RAND McNALLY

THE
MAPMAKER'S
ART

THE MAPMAKER'S ART

An Illustrated History of Cartography

JOHN GOSS

Introduction by
VALERIE SCOTT

 RAND McNALLY

Rand McNally
The Mapmaker's Art
An Illustrated History of Cartography

Published by Rand McNally in 1993 in the U.S.A.
Copyright © Studio Editions Ltd., 1993

ISBN 0 528 83620 X

Design by Joy FitzSimmons
Design assistance by Sheila Sherwin
Picture research by Susan Bolsom-Morris
and Marcus Harpur
Typeset by MC Typeset Ltd.
Printed and bound in Hong Kong

Library of Congress Cataloging-in-Publication Data

Goss, John, 1947-
    The mapmaker's art: an illustrated history of cartography / John
Goss.
        p. cm.
    Includes bibliographical references and index.
    ISBN 0-528-83620-X
    1. Cartography—History. I. Title
GA201.G67 1993   − 93-4963
526′.09—dc20   CIP

PLATE 1 *(frontispiece) An engraved frontispiece from the* Zee-Fakkel *chart atlas by Johannes van Keulen, Amsterdam, issued in the early eighteenth century, c.1710.*

PLATE 2 *(opposite) The southeast Asia peninsula and* Jave le Grande *from the* Boke of Idrography *by Jean Rotz of Dieppe, 1542. The map depicts the native peoples and flora and fauna observed on voyages in these waters.*

PLATE 3 *(overleaf)* Grande Jave *from* Cosmographie universelle *by Guillaume Le Testu, manuscript, c.1556, with east at the top. The* Cosmographie universelle, *a manuscript atlas of fifty-six maps, is one of the most detailed and beautifully decorative works produced by the Dieppe school of cartographers, which flourished in Normandy in the middle of the sixteenth century.*

ACKNOWLEDGEMENTS

Compilation of a book of this nature involves the co-operation of many people, consciously or sub-consciously. In no particular order of merit, I wish therefore to thank the following individuals and organizations: the ever-patient staff of the Map Rooms of the British Library and of the Royal Geographical Society; the Bibliothèque Nationale, Paris; my colleagues in the Book Department at Sotheby's, London; Valerie Scott of Map Collector Publications; 'Bic' Wardington; Dr Helen Wallis; H.A.M. van der Heijden; Peter de Jonge; Nico Israel; Paul Carter; Dr Peter Jarvis; Dr David Woodward; Ken Webb; Belinda Wilkinson; Emma Wish; Susan Bolsom-Morris; Joy FitzSimmons; Caroline Bugler; Debbie Kennett; Fiona Hunter; Doug Adams; Jonathan Potter; my parents; Graham and Maria Young; Mike Jones; Cécille Kruyfhooft; and all those who first suggested this book a long time ago but whose persuasions and cajolings I resisted until now. Any errors and omissions are entirely my own.

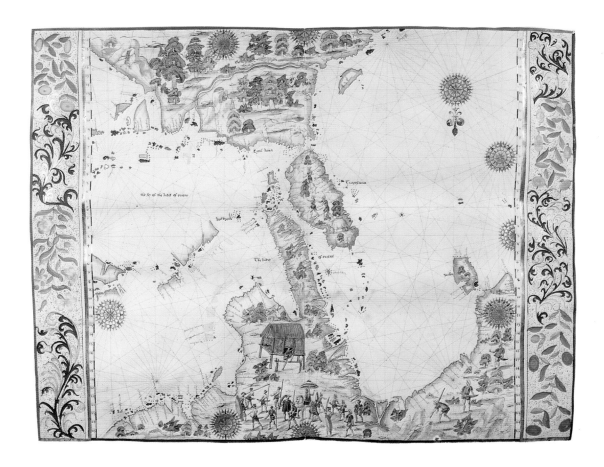

CONTENTS

INTRODUCTION
by Valerie Scott

THIS BOOK ENTERS the scene at an exciting time for lovers of early maps and the history of cartography. More people than ever before are becoming collectors, lured by the fascination of an antique which combines art, geography, history, and even heraldry, and which can be secured at a price which is well within reach of the average person. The growth in the popularity of map collecting has heightened interest in the 'how and why', generating more research which, in a number of cases, has already led to the discovery of maps and atlases previously thought lost. Such 'finds' can emerge from all sorts of different places ranging from existing library map collections to the dusty attics or damp cellars of private homes.

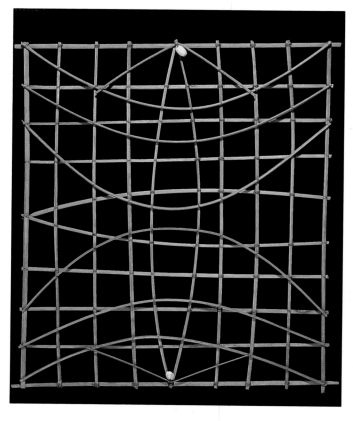

PLATE 4 *A stick and shell chart showing seasonal wave swells, used by the Marshall Islanders for navigating between the islands.*

One such example was a sixteenth-century miniature atlas of sea charts which came to light in London recently. These charts were the work of Sir Robert Dudley (1574–1649), the illegitimate son of the Earl of Leicester. Whilst the larger versions, bound into an atlas entitled the *Arcano Del Mare* ('Secrets of the Sea', published in Florence, 1646–1647) have been known for some time, there was no previous record of the smaller charts. Apart from the obvious interest generated by such a 'find' the charts provided an answer as to how early navigators could have used the original bulky charts, measuring fifty by seventy-one centimetres, in any practical way at sea. They probably did not; they took the smaller ones. Mystery solved! (see Chapter IX.)

Auction houses, particularly those in North America, Great Britain, and Germany, are reflecting the increased interest in maps and atlases by holding specialist sales. The publication of books like *The Mapmaker's Art* also plays an important part in popularizing the subject.

The Mapmaker's Art is an ideal reference for those who know a little about the history of mapping and would like to know more. Many interesting facts emerge from the text. For instance, we are told that it is impossible to pinpoint the first map or mapmaking tradition because maps in some form or other have been used throughout the world from the beginnings of mankind. It is in fact a fair claim that maps represent one of the earliest forms of communication devised by man.

The study of the 'history of cartography' – the subtitle of this book – is at an important crossroads. John Goss tells the story of mapmaking from the earliest times to the modern day as seen by Europeans, but he also touches on the mapping of more distant lands like China and the Far East. This is very much to the author's credit since it is vital that we begin to look away from the traditional, Eurocentric story, to a more distant horizon embracing the history of other cultures.

One of the reasons why such horizons have not been more fully explored by Western Europeans is the obvious one of proximity; it is much easier to study things nearer home which are familiar and therefore more easily understandable. There has also been much easier access to European material. But another, less obvious, reason is that printing arrived earlier in Western Europe than in non-western countries (apart from China which had a very early tradition of 'printing' by means of stone rubbings) which meant that material was far more readily available for study. Much early Asian and Islamic cartography was manuscript or hand-drawn, as opposed to printed, and so has been lost with the passage of time.

This wider, more enlightened, approach is reflected in another *History of Cartography* being published in six volumes in Chicago.[1] Volume Two, Part One, which appeared recently, is devoted to the mapping of traditional Islamic and South-Asian societies, whilst Part Two will explore the cartography of the traditional East and Southeast-Asian societies. An earlier work, which bore the same title and was published in 1964,[2] only devoted six pages to Islamic cartography, half a page each to Indian and Persian, and three to Ottoman cartography, and this imbalance obviously had to be put right.

I wonder how many people know that the word 'map' is derived from the Latin *mappa* meaning table-cloth or napkin? *The Shorter Oxford English Dictionary* defines a map as a 'representation of the earth's surface or a part of it, its physical and political features etc., or of the heavens, delineated on a flat surface of paper etc., according to a definite scale or projection'. However, the authors of this new *History* have revised that definition to 'a graphic representation that facilitates a spatial

PLATE 5 Planisphaerium sive universi totius . . . *by Nicolaus Copernicus from* Atlas coelestis seu harmonica macrocosmica *by Andreas Cellarius, Amsterdam, 1661. This celestial chart illustrates the sun-centred system outlined by Copernicus. Seated at bottom right, Copernicus is popularly remembered as the astronomer who laid the foundations of our modern view of the universe.*

understanding of things, concepts, conditions, processes, or events in the human world'. A map, of course, does not have to be represented on paper. Who are we to say that an arrangement of sticks put down by North American Indians to record migrations of tribes or herds, or inter-tribal battles; the map drawn on the bark of a tree; or the directional inscriptions engraved on the powder horn employed by the North American scout, are not maps?

G. Malcolm Lewis has stated that Indians could draw maps before their first contact with Europeans,[3] although they may not have been in a form recognizable by us. In the same way, an arrangement of sticks and shells formed the basis of another form of communication made by the Marshall Islanders in earlier times (Plate 4). These stick-charts represented the patterns of the waves and helped them to navigate between different islands. These clearly qualify as sea charts.

Nowadays we tend to associate maps with the earth rather than the sky so it may seem strange that John Goss devotes the whole of Chapter X in this book to celestial globes and charts (Plate 5).

However, it must be remembered that the study of the stars was immensely important to early earthbound navigators who knew little of the lands that lay beyond their own. China in particular has a long tradition of celestial mapping. The study of astronomy was an important branch of the natural sciences in the seventeenth century and the foundation of the Observatory at Greenwich in 1675 was born out of the recognition of a need for accurate observations of the heavens. One of the most perplexing problems facing the navigators and scientists of the time was the precise determination of longitude – a dilemma eventually resolved with the establishment of the Greenwich Meridian.

How appropriate that this book should be published almost exactly 500 years after Christopher Columbus returned from his famous voyage of discovery to America (known as the New World). In 1992 there were commemorations on both sides of the Atlantic in recognition of this quincentennial. However, 1493 was the year when Columbus set out on his second voyage to establish a colony in the Indies and to explore Cuba and Hispaniola. Columbus has now become more of a symbol than a hero and few believe that he was the first European to reach the shores of America. In fact, Columbus himself thought he had reached Japan and the continent of Asia! The exact place where he landed in America is still in dispute amongst scholars and will probably never be proven. No matter, symbolic or factual, this was a turning point in history as it meant that Europeans had the information to help them begin to learn the true configuration of the world.

The history of maps and mapping is no different from any other branch of history as soon becomes apparent from reading this book. One particular country will come to the fore for a time only to be succeeded by another. The fifteenth century, for example, was dominated by the Italian school of mapmaking (Plate 7), and this was followed by the golden age of mapmaking in the Netherlands which continued for most of the late sixteenth and early seventeenth centuries (Plates 8, 9). This age gave birth to the famous publishing firms like those of Ortelius and the Blaeu family who left a legacy of outstanding atlases and globes. From this period and this part of the world came Gerard Mercator, who is probably the most widely known figure in the history of cartography. His basic projection (the Mercator projection), which he first used on his great world map of 1569, is still used today, more than 400 years later, and was an outstanding achievement. (See Chapter IV.)

The British Isles have a long history of mapmaking and there are a number of manuscript maps of the world on animal skin, known as *mappaemundi*, surviving to prove the fact. The best known of these is the large map showing all sorts of mythical beasts and strange humans, one without a head, which hangs in Hereford Cathedral. This priceless artefact narrowly missed being put into auction to raise money for repairs to the roof of the cathedral only a few years ago. Luckily it was saved for the nation by the generosity of a number of benefactors.

England was also at the forefront of the design of instruments and techniques to further the progress of cartography, so it is surprising that the first national survey of a country took place in France (Plate 10). The work was carried out by an Italian, Giovanni Domenico Cassini (1625–1712), who settled in Paris in 1669 under the auspices of the Royal Academy of Sciences. When Louis XIV saw the new maps made from the survey he is said to have remarked that the survey had cost him more territory than if he had fought a disastrous military campaign!

The subject of early globe-making opens up

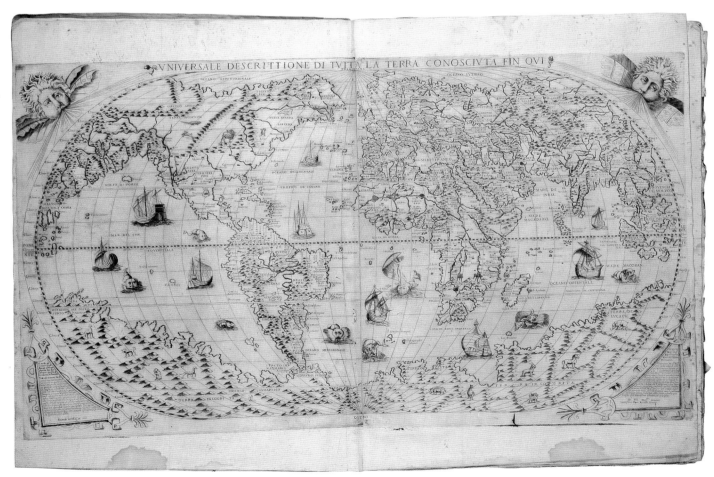

PLATE 7 *World map on an oval projection,* Universale descrittione di tutta la terra conosciuta fin qui, *by Paolo Forlani, copper engraving, Venice, 1565. A close copy of Giacomo Gastaldi's map issued in 1546. In this map, North America is joined to Siberia by a broad land bridge, even though a similar map issued by Gastaldi in 1561 shows a strait here.*

PLATE 8 *(right)* Haga
Comitis *(The Hague) from
Joan Blaeu's Townbooks of
the Netherlands, 1648.
Blaeu's magnificent
townbooks are a continuing
object of pride, beautifully
engraved with highly
detailed plans.*

PLATE 9 *(below)* Les
deux poles *by Nicolas
Sanson, Amsterdam,
c. 1700. This unusual
world map shows the world
in hemispheres viewed from
the two poles, here in a
Dutch version issued by
Pieter Mortier.*

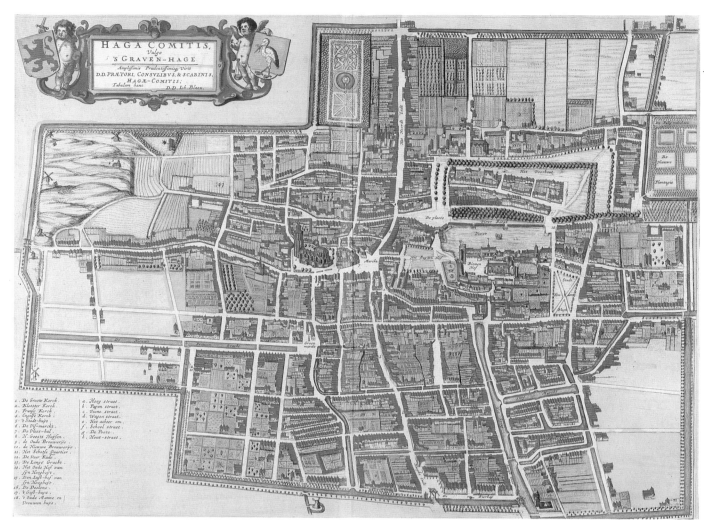

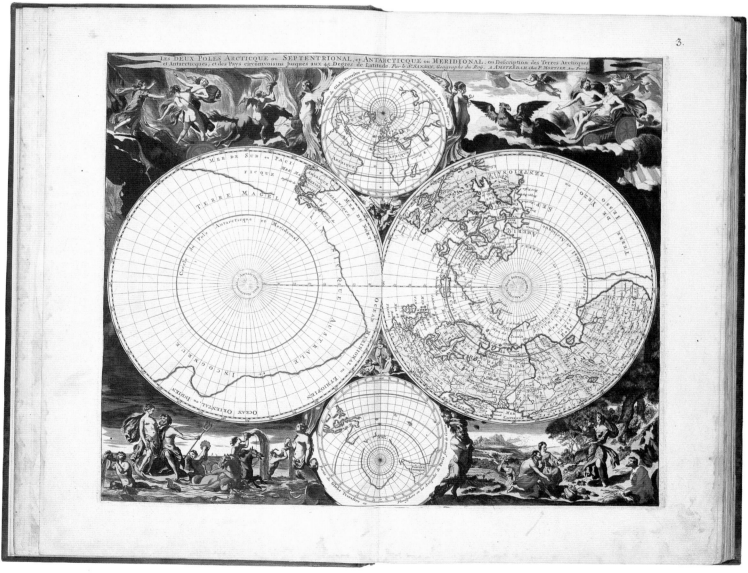

another fascinating area for study and collecting. Globes date back to the time when man first perceived the world as a sphere and were frequently used as tools for teaching geography. They were often created in pairs, one terrestrial, one celestial. In the sixteenth century the Blaeu family of Amsterdam (see Chapter IV) made globes which were well known throughout the world. Their work was surpassed later in the century by that of Father Vincenzo Coronelli of Venice who created even more beautiful globes and was probably the most prolific of all globe-makers. His work included a huge pair of globes for Louis XIV of France which were on display a few years ago in the ultra-modern Pompidou Centre in Paris after undergoing restoration. They measure just under five metres in diameter and display a portrait of Louis with an inscription saying, 'to the august majesty of Louis the great, the invincible, the happy, the wise'.[4]

The hobby of map collecting is still in its infancy, but it is becoming increasingly popular and this popularity is catered for in a number of ways.[5] There is a network of map dealers around

the world; there are specialist auction sales of both maps and atlases; and there are numerous books being published to aid collectors. There are two specialist periodicals for map collectors: the lively quarterly magazine *The Map Collector*, which covers all aspects of map collecting and caring for maps, and the more scholarly journal *Imago Mundi*. There are also a number of map societies around the world including the British-based International Map Collectors' Society.

When I say that map collecting is a new hobby I do not mean to imply that there have not always been great collections. There have, but until recently these tended to be formed by wealthy people who founded great libraries and who collected atlases, often alongside other books and works of art. If it had not been for some of these, our libraries and institutions would have been the poorer. For instance, the collections at the British Library (formerly the British Museum, established in 1753) are founded on collections made by Sir Robert Cotton, the sixteenth-century antiquary; Edward and Robert Harley, the Earls of Oxford; and Sir Hans Sloane. These were aug-

PLATE 10 *Illustration showing the measurement of the Paris meridian from a base-line, from* Discours du méridien *by Jacques Cassini, 1749. France was the first country to undertake a national survey.*

mented by the royal collections presented by George II of England in 1757. Many American cartographical libraries are also founded on collections by wealthy collectors like Lessing J. Rosenwald and Hubert Howe Bancroft. A.E. Nordenskiöld (1832–1900), discoverer of the Northeast Passage and Director of the Minerology Department at the Swedish Museum of Natural History in Stockholm, collected literature on voyages and exploration which now forms the base of the cartography section at the University of Helsinki Library, one of the few collections which has preserved the documents showing how it was formed.[5]

If you do decide to become a collector start by defining your collecting genre. This can be almost anything from an expensive collection of double-hemisphere world maps to something more humble like English county maps by Thomas Moule. These were produced in Victorian times and contain charming vignettes depicting the life of the country at that time (Plate 13). Some of the strangest maps ever produced are also collectable – those of Michael Drayton, who was an English poet living in the late sixteenth and early seventeenth centuries (Plate 12). A song or poem about each English county was accompanied by a map in

a book entitled the *Polyolbion* which Drayton dedicated to the then Prince of Wales. He implores the Prince to take a natural interest in his work so that the influence of 'so glorious and fortunate a Starre, may also reflect upon me: which hath power to give me new life, or leave me to die more willingly and contented'.

This introduction to the history of cartography should act as a taster and give those who read it a hunger for more knowledge. In the words of one writer: 'I am told there are people who do not care for maps, and find it hard to believe. The names, the shapes … the courses of the roads and rivers … are an inexhaustible fund of interest for any man.'[6]

References
1. J.B. Harley and D. Woodward, *ed* six-volume *The History of Cartography*, Volume I, 1987.
2. Leo Bagrow, *History of Cartography*, English edition, 1964.
3. G. Malcolm Lewis, 'The Indigenous Maps and Mapping of North American Indians', in *The Map Collector*, Issue 9, Map Collector Publications, Tring, 1979.
4. *Cartes et Figures de la Terra*. Catalogue of an exhibition held at the *Centre Georges Pompidou*, Paris, 1980.
5. Anna Maria Mickwitz, 'Dear Mr. Nordenskiöld, your offer is accepted', in *The Map Librarian in the Modern World. Essays in honour of Walter W. Ristow*, 1978.
6. R.L. Stevenson, *Treasure Island*.

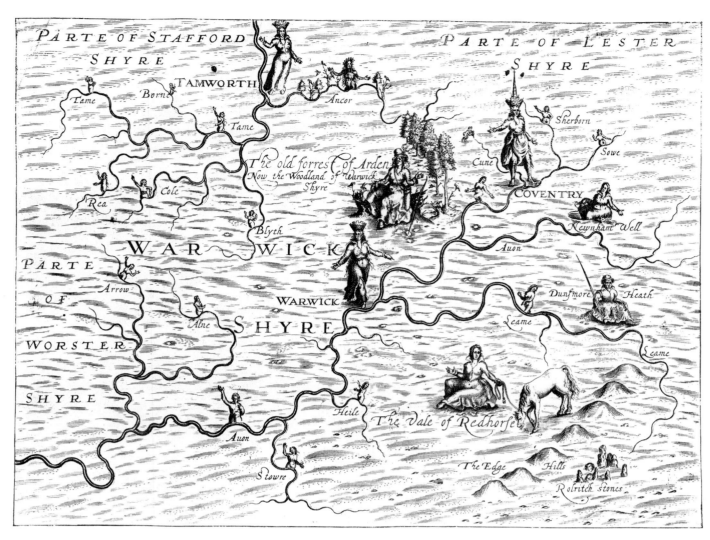

PLATE 12 *(left)*
Warwickshyre *by Michael
Drayton, from* Polyolbion,
*1612. This rather eccentric
map is one of a series on the
English counties which
accompanied Drayton's book
of songs and verses on
England. Note the old forest
of Arden, once part of a
large Midland forest,
famous as the probable
setting of Shakespeare's* As
You Like It.

PLATE 13 *(below)* Sussex
by Thomas Moule from
Moule's English
Counties, *London,
c. 1836. Note the charming
vignettes of Chichester
Cathedral, Arundel Castle
and the Chain Pier at
Brighton.*

Sardona

N

Castello firmani

R. Tenna Cupra maritima

vi fluor. fr. Tenna ii xii

viceno E x fisternas iii Cirulos vii Pitinum xii

V

Interocrio Aque cutilie

ocri xii vii viii Reate xvii Ad nouas viiii

inter manana xii Aequo falisco xvi Cieto viiii

Farfar R.

Aqua uiua

vii Ad uicesimu xv Ad ubrias vi

Ad septium via clodia iii Fonte adriani

enos ii .co. falis

v, uiarum

vuii Av sco Pe TRUO

Turres

Bebiana lorio xii via aurelia

x Alsium vi

viiii

allum uallinacium xv

CHAPTER I

THE FIRST MAPMAKERS

2100 BC – 1200 AD

WHO 'INVENTED' MAPS? We are used to consulting history books or encyclopaedias to check the exact date of an item's discovery or invention. All the more fascinating, therefore, to realize that mapmaking defies this precision. It did not come into being as a result of a conscious decision of some unknown person, many centuries or even millennia ago, to take a piece of papyrus, or perhaps a block of stone, and produce a 'map'. We cannot point to a particular date for the invention of mapmaking. On the contrary, it seems that maps of one kind or another have evolved independently in different cultures around the world. In cultures as far afield as China and Greece, North America and Australia, maps were produced for a variety of purposes.

In common with many other inventions, the first maps in any community were undoubtedly made in answer to a need. It is likely that the first recognizable maps were drawn to show sources of water or fertile land on which to raise crops or domesticated animals. Somewhat later perhaps, maps may have served as a type of early cadastral survey, that is to say, a map which shows the location, size and boundaries of one or more plots of land in order to distinguish ownership. Such maps were usually drawn on a large scale or sometimes without a scale at all.

PLATE I.I *Detail from the* Tabula Peutingeriana, *one of the best-known examples of Roman mapmaking, dating from the first century AD. The map is known to us through a medieval copy believed to have been drawn by a monk in Colmar in 1265.*

PLATE 1.2 *(above and right) A building-plan (above), carved on stone, lies in the lap of a statue of Gudea (right), ruler of Lagash in Sumer, Babylonia, dating from around 2100 BC. This plan is our earliest evidence for plans drawn true to scale: traces of a scale-bar can be seen in the damaged corner of the tablet. Confirmation is provided by later actual scale-plans from Mesopotamia, drawn on clay.*

tablets containing long lists of names of places, rivers, mountains and other features have been found dating from 2500–2000 BC, which may have been used for record purposes. In 2330 BC, Sargon of Akkad knew of places as far to the west as the Mediterranean shores of the Levant, and some later clay tablets make references to military expeditions and itineraries, although none record distances in any recognizable form. The boundaries of some territories are shown in descriptive form in tablet records, but it is not known whether maps were used to illustrate such records and we cannot prove the existence of maps as such, however tempting the implications may be.

Ancient Mesopotamia

In Mesopotamia, plans are known to have been made as early as about 2100 BC for Gudea, the ruler of Lagash in Sumer, Babylonia. One of these has survived in the form of a large-scale building plan inscribed across the lap of the king's robes on a monument, which is now in the Louvre in Paris (Plates 1.2 A and B). Other large-scale plans of the time of Sargon appear to show rivers, city walls and streets. A well-known example is the plan of Nippur, the religious capital of Sumer, dating from about 1000 BC. This shows the Euphrates river, canals, walls and named city gates, with measurements given in units of cubits. (A cubit is an ancient measurement corresponding to the length of the arm from the elbow to the tip of the middle finger — about fifty centimetres.) The best known of these ancient Babylonian maps is the so-called Babylonian World Map, dating from about 600 BC, which is incised on a clay tablet (Plate 1.3). It depicts the region at the head of the Persian Gulf and the Euphrates and Tigris rivers, with Babylon itself at the centre of the circular design and the whole enclosed by the ocean. The map is now in the British Museum.

Ancient Egypt

We know that Egypt was a land of accurate measurement. Much of this technique was born of the need to re-establish the boundaries of lands subject to the annual flooding of the Nile. Professional surveyors made their measurements in squares, which were determined by lengths of

Following the invention of cuneiform writing by the Mesopotamians, Persians, Sumerians and others, some time during the fourth millennium BC, early pictographs (picture writing) may possibly have depicted and defined the lands of kings or tribal leaders. Logic suggests that if pictographs were being used at an early stage in the development of organized society to represent single or multiple objects, and perhaps even ideas as well, then it is not a far step to the use of symbols of one kind or another to represent human environments. In other words, it is possible that maps of some type may be nearly as old in concept as the use of writing. Many incised clay

PLATE 1.3 *A small clay tablet with a descriptive cuneiform text showing the world according to the Babylonians from about 600 BC. The world (the disc shape) is surrounded by the 'Bitter River' (the salt water of the ocean). The two vertical curved lines represent the Euphrates River, while the smaller circles show the names of cities and neighbouring countries. The triangular symbols beyond the ocean may represent supposed hazards or lands of twilight.*

knotted rope. Circular and triangular plots were also made. Such measurements were recorded on mathematical papyri, such as the Rhind Papyrus of about 1600 BC, now in the British Museum. The greatest extant monument of Egyptian map-making is the so-called Turin Papyrus, a painted map dating from about 1300 BC. It covers the lands between the Nile and the Red Sea, and shows the gold and silver mines and the roads of the region. The Turin Papyrus appears to have been an early form of land registry map in that it delineates the ownership of the gold and silver mines, which were located at Umm Fawakhir in the Wadi Hammamat region.

Religion in Egypt also seems to have played a part in the development of mapmaking. It

PLATE 1.4 *Alexander the Great, detail from* The Battle of Isos between Greeks and Persians, *floor mosaic, Pompeii, c. 100 BC. The great military expeditions of Alexander the Great expanded Greek knowledge of the ancient world.*

manifests itself in the *Book of the Dead*, compiled in about 1400 BC, in which are shown the delineations of the ideal plot of land tilled by the deceased in the kingdom of Osiris, the god of the underworld: a rectangular plot bounded by canals, vividly painted in colours.

The Greek world

A major, recognizable stage in the development of mapmaking seems to have occurred some time before AD 325 during the latter years of the pre-Christian era in Alexandria, the Roman capital of Egypt and the centre of the Hellenic world. Then, as now, the area was at the crossroads of many trade routes to and from all parts of the Near and Middle East and far beyond. It was the emporium of the inhabited world, and a great centre of learning. The rulers of Alexandria were zealous collectors and hungry for knowledge.

Our knowledge of the ancient world, frustratingly imperfect as it is, rests on the writings of these early Greek sages and philosophers, travellers and writers. Homer (*c.* 700 BC), the epic poet, saw the world as a flat shield surrounded by the waters of a broad river, or *oceanus*. The centre of this world was at Delphi, itself the centre of Greece and the nucleus of the habitable world. This idea of an all-encircling ocean was restated by such eminent men as Hesiod the poet, Hecataeus, Strabo and Anaximander, the geographer and philosopher from Miletus (in central Anatolia, Turkey). Anaximander (611–547 BC), a pupil of Thales (624–565 BC), is said to have devised a globe (possibly in map form) of the world in the sixth century BC. He was also responsible for introducing the sundial to ancient Greece and, as one of the early pioneers of exact science, he taught that the ecliptic was in fact oblique.

Somewhat later, around 500 BC, Hecataeus, also of Miletus, compiled the first formal 'geography', entitled *Periegesis*, or *Travels around the Earth*. Hecataeus's geography took the form of a *periplus*, or coasting pilot, which gave descriptions of a voyage and sailing directions. The earliest known Greek *periplus* is a pilot-guide to the Mediterranean, attributed to one Scylax of Caryanda (in Asia Minor) in about 500 BC, the existing text probably dating from around 350 BC. No charts survive from this, or indeed any other,

Greek *periplus*, but such guides gave details of the number of days' sailing from one trading port to another along the shores of the Mediterranean.

The historian Herodotus (*c*.485–425 BC) visited Egypt, Babylonia and Persia in the pursuit of historical evidence. In his *History*, completed about 425 BC, he added considerably to the knowledge of the known world. The great military expeditions of Xenophon (444–359 BC) and Alexander the Great (356–323 BC) took Hellenistic civilization far beyond the Mediterranean, as far east as Tashkent in central Asia and to the banks of the Chenab in northern India (Plate 1.4).

We cannot know to what extent Greek writers on geography made, or even consulted, maps in any recognizable form, but a hint about the increasing importance of world maps is given in the will of Theophrastus (*c*.370–*c*.286 BC). With the general aim of educating the public of Athens, he requested that 'the *pinakes* [panels] showing the *periodoi ges* [maps of the world] should be set up in the lower cloister' in the Agora in Athens. These were evidently wooden panels which, like pictures, could easily be removed when required.

As the Greeks grew more confident in their practical and intellectual mastery of the world around them, they initiated a broad enquiry into the geography and the inhabitants of the *oikoumene* (the area centred on the Mediterranean which represented the Greek conception of the inhabited earth). As a result of these investigations Greek ideas of time and space were altered for ever. From Greek explorations of the coastal areas of the Mediterranean and the Black Sea, the Middle East, and even short stretches of the Atlantic coasts, came new descriptions of the ever-expanding world known to the Greeks.

Pytheas, from the Greek colony of Massilia (Marseilles) in the western Mediterranean, made a pioneering voyage in about 330 BC. The purpose of his journey seems to have been to determine latitudes for the remoter parts of the world either through a knowledge of the length of the longest day or through the altitude of the sun on the winter solstice. Pytheas knew the location of the celestial pole, and calculated the latitude of Massilia, very accurately, at 43°12′N, only three minutes less than the modern correct value – an astounding achievement for those early times. Pytheas subsequently voyaged to the Cassiterides, or Tin Islands

(thought to have been the Isles of Scilly, off the southwest coast of Britain), from where he circumnavigated the British Isles and possibly even ventured into the Baltic. He travelled as far north as a place he called Thule, where the sun was visible for twenty-four hours a day in midsummer (Plate 1.6). However, as neither Pytheas's own text nor any map which he may have drawn has survived, it is impossible to say exactly where Thule was although it may have been an island or stretch of coastline in northern Scandinavia.

Another Greek, Dicaearchus, who came from the Greek colony of Messana (Messina, in Sicily), wrote a *Periegesis*, like that of Hecataeus. Dicaearchus was a pupil of Aristotle and lived around 320 BC. He initiated a base-line running from the Pillars of Hercules, to Sardinia, to Sicily, to the Peloponnese in southern Greece, to southern Asia Minor, the Taurus mountains, and as far as the western reaches of the Himalayas. This line divided the known world into two more or less equal halves, from which Dicaearchus was able to give estimates of distances.

The information collected by the early Greek travellers, and others, was summarized by Eratosthenes in about 200 BC. It was Eratosthenes (*c*.275–194 BC) (Plate 1.8) who arrived at a remarkably accurate estimate of the circumference of the globe. He did this by measuring the shadow of the noonday sun on the summer solstice at Alexandria and Syene (the modern Aswan) on the First Cataract of the Nile in Upper Egypt, which

PLATE 1.5 *(below)*
A Greek attic-red figure vase from Starnos, c. 490 BC, depicting Odysseus with the Sirens. The ancient Greeks were accomplished sailors who actively explored the coastal areas of the Mediterranean and the Black Sea. Odysseus, the archetypal Greek adventurer, is seen here on his epic voyage of discovery.

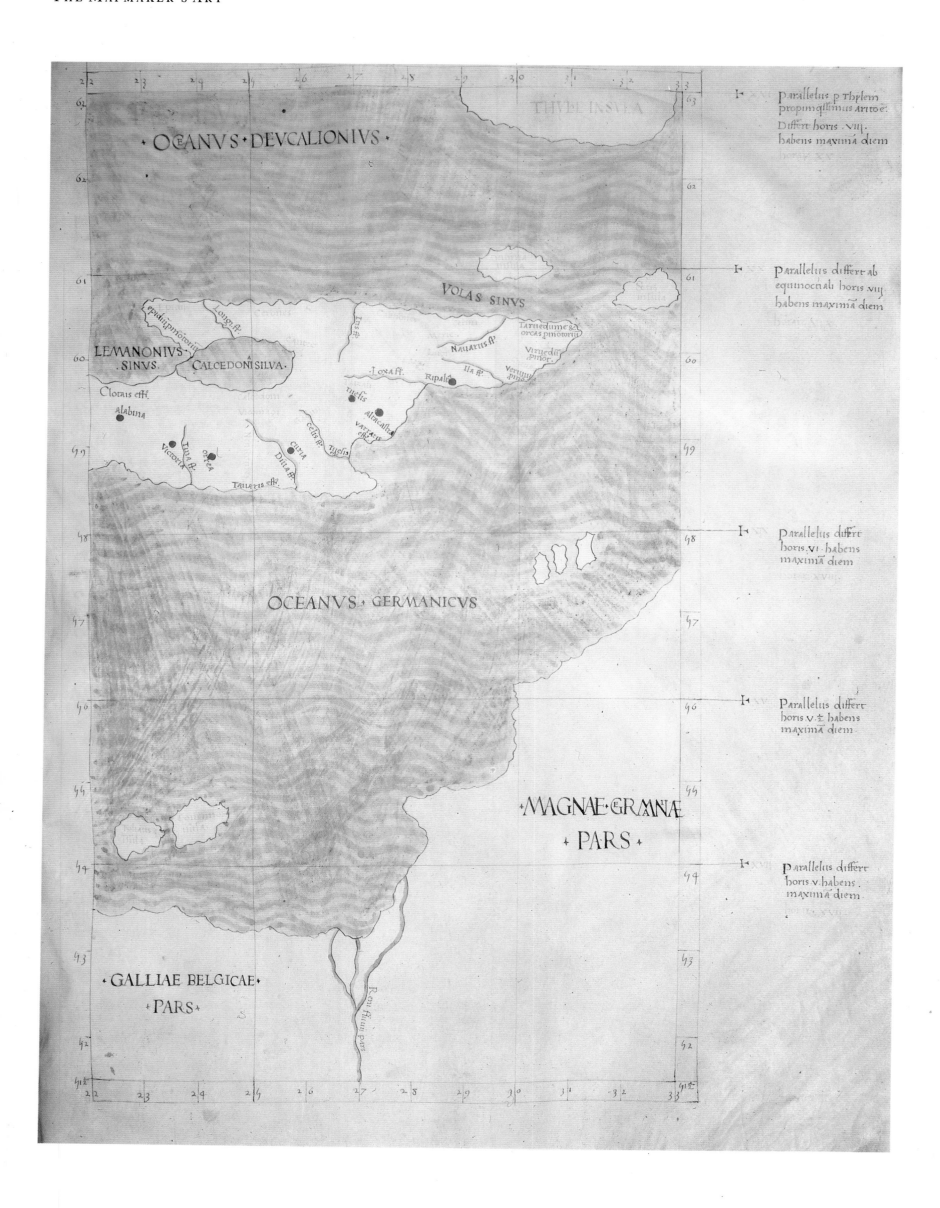

he assumed to be on the same meridian, arriving at a figure of 252,000 stades, or about 40,250 geographical kilometres. (A stade was originally the distance covered by a plough before turning, and was equivalent to about 185 metres.)

Eratosthenes was invited by Ptolemy III Euergetes (*r.* 246–221 BC), King of Egypt at that time, to come to Alexandria as tutor to the King's son, and to become director of the great library there. Ptolemy III Euergetes used to have all visitors to the city searched on entry. Any texts found among their possessions were confiscated and copied, the original being deposited in the library and the copy given to the traveller, without thanks or reward. Anything and everything was collected by Euergetes, in Egyptian, Greek, Hebrew or any other language, which could be translated for deposit in the library (Plate 1.7). By the time Euergetes relinquished his rule in Alexandria, his librarian estimated that the collection numbered some 490,000 volumes.

Neither of Eratosthenes' two texts, *On the Measurement of the Earth* and the *Geographia*, has survived, but the latter was discussed later by Strabo (see below). In his *Geographia*, Eratosthenes discussed the best methods of making a map of the known world. He worked out the distance along the meridian of Alexandria, from the latitude of the 'Cinnamon country' (approximately 12°N, somewhere in Ethiopia) in the south, to that of Thule in the north. A reconstruction of Eratosthenes' map, of about 220 BC, shows the known world to be a more or less rounded-off rectangle, some 77,800 stades east-west and 37,600 stades north-south (Plate 1.9). Ancient methods of reckoning longitude, however, were unreliable compared with those for calculating latitude derived from solar or stellar observations. Although it was known that a reliable result could be obtained from simultaneous eclipse observations, it was difficult to communicate such results and even more so for scholars to correlate them. Nevertheless, the map of Eratosthenes was a remarkable achievement, and it may be considered as the first scientific Greek map. Its physical dimensions are not known to us, but when it was presented before the court of Ptolemy III Euergetes, it must have been a large and impressive sight. It is likely that it was drawn to scale as far as possible, and its influence on later Greek and

Roman mapmaking was considerable. Notwithstanding Claudius Ptolemy's later work, 'it can be said to have affected world maps right down to the Age of Discovery'.[1]

In about 168 BC, the Greek polymath Crates of Pergamum (*fl. c.*180–145 BC), who wrote on Homer and the travels of Odysseus, visited Rome. While there, he fell and broke his leg. He stayed on in Rome while his leg healed and filled up his days by giving lectures, which are said to have made a great impression on the Romans. Crates considered that the shape of a map would be correct only if it were drawn on the surface of a globe, and that the optimum diameter of such a globe would have to be at least three metres in order to give an effective and accurate scale. Crates favoured an unusual symmetry: he said that the world comprised four symmetrical landmasses separated by two intersecting belts of ocean. In the north lay Europe, Asia and the parts of Africa then known; to the south were the lands of the *Antoikoi* or 'dwellers opposite'; to the west were the regions of the *Perioikoi* or 'dwellers round'; and to the south of the *Perioikoi* lay the Antipodes. The division between the known lands and the

PLATE 1.7 *(above)*
An artist's impression of the library at Alexandria taken from a Victorian engraving. By the end of the reign of Ptolemy III Euergetes (r. 246–221 BC) the library contained some 490,000 volumes. Visitors were searched on entry to the city, and any texts in their possession were copied.

PLATE 1.6 *(opposite)*
A Ptolemaic manuscript map showing northern Britain and the German coast. 'Thule insula' appears in the far northeastern corner. The Greek traveller and writer Pytheas journeyed as far north as a place he called Thule, which is believed to be somewhere in Scandinavia.

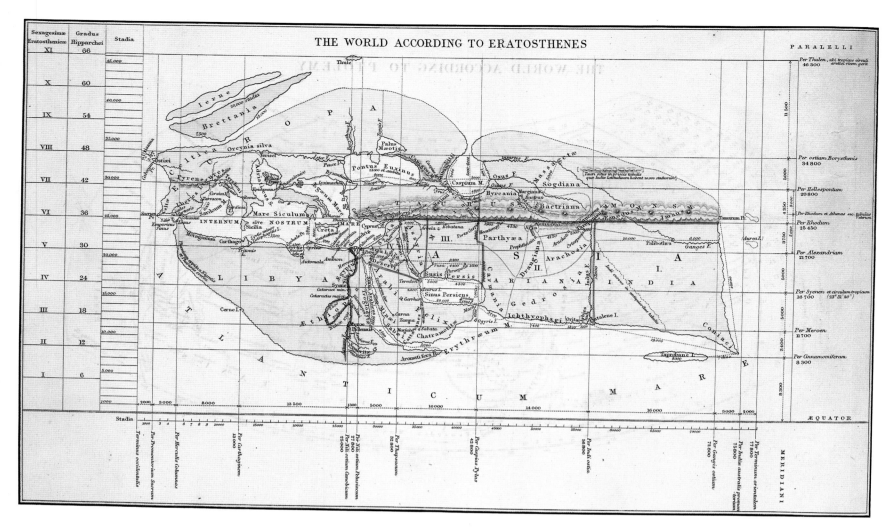

PLATE 1.8 *A bust of the Greek geographer Eratosthenes (c. 275–194 BC), director of the great library at Alexandria. Eratosthenes arrived at a remarkably accurate estimate of the circumference of the globe by measuring the shadow of the noonday sun on the summer solstice at Alexandria and Syene.*

Antipodes came at an ocean belt on either side of the Equator. *Aethiopes* (Ethiopians, or 'black faces') lived on each side of this great divide, as Homer noted near the beginning of the *Odyssey*:

> . . . the Ethiopians, split in two,
> Some in the east, some by the setting sun.

With a little poetic imagination, the world according to Crates bears a remarkable resemblance to a modern globe: Europe and Asia in the northeastern quadrant, Africa in the southeastern, South America in the southwestern, and North America in the northwestern quadrant.

The great stoic and sage Strabo (*c.* 50 BC to AD 25) visited Alexandria in 25 BC. An itinerant scholar, he travelled as far west as Etruria in the peninsula of Italy, and as far south as the frontier regions of Ethiopia. He had seen such places as Rome, Corinth, Magnesia, Smyrna and Beirut: 'You could not find another person among the writers on Geography who has travelled over much more of the distances just mentioned than I', he wrote, modestly. It is possible that a large proportion of Strabo's travels were carried out through the medium of the great library, for he is said to have spent at least five years studying the writings of the ancient philosophers and writers collected there, gathering materials for his own *Geography*. It is this work which, in the many printed editions and translations that have come down to us from the fifteenth century, forms the principal key to the history of ancient geography and mapmaking, although there is no evidence to suggest that Strabo himself ever made a map. As Lloyd Brown commented: 'It is doubtful whether he [Strabo] . . . ever compiled a map. If he had done so or if he only thought he had, he would have said so. His ego was sublime!'[2]

Commenting on his sources, Strabo himself wrote in *Geography I*:

If I shall, on occasion, be compelled to contradict the very men whom in all other respects I follow most closely, I beg to be pardoned; for it is not my purpose to contradict every individual geographer, but rather to leave the most of them out of consideration — men whose arguments it is unseemly even to follow — and to pass upon the opinion of those men whom we recognize to have been correct in most cases. Indeed, to engage in philosophical discussion with everybody is unseemly, but it is honourable to do so with Eratosthenes, Hipparchus, Poseidonus, Polybius, and others of their type.[3]

Nearly all that is known of ancient Greek geography prior to the work of Claudius Ptolemy (see below) in the second century AD can be traced back to the writings of Strabo and the fruits of his five years' labour at Alexandria, which contained references to the geography of the Near and Middle East and the Mediterranean.

Claudius Ptolemy

Even today, by far the best-known and still the most influential of the early works on geography is the *Geography* of the Alexandrian Claudius Ptolemy (*c.* AD 90–168) (Plate 1.10). This text marks the zenith of Greek geographical thought and contains the first recognizable and scientifically calculated map projections. By the time of Ptolemy, the use of parallels and meridians was well established, but a method was still needed to show these on a map which represented the curved surface of the earth with the minimum of distortion – a problem which occupies cartographers to a greater or lesser degree to this day. Strabo had recommended the construction of a globe three metres in diameter. Ptolemy's concept was to plot meridians at five-degree intervals along the equator and to have them converge at the northern pole. Parallels were spaced according to the length of the longest day of the year at half-hourly and hourly intervals northwards from the Equator.

The text of Ptolemy's *Geography* describes a large world map and twenty-six regional maps of the then known world in Europe, northern Africa and southern and western Asia, but it is unclear whether Ptolemy himself ever drew maps to illustrate his text. For twelve centuries after his death, the tradition survived. The oldest extant manuscript copy of the *Geography* was written by monks at Vatopedi on Mount Athos in the early fourteenth century. This manuscript contains maps based on the descriptions and co-ordinates given by Ptolemy. It was on this manuscript – and the several copies of it which were made thereafter – that the first printed western atlas of maps was based, the first illustrated edition of Ptolemy appearing at Bologna in Italy in 1477, containing twenty-six copper-engraved maps. A fine example of a Ptolemaic world map is that which occurs in a twelfth- or thirteenth-century Byzantine manuscript, the *Codex Urbanus Graecus 82* (Plate 1.11). Names are written in Greek and simple wind-

heads are depicted. Such manuscripts are among the earliest known to contain maps based on the texts of Ptolemy's *Geography*. The influence of the work of Ptolemy will be discussed at greater length in Chapter V.

The Roman world

After the decline of Greek science, the Romans continued the practice of mapmaking, although they did not make many advances on the techniques of their predecessors. Much Roman mapmaking appears to have been based on itineraries, which were essential in such a far-flung empire as that of Rome at its zenith, stretching from northern Britain to the gates of the East. The best-known example of the type of maps compiled by the Romans is the so-called *Tabula Peutingeriana*, known to us as a medieval copy of a first-century AD road map locating towns, way stations and forts in the territories of the empire (Plates 1.1 and 1.12). The map was named after one Konrad Peutinger, the scholar who owned the map from 1508. It was originally a long roll of parchment, some 6.75 metres in length by 0.34 metres wide, but has been divided into more manageable sections for ease of preservation.

PLATE 1.9 *(opposite)*
A reconstruction of a world map by Eratosthenes, of about 220 BC, summarizing the information collected by the early Greek travellers. The known world appears as a rounded-off rectangle. Eratosthenes's map was drawn to scale as far as possible and may be considered as the first scientific Greek map.

PLATE 1.10 *A woodcut portrait of Claudius Ptolemy* (c. AD 90–168) *dating from the sixteenth century. Ptolemy's* Geography *is the best-known and most influential of the early works on geography. The text marks the zenith of Greek geographical thought and contains the first recognizable and scientifically calculated map projections.*

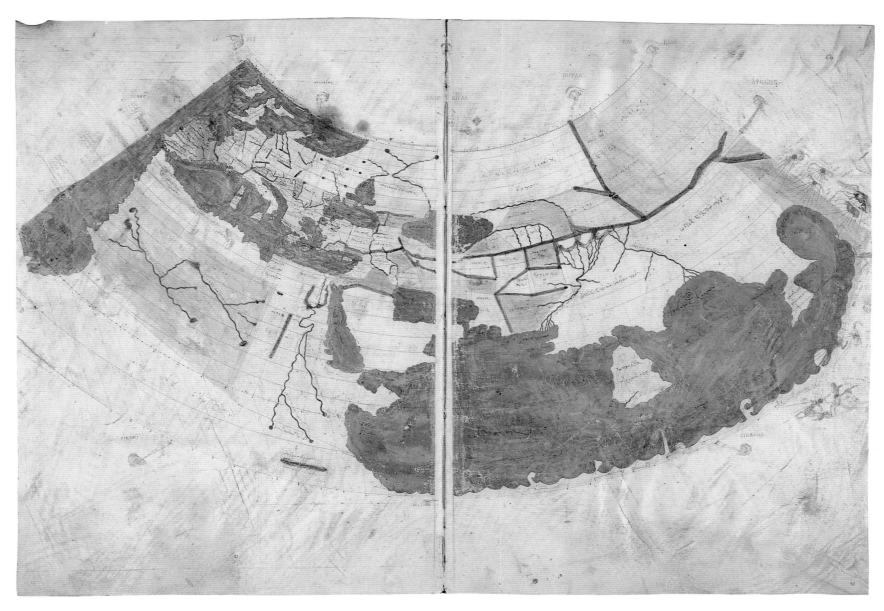

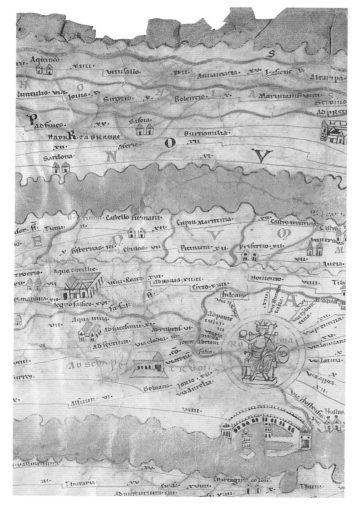

PLATE I.II *(above)*
A manuscript Ptolemaic
world map from the Codex
Urbanus Graecus 82
dating from the twelfth or
thirteenth century. The
names are written in Greek,
and simple wind-heads are
shown. Such manuscripts
are the earliest known to
contain maps based on the
texts of Ptolemy's Geography.
The map is now in Rome.

The copy which has survived was drawn in the twelfth or thirteenth century, and was once thought to have been the work of a monk at Colmar, who copied the map onto twelve sheets in 1265. The most obvious feature of the map is that its total width east-west is about twenty times its height north-south, and it was probably even longer originally. North-south distances therefore appear very short, while east-west distances appear correspondingly much too long. Nevertheless, the map served a particular purpose: to show the main roads and the staging-posts along them, with distances between each.

The earliest version of the map may have had its origins some time during the first century AD, since the towns of Pompeii and Herculaneum, destroyed and buried by the great eruption of Vesuvius in AD 79, are included. Names of regions inside and outside the Roman Empire are given, but no boundaries are shown. Roads are represented by continuous lines, but without any distinction between major and minor roads. No military installations appear to be named, so it is

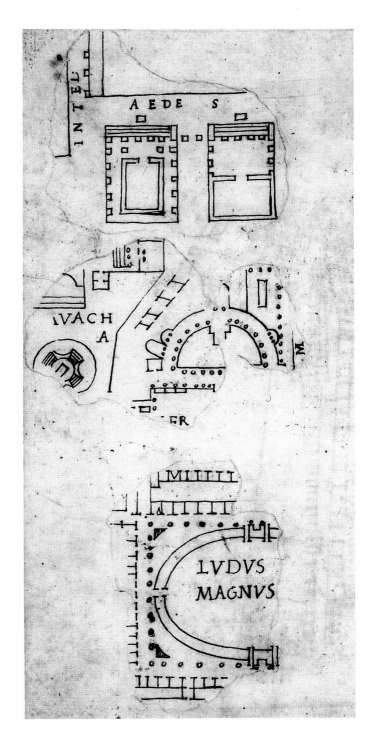

from Lympne to Exeter remains, with some of the places to the north of the Thames, in modern Essex, also visible. O.A.W. Dilke comments:

It should not be thought that the Peutinger Table was typical of Roman maps, or that the Romans were incapable of drawing a map to scale. General maps, land surveyors' maps and town plans were drawn to scale, with reasonable approximations to cartography. If this road map was not, either it alone or the type constitutes an exception. Today's underground maps are not drawn to scale, but are really stylized topological models, simpler and more rapidly interpreted than a map to scale and in correct shape.[4]

Even in the present day, modern road maps in atlases such as the British AA handbooks show the motorways in similar, readily recognizable strip form as itineraries rather than maps drawn to scale, but are easily interpreted by the user as a ready reference.

Another, rather different example of Roman mapmaking is the scale plan of Rome, dating from AD 203–211 (Plate 1.13). Carved in marble at a scale of 1:240, it is an impressive record of the skills of Roman surveyors.

PLATE 1.12 (*opposite*) *A small section of the so-called* Tabula Peutingeriana, *a medieval copy of a road map of the Roman Empire. Note that it is drawn in strip form – a form still familiar to the road-user today – with all but the more essential detail omitted or compressed. The city of Rome and its seaport at Ostia are easily seen, with individual roads leading to and from the Eternal City clearly marked and named. The greenish-blue wavy lines represent rivers.*

PLATE 1.13 (*left*) *Small fragments of a scale-plan of Rome are shown in this tracing carved in marble at a scale of 1:240 dating from AD 203–211. This impressive cartographic record of the skills of Roman surveyors is likely to have been made for official purposes, and may have been done for the then Prefect of Rome, Lucius Fabius Cilio.*

Non-European cultures

So far then, we have concentrated on the origins and early history of maps in an Old World context. But it must not be imagined that cultures beyond Europe, in its broadest sense, had no knowledge of maps or of mapping techniques. North American Indians, Australian Aborigines, Eskimos, Pacific Islanders and others are known to have developed for themselves some techniques of representing their environment in graphic form, whether as a result of contact with Europeans or quite independently before any known contacts with other peoples. Most of these maps have only come to our knowledge in the West in the last few centuries, following the discoveries of the early explorers, but it is likely that the mapmaking traditions found in these cultures were established many centuries ago.

North American Indians
There is plenty of evidence to demonstrate that the North American Indians drew maps, whether to express cosmological ideas or to record migrations

assumed that the *Tabula Peutingeriana* served a civilian rather than a purely military purpose. Some 555 towns are marked, most by what we would nowadays call a conventional sign (usually in the form of a small building). Granaries, altars and lighthouses are also shown. Three large cities – Rome, Constantinople and Antioch – are given special treatment and shown by their representative goddesses. Rome and Constantinople were singled out because they were the capitals of the western and eastern empires, while Antioch (Antakya in southeastern Turkey) was chosen because of its important role in the defence of the eastern empire. In the extreme west, only a fragment of Britain survives, the part which extended beyond the original first sheet of parchment. London is not shown, but the coastal area

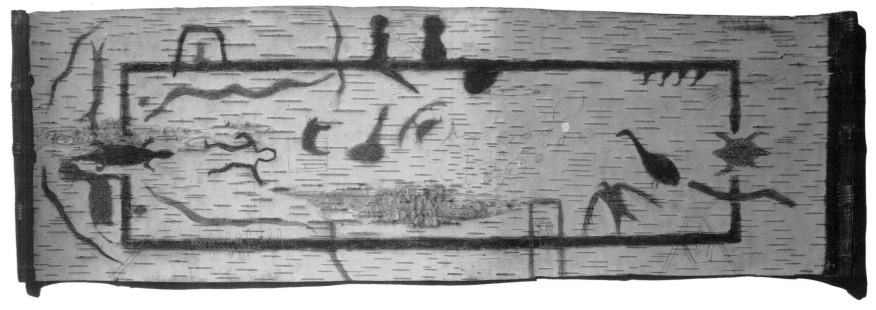

PLATE 1.14 *An unusual example of a North American Indian chart, which has been interpreted as a migration, or* midéwegun, *chart of an area near Lake Superior.*

PLATE 1.15 *(opposite) Portions of maps carved on driftwood showing part of the coast of King Christian IX Land in eastern Greenland. The long thin strip represents the offshore islands facing the coast near Sermiligaaq (65°55′N; 36°30′W).*

of tribes or herds, or inter-tribal battles. An early example is found in Captain John Smith's account of Virginia in 1607, in which he describes how the Powhatan Indians used three circles of corn and meal centred on a fire to represent: first, their own country as the inner circle; second, the coastline of North America; and third the edge of the supposedly circular world, with Captain Smith's own country of origin, the British Isles, placed as a pile of twigs between the second and the outermost circles. A later example, described by G.M. Lewis, showed how a Delaware Indian preacher used a map drawn on deer hide, from which he made copies for trading purposes:

[The map] consisted of two concentric squares, the outer of which enclosed the land and the inner the habitat of the Indians in their after-life. The area between the two squares was further divided into the habitat of the Indians in this life and their former habitat, which had been lost to the whites. Opposite corners of the inner square represented a former avenue to after-life, access to which had been closed by the whites, and a newly opened but dangerous alternative.[5]

It was, however, a more basic need – the desire to communicate with other members of a tribe, or perhaps warn off members of other tribes, or simply to leave messages – that created the necessity for mapping among the Indians. In the north, white birch bark was widely used as a medium for drawing maps with charcoal sticks or stones dipped in paint. Until the middle of the nineteenth century such maps were relatively common in the upper Mississippi valley and Great Lakes region, where they would be found placed on the end of a pole to make them conspicuous. They indicated the number of the tribe, their direction of travel, and so on. Usually, the location of a lake or river, camp sites and details of routes used for transport made up the cartographic content, in a manner easily understood by those with a knowledge of the region. An example of a migration chart showing the region around Lake Superior can be seen in the British Museum (Plate 1.14). Other examples would depict hunting activities, either to locate buffalo herds or to show places where good fishing was to be had. Few examples have survived, possibly because of their ephemeral and fragile nature or because they were considered primitive and unimportant by the white people who first saw them when they encountered the Indians.

Sometimes, however, whites recognized this particular skill of the Indians, and would commission them to make maps, some of which were drawn on paper or animal hide. Before the middle of the nineteenth century, maps of this type would have been commissioned by explorers, traders or missionaries. Spanish missionaries in the southwest produced hundreds of such maps from local sources, and tribes friendly to French traders in upper midwestern regions made maps to show the French which rivers might be used to reach distant tribes in their quest for furs and hides.

Eskimo maps

Elsewhere in North America, among the Eskimo peoples of the Canadian Arctic, mapping traditions have evolved which appear to demonstrate the results of highly developed skills of observation, or perhaps the development of mapping techniques as a result of contact with outside cultures. In the southeast part of Hudson Bay in northern Canada is a small group of islands, the Belcher Islands, which appear on maps and charts in a highly complicated outline. The true nature of this outline was not established until the explorations and researches of R.J. Flaherty during the years 1912–1916. The reason for Flaherty's expedition was an outline map drawn in manuscript by an Eskimo named Wetalltok, in about 1895, which showed the island group's outline completely at odds with the current Admiralty charts. As a result of the Flaherty expedition, the Eskimo's charts were proved to be remarkably accurate. As P.D.A. Harvey points out, 'This says a great deal for Wetalltok's sense of topography as well as for his skill in mapping, but it tells us nothing of native Eskimo cartography, for he had been in close touch with Europeans'.[6] Nevertheless, this does not explain how the Eskimo could draw such an accurate outline. A possible explanation is that Wetalltok and his people, being expert hunters and sailors, were in such close touch with their immediate surroundings that they were used to taking detailed note of the lie of the land.

A more recent instance of contacts with outside cultures may also be illustrated by the example of native charts carved on pieces of driftwood and bone, showing parts of the coastline of Greenland (Plate 1.15). These are remarkable and accurate charts, made as a result of close observation of the lie of inlets and offshore islands. Such skills have, however, gradually become corrupted because of the thriving tourist trade, which has led to the production of debased examples for eager buyers.

The Marshall Islands

Farther afield, in the western Pacific Ocean, among the Marshall Islanders, another type of mapping tradition grew up – one of the most interesting examples of native mapping skills. This is the tradition of the 'stick-charts', first reported as recently as 1862. The stick-charts of the Marshall Islands are made from the strong but flexible centre ribs of palm leaves (Plate 1.16). They are lashed together to make either straight or curved lines, and many also have small shells attached at the intersections of the ribs. Some of the charts are quite large, measuring some 600 mm square, and sometimes as much as 1,500 mm long. Their main purpose is to show the directions

of deep-sea swells and currents. Three types have been identified: *mattang*, which show the main principles involved; *meddo*, which show smaller parts of the island group or individual islands; and *rebbelith*, which are charts of either one or both of the main chains of the Marshall Islands. The charts have continued to be used by the islanders alongside navigational aids brought in as a result of contact with European and other peoples.

These stick-charts are not meant to be used to plot a course as one can with conventional charts, although at one time it was thought that the *meddo* type was used in this manner. The interpretation

PLATE 1.16 *(overleaf) A Marshall Islands stick-chart of the* mattang *type showing a portion of the archipelago. The small shells mark either single islands or island groups: The curved strips indicate prevailing wave directions. At a glance primitive, it is in reality a highly complex and sophisticated piece of chartmaking based on direct observation.*

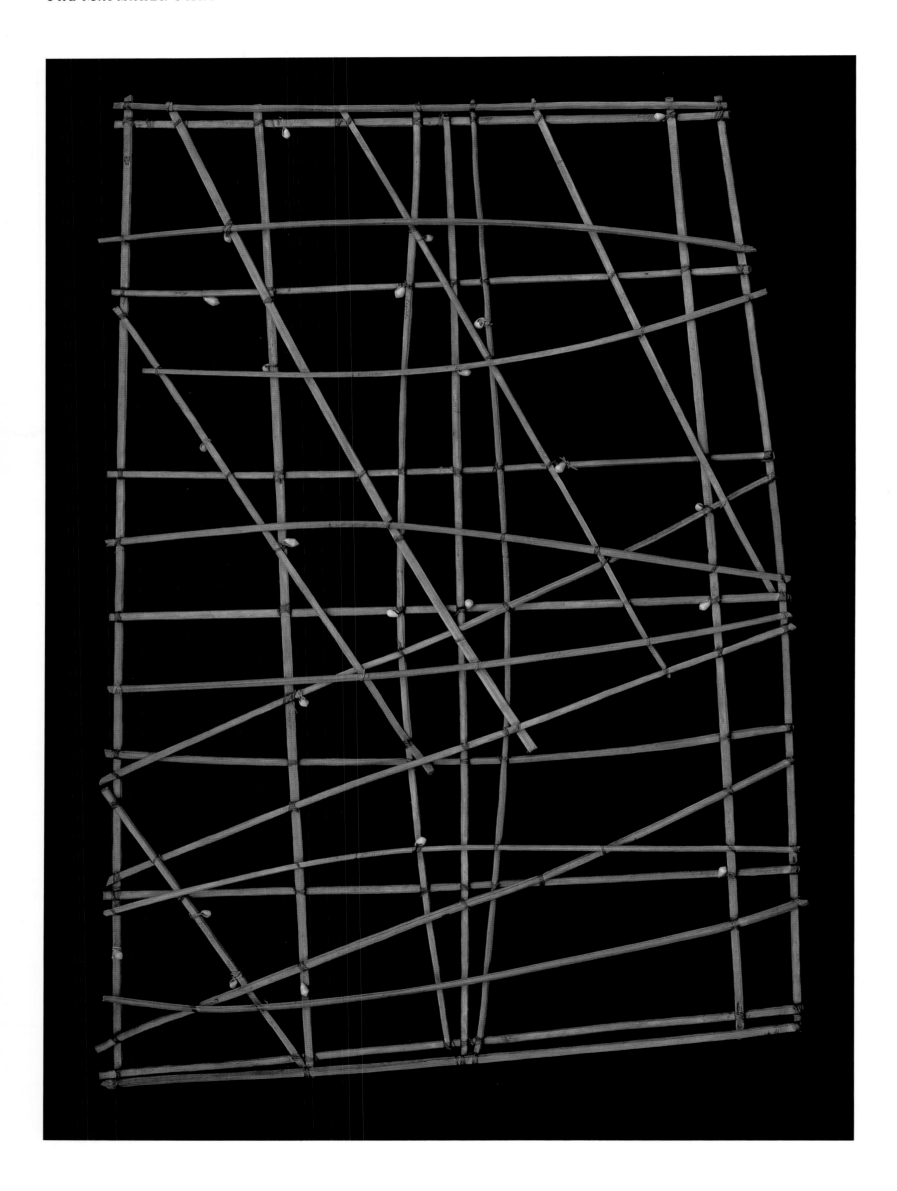

of the stick-charts was a closely guarded secret of the master mariners of the islands for many years, but it has now become apparent that the charts were used for instructional purposes. The techniques were learned on dry land and the pattern was then memorized by the individual navigator. We cannot be certain how widespread the use of these charts was throughout the islands, for the only known examples originate from the southern parts of the Marshall Islands. That these stick-charts are still in use and that they can be used for navigating seemingly featureless waters over several hundred nautical miles is surely testament to the sophistication of the culture in which they were developed. Indeed, the very currents and swells observed by the islanders have only been observed in clear detail on the ocean surface since the NASA satellite surveys began intensive coverage of the earth's surface in the 1970s.

Australian Aborigines

Mapmaking also developed in unique ways in Australia among the various tribes of the Australian Aborigines. Much of our knowledge on these matters comes from the earliest colonists and explorers, and has depended very largely on chance and the curiosity of particular observers. One such example is from the island of Mer in the Murray Islands, situated between Papua New Guinea and Queensland, northern Australia. If examples of such maps had not been collected by Europeans in early days, they might have languished in the basements of anthropological collections, uncatalogued and slowly gathering dust.

It would be extremely difficult to find out how such mapmaking skills existed among less developed societies, or to work out any pattern of distribution. However, it would be naive of us to suppose that the only reason why such peoples made maps was to help them find their way. Symbolic maps were probably just as important to Aborigines as practical maps (Plate 1.17). As Harvey points out:

[It is] perfectly possible that the Bindibu carved their spear-throwers with maps of the tribal waters as a handy *aide-mémoire* that one would always have with one . . . But it is no less possible that the maps were symbolic in purpose as well as in form, representing an assertion of rights, a statement of sovereignty . . .

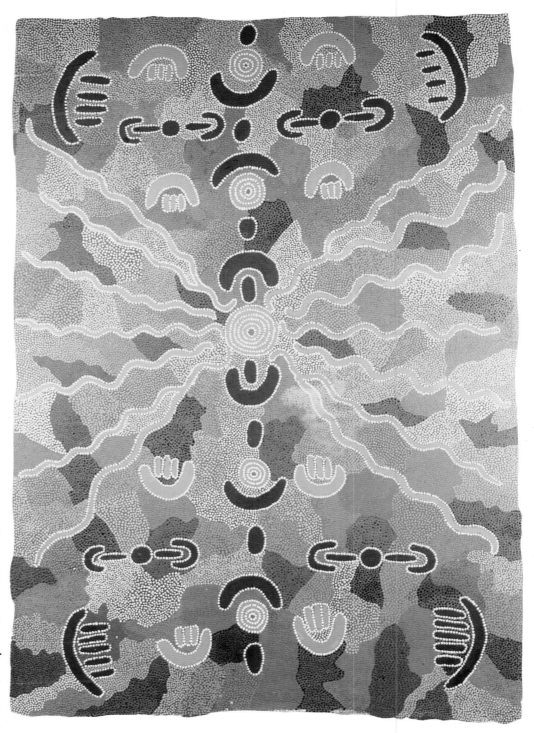

And we must remember that the range of purely practical purposes that a map might serve in such societies would be rather wider than in our own, which takes a more limited view of causation: designs or objects representing houses, villages, fields, rivers and other features of the landscape would be an obvious vehicle for sympathetic magic, like the shells that represented villages on the island of Mer.[7]

PLATE 1.17 Maliki *Jukurrpa (Dingo Dreaming) by David Jupurrula Oldfield. An example of an Australian Aboriginal map, here showing the Ngama country near Yuendumu (northeast of Alice Springs, Northern Territory). The lines radiating from the central circular motif represent the tracks and paths taken by the dingoes.*

References
1. O.A.W. Dilke, *Greek and Roman Maps*, page 35, 1984.
2. Lloyd A. Brown, *The Story Of Maps*, reprint edition, page 17, 1977.
3. Strabo, *Geography I*, pages 51 & 53, 1917.
4. O.A.W. Dilke, *op. cit.*, page 120.
5. G.M. Lewis, *The Map Collector*, 9, 1979.
6. P.D.A. Harvey, *The History of Topographical Maps*, page 34, 1980.
7. P.D.A. Harvey, *op. cit.*

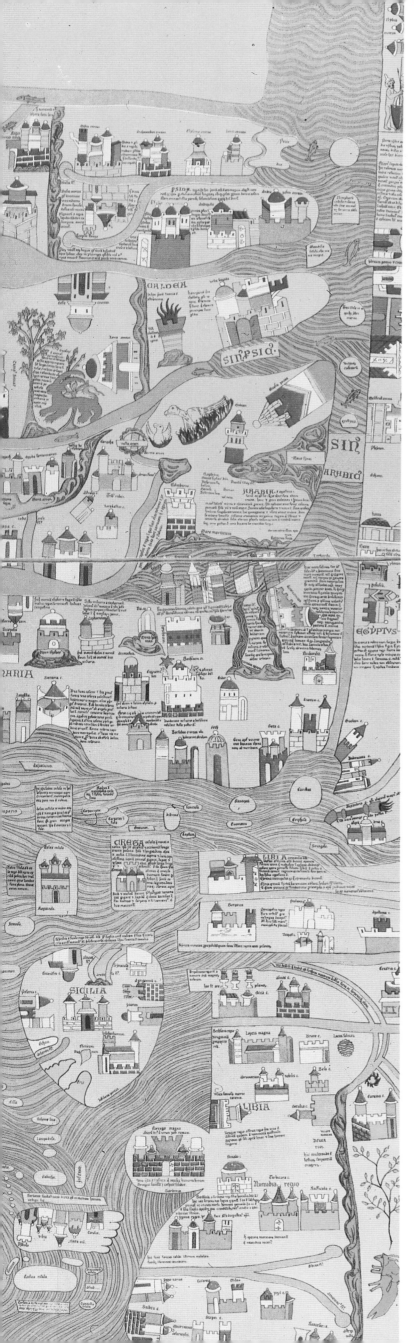

CHAPTER II

MEDIEVAL MAPMAKING

700 – 1500 AD

AFTER THE DECLINE of the Roman Empire, and of Greek science, mapmaking in western Europe entered a period of relative decline. This is not to suggest, however, that maps were not being made in Europe at this time – some 1,100 world maps are known to have survived from the period AD 700–1500, according to the survey of Marcel Destombes.[1] We know that the globular form of the earth was recognized by most scholars and geographers of the Middle Ages, but medieval mapmakers were rooted in the dogmas of the Christian church and scientific precision was not a primary concern. While many of these maps were very elaborate and often highly decorative, the geographical knowledge was crude and inaccurate. The only reasonably accurate maps made in Europe at this time were the early portolan charts, which were based on the practical observations of skilled navigators and seamen. During the corresponding period in the East, however, the Chinese developed the art and science of cartography to a high degree, and their example was later followed by the Arabs.

PLATE 2.1 *Detail from the Ebstorf* mappamundi *made for the convent at Ebstorf near Lüneberg, c. 1339. This highly decorative map is a typical example of cartographic work produced in Europe in medieval times and is one of the most elaborate maps of its kind. The map is full of information, containing illustrations of mythical creatures, and strange peoples such as archers with four eyes and people who use sign language.*

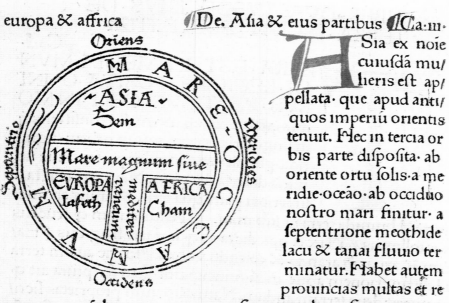

europa & affrica

De Afia & eius partibus Ca. iii.

ASia ex noie cuiufdā mu/ lieris eft ap/ pellata· que apud anti/ quos imperiū orientis tenuit. Hec in tercia or bis parte difpofita· ab oriente ortu folis·a me ridie·oceāo· ab occiduo noftro mari finitur· a feptentrione meothide lacu & tanai fluuio ter minatur. Habet autem prouincias multas et re giones·quarū breuiter nomina et fitus expediam· fumpto initio a paradifo Paradifus eft locus in orientis partibus conftitu/ tus·cuius vocabulum ex greco in latinum vertitur ortus. Porro hebraice eden dicitur·quod in noftra lingua delicie interpretat· quod vtrumq; iunctum facit ortum deliciarum·eft enim omni genere ligni & pomiferarum arborum confitus habens· etiam lignum vite. Non ibi frigus· non eftus· fed perpetua aeris tem/ peries·e cuius medio fons prorumpens·totum nemus irrigat· di uiditurq; in quatuor nafcentia flumina. Cuius loci poft pecca/ tum hominis aditus interclufus eft. Septus eft eni vndiq; rom phea flammea·id eft muro igneo accinctus· ita ut eius cū caelo pene iungatur incendium. Cherubin quoq; id eft angelorum prefidium arcendis fpiritibus malis fuper romphee flagrantiā ordinatum eft·ut homines flamme·angelos vero malos angeli boni fubmoueāt·ne cui carni vel fpiritui tranfgreffionis aditus paradifi pateat. India vocata ab indo flumine· quo ex parte occidentali clauditur. Haec a meridiano mari porrecta vfq; ad ortum folis·& a feptentrione vfq; ad montem caucafum perue/ nit·babens gentes multas & oppida· infulam quoq; taprobane gemmis & elephantibus refertam. Crifam & argiram auro ar/ gentoq; fecundas·vtilem quoq; arboribus foliis nunqm caren tibus. Habet & flumina gangen & nidan & idafpen illuftran/ tes indos. Terra indie fauonio fpiritu faluberrima. In anno bis

PLATE 2.2 A T–O world map from an edition of Bishop Isidore of Seville's Etymologiae printed by Gunther Zainer at Augsburg in 1472. The map, measuring some 65 mm, was the first printed map in Europe.

T–O maps

In western Europe world maps from the Middle Ages are essentially diagrammatic in form and have been given the generic name of 'T–O' maps. There is very little map-like about them, however – rather they are a sort of 'shorthand' view of the world as we shall see below.

The concept of the T–O map arose in the writing of Isidore, Bishop of Seville from AD 600 to 636, in his *Etymologiarum sive originum libri xx* (usually known as the *Etymologiae*). In this work,

Isidore devised a 'map' of the world in which it was shown surrounded by the encircling ocean (*Mare Oceanum*) (Plate 2.2). This was represented by the letter O, in keeping with the ancient concept that the world was surrounded by water. Within the O, a T shape was drawn. This T divided the world into the three known continents, Asia, Africa and Europe. The vertical stroke of the letter represented the Mediterranean (literally 'the middle of the earth'), while the cross-stroke of the T represented the great rivers, the Don (*Tanais fluvius*) and the Nile (*Nilus fluvius*). The cross-stroke was also intended to represent the Black Sea, the Bosphorus, and the eastern Mediterranean. In the east, above the cross-stroke of the T, was often placed a representation of the Garden of Eden, following the words of Genesis 2:8 – 'And the Lord God planted a garden eastward in Eden' – thus according Eden a place of honour on the map. Four rivers were also described as flowing from the Garden of Eden: Pishon, Gihon, Tigris and Euphrates.

The idea that the T–O maps might be considered as a shorthand picture of the world, especially in its religious context, is further emphasized by the fact that the letter T derives from the Greek letter *tau*, which was often used as an ancient representation of that most important of Christian symbols, the cross. The purpose of the T–O maps was in part to disseminate Christian doctrine, bearing in mind that the maps were made by monks, and that monasteries were the main centres of learning in the Middle Ages. The junction of the vertical stroke and the cross-stroke of the letter T formed the centre of the T–O map. This centre represented the centre of the Christian world, namely Jerusalem, the holy city of Christendom: 'Thus saith the Lord God; this is Jerusalem: I have set it in the midst of the nations and countries that are round about her.' (Ezekiel 5:5).

The four main directions, north, east, south and west, were marked as *septentrio*, *oriens*, *meridies* and *occidens* respectively, with *septentrio* (north) referring to the seven stars of the constellation of the Great Bear and *meridies* (south) to the midday position of the sun on the meridian. The *Etymologiae* of Bishop Isidore was first printed with his T–O map in 1472, seven centuries after the book was first written. It continued in print for about another century, illustrating how rooted and far-reaching were the religious beliefs of the Middle Ages, deeply colouring people's perception and representation of the world.

Mappaemundi

During the Middle Ages some highly elaborate and often extremely beautiful world maps, *mappaemundi*, were made. (The word 'map' is derived from the Latin *mappamundi*, which literally means 'cloth of the world'.) *Mappaemundi* were produced under the influence of Christian theology within a rigid framework prescribed by the conventions of the Church. A smattering of detail based on contemporary travel was added wherever it could be fitted into this framework. The most famous and the largest extant example is the so-called Hereford map, measuring some 1,630 mm by 1,370 mm and drawn on a large sheet of vellum (Plate 2.3). The Hereford map was designed by one Richard of Haldingham and Lafford, presumed prebendary of Lafford in Lincoln Cathedral, in about 1276. Some of the sources of the Hereford map are classical in origin, references being made, for example, to the cartographers employed by Julius Caesar to prepare a world map. The basic plan of the map is of the T–O type, but without the strictly formal divisions. The names of Paris, Rome and Antioch stand out, as do those of two Alpine passes, which suggests that one of the purposes of the map was to indicate routes for pilgrims intending to make their way to Rome and, ultimately, to Jerusalem. Vivid pictorial elements include scenes from the Bible, mythical beings and hideous and malformed monsters and people, no doubt intended to prevent the fearful (and illiterate) spectator from straying from the path of righteousness.

The very crudeness of the geography of the Hereford map reflects a marked deterioration in geographical knowledge from the time of Ptolemy, a thousand years earlier. Accuracy and objectiveness in geography were not of primary concern to the medieval mind, though the map is based on complex itineraries and much secular history. The many illustrations served to educate the viewer in the principles of the Church, laced with dogma, mythology, folklore and symbolism. Indeed, these very symbols and monsters appeared in one of the first great encyclopaedic works to be

PLATE 2.3 *(above) The Hereford mappamundi, attributed to Richard of Haldingham and Lafford, c. 1290. This celebrated world map is one of the best known of all mappaemundi and is one of the largest of its kind. The traditional T–O form can clearly be seen, with the British Isles appearing at lower left.*

PLATE 2.4 *(left) The so-called Psalter world map in a thirteenth-century English psalter. Jerusalem in the centre of the map is surrounded by numerous mythical creatures and faces. The map measures only c. 10 cm across.*

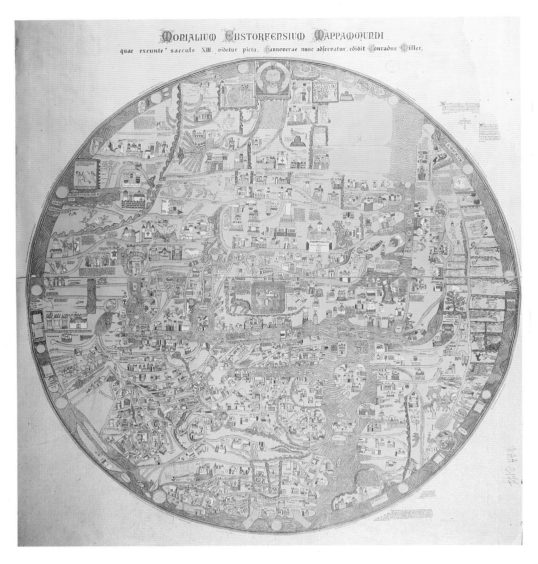

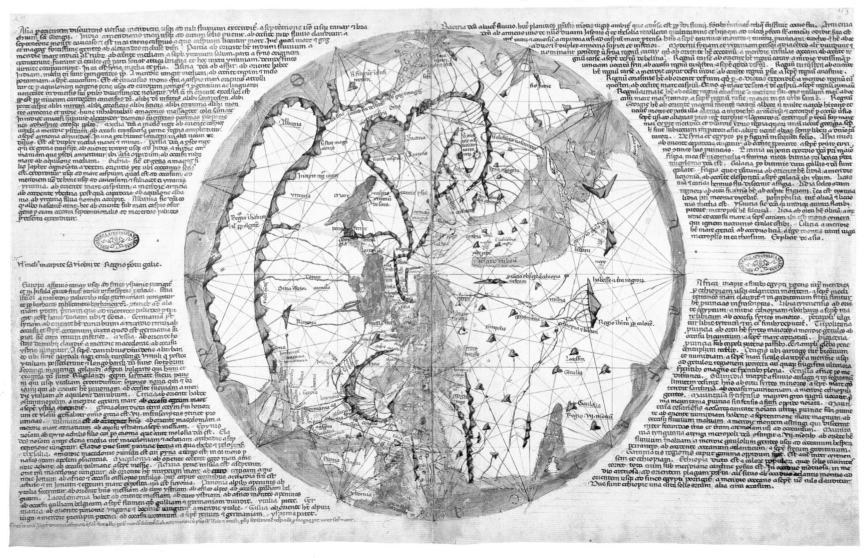

printed, the *Liber chronicarum* (the 'Nuremberg Chronicle'), compiled by Hartman Schedel and printed in 1493. This work was replete with all the beasts, monsters, hideous dwarfs and angels of death of medieval imagery. A recent commentator on the Hereford map wrote that:

It has many of the attributes of Isidore's . . . *Etymologiae* . . . Both are eclectic, uncritical, illogical, unoriginal in that they depended entirely on outside sources, and consistent only in their unswerving loyalty to Christian principles. Taken together, these attributes of medieval times reflected a manner of thought which contrasts with that of both preceding and following times. A basic difference appears to be in medieval otherworldliness taken to the point of indifference to the realities of the physical world. That was viewed, not from first hand, but as it was described in ancient sources, without thought of their possible errors or widely varying quality and without attempts to evaluate their validity or to improve upon them. The attitudes of the Greeks and Romans which prevailed before the Middle Ages were dissimilar, but neither were so sharply divorced from reality, and the contrast of medieval with modern attitudes is equally clear. But

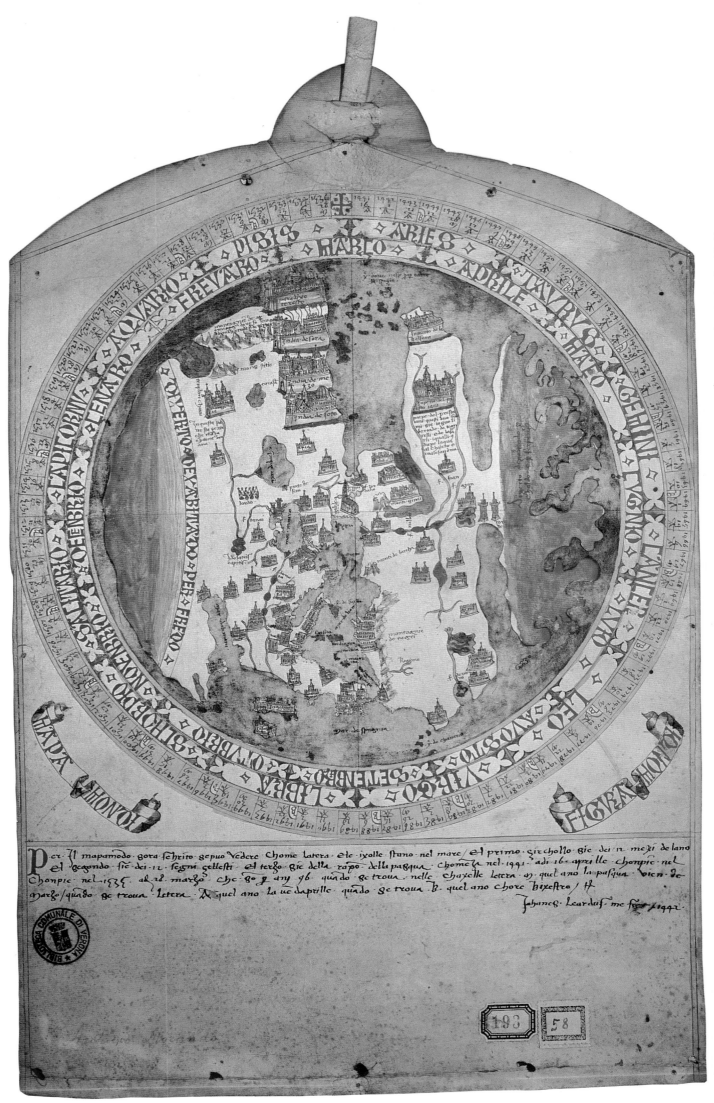

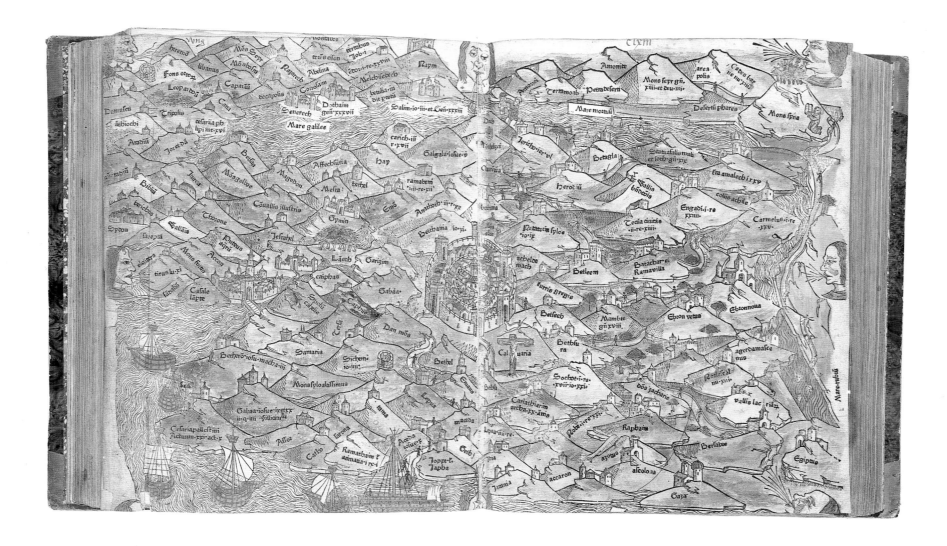

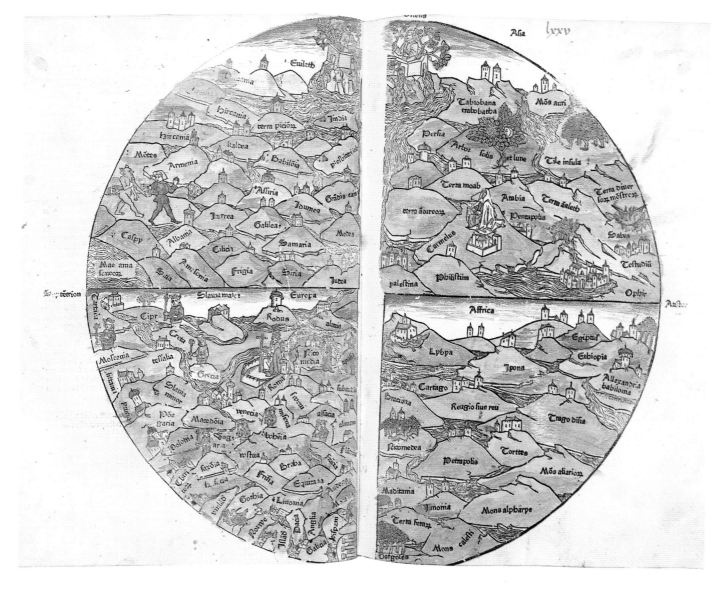

PLATE 2.8 *(above and right)* A map of Palestine *(above)* and a circular world map *(right)* printed by Lucas Brandis in Rudimentum novitiorum *at Lübeck in 1475. The world, in traditional medieval circular form, is oriented with the east to the top and with Jerusalem at the centre.

PLATE 2.9 *(opposite)* Das ist die mapa mu[n]di un[d] alle Land un[d] kungk reich wie sie ligend in der ga[n]tze Welt *by Hans Rüst, separately published woodcut, Augsburg, c. 1480. A very rare example of a printed medieval* mappamundi, *known from only one surviving copy. Note Jerusalem at the top centre, with the Pillar of Hercules at the opposite end of the Mediterranean.*

PLATE 2.10 *Medieval sailors charting their course across the seas. Detail from* Livre des Marveilles, *a fourteenth-century French illuminated manuscript.*

the Hereford map has one positive attribute which merits our consideration. Much attention was given to make it beautiful, both in its overall organization and in the quality of its individual illustrations. Medieval drawings have an undeniable charm. They may seem naïve, but somehow they catch the essence of what they were intended to portray in a way that a photograph or modern drawing does not always do.[2]

Another fine example of medieval mapmaking is the Ebstorf *mappamundi* (*c.* 1339) (Plates 2.1 and 2.5). Made for the convent at Ebstorf, near Lüneburg, it was sadly destroyed in an air-raid in 1943, and is reproduced from a facsimile. A huge map, it measured more than three metres in diameter. It was one of the most elaborate of its kind, full of information and illustrations of strange peoples. East, represented by the head of Christ, appears at the top of the map. A close relation to the Ebstorf map is the so-called Psalter world map which appears in a thirteenth-century English psalter (Plate 2.4). In contrast to the huge Ebstorf map which is some thirty-five times larger, the small but priceless Psalter map measures only ten centimetres across.

A fine example of a *mappamundi* oriented in the traditional manner, with east at the top, is Giovanni Leardo's *Mapa Mondi Figura Mondi* of 1442 (Plate 2.7). An interesting feature is the surrounding Easter calendar and zodiac.

At some time during the early fourteenth century, *mappaemundi* began to include the kind of information depicted on portolan charts. A notable example is Pietro Vesconte's *mappamundi* of *c.* 1321 (Plate 2.6). Note, for instance, the outline of the Mediterranean Sea and a network of rhumb-lines – features seen on early portolan charts. The first European printed maps to show land form and coastlines in some topographical relation to each other were the maps included in the *Rudimentum novitiorum*, printed at Lübeck in 1475 (Plates 2.8 A and B). A very rare example of a printed medieval *mappamundi* is the fine *mappamundi* of *c.* 1480 by Hans Rüst (Plate 2.9).

Portolan charts

While western cartography was dominated in the Middle Ages by Church doctrine and mythology, a much more practical type of map was evolving in the Mediterranean, based on actual observation rather than religious beliefs. Portolan charts (sea charts giving accurate sailing directions) evolved some time during the thirteenth century and were a major advance in medieval and hydrographic mapping, with an influence that lasted for some four hundred years.

It is possible that portolan charts had their origins in the written directions for coastal passages from one seaport to another, which originated in the private notes and logs kept by navigators and pilots for personal reference. These written notes, known as 'portolans', were non-pictorial. They gradually accumulated more and more local experience, and by the late thirteenth century many of the directions contained in the local accounts had been collected into a pilot-book called *Il Compasso da navigare*, published in 1296. This book covered the entire Mediterranean and Black Sea coasts; the directions given in it run clockwise around the Mediterranean coasts from Cabo de São Vicente at the southwestern tip of Portugal to Safi in Morocco. The information includes bearings, distances in Italian miles, guides to entering harbours, dangers, shoals and reefs, together with facts on safe harbours and anchorages. There are also directions for several long-distance passages between particular reference points, such as well-known or distinctive islands, headlands and similar features.

The portolan charts, then, were in essence these same sailing directions but based on actual observation and depicted pictorially and cartographically. It has been suggested that some form of nautical chart, based on Greek *periploi* (written descriptions of coastlines for navigational use), may have existed in classical times, but if such charts were ever drawn, none has survived, and it is unlikely that they were the inspiration for portolan charts. Use of the term 'portolan chart' to describe these sea charts is relatively recent, and seems first to have been used in this way at the end of the nineteenth century by A.E. Nordenskiöld in his descriptive work, *Periplus*.

Features of the charts

The charts have several distinctive features:

1. A network of intersecting straight lines (usually called 'rhumb-lines') originating from sixteen equidistant points was spread about the circumference of a 'hidden' circle. The lines frequently extended beyond the circle and there was often a fairly elaborate compass-rose at one or more of the intersecting points.

2. Place and feature names were written perpendicular to the coastline, in sequence along the coast. Some would inevitably appear upside down to the viewer when read in the conventional manner, but they could easily be followed if they were read in the same direction as that of a vessel plying the coast.

3. The charts were drawn in ink, on skins of vellum or parchment, according to certain colour conventions. The most important names were shown in red, the rest in black; the lines depicting the four main wind directions according to Mediterranean tradition were drawn in black or sepia, those for the eight half-winds in green and those for the sixteen quarter-winds in red.

4. Coastlines were shown in a generalized manner, but with particular emphasis on bays and headlands, as well as on hazards such as rocks, reefs and shoals. These were marked with dots or small crosses in a manner clearly distinguishable from the rest of the detail given on the chart.[3]

From this it may be gathered that portolan charts were quite unlike contemporary medieval maps. They often incorporated detail of remarkable accuracy, based on close and actual observation, rather than the conventional medieval habit of repeating cartographical and mythical information issued by the Church. Indeed, from the outset, portolan charts appear to have been remarkably accurate, with little evolutionary development from the earliest known examples to the later charts made towards the end of the seventeenth century; however, although the coastlines on these charts have remained consistent, the place-names have evolved over the centuries.

Portolan charts were mainly produced by chartmakers of Italian or Catalan origin. Most of the Catalan 'school' came from Mallorca in the Balearic Islands in the western Mediterranean and, as one might expect, most of the chartmakers in Italy worked in or near the great port cities of Genoa or Venice, or from other towns with

PLATE 2.11 *The* Carte Pisane *dating from c. 1300, the oldest known surviving portolan chart. Most of Europe and the Mediterranean is shown in recognizable outline. The chart has rhumb-lines joining points on two circles as direction-finding aids, as well as rectangular grids.*

PLATE 2.12 (above) A
portrait of Pietro Vesconte
on part of a section from a
portolan chart atlas by
Vesconte, 1313. Vesconte
was one of the earliest
known chart-makers.

PLATE 2.13 (right)
Part of the eastern
Mediterranean and the
Greek archipelago, Cyprus
and the Nile delta from a
portolan chart by Pietro
Vesconte, 1320. The large
island coloured in full is
Crete (left of centre),
with Rhodes immediately
northeast. Such charts
could be made up into an
atlas mounted back to
back between wooden
or card boards.

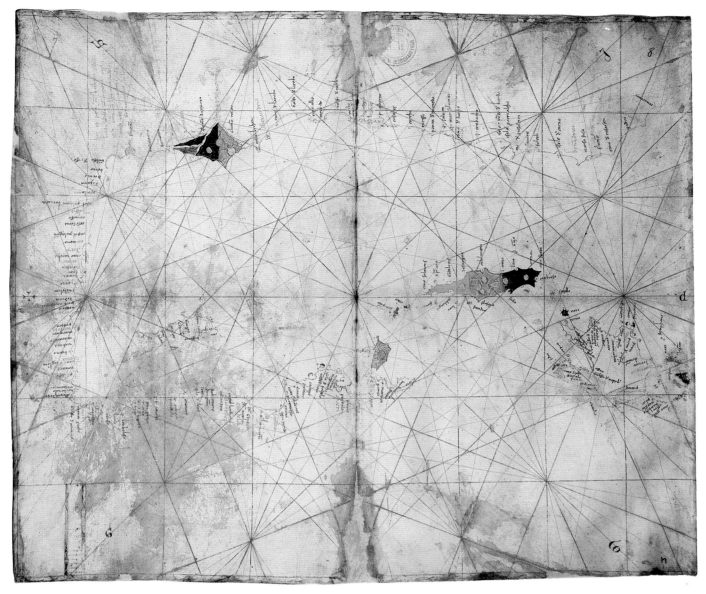

well-established maritime trading links, such as
Naples. It is not certain which of the two main
schools of portolan chartmakers came first, Catalan or Italian. At any rate, while the geographical
source material was obviously the same, Catalan
charts show some gradual change, in contrast to
their Italian counterparts.

Nevertheless, barring some decorative features
and elements, portolan charts were generally similar in form and appearance. This may be due to
the fact that, in the case of the Mediterranean
charts at least, the considerable number of seaports, and the relatively short distances between
them, reflected a need for easily read information.
This was particularly important for voyages carried out in the hours of daylight, with the
consequent need to find safe anchorage by night-
fall. Portolan charts were drawn to scale, and were
the first charts in late medieval and early modern
Europe made in this way.

The oldest known portolan chart is believed to
be the so-called *Carte Pisane*, from about 1300,

thought to have been made in Genoa for a Pisan
patron (Plate 2.11). One of the earliest recorded
portolan makers was Pietro Vesconte, who made
and dated charts from 1311 onwards (Plates 2.12
and 2.13). One of Vesconte's charts, made in
1325, was sold at Sotheby's in London in 1980.
Like some other early portolan charts, it once
formed part of the binding of a book and consequently had been cut down, folded and stitched.
Such treatment may seem drastic, but when a chart
was considered to have outlived its usefulness, and
binding materials were needed, what better material to use than an old vellum chart? Ironically,
such treatment has led to the survival of a large
number of cartographic treasures which would
otherwise have been thrown away or destroyed.

Design and illustration
Even though portolan charts were made for practical use, they were often works of art in their own
right, illuminated in bright colours and sometimes even with gold highlighting. It is these

decorative elements which most often attract the appreciation of today's collectors. Many fine examples exist with vignette illustrations of the major seaports or pictures of rivers and mountains. Sometimes the charts are embellished with flags and banners or, occasionally, caravans of merchants and traders, monarchs and kings. Often there are scenes of religious content, such as depictions of the Crucifixion or of the Virgin and Child, drawn at the neck-end (or narrow point – usually at the western edge) of the sheet of vellum or parchment. The most elaborate examples were probably never intended to be taken on board ship: they would soon have suffered surface damage through exposure to the elements, from less than careful handling, or from the simple plotting of courses. Many of these elaborate charts were intended to adorn the walls of the wealthy as valued possessions, which is why so many of them have survived in good condition to this day.

Charts used at sea, while not so beautiful to look at, also contained some decorative elements, such as religious symbols, intended perhaps as talismans or good luck charms for superstitious seafarers. Often town symbols were retained; pictures of Lisbon, Cadiz, Marseilles, Genoa, Venice, Ragusa or Constantinople appeared with great frequency, with other port cities indicated in different-coloured inks or in slightly larger lettering. Flags, banners and other symbols served a practical purpose also, for it should be remembered that many sailors, while skilled in their particular craft, were often barely literate. Sailors recognized very readily, for example, the symbol of Venice, the Lion of St Mark, or in later years the crescent symbol placed at Constantinople (which was taken by the Turks in 1453). These were useful precautions, for a crescent shown above a Muslim city might prevent a Christian sailor inadvertently travelling in that direction.

PLATE 2.14 *(below) Part of a portolan chart extending from northern Europe to the north African littoral by Angelino Dulcert, dated to c. 1339. The map is drawn in the manner of Catalan charts. Note the depiction of inland features, such as mountain ranges and major rivers, and the use of flag symbols to denote major towns and cities.*

PLATE 2.15 *(opposite)*
A Catalan (or Estense)
mappamundi, c. *1450.*
The Mediterranean basin
and Black Sea are well
defined but beyond this the
detail is merely imaginary.
The map is similar in style
to portolan charts, with a
network of rhumb-lines
radiating from the centre
of the map. Legendary
potentates are seen in Africa
and southwestern Asia.

An example of a portolan chart displaying many of these features is Angelino Dulcert's chart of *c.* 1339 (Plate 2.14).

Another convention found on portolan charts was the colouring of the island of Rhodes, off the coast of southwestern Turkey, in solid red with the white cross of the Order of St John superimposed on top. This was a common practice even on some charts (particularly those of Italian origin) made long after the expulsion of the Order by the Turks in 1522 and their removal to Malta, where they were re-established in 1530. Appropriately enough, the Red Sea was often coloured in red, particularly on Catalan charts. Again, many examples show the Moorish kingdom of Granada in southern Spain coloured in green, even after the final expulsion of the Moors in 1492.

Catalan trade

The Catalans were not only skilled navigators and accomplished map and chartmakers, but also highly esteemed traders, ranging as far as the Volga valley in southern Russia in the east and the Baltic shores in the north. They also developed trade with the Arabs, ignoring the papal ban on trading with Muslims which was in any case barely enforceable. Indeed, it should not be forgotten that Mallorca, where most of the Catalan charts were made, was ruled by the Muslims until 1248. It is therefore not unreasonable to suppose that contacts between Catalan and Arab geographers existed over several centuries, thus promoting knowledge of Arab geography and the development of cartography.

The Catalans were regular visitors to French, Italian, English and Low Countries seaports during the fourteenth century, and even established consulates to represent their interests abroad. In this way they could acquire information on these lands for possible future incorporation into their portolan charts. Descriptive notes are a feature of Catalan charts, as are geographical names, no doubt compiled from information received from their representatives abroad. It may be said that Catalan charts are at one and the same time sea charts and terrestrial maps, concerned, as many examples are, with the geography of coastal hinterlands. The masterpiece of the Catalan chartmakers is the so-called *Catalan Atlas*, made in 1375 by the Mallorcan Jew Abraham Cresques

(Plate 2.16). He was 'master of *mappaemundi* and of the compasses' to the King of Aragon, and presented his work to Charles V of France in 1381. Drawn on eight panels of wood, Cresques' large map stands as the most complete picture of geographical knowledge of the later Middle Ages.

Special features

In general, Catalan charts all contained the following features. The 'neck-end' of the vellum sheet was always at the left-hand side (or western edge). Directions were indicated by small discs showing the Pole Star for the north point, with the earth depicted by a sphere half-shaded at the top (north) to show the south orientation, a cross to represent the east and a rosette for the west point. Sometimes the discs were painted in the colours of Aragon (red and yellow), while inland waterbodies were painted with vertical wavy lines with their geographical names written within a coloured frame. Toponomy (place-names) and notes were usually written in Catalan or medieval 'dog' Latin. A particularly attractive example is the portolan chart made in 1456 by Jacobo Bertran and Berenguer Ripol in Barcelona, and clearly signed and dated. It shows the Mediterranean and part of the Atlantic seaboard stretching as far north as the coast of the Low Countries and the coasts of England and Wales. Another excellent example is the Catalan Atlas mentioned earlier (Plate 2.16). Here are many typical features of Catalan portolan charts: the Red Sea in the appropriate colour, the Atlas mountains and Andalusia (in Moorish hands) tinted green, the large-profile illustrations of towns and cities, the flags and standards of seafaring states and kingdoms. A slight oddity in this cannon of maps and charts is the Catalan (or Estense) *mappamundi*, *c.* 1450 (Plate 2.15). While the Mediterranean and Black Sea are well-defined, the detail beyond is purely imaginary. A characteristic network of rhumb-lines radiates from the centre of the map, and legendary potentates are shown in rich colours.

Italian charts generally showed only the Mediterranean coasts with parts of adjacent seas, and perhaps part of the Atlantic seaboard as far northwards as the Low Countries. A particular example is the *Medici Atlas*, dated some time during the first half of the fifteenth century, perhaps after 1415, which was probably inspired

by Catalan influences as it incorporates interior detail in abundance. In fact, it is likely that many Italian chartmakers learned their craft from chartmakers in Mallorca before establishing themselves in Italy. It is interesting to note that the world map in the *Medici Atlas* shows the southern part of Africa long before it was rounded by Bartholomew Dias and Vasco da Gama, though no doubt this was a later addition or modification. A later example of Italian chartmaking is the portolan chart of 1563 produced by the Maggiolo

family (Plate 2.17). An attractive feature is the fine, gilded decorative detail.

Methods of work

We know little about how chartmakers organized their affairs; it is generally assumed that portolan charts were made in workshops, but we cannot always be certain how many people were in fact involved in the actual construction of such charts. Illuminated manuscripts from the great monastic

(continued on page 50)

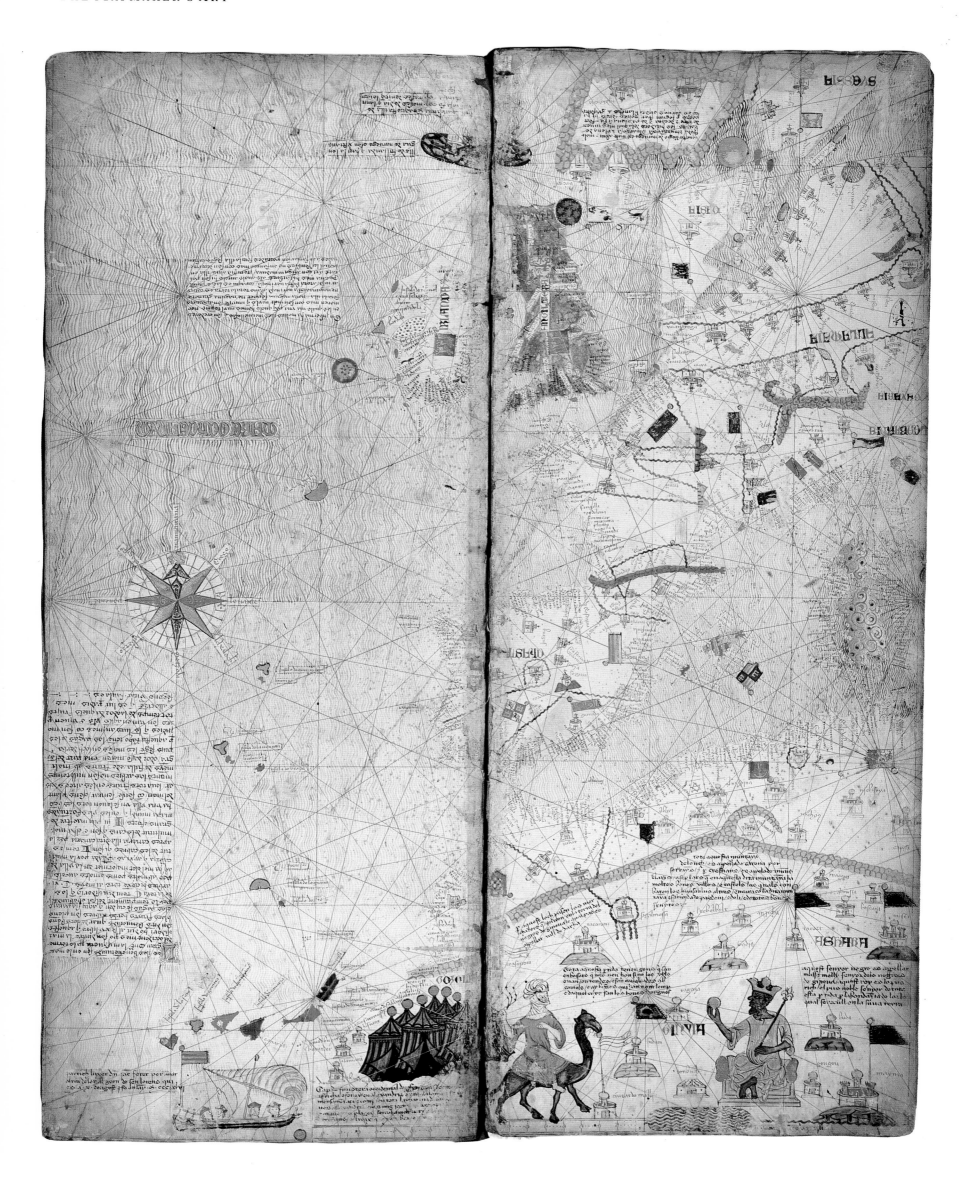

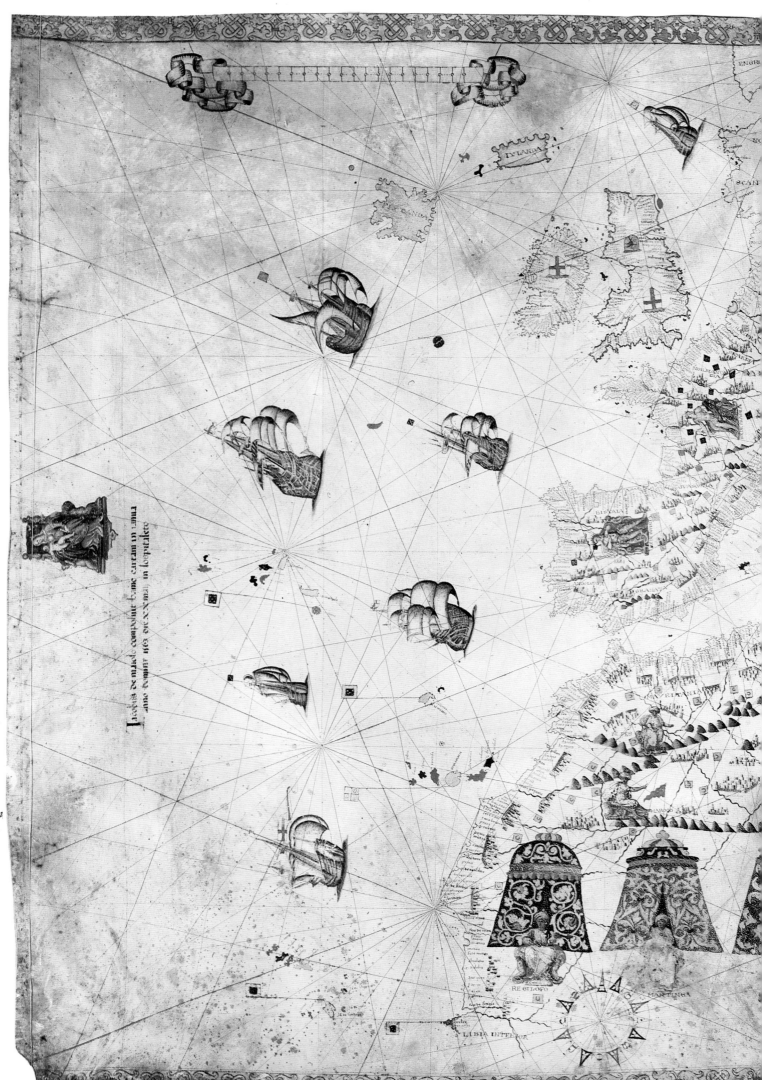

PLATE 2.16 *(previous page) Part of the western end of the Catalan Atlas, constructed from twelve sheets forming a large* mappamundi, *c. 1375. Note the colourful illustrations of native rulers and traders in North Africa. Farther north can be seen the British Isles and part of Scandinavia. The outline of the Mediterranean is taken from portolan chart outlines.*

PLATE 2.17 *(right) A portolan chart by the Maggiolo family, 1563. The Maggiolos had a large output of portolan charts and atlases, of which this is a representative example. Note in particular the symbols and details inland in Europe, embellished in North Africa by a line of gilded tents.*

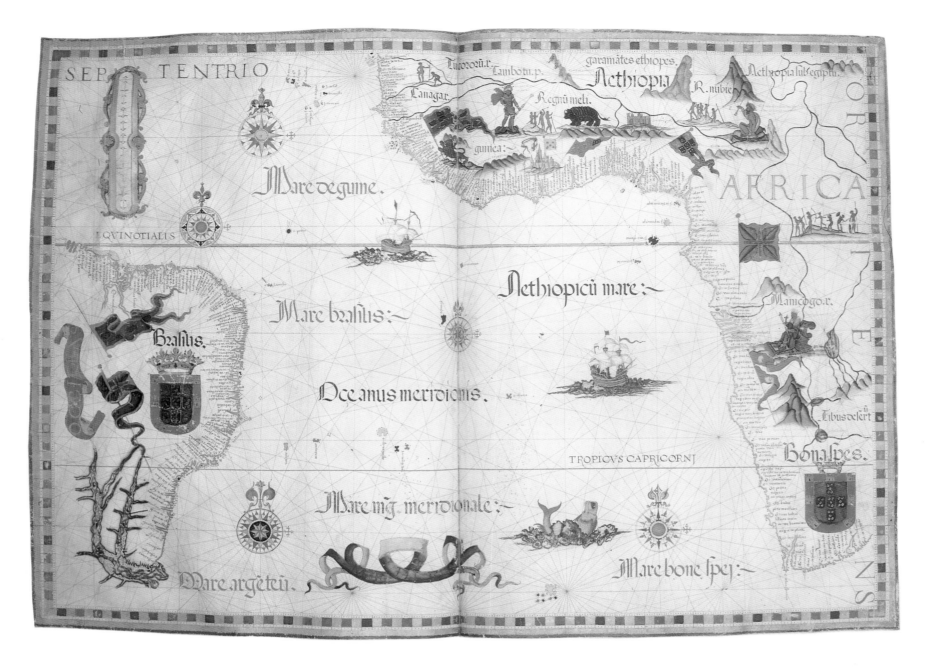

PLATE 2.18 *Chart of the South Atlantic by Diego Homem, 1558. The map shows those parts of South America and Africa claimed by Portugal. Homem was commissioned by Queen Mary of England and Philip II of Spain, her husband, to make the atlas in which this chart appeared.*

workshops in France, Germany and the Low Countries might perhaps be the work of one man, with certain tasks apportioned to scribes, rubricators and others. It may be that some of the decorative features on Pietro Vesconte's charts, for example, were drawn by another hand. In 1271, an artists' guild was established in Venice which embraced many craftsmen. It is possible that chartmakers such as Vesconte and others may have been active members of this guild.

Extant legal records dating from 1399 show that a wealthy Florentine merchant, Baldassare degli Ubriachi, commissioned four large maps for presentation to European monarchs from Jefuda (son of Abraham) Cresques and Francesco Beccari, both of whom were in Barcelona at the time. In the documentation, it is noted that Cresques (described as *maestro di charta da navichare*) was employed to draw the basic maps, while Beccari (called *dipintore*, or painter) was commissioned to decorate and illuminate them.

Printing and portolan charts

Portolan charts continued to be made long after the technique of printing was first used for maps in the late fifteenth century. The first printed portolan chart of the Mediterranean was made in 1539, in Venice, by Giovanni Andrea di Vavassore. During the early sixteenth century latitude scales were added to the charts, and in the seventeenth century a projection like that devised by Gerard Mercator (that is, with increasing degrees of latitude) was introduced. Other famous examples of printed portolan charts include a map of the Mediterranean by Diego Homem (of Portuguese extraction). It was engraved in 1569 by Paolo Forlani, who stated:

. . . but as [the earth's] description according to the use of mariners has not yet been published, nor the sailing chart, a thing necessary to every sort of person, I being desirous of serving the world, am doing so, and have requested and obtained from S. Giacomo

Homem, Portuguese, a man excelling in this, a description of Europe and part of Africa and Asia, according to the use of mariners . . . and other things needed for good navigation.[4]

Long after printed charts and maps were made available, chartmakers continued to produce extremely attractive examples of their art, more often for presentation purposes than for practical use. A particularly outstanding example of this kind of decorative manuscript chart is Diego Homem's chart of the South Atlantic, drawn in 1558 (Plate 2.18).

The impact made by portolan charts was, clearly, both great and long-lasting. In summary, T. Campbell lists their attributes:

From the earliest extant copies, probably a little before 1300, the outline [that portolan charts] gave for the Mediterranean was amazingly accurate. In addition, their wealth of place-names constitutes a major historical source. Their improvement over Ptolemaic maps relating to the same area is obvious at a glance . . . moreover, the Ptolemaic maps began to circulate widely through Europe only in the fifteenth century, by which time portolan charts were well established. . . . The medieval sea chart is the clearest statement of the geographic and cartographic knowledge available in the Mediterranean. . . . The medieval *mappaemundi* are the cosmographies of thinking landsmen. By contrast, the portolan charts preserve the Mediterranean sailors' firsthand knowledge of their own sea, as well as their expanding knowledge of the Atlantic Ocean.[5]

The Far East

The art and science of mapmaking was developed by the Chinese to a high degree early on in their civilization. It was the mapmaker Chang Heng who first invented and developed quantitative cartography during the second century AD, in other words roughly contemporary with Ptolemy's work in the West. It has been thought that Chang Heng applied some sort of grid system to maps so that positions, distances and routes could be calculated in a scientific, systematic manner. If this were so, then geographical positions on such maps would presumably be determined by counting the X and Y co-ordinates of the 'grid' rather like some of the computer-generated maps of our own times.

Unfortunately, Chang Heng's own writings on cartography have not survived. He wrote a book entitled *Suan Wang Lun*, or 'Discourse on Net Calculations', which laid the groundwork for the mathematical use of some form of grid system on maps. In AD 116 he presented a large map called *Ti Hsing Thu* to the emperor. An important piece of evidence regarding Chang Heng is found in the *Chien Han Shu*, the official history of the Han dynasty (207 BC to AD 220), which states that he 'cast a net around heaven and earth, and reckoned on the basis of it'. However, there is some doubt about the meaning of this statement and it is possible that Chang Heng is merely referring to the celestial system of declination and right ascension, which is more like a polar co-ordinate system, rather than a grid. Equally there is some doubt about the meaning of 'earth' which probably should not be taken to imply terrestrial cartography.

During the third century AD, Chang Heng had a successor in the scientific study of mapmaking. He was P'ei Hsiu, who in AD 267 was appointed minister of works by the first emperor of the Ch'in dynasty. The *Chin Shu*, which is the official history of the dynasty, quotes an extract from the preface of P'ei Hsiu's large eighteen-sheet map:

The origin of maps and geographical treatises goes far back into former ages. Under the three dynasties [Hsia, Shang and Chou] there were special officials [Kuo Shih] for this. Then, when the Han people sacked Hsien-yang, Hsiao Ho collected all the maps and documents of the Ch'in. Now it is no longer possible to find the old maps in the secret archives, and even those which Hsiao Ho found are missing; we only have maps, both general and local, from the later Han time. None of these employs a graduated scale and none of them is arranged on a rectangular grid. Moreover, none of them gives anything like a complete representation of the celebrated mountains and the great rivers; their arrangement is very rough and imperfect, and one cannot rely on them. Indeed some of them contain absurdities, irrelevancies and exaggerations, which are not in accord with reality, and which should be banished by good sense.[6]

The history goes on to describe the principles of Chinese mapmaking:

In making a map there are six principles observable: (1) The graduated divisions, which are the means of determining the scale to which the map is to be drawn. (2) The rectangular grid (of parallel lines in two dimensions), which is the way of depicting the correct relations between the various parts of the map. (3) Pacing out the sides of right-angled triangles, which is the way of fixing the lengths of derived distances (i.e., the third side of the triangle which cannot be walked over). (4) Measuring the high and the low. (5) Measuring the right angles and acute angles. (6) Measuring curves and straight lines. These last three principles are used according to the nature of the terrain, and are the means by which one reduces what are really plains and hills to distances on a plane surface. If one draws a map without having graduated divisions, there is no means of distinguishing between what is near and what is far. If one has graduated divisions, but no rectangular grid or network of lines, then while one may attain accuracy in one corner of the map, one will certainly lose it elsewhere (i.e., in the middle, far from guiding marks) . . . But if we examine a map which has been prepared by the combination of all these principles, we find that a true scale representation of the distances is fixed by the graduated divisions . . . When the principle of the rectangular grid is properly applied, then the straight and the curved, the near and the far, can conceal nothing of their form from us.[7]

Again, unfortunately, P'ei Hsiu's actual map has not survived. Nor was it lodged in the official secret archives. This is not exceptional, for throughout Chinese history (just as in the history of the making of maps and charts in the West in later centuries) the possession of superior mapping was the key to political and military power and success, in much the same manner that the possession of strategic weapons systems has been a guarantee of power in our own times. An instance of this is given by one Shen Kua, who wrote:

In the Hsi-Ning reign period [1068–1077] ambassadors came from Korea bringing tribute. In every *hsien* city or provincial capital which they passed through they asked for local maps, and these were made and given to them. Mountains and rivers, roads, escarpments and defiles, nothing was omitted. When they arrived at T'iehchow they asked for maps, as usual, but Ch'en Hsiu, who was then prefect of Yangchow, played a trick on them. He said that he would like to see all the maps of the two Chekiang provinces with which they had been furnished, so that he could copy

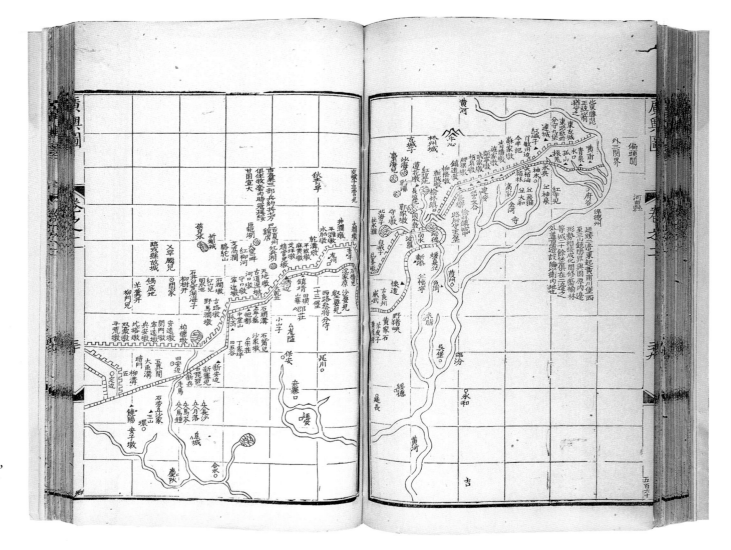

PLATE 2.19 *Map of Northern China from* Illustrations of Objects mentioned in the Six Classics (Liu Ching Thu), *edited by Yang Chia, 1155 and later. The map shown here is a later version.*

them for what was now wanted, but when he got hold of them, he burnt them all, and made a complete report on the affair to the emperor.[8]

It is therefore easy to see how and why many early maps simply did not survive; they were rarely, if at all, copied, and more often than not were destroyed. The information contained therein was too dangerous and sensitive to risk its falling into the wrong hands.

But all has not been lost to us from Chinese cartography. Preserved in the Pei Lin Museum at Sian are two remarkable maps carved in stone, dating from the twelfth century. One, entitled *Yü Chi Thu*, or 'Map of the Tracks of Yü the Great' (1137), is the most remarkable map of its age in any culture. It measures some 914 mm square, and has a rectangular grid superimposed on it. The map shows a very accurate coastal outline, extending from the Shantung peninsula region in the north to Hainan in the south, and includes precise detail with regard to the river systems of China. The other map, called *Hua I Thu*, or 'Map of China and the Barbarian Countries', is of the same size and date, but is not quite so accurate in general outline.

An object of pride in the West is the 'invention' of the printing-press by Johann Gutenberg in 1458. However, the Chinese had already developed a method of printing by the eighth century, though not with a printing-press; the Chinese technique was achieved with rubbing. Chinese printed maps were similar to those produced by rubbings taken from great stone steles (*c.*704). The Chinese applied this technique to cartography in 1155 in a work edited by Yang Chia called *Liu Ching Thu*, or 'Illustrations of Objects mentioned in the Six Classics' (Plate 2.19). This contains a map of western China showing the Great Wall, rivers and many names of places and features. It is the oldest printed map in any culture and, although somewhat crude in nature, it shows no tendency to compress geographical information into a rigid framework laid according to the dogma of religion, unlike the European maps of the time.

Perhaps the most famous (in the West, at least) lasting monument of Chinese mapmaking is the great map compiled by Chu Ssu-Pên (1273–1337), who was the inheritor of the traditions of

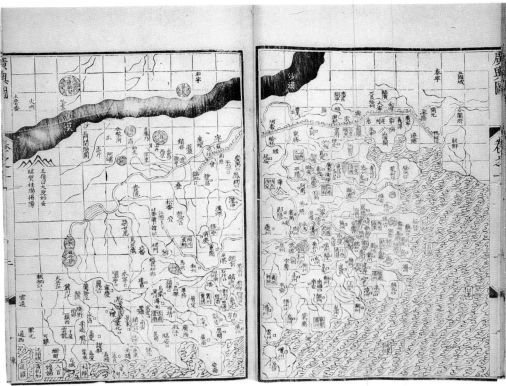

Chang Heng and P'ei Hsiu. He was probably able to make use of information brought into China as a result of contacts with Arab geographers, traders and merchants. The work of Chu Ssu-Pên was roughly contemporary with the early portolan charts in the West. Chu Ssu-Pên's great work, the *Yü Thu*, or 'Earth-Vehicle Map', was compiled between 1311 and 1320 but remained in manuscript form for another 200 years until about 1541. It was then revised and enlarged by Lo Hung-Hsien (1504–1564) and printed in about 1555, bearing the title *Kuang Yü Thu*, or 'Enlarged Terrestrial Atlas' (Plate 2.20). Such was the importance of Chu Ssu-Pên's map that it remained in use until the early nineteenth century. Lo Hung-Hsien's preface stated:

Chu Ssu-Pên's map was prepared by the method of indicating the distances by a network of squares, and thus the actual geographical picture was faithful. Hence, even if one divided the map and put it together again, the individual parts in the east and west fitted faultlessly together . . . His map was two metres long and therefore inconvenient to unroll; I have therefore now arranged it in book form on the basis of its network of squares.[9]

Concerning those lands beyond China, and contacts with them, Chu Ssu-Pên was somewhat wary. He commented:

Regarding the foreign countries of the barbarians south-east of the South Sea, and north-west of Mongolia,

PLATE 2.20 *The region of the Great Wall of China based on Chu Ssu-Pên's map prepared between 1311 and 1320. This woodblock-printed section comes from the sixteenth-century or later version known as the* Enlarged Terrestrial Atlas, *c. 1555. The preface of the atlas stated: 'Chu Ssu-Pên's map was prepared by the method of indicating the distances by a method of squares, and thus the actual geographical picture was faithful'.*

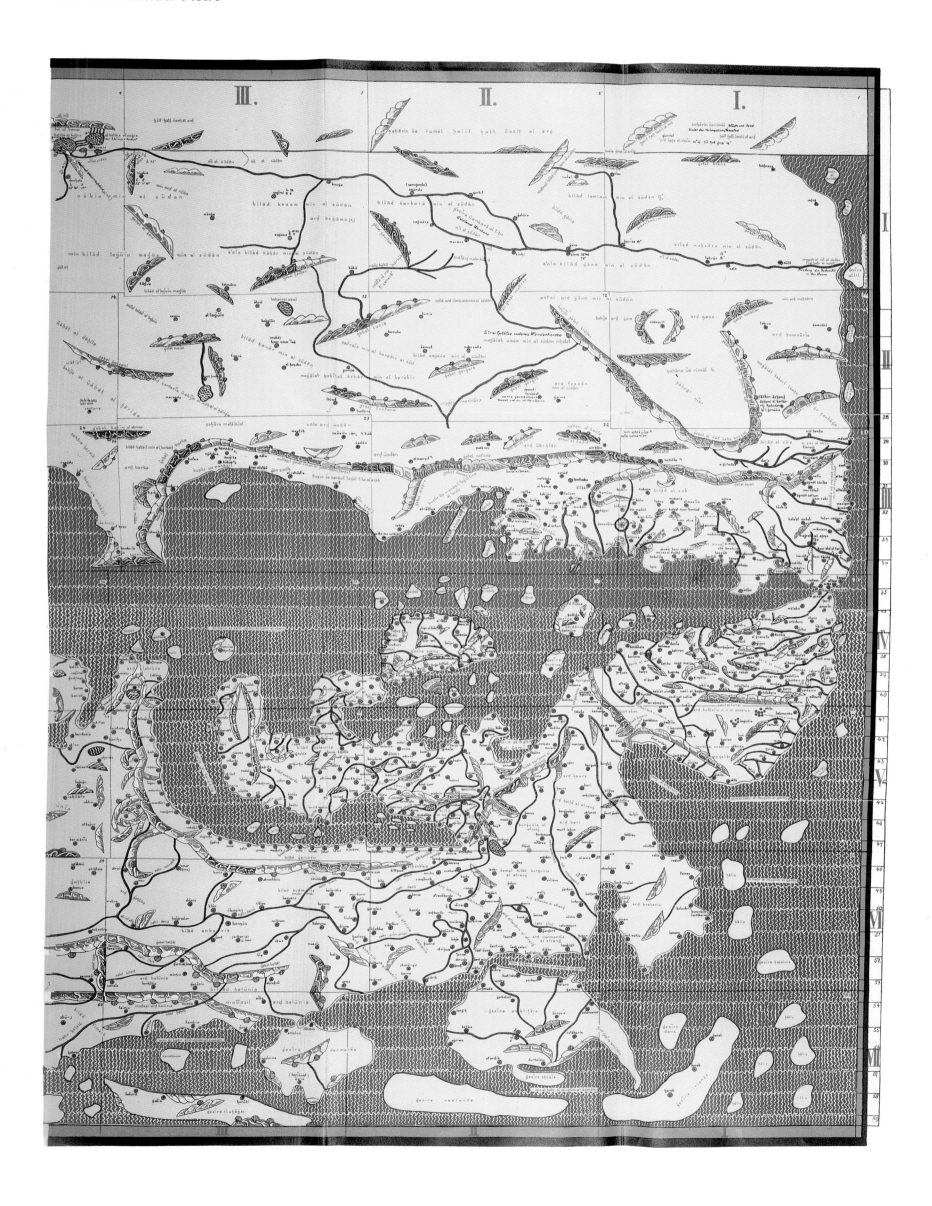

there is no means of investigating them because of their great distance, although they are continually sending tribute to the court. Those who speak of them are unable to say anything definite, while those who say something definite cannot be trusted; hence I am compelled to omit them here.[10]

China was not the only Far Eastern country with an interest in mapmaking. In 1402 a map was compiled in Korea by Li Hui and Chhuan Chin entitled *Hin-I Chiang Li-Tai Kuo Ku*, or – rather less succinctly! – 'Map of the Territories of the One World and the Capitals of the Countries in Successive Ages'. The original has not, apparently, survived, but there are several copies from about the fifteenth century, now preserved in Japan. The Korean map is quite large, measuring some 1,520 mm by 1,220 mm, and includes interesting detail of Western countries, for some one hundred place-names in Europe and thirty-five in Africa are mentioned. Furthermore, the continent of Africa is drawn in its correct, roughly triangular shape, pointing southwards. As if somehow to make a link with the classical centre of learning at Alexandria, this city is indicated on the map by a large pagoda-like feature, representing the famous lighthouse there.

Such knowledge of the West can only have come about as a result of contact with Arab or Persian merchants, traders and navigators, and from knowledge of a globe brought to Peking in 1267 by the Persian traveller Jamal al-Din. There was an Arab colony established at Canton in the south of China by the middle of the eighth century, and the Arab travellers Sulaiman the Merchant and Ibn Wahb al-Basri made extensive journeys throughout China during the ninth and tenth centuries. The Mongol conquests in the west of Asia in the thirteenth century also brought the Arab and Chinese cultures into some contact. It follows, therefore, that there must have been some exchange of geographical information during these periods.

The Arab world

The Arabs maintained close links with the Byzantine culture of the old Roman Empire in the east, which allowed them early contact with what remained of Greek science and access to the works of

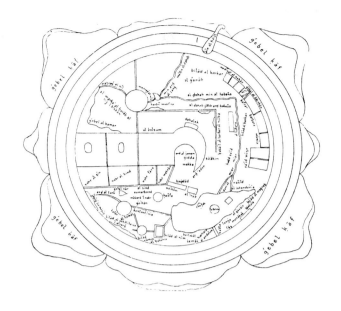

Ptolemy (by the ninth century). The best known of the Arab mapmakers is Abu 'Abdallah al-Sharif al-Idrisi (1099–1166), better known by the abbreviated form of his name, al-Idrisi. Al-Idrisi made a world map in 1154 for the Norman king of Sicily, Roger II, at Palermo (Plate 2.21). It has rectangular sheet lines, laid out according to the climates.

In the early fourteenth century, another Arab mapmaker, Hamdallah ibn abu Bakr al-Mustaufi al-Qazwini (1281–1349), made maps to illustrate his *Ta'rikh-i-Guzida*, or 'Select Chronicle'. We know that he had contacts with the Far East, for his text gives, for example, the Mongol names of various flora and fauna found there. He made three maps of Persia, with nothing but place-names, using grids like those used in Chinese mapmaking. It seems that in their mapmaking the Arabs made use of cross-fertilizations from both the Ptolemaic tradition and their knowledge of China; it follows that information must have been communicated to the Arabs in their colony at Canton and through their meeting with Chinese navigators in the Indian Ocean ports where Arabs had long been established.

References
1. Marcel Destombes, *Mappemondes*, Amsterdam, 1964.
2. J.T. Lanman, *Glimpses of History from Old Maps*, page 42, 1989.
3. *Cartographical Innovations*, section 1.0320D.
4. Quoted in D. Howse & M. Sanderson, *The Sea Chart*, page 38, 1973.
5. T. Campbell, *The History of Cartography I*, pages 371–372.
6. Joseph Needham, *Science and Civilisation in China*, *III*, page 539, 1959.
7. Joseph Needham, *op. cit.*, pages 539–540.
8. Shen Kua, *Meng Chi Pi Than (Dream Pool Essays)*, 1086.
9. Joseph Needham, *op. cit.*, page 552.
10. Joseph Needham, *op. cit.*, pages 551–552.

PLATE 2.21 *(opposite) Western Europe and northwestern Africa from the world map by al-Idrisi, 1154. This beautiful map was commissioned by King Roger II of Sicily and was compiled using eastern and western knowledge. It is here reproduced from a facsimile.*

PLATE 2.22 *(left) A map of the Middle East centred upon Jiddah from* Ta'rikh-i-Guzida (Select Chronical) *by Hamdallah ibn abu Bakr al-Mustaufi al-Qazwini, dating from the early fourteenth century. Baghdad, Alexandria, Cyprus and the Nile Valley can be clearly seen. (The map has been re-drawn for clarity.)*

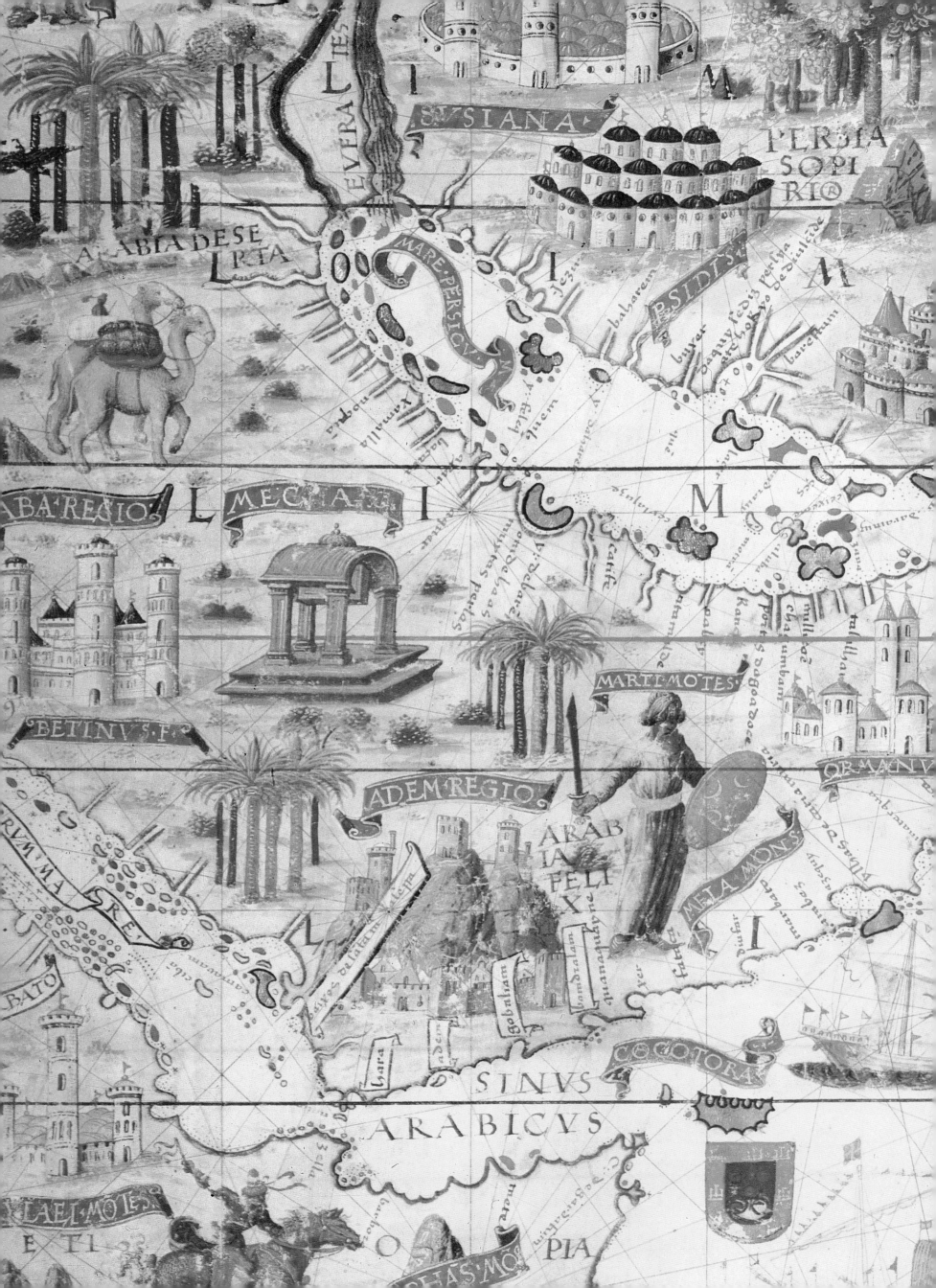

CHAPTER III

THE AGE OF DISCOVERY

1100 – 1800 AD

WHAT HAS BECOME generally known as the Age of Discovery came about as the result of the daring exploits of a small number of adventurers originating from the well-travelled sea routes and seaports of the Mediterranean and the western shores of Europe. Unfortunately, very few reliable accounts and records of travels made before the middle of the fifteenth century have survived. Until the late fifteenth century most of the sea passages leading away from Europe were largely unknown to Europeans, and probably to anyone else. The only straits and passages which were known and in regular use were those which connected the Mediterranean with the Atlantic and the Black Sea with the Mediterranean. The Chinese, on the opposite side of the globe, were familiar with the long sea passages westward into the Indian Ocean and beyond, towards and round Africa via the Indonesian archipelago and the China Sea. There was even a persistent legend about an island mountain paradise called *P'end hai* in the Pacific Ocean, which may possibly have been Hawaii, or even the north-western coast of North America. But, as yet, no European ships had dared to travel to these strange new continents.

PLATE 3.1 *Detail from an untitled manuscript chart extending from Arabia to Sumatra, one of five charts in the so-called* Miller Atlas *by Lopo Homem and Pedro Reinel, c. 1519. Note the crowded interior detail comprising realistic miniatures of warriors, lions, rhinoceroses, elephants and various flora.*

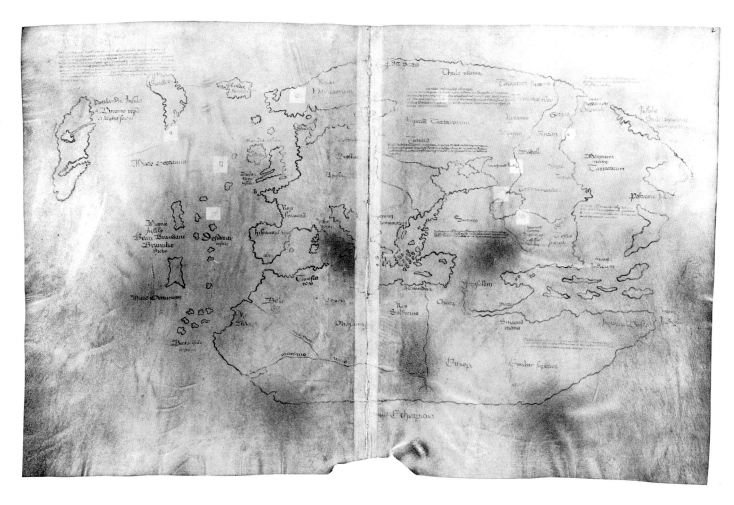

Norse expansion

In the late tenth century, Europeans *had* ventured across the North Atlantic, to Iceland and on to Greenland. According to the *Greenland Saga*, Bjarni Herjolfsson was blown off course while en route from Iceland to Greenland in AD 985, but he made no recorded landfalls, noting only that he had seen land as he plied his way northeastwards back to Greenland. Then, around the year 1000, Leif Eriksson set out from Greenland to retrace Herjolfsson's course, overwintering somewhere to the south of the mouth of the St Lawrence river in eastern Canada. The rocky New England coast must have seemed reassuringly familiar to a sailor from the rockier shores of northwestern Europe.

The first known contact between indigenous North Americans and Europeans took place at a site called Kjalarnes (or Keel Cape), where Algonkians (North American Indians living in the valleys of the Ottawa and St Lawrence rivers) skirmished with Norsemen. From archaeological evidence, this site is believed to have been near Lake Melville in Labrador, well to the north. Attempts were later made to establish a colony at Vinland. The chronicle of Adam of Bremen (written in 1072) recorded information that had been heard from the king of Denmark:

He told me too of yet another island, discovered by Norsemen in their ocean [ie, the North Atlantic], which is called Wineland from the circumstance that vines grow there of their own accord, and produce most excellent wine. That there is abundance of unsown corn there we have learned . . . from the trustworthy report of the Danes.[1]

No known contemporary cartographic evidence of the Norse voyages in American waters has survived. For several years, considerable controversy surrounded the so-called 'Vinland Map', which purported to show cartographic knowledge of the Greenland settlements and of the voyages from Greenland to the North American mainland at the turn of the tenth and eleventh centuries (Plate 3.2). It was believed to have been compiled in about 1440. There is still some dispute as to the authenticity of the map, whether it was indeed produced in the middle of the fifteenth century on the basis of a world map by Andrea Bianco made in 1436, or whether it is a modern forgery. The archaeological evidence of the discoveries made in Newfoundland (at L'Anse aux Meadows [Cove of Meadows], a Norse site) cannot be so easily disputed. It is surprising, however, that the Norse discoveries of a great landmass across the North Atlantic were not more widely known.

Portuguese expansion

It was not until the early fifteenth century that Europeans made further recorded sea voyages beyond their home continent. The origin of such expansion can be traced back to the Crusades, the long series of holy wars which were waged from 1096 to 1204 by Christian forces from western Europe against Islam in the Levant and Egypt, and are indicative of the first attempts at European recovery from centuries of shrinkage and decline. Overland travellers and merchants, such as Marco Polo, attempted to keep alive contacts with the outside world, but the mighty power of the Ottoman empire in the fifteenth century threatened more than once to sever such overland links between western Europe and markets in Asia. It became necessary, therefore, to search for new routes by sea – round Africa and into the Indian Ocean – in order to circumvent the threat from the Ottoman empire.

Although only a small maritime nation on the extreme fringe of Europe, Portugal had certain advantages in the early fifteenth century over its larger, more powerful neighbours to the east. It had not suffered from the ravages of the Hundred Years' War, had not been severely laid low by the Black Death, and was ruled by a rather wealthy monarchy. The Portuguese took on the Castilians in Spain during the early fifteenth century, which gave them a certain sense of a national identity. The exploring achievements of Portugal became enshrined in the 1572 epic poem *Os Lusíadas* of Luís de Camões, which begins:

This is the story of heroes who, leaving their native Portugal, opened a way to Ceylon, and farther, across seas no man ever sailed before.

The ambitions of Portugal were organized into a sustained effort in order to achieve the desired results. Unlike Columbus's discoveries in the New World, which turned out to be a bold stroke of good luck, Portuguese voyagers undertook a rational, perhaps even systematic, process of exploration. Their journeys involved political direction, particular objectives, careful evaluation of risks and the expectation of reward. Portuguese endeavours may justly be regarded as a prototype of modern exploration.

The official chronicler of the kings of Portugal, Gomes Eames de Zurara, summarized the objectives of the Portuguese explorers most succinctly:

To discover what lay beyond the Canaries and Cape Bojador; to trade with any Christians who might dwell in the lands beyond; to discover the extent of the Muslim dominions; to find a Christian king who would help him fight the Infidel; to spread the

PLATE 3.3 *Detail of* Portuguese Carracks off a Fortified Coast, *an oil painting by Cornelsz. Anthonisz* c. *1520. Columbus would have sailed in ships like these on his voyages of discovery.*

Christian faith; to fulfil the predictions of his horo-scope, which bound him to engage in great and noble conquests and attempt the discovery of things that were hidden from other men; to find Guinea.

Henry the Navigator

Prince Henry the Navigator (1394–1460) (Plate 3.4) has been seen as the prime motivator behind Portuguese achievements in the early part of the 'Age of Discovery', even though he was not a sailor and did not participate in any voyages of discovery. Henry was involved in the sponsorship of some eight voyages between 1419 and 1460, his appetite no doubt having been whetted by his taking part in the capture of the Moroccan port of Ceuta from the Moors in 1415.

At Ceuta, Henry probably learned of the legendary kingdom of Prester John and the mines of gold said to exist somewhere in the interior of Africa. No doubt the possibility of great riches offered by a discovery of gold was one of Henry's motives in sponsoring expeditions and voyages – perhaps Christian motives also contributed, not to mention sheer curiosity about what lay beyond Cape Bojador (the bulging cape of the West African mainland).

The early discoveries

The first rewards from Portuguese endeavours came in the form of Atlantic islands. The Portuguese settled in Madeira in 1419 and the Azores in 1431, and began to establish trading links with these islands. Madeira was already well known beyond Portugal and continued to enjoy a prosperous wine trade with Europe during the fifteenth and sixteenth centuries. The Canaries had been discovered during the fourteenth century, probably by sailors leaving from Genoa, but were colonized and settled by the Portuguese early in the fifteenth century.

The Portuguese reached Cape Bojador in 1434, but sailors would not venture beyond this latitude for several years. Between Cape Drâa and Cape Bojador the coast must have seemed extremely dangerous, with heavy swells, strong currents and a sea often coloured red in the summer by the sand blown offshore from the Sahara. To susceptible imaginations confronted with the unknown, this must have had the appearance of bloody water. The Portuguese finally ventured farther south to

Cape Blanco in 1441, Cape Verde in 1445 and round the Guinea Coast in the 1460s. With the gradual Portuguese advance along the western and Guinea coasts of Africa, new sources of trade were opened up for goods and commodities.

In 1462, Pieno da Sintra passed beyond Sierra Leone. Successive voyages gradually ventured round Cape Palmas and Cape Tres Puntas to the Gold Coast, where in 1481–1482 the trading and slaving fort of São Jorge da Mina (Elmina) was eventually established. Beyond the fort lay the head of the Gulf of Guinea and the Equator to the south. The Gold Coast was reached by João de Santarém and Pedro de Escobar in 1471. Their report that the coast tended southwards instead of east here at the head of the Gulf of Guinea in the Bight of Benin caused King Afonso V of Portugal (1438–1481) to consult the Florentine Paolo Toscanelli, a physician resident in Lisbon, in 1474. Toscanelli supplied copies of a letter, together with a world chart in which he provided information, based largely on Marco Polo's accounts of the Far East. These supported Polo's authority against the currently held beliefs of Ptolemy, extending Asia eastwards and thereby reckoning the journey from Lisbon to Quinsay (Hangzhou) as some 10,400 kilometres and from Antillia in the west to Cipangu (Japan) as 4,000 kilometres. Toscanelli's information was considered authoritative, but his chart is now unfortunately lost.

In 1482–1484 Diego Cão travelled as far as the Congo several degrees south of the Equator, reaching 13°S at Cape Lobo. At the mouth of the Congo, Cão set up a stone pillar with an inscription in Latin, Portuguese and Arabic, calling the site Rio de Padram. This was the first of the *padrões* (stone pillars or crosses) erected by the Portuguese voyagers on the orders of King João II (r. 1481–1495), to mark new discoveries. It was from Cão's discoveries that Portuguese efforts to discover new lands were rekindled with vigour – the hope and will to discover India and perhaps the land of the fabled priest-king Prester John. In medieval travellers' tales, this kingdom had been set in central Asia, but by the middle of the fifteenth century, Prester John was believed to rule Ethiopia; Fra Mauro's map of 1459 depicted Prester John's kingdom as 'Abassia' (Plate 3.6). Abyssinian monks had even visited Portugal and João II sent expeditions via the Cape and overland

PLATE 3.6 *A world map by Fra Mauro made at Murano, Venice, and finished in 1459. This is the largest extant late medieval or early world map. It measures some 1,960 by 1,930 mm and is drawn to show south at the top. The Mediterranean therefore appears inverted — to the right-hand side shown in a reasonably accurate outline. Africa is the roughly triangular landmass occupying the near right-hand quadrant, and is separate from the Asian landmass.*

from Guinea in an attempt to reach the kingdom via the Nile valley.

The first Portuguese navigator to reach India was Pero da Covilhão, who travelled by way of Egypt and the Red Sea in 1487–1488. He reported in 1490 that he had visited Calicut, Cananor and Goa. He later settled in Abyssinia.

Also in 1487, Bartholomew Dias (Plate 3.5) set out on what was to prove to be a most remarkable voyage. Out in the Atlantic, Dias had been blown far out to sea by a northerly gale and had spent nearly fourteen days and nights out of sight of land. Dias had tried to head east, but when he made his landfall it turned out to be the east coast of Africa, beyond the promontory we now know as the Cape of Good Hope.

Dias erected a column at a point east of what is now called the Bushman's River, naming it Cabo de Padram. The Cape itself was named by João II after Dias's return in 1488 as the Cabo de Boa Speranza in the expectation of 'the great hope' of the discovery of India. Until this time, no Western European had dared, or been able, to pass the Cape. Now, however, the sea route to India and the Far East lay clear for the Portuguese.

The discovery of India

However, before the Portuguese could send out their first, properly equipped expedition to India, news arrived from Spain that one Christopher Columbus had succeeded in reaching India and the East by sailing west. In order to avoid conflicting claims in the newly found lands, Portugal and Spain entered into a joint agreement in the form of the Treaty of Tordesillas, signed in 1494. The treaty decreed that Portugal would be granted possession of all newly found lands between about 45°W (about 480 kilometres west of the Azores) and 130°E, and Spain all discoveries to the west of that line. In other words, Spain would have the whole of the New World apart from the northeastern part of Brazil, while Portugal would retain a monopoly on the Cape routes to India and the East.

The first Portuguese expedition to India via the Cape sailed under Vasco da Gama (*c.*1460–1524) in 1497–1499. Da Gama was sent out by Manuel I (*r.*1495–1521), João's successor, to reach Calicut. He arrived there in 1498. A second fleet, led by Pedro Alvares Cabral, set sail in 1500–1501, this time sailing via Brazil on da Gama's advice to avoid the calm of the Guinea coast.

The earlier voyages had exposed and demonstrated the weaknesses of the traditional Portuguese vessel, the caravel, in open waters. In any case, the trade with India called for vessels of larger carrying capacity. Dias designed ships for da Gama's fleet, heavier and broader in beam. These were the prototypes of the *nao* (or 'ship'), which was the characteristic ocean-going vessel of the Portuguese fleets of the sixteenth century. The flagship of da Gama, the *São Gabriel*, was an example, square-rigged on the fore and main masts, fore-and-aft on the mizzen.

The rise and fall of the Portuguese Empire

Following the pioneering voyages of da Gama and Cabral, a Portuguese seaborne empire was rapidly established, with Manuel I assuming the title and style 'Lord of the conquest, navigation and commerce of Ethiopia, Arabia, Persia and India'. This empire was a commercial rather than a political one, based on trading ports and factories commanding the Indian Ocean trade routes.

At first, trade with India was difficult because the Arabs, who had controlled the coastal waters of the Indian Ocean for centuries, tried to keep out all rival traders. It took some fourteen years before Portugal established herself in trading ports. The primary base was at Goa on the west coast of India, conquered by the Portuguese in 1510, with secondary bases established at Hormoz (1508) in the Persian Gulf region and Malacca (1511), which commanded the Malay peninsula and the East Indian archipelago. Trading ports were also set up at Moçambique and Calicut in

1498, at Socotra in 1503 and Muscat in 1507. The key to Portugal's success was essentially naval power; their naval architects had learned to combine the old square sails (which gave good speed at full sail) with the Arab lateen sails (which gave increased manoeuvrability). The Portuguese also provided effective fire-power in the knowledge that cannons, not soldiers, were better at sea and were also an effective means of preserving naval and trading power.

The trading empire created by Portugal remained dependent upon naval power rather than overseas settlements. The Portuguese established a long chain of trading bases, comprising warehouses and forts supplied by sea, stretching all the way from West Africa to China. Contacts with Africans and Asians were generally restricted to trade and occasional missionary activity, with no attempts made to conquer for the purposes of gaining political power. By the middle of the fifteenth century, the Portuguese began to profit from their explorations, particularly from the slave trade. Between 1442 and 1446, almost 1,000 slaves were brought from Africa. During the sixteenth century Portugal's wealth increased through their virtual monopoly of the market in luxury goods from the East, such as costly spices, which were in great demand as medicines and preservatives.

The Portuguese achievement had all the ingredients of the western rise to worldwide power: technical superiority of ships and weapons, tactical skills, commercial expertise supported by military force, careful planning and organization at home. Spain soon determined to counter her Iberian neighbour, and later the Dutch, the English and the French all became determined to outdo each other in the scramble to build overseas empires. It was this competition which gave Europeans the vital stimulus other peoples lacked, and it was to project them to a dominance over much of the globe for nearly half a millennium.

Such a far-flung empire, however, proved costly to maintain, and by the end of the sixteenth century it was in decline. Between 1580 and 1640, the Portuguese crown was united with that of Spain, and most of the Portuguese strongholds fell to either the Dutch or the English, so that only Goa, Diu, Macao and part of Timor in the East Indies remained under Portuguese control.

Mapping the Portuguese discoveries

Although the Portuguese almost certainly mapped their discoveries, very few charts prior to the beginning of the sixteenth century have survived. The Portuguese discoveries in Africa and in the Indian Ocean following the voyages of Vasco da Gama in 1497–1499 are depicted only on maps of Italian origin. Most of these Italian mapmakers were either Venetian or had worked at some time in Venice – itself of course a considerable maritime power. In 1448, Andrea Bianco, who was master of a Venetian galley in the lucrative Flanders trade, made a chart, signed in London. It showed the African coast as far as Cape Verde (with its welcoming green forests which gave the area its name) and Senegal as known from Portuguese sources up until 1441. The Portuguese sources used by Bianco were either not very up to date or more recent charts were not available to him, and as a result he did not, or could not, include Gambia or the shores to the south and east.

In 1459, shortly before the death of Prince Henry the Navigator, the monk Fra Mauro compiled what was to be one of the last, and indeed greatest, of the medieval *mappaemundi* (Plate 3.6). Although typically medieval in appearance, being circular in form, it was considerably more up to date than the printed versions of Ptolemy's maps that were to follow around twenty years later. The map was made with the assistance of Andrea Bianco and gives somewhat more information on West Africa than Bianco's chart. It has been thought to provide evidence of Portuguese penetration as far south as the Congo, which was not reached by Diego Cāo until 1484. East Africa is shown in some detail and is quite definitive in refuting Ptolemy's notion of a land-bridge between Africa and Asia, thereby rejecting the Greek concept of a land-locked Indian Ocean and showing an open sea route round the presumed southern cape of Africa.

Henry the Navigator's death in 1460 brought major Portuguese exploration of the shores of Africa to a halt for more than twenty years. However, the later voyages, which he sponsored just before his death, taking the Portuguese as far south as Sierra Leone, are recorded in charts, again made in Venice, from 1467 onwards, by

PLATE 3.7 *A section of the globe, some 51 cm dia., made by Martin Behaim in Nuremberg in 1492, the oldest surviving European globe. The geographic information appears to have been derived from the world map of Henricus Martellus showing the world seen by Columbus on the eve of his first voyage in 1492.*

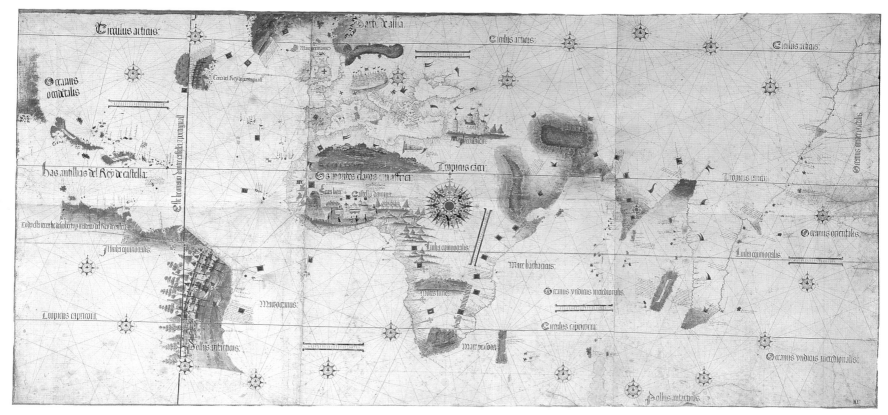

PLATE 3.8 *The* Cantino planisphere, *drawn on three leaves of vellum joined, Lisbon, 1502. A remarkable chart, showing the extent of Portuguese discoveries by the early sixteenth century. Note the Portuguese standards along the Brazilian coast, acknowledging the discoveries of Pedro Alvares Cabral in 1500, and note too the prominently drawn demarcation line of the Treaty of Tordesillas.*

people like Grazioso Benincasa d'Ancona. D'Ancona's charts were based on the reports of the Venetian navigator Alvise da Ca'damosto who made two voyages to the Indies for Prince Henry in 1455 and 1456, and also travelled to the Gambia and the Rio Grande. Ca'damosto's discoveries were also included in Benincasa's map.

Both Cão's and Dias's voyages are recorded on the manuscript world map by Henricus Martellus drawn in 1490, shortly after the return of Dias in 1489. This map, although plainly Ptolemaic in inspiration, abandons the classical notion of the landlocked Indian Ocean in the light of the Portuguese discoveries, the southeastern coast of Africa being left blank beyond Bartholomew Dias's farthest eastern point.

In 1502, a manuscript world map showing the discoveries of the Portuguese navigators up to those of Cabral was obtained and smuggled out of Lisbon by one Alberto Cantino, the agent there of Ercole d'Este, duke of Ferrara. It is still preserved today, half a millennium later, at the Biblioteca Estense at Modena. This map, known as the 'Cantino' planisphere (Plate 3.8), is the oldest extant cartographic document of the Portuguese discoveries in both the eastern and the western hemispheres.

It may seem strange that no earlier original Portuguese charts survive (as far as we know). This is mainly because of a policy of official secrecy (particularly under João II) by which the

Portuguese authorities sought to restrict access both to lands discovered by the Portuguese and to any relevant information which may have been of value to a rival foreign power.

An office known as the Casa da Mina e India was the body responsible for overseas territories and colonies, and it was this office which produced and revised charts, issuing them to pilots for use on voyages, subject to their being handed in again on return to Portugal. An Italian agent in Lisbon declared that it was impossible to secure any charts of Cabral's voyage because 'their king had instituted a death penalty for anyone sending one out of the country'. A possible explanation for the lack of any known charts drawn for Prince Henry or for João II is that any charts which were made may have been lost during the great earthquake which destroyed much of Lisbon in 1755.

From this it can be seen, therefore, that the only cartographic evidence of Portuguese discoveries prior to the beginning of the sixteenth century is found in maps and charts based on Portuguese originals or copied from them with the help of information then only available in Portugal. Such information may have been taken from there by word of mouth or smuggled (as in the case of the Cantino map) out of Portugal by foreign agents by one means or another and passed to Italian chartmakers, such as Bianco, Fra Mauro, Benincasa and others, all of whose maps contain Portuguese names. Cortesão comments:

It is very sad that so many fifteenth-century Portuguese charts, which we know to have certainly existed, have disappeared, with the exception of three or four, but at the same time it is fortunate that many of these charts served as prototypes for Mediterranean cartographers, particularly Italian, as had doubtless already happened in the fourteenth century; we can thus visualize fairly well what was represented in some of the charts that have disappeared but were used for drawing many of the charts that have survived . . . and we can also be tolerably certain that Portuguese cartography did not improve, rather the contrary, when it was copied and translated by the Mediterranean cartographers.[2]

Spanish expansion

The second wave of expansion overseas was that of the Spaniards, inspired by the successes of their Portuguese neighbours. Spain was a much larger nation than Portugal, and founded its empire on conquest and colonization rather than purely on trade and commerce. The initial stimulus, however, came from a stroke of ironic good fortune – namely, the refusal of the Portuguese to underwrite a venture proposed by a Genoese sailor, Christopher Columbus (Plate 3.9), who was motivated by the belief that 'gold is most exquisite of all things . . . whoever possesses gold can acquire all that he desires in this world'.

Columbus (1451/2–1506), born in Genoa, had contacts with all of the leading Italian geographers of his day and was convinced that the far shores of Asia could be reached only 5,400 kilometres to the west of the Canary Islands in the Atlantic. This belief was based on the Ptolemaic estimate of the circumference of the globe at some 28,800 kilometres (that is, about 9,600 kilometres short of the true figure) and possibly on Marco Polo's later estimate that Asia extended 2,400 kilometres farther to the east than it does in reality.

Columbus was convinced that the East could be reached by sailing west across the Atlantic, and in 1484 put his proposal, 'The Enterprise of the Indies', before the Portuguese government. He was turned down by João II on the advice of his counsellors, who asserted that Columbus had underestimated the distance from Iberia to Cathay by such a western route. As a result, the Genoese captain offered his services to the Spanish crown,

gained the financial support and blessing of Ferdinand V and Isabella I, and set sail from Palos in southern Spain on 3 August 1492, but not before a board of advisors, mainly ecclesiastics, had taken seven years to decide to back his plans, having at first rejected them and then deciding to support them.

For thirty-three days Columbus sailed west without sight of land. His flotilla of three, the *Niña*, the *Pinta* and the *Santa María* – a *nao* and two caravels – with the *Santa María* in the lead, was at times entangled in the floating mass of weed in the Sargasso Sea in the North Atlantic Ocean. He countered the sinking morale of his crewmen by maintaining a second, false, log which recorded less progress than that actually made, so that his men were unable to tell just how far they were from home. Columbus reported to Ferdinand and Isabella: '. . . it was always feigned to them [the crew] that distances were less, so that the voyage might not appear so long. Thus two reckonings were kept . . . the shorter being feigned, and the longer being the true one.' Landfall was made on 12 October 1492 somewhere in the outer islands of the Bahamas (Plate 3.10). Columbus ceremoniously named the island San Salvador, but the exact site of Columbus's landfall has been hotly disputed over the last two

PLATE 3.9 Columbus as a Young Man *by Martin Alonso, oil painting, fifteenth century.*

few little gold trinkets and ornaments that the natives (whom Columbus naturally called 'Indians') wore in their noses suggested to Columbus that he was anywhere near the East. By some means the natives indicated to him that the gold originated from islands to the west of the landfall site, called Guanahaní by the natives, and he set sail in search of his prize. Columbus reached Cuba – which he at first thought was Cipangu – on 28 October. On 1 November, Columbus wrote: 'It is certain that I am before Zayt and Quinsay [in China], a hundred leagues, a little more or less, distant from one and the other.'

From mid-November to early December, the three vessels explored the northern shore of Cuba. On 21 November, Martín Alonzo Pinzón, commander of the *Pinta*, learned of gold to be found on the island of Great Inagua and deserted the others, leaving the *Santa María* and the *Niña* to proceed along the Cuban coast. On 5 December, they crossed the Windward Passage and found Hispaniola. Here, Columbus heard of gold in quantity in the interior, at a place called Cibao. Naturally enough, to a hopeful Columbus, this name sounded more than enough like Cipangu to

(continued on page 71)

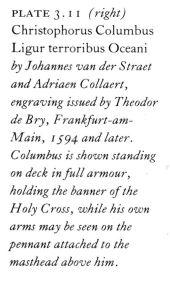

PLATE 3.10 Indians Greeting Columbus on the Shores of the New World *by Theodor de Bry, an engraving from* America, *1613.*

centuries. A number of different islands have been proposed as the original landfall site, among them, Watling's Island, Samana Cay, Cat Island, Mayaguana and Caicos.

Columbus found no oriental inhabitants there as he had hoped, but he was still convinced that he had reached Cathay or Cipangu in Japan. Only the

PLATE 3.11 *(right)* Christophorus Columbus Ligur terroribus Oceani *by Johannes van der Straet and Adriaen Collaert, engraving issued by Theodor de Bry, Frankfurt-am-Main, 1594 and later. Columbus is shown standing on deck in full armour, holding the banner of the Holy Cross, while his own arms may be seen on the pennant attached to the masthead above him.*

PLATE 3.12 *(opposite) Brazil from the* Miller Atlas *by Lopo Homem and Pedro Reinel, c. 1519. The map shows the coasts explored by Pedro Alvares Cabral in 1500 – covering the area between the Amazon delta and the estuary of La Plata.*

REGION FROIDE

CANADA

MER DE FRANCE

MER DESPAIGNE

MER OCCEANE

DE CANCER

MER DES
ENTILLES

LE PERV

MER DV SV

AMERIQVE

MER DE MAGELLAN

EVROPE

AFRIQVE

LA LIGNE

LA ZONA TORRIDA

TROPIQVE

MER AVSTRALLE

LA TERRE

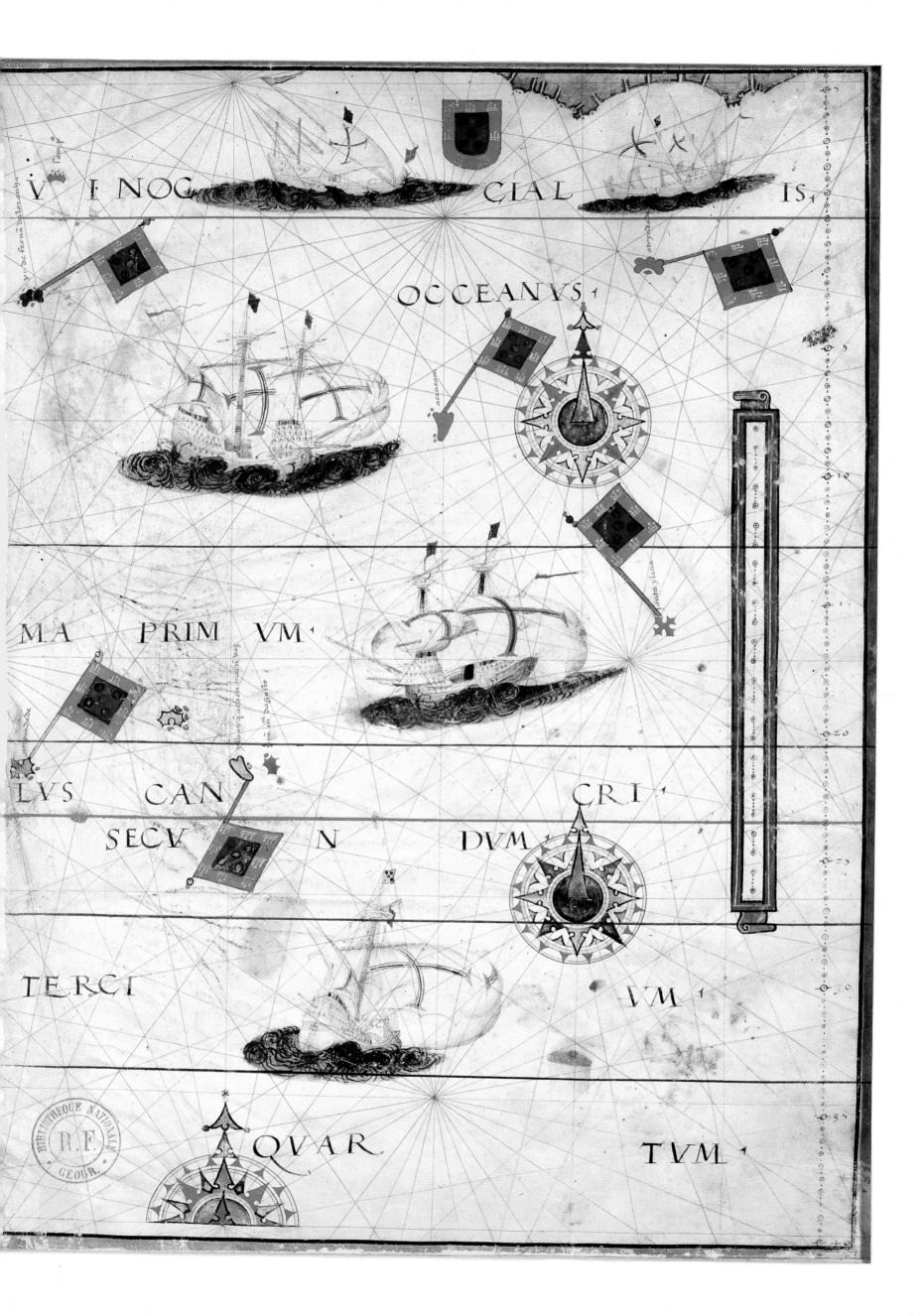

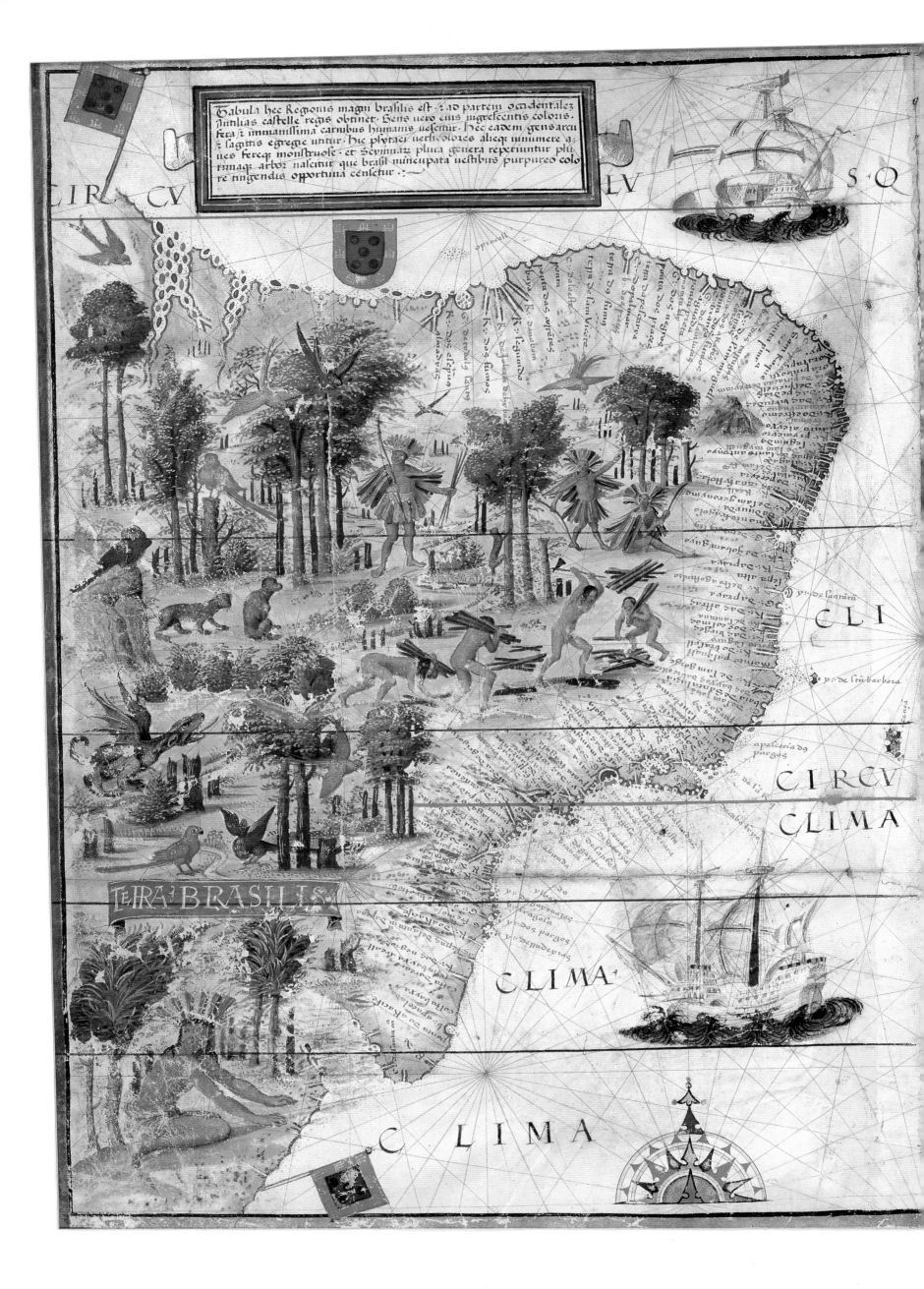

convince him that his objective was at last close at hand. On Christmas Eve, however, the *Santa María* grounded on a reef and was wrecked, leaving Columbus with only the *Niña*. He decided to return to Spain at the earliest opportunity, leaving a party of thirty-nine men behind at a fort settlement suitably named La Navidad ('Christmas'), departing in early January 1493. Two days out, off the Hispaniola coast, the *Niña* met up again with the *Pinta* and together the two vessels arrived safely home, after a difficult return passage across the Atlantic.

Columbus's later voyages

In Barcelona, Columbus was received by Ferdinand and Isabella (Plate 3.14) and almost immediately afterwards began preparations for a second voyage. This voyage lasted from 1493 to 1494, Columbus embarking from Cadiz on 25 September with a fleet of seventeen vessels carrying 1,500 men, with the intention of establishing a permanent colony in the Indies. This Columbus duly did, at Isabella in Hispaniola, with his brother Diego as governor. From Isabella Columbus moved on to Cuba, exploring the southern coasts and satisfying himself that Cuba formed, as he had always convinced himself, a peninsula of eastern Asia. Returning to Hispaniola, Columbus joined his brother Bartholomew, who had recently arrived there. The colony at Isabella was in some disarray, Diego Columbus having proved an ineffective administrator. In order to re-establish control, Christopher Columbus turned upon the inoffensive, innocent native population as scapegoats, many of them being rounded up and dispatched to Spain as slaves. This established the beginnings of a trade which for centuries was to stain the history of European contact and activity in the New World.

Columbus made a third voyage to the West Indies from 1498 to 1500. During this voyage he saw for the first time the northern shores of South America, leading him to suppose that this was the seat of Earthly Paradise and that he had found 'a very great continent . . . until today unknown', declaring that God had made him the 'messenger of the new heaven and earth' and that 'He had showed me the spot where to find it'. Observing the large quantities of fresh water in the seas off what is now Venezuela, Columbus deduced that he

was off a great continent. Nevertheless, he remained convinced that he could still reach Asia, believing that this southern continent was separated from Asia by a strait that led directly to the Spice Islands and India.

In 1502–1504 Columbus made his fourth, and final, voyage, this time exploring the Caribbean coast of Central America. He declared that this land was 'Catigara' (Indochina) – from Nicaragua to Darien. Still he searched for that elusive strait leading to the west, perhaps Ptolemy's 'Sinus magnus' or Great Gulf. At this point Columbus believed himself to be a mere nineteen days' voyaging from the Ganges river in India.

Mapping Columbus's voyages

Of the many maps and charts that Columbus must have made for his four voyages, none are now believed to have survived. A simple sketch map of

PLATE 3.13 *(opposite)*
A chart by Pierre Desceliers, 1550. This remarkable and extremely beautiful chart is an example of the work of the so-called 'Dieppe school'. Note that some names appear inverted: the intention was to allow names to be read from the upper or the lower border inwards towards the Equator.

PLATE 3.14 *(above)* The Reception of Christopher Columbus by Ferdinand and Isabella *by Eugene Deveira, oil painting, nineteenth century. Columbus is being greeted by the Spanish monarchs before setting out on his 1493 voyage.*

71

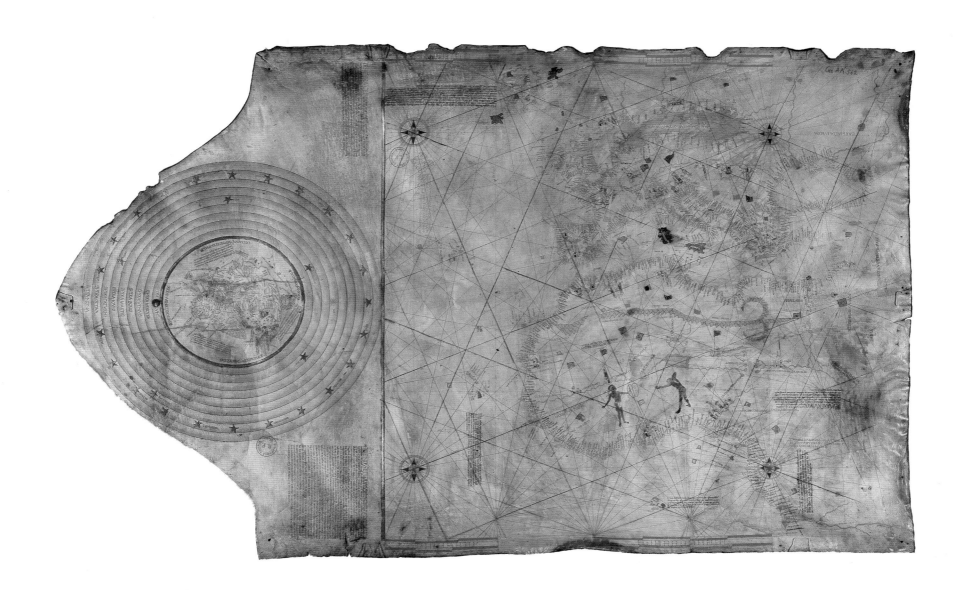

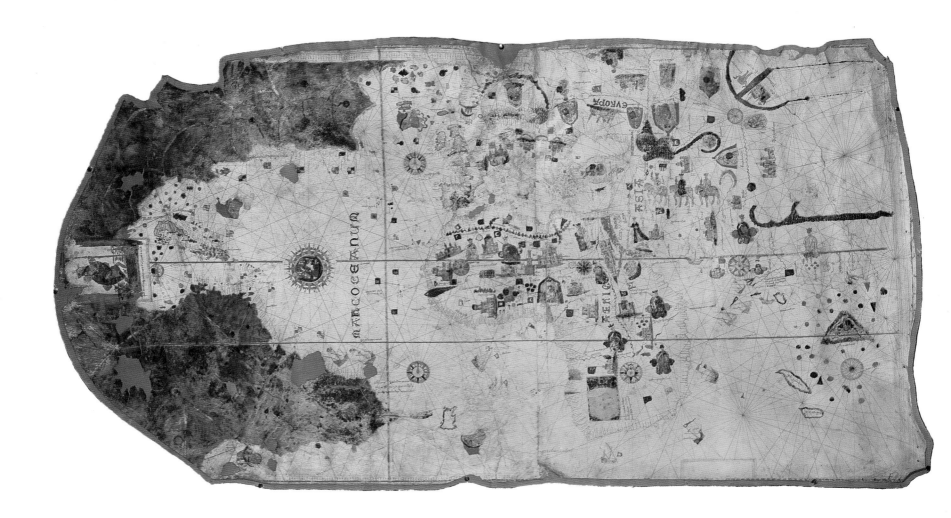

the northern coast of Hispaniola has been attributed to Columbus, but recent research suggests that it may be a fake.[3] The map itself names Cape San Nicolas, the island of Tortuga and the headland of Monticristi. Also indicated is the small settlement of La Navidad, which Columbus set up as the first *recorded* European settlement in the New World, built from the timbers of the wrecked *Santa María*.

There is also a sketch map (*c*.1520), made by Alessandro Zorzi, of Venice, based on a map by Bartholomew Columbus, himself an experienced chartmaker. This sketch shows the coasts of central and northern South America and the facing African and Spanish littorals across a very narrow Atlantic, reduced to the proportions of a broad strait. The chart summarizes the discoveries made on the fourth voyage, indicating the Far East with Ptolemaic names and showing how Columbus connected his discoveries to his firmly held belief that he had found the eastern shores of Asia. The name 'Mondo Novo' (New World) is appended to Columbus's 'hitherto unknown' southern continent. Echoes of this name are preserved in Martin Waldseemüller's map, *Tabula Terre Nove* (Plate 3.21), printed in the 1513 edition of Ptolemy, which bears the legend *Hec terra cum adiacenti-*

b[us] insulis inventa est per Columbu[m] ianuensem ex mandato Regis Castelle. Another particularly important map from Columbus's voyages is that of Juan de la Cosa, drawn in 1500 (Plate 3.16). Juan de la Cosa accompanied Columbus on his second voyage in 1493–1494 as pilot, and also Alonso de Ojeda and Amerigo Vespucci on their explorations of the northern South American coasts and the Caribbean in 1499. De la Cosa's map emphasizes in scale the section covering Central and South America, showing Spanish discoveries down to 1499 on the western side of the demarcation line laid down at Tordesillas. The map gives not only the Spanish discoveries, but also discoveries made much farther north on the Atlantic seaboard of North America by John Cabot in 1497–1498, when these coasts in either Newfoundland or Nova Scotia were taken as being part of the Asian mainland. Cabot's discoveries are indicated by English flags and by the legend 'Cauo de Ynglaterra' (English coast, probably either Newfoundland or Nova Scotia) and 'Mar descubierta por Ynglese' (sea discovered by the English). The westward extension of the landmass here seems to indicate a connection with the Asian mainland. This is echoed on the Contarini-Roselli world map of 1506 (Plate 3.18), the earliest known printed

PLATE 3.15 *(opposite, top) An anonymous portolan chart sometimes attributed to Christopher Columbus with a small* mappamundi *and cosmographical diagram at the 'neck end'. The information depicted suggests a date of compilation of no later than the early 1490s: note that the Spanish standard flies over Granada, but that no discoveries made after 1493 are shown. The map is possibly based on Portuguese sources – note that the Portuguese standard is shown near many places on the coasts of Africa.*

PLATE 3.16 *(opposite, bottom) An untitled portolan world chart by Juan de la Cosa, 1500. This is the earliest extant map showing part of the continent of the New World. It is the only authentic cartographic record of John Cabot's expedition to North America in 1497. The new lands are drawn as an extension of the Asian landmass.*

PLATE 3.17 *(left) Florida, the Gulf of Mexico and a plan of Mexico City from the second letter of Hernando Cortés, the Spanish conqueror of Mexico, first published at Nuremberg in 1524. It shows 'La Florida' (here at the extreme left-hand side) on a printed map. The adjacent plan of Mexico City shows the city as it was found by Cortés before he destroyed it in 1521.*

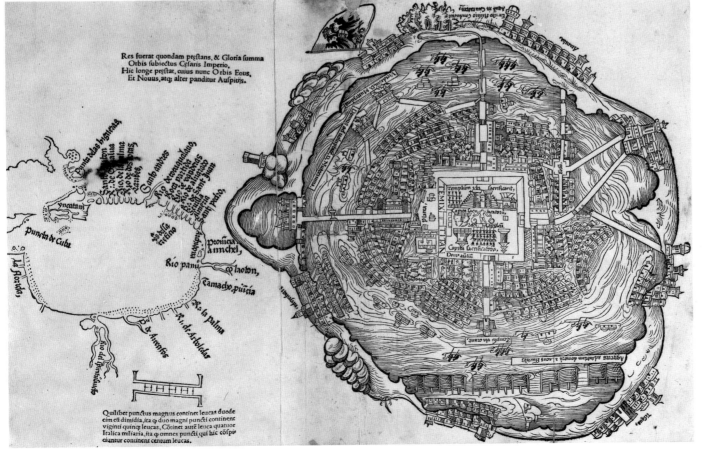

PLATE 3.18 *(above) A fan-shaped world map designed by Giovanni Contarini, engraved on copper by Francesco Rosselli, printed at Venice or Florence in 1506. This map was discovered as recently as 1922. It is the first printed map to indicate parts of the New World discovered by the Spanish and Portuguese.*

PLATE 3.19 *(right)* Universalior cogniti orbis tabula *by Johannes Ruysch, Rome, 1507–1508. Copies of this revolutionary map of the world appeared in Ptolomy's* Geography.

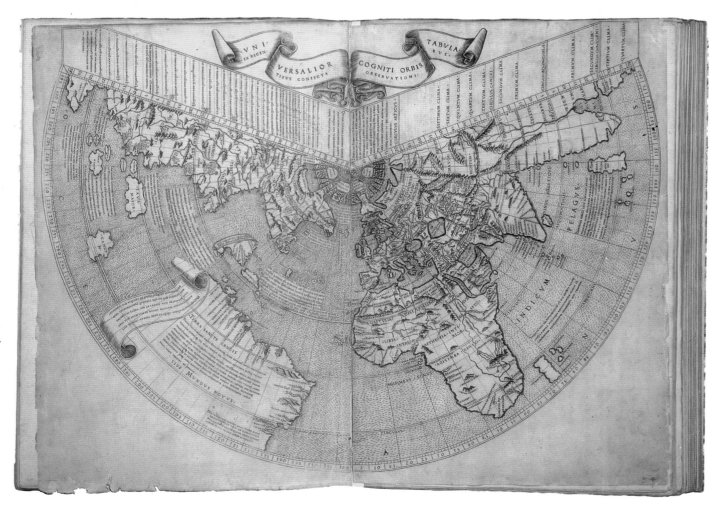

map to show any part of the New World, and the famous Ruysch map (Plate 3.19), which resembles it in many ways, printed at Rome in 1507–1508 and included in copies of the Rome edition of Ptolemy in 1508.

Further developments

The rapid spread of printing in western Europe during the late fifteenth and early sixteenth centuries brought with it the means to disseminate information about the new discoveries in the East and West. These early printed maps are Italian, German or Portuguese in origin, such as the Contarini-Roselli and Ruysch maps already mentioned, and Martin Waldseemüller's great world map, *Universalis Cosmographia* dated 1507 (Plate 5.7). This was printed in an edition of 1,000 copies only one of which (re-discovered at the beginning of the present century) is known to have survived. Waldseemüller's map is based partly on Ptolemaic sources for the Old World, but credits Amerigo Vespucci as the source of the information relating to the New World, relegating the discoveries of Columbus to a brief legend referring to his sighting of Trinidad on the third voyage in 1498. Such was the influence of Waldseemüller's map that almost every successive mapmaker of any importance placed great reliance on it. Despite its limitations and reliance on Ptolemaic conceptions for India, Asia and so on, Waldseemüller's map was recognized immediately as a masterpiece of practical cartographical research. Virtually every significant mapmaker for the next quarter of a century relied upon the Waldseemüller map almost exclusively. Waldseemüller, incidentally, was the person who first suggested that the new continent be named America, after the Florentine explorer Amerigo Vespucci.

The western hemisphere

During this time, at around the turn of the fifteenth and sixteenth centuries, English and Portuguese navigators had made discoveries elsewhere in the New World, or western hemisphere, according to the concept of Pietro Martyr d'Anghiera in 1494. In a letter written during that year he referred to '*ab occidente hemispherii antipodum*' (the antipodes in the western hemisphere) and the idea was illustrated a few years later, in 1511, in

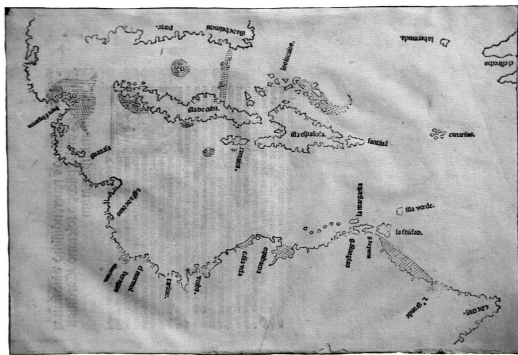

his *De rebus oceanis et novo orbe* from his *Opera*, published at Seville. This is the first printed Spanish map of any part of the Americas, recording landfalls in Florida and marking, for the first time, Bermuda (see Plate 3.20).

Newfoundland, Greenland and Labrador

There is no known written record or account of the landfalls of Cabot in Newfoundland (Juan de la Cosa's 'English coast') in 1497–1498, but in 1500–1501 Gaspar Corte Real, a navigator from the Azores, sailed across the North Atlantic, rediscovered Greenland and saw the facing coast of Labrador. These discoveries are recorded on the large planisphere drawn in 1502 by Alberto Cantino (Plate 3.8). This map is the earliest to

PLATE 3.20 *(above) Untitled map of the West Indies from Pietro Martyr d'Anghiera's* Opera *printed at Seville in 1511, being the first printed Spanish–American map.*

PLATE 3.21 *(below)* Oceanus Occidentalis seu terre nove *by Martin Waldseemüller, Strasbourg, 1522. Waldseemüller is said to have been the first person to suggest that the new continent be named America after Amerigo Vespucci.*

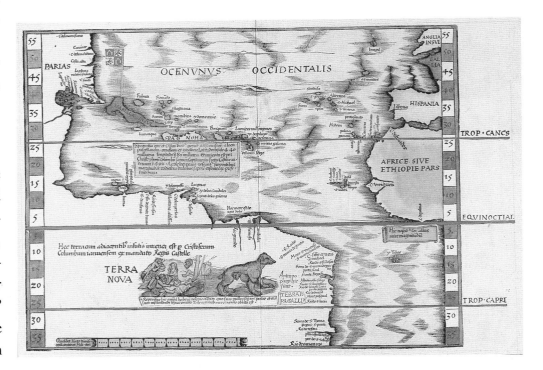

record the Portuguese discovery of India; subsequent Portuguese maps show in increasing detail and precision the results of discoveries in the Indian Ocean and in the East Indian archipelago.

Cantino's map illustrates the discoveries made on the eastern – or Portuguese – side of the line of the Treaty of Tordesillas of 1494. The second Portuguese fleet to India, which sailed in 1500 under the leadership of Cabral, headed southwest for the Cape Verde islands, to make good use of the trade winds and to avoid becoming becalmed off the African coast, and perhaps also to make further discoveries on the Portuguese side of the demarcation line. Thus Cabral, acting on the advice of Vasco da Gama, found the coast of Brazil, where he made landfall at about 17°S, thence resuming his course for the Cape of Good Hope. Then, in 1501–1502, Amerigo Vespucci continued exploration of the eastern coasts of South America to a point beyond the estuary of the

Rio de la Plata, probably as far as 50°S. These discoveries, among others, are recorded on a manuscript world map drawn about 1508 and attributed to a Genoese mapmaker, Vesconte Maggiolo, which is now preserved at the British Library in London.

The Pacific Ocean

Elsewhere in the New World, the first European to see the Pacific made his discovery from a peak in the Darien region of Panama in September 1513. He was Vasco Nuñez de Balboa, who climbed the peak 'from whiche he myght see the other sea soo longe looked for, and never seen before by any man commynge oute of our Worlde'.[4] The newly discovered ocean was called by the Spanish *Mar de Zur* in contrast to their naming of the Atlantic *Mar del Norte*, which lay to the north and northeast of the isthmus where Balboa was situated at the time of his discovery.

PLATE 3.22 *A world map by Giacomo Maggiolo, manuscript 1561. This is a fine example of the work of the celebrated Genoese portolan chartmaking Maggiolo family. A most unusual feature is the inset of the New World.*

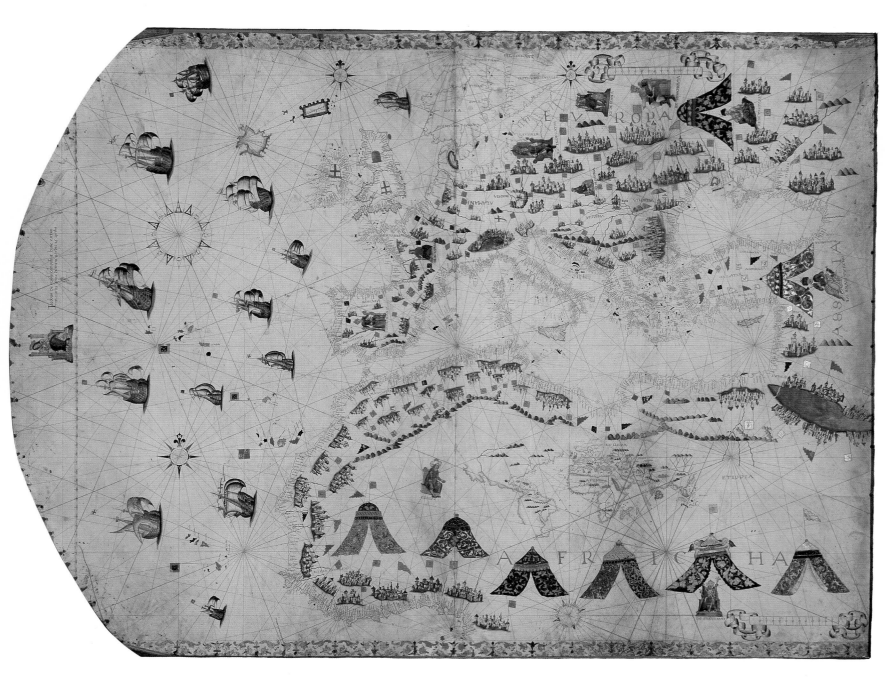

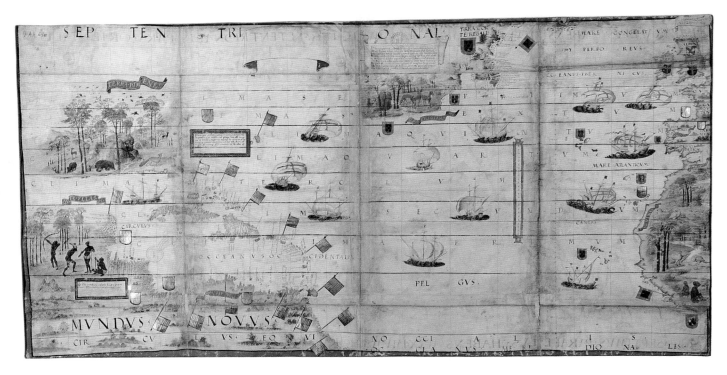

PLATE 3.23 *The Atlantic Ocean and the West Indies from the* Miller Atlas *by Lopo Homem and Pedro Reinel, c. 1519. The map depicts the lands explored by Corte Reals in the north in 1500–1504 and the northern shores of South America, with hints of Florida, here labelled 'Terra Bimene', not to be confused with Bimini in the Bahamas.*

PLATE 3.24 *Untitled manuscript chart extending from Arabia to Sumatra, one of five charts in the so-called* Miller Atlas *by Lopo Homem and Pedro Reinel, c. 1519. The map shows the coasts observed by Portuguese navigators such as Vasco da Gama, Pedro Alvares Cabral and others from 1498 to c. 1515.*

By one of those remarkable facts which characterize human history, Balboa's discovery of the Pacific seemed to provide the key which unlocked the coast of the Americas northwards and southwards on its western side.

In 1540, less than thirty years later, Sebastian Münster was able to issue the first separate map of the Americas shown as a landmass in its own right (Plate 3.25). The map emphasized the continuity of the two continents, North and South America, which were joined just north of the Equator at Balboa's narrow isthmus, and proved for all time that no strait leading to Cathay and the other countries of the Far East existed.

A few years after Balboa's sighting of the Pacific, Spanish ships actually circumnavigated the world in 1519–1522. Spain now had access to the Pacific and, with the Philippines, the beginnings of an empire in the East, firmly linked to the Spanish–American Empire.

(continued on page 82)

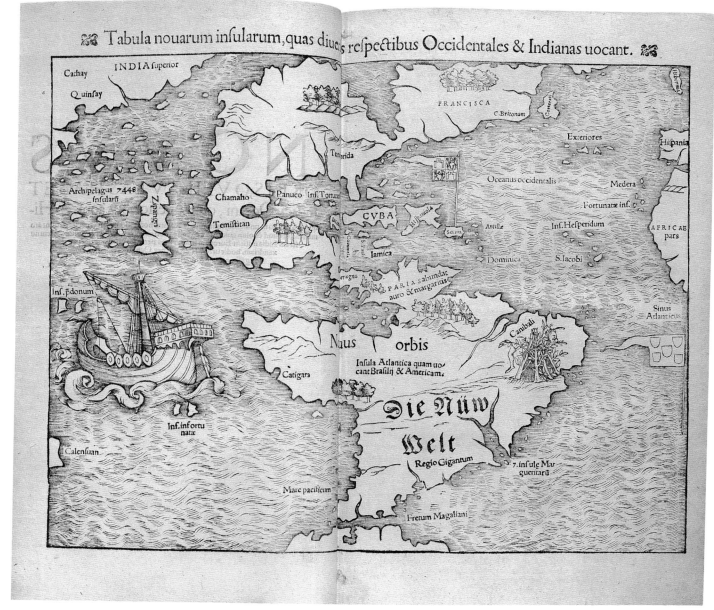

PLATE 3.25 *(right)* Die nuw welt *by Sebastian Münster, woodcut, 1540 and later. This was the first printed map devoted to the western hemisphere, and it improved on previous prints by showing North and South America as separate continents.' Münster was Professor of Hebrew at the University of Basel and a prominent German mathematician, cartographer and cosmographer. Among his publications was an edition of Ptolomy's* Geography.

PLATE 3.26 *(right) Untitled world map by Guillaume Brouscon, 1543. The map shows the arms of Arthur de Cossé,* maréchal de France. *Note here that South America (in the lower left-hand quadrant) is shaped oddly like an outline of Australia, even to the extent of including Tasmania as a southern peninsula. Brouscon, a Breton seaman, compiled nautical guides, tables and nautical almanacs.*

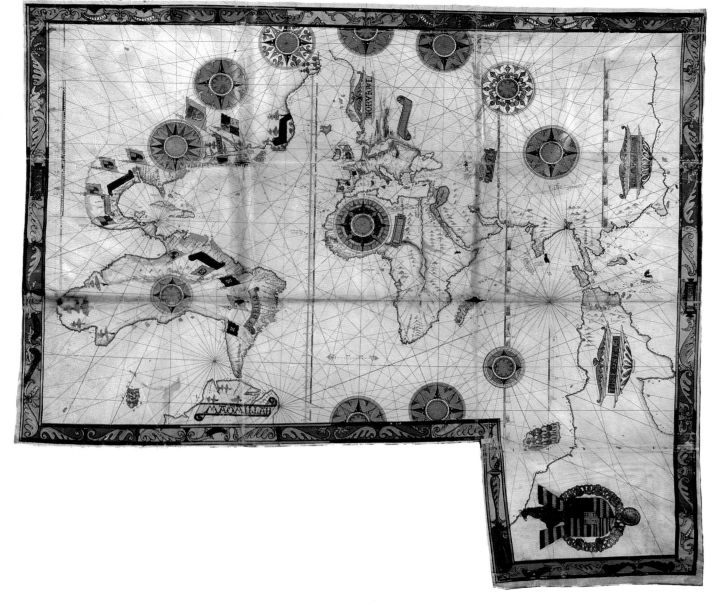

PLATE 3.27 *(above)* One of a group of original maps and drawings by John White. This map charts the coast of the southeastern part of North America from Virginia to Florida, illustrating the early European sphere of active colonization on the mainland.

PLATE 3.28 *(left)* America sive Novus Orbis respectu Europaeorum inferior globi terristris pars, *1596, from Part VI of the* Great Voyages *series by Theodor de Bry, Frankfurt am Main, 1597. Sometimes decorative maps such as this were included in travel books. Note the portraits of Vespucci, Pizarro, Magellan and Columbus.*

TARTARIA

SINA

IAPAN

MAR NEGR

Tropicus Cancri dat is Creefts Sonnewend of Noorder Sonn

Islas

Filipinas

Islas de las
velas, o
de los Ladrones

ARCHIPELAGO DE S. LAZARO

BORNEO

WEST

Linea Aequinoctialis dat is de Middellijn

Nueva Guinea

Illas de Salomon

Tropicus Capricorni dat is Steenbock Sonnewend of Zuyder

M

By Hessel Gerrits z.
met Octroy
vande E. H. M. Heeren
de Staten Generael
der Vereenichde Nederlanden
ch. lc xxiii

SVYDT

PLATE 3.29 Mar del Sur, Mar Pacifico *by Hessel Gerritsz, manuscript on vellum, drawn in 1622 (with amendments dated to 1634, probably by Gerritsz's successor, Willem Janszoon Blaeu). The chart shows the coasts discovered in New Guinea in 1605–1606, as well as all Spanish and Dutch discoveries in the Pacific known to Gerritsz.*

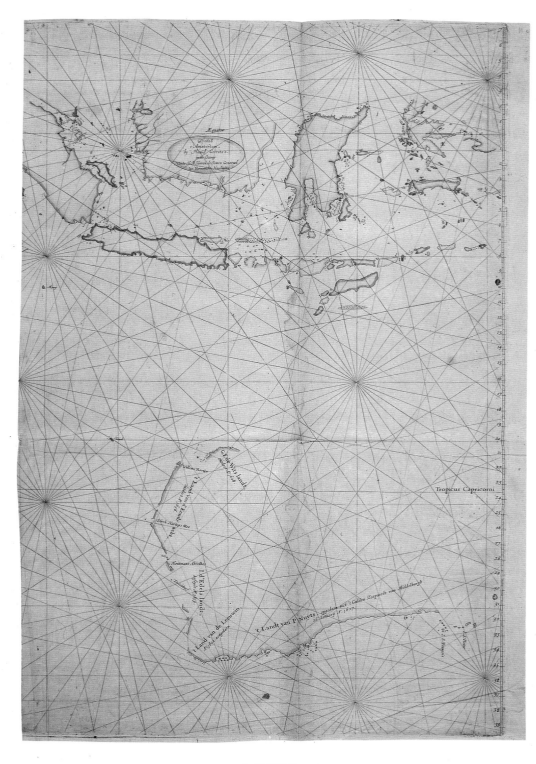

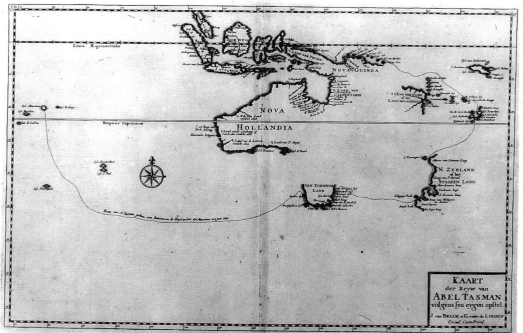

The discovery of Australasia

The notion of a circumpolar southern continent had been widely accepted since Antiquity. Early geographers believed that another continent (*antichthon*) existed in the southern hemisphere as a balance or counterpart to the inhabited world (*oikoumene*) of the northern hemisphere. In the sixteenth century the celebrated Dutch mapmakers Gerard Mercator and Abraham Ortelius (see Chapter IV) perpetuated the conception of a southern continent centred on the South Pole to balance the known lands in the north. Mercator's world map of 1569 included a '*Continens australis*' located in the far south. A year later, in 1570, Abraham Ortelius indicated a vast '*Terra australis nondum cognita*' on the world map in his atlas *Theatrum orbis terrarum*.

The Dutch discoveries

Dutch navigators made a series of exploratory expeditions into the southern hemisphere in the first decades of the seventeenth century. In 1606 a Dutch vessel reached the northern coast of Australia. Ten years later Dirk Hartog, in the *Eendracht*, landed on the western shore of the continent. Many Dutch ships sailed in the vicinity of *Terra australis* between 1618 and 1623. Hessel Gerritsz (1581–1632), the chief cartographer to the Dutch East India Company until 1633, published an untitled sea chart in 1618 showing the Dutch discoveries in southern and western Australia up to 1628 (Plate 3.30). Fragments of the southern coastline appeared on some Dutch maps, discovered around 1626.

In August 1642 an exploratory party headed by the Dutch navigator Captain Abel Janszoon Tasman (1603–1659) set sail with two ships on a systematic exploration of the South Pacific. The ships sailed south from Mauritius in October and skirted Australia without apparently seeing it, owing to the cold, stormy weather. They reached a landmass which Tasman christened Van Diemen's Land in honour of the Governor General of the Dutch East Indies who commissioned the voyage. The island was renamed Tasmania when it was colonized by the British in 1803 when they set up a convict settlement. On 13 December Tasman came upon States' Land, which was later named as New Zealand by the Dutch.

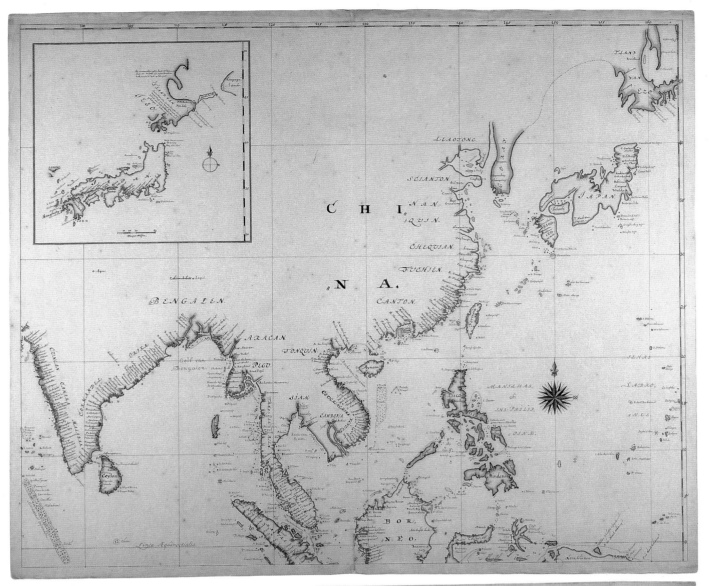

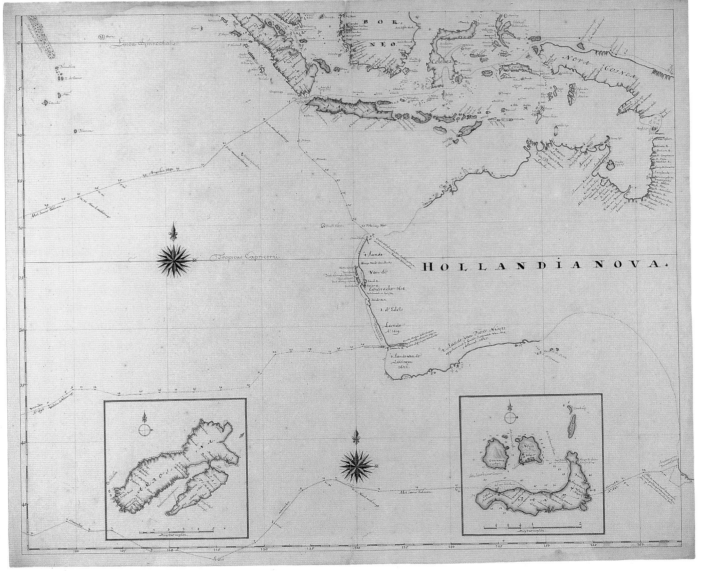

PLATE 3.30 (opposite, top) Untitled chart showing the Malay Archipelago and the Dutch discoveries in Australia by Hessel Gerritsz, Amsterdam, 1618 (but 1628 or later). This chart shows discoveries up to 1628 in southern and western Australia. Until 1633 Gerritsz was chief cartographer to the Dutch East India Company.

PLATE 3.31 (opposite, bottom) A synoptic Dutch chart of the voyages and discoveries of Abel Janszoon Tasman, published in Oud-en Nieuw Oost-Indien by François Valentijn in 1726. Place names and dates are given for various isolated stretches of the Australian coast as found by Dutch navigators up to 1644.

PLATE 3.32 (left, top and bottom) Two of a group of four charts which cover the Indian Ocean from the Cape of Good Hope to Australia and New Zealand and northwards to the East Indies and Japan, attributed to Isaak de Graaf. The charts show inter alia the routes of Abel Janszoon Tasman in 1642–1643 and of Willem de Vlamingh in 1696 in search of the trace of a lost Dutch vessel.

PLATE 3.33 *(right)* The Drake Silver map of the world, *silver medallion with the western hemisphere (obverse) and eastern hemisphere (reverse), 71 mm dia., said to have been struck or cast in 1581 after the return of Sir Francis Drake from his circumnavigation.*

PLATE 3.34 *(below)* A chart of New South Wales or the east coast of New-Holland *by James Cook, 1770. This coast, which Cook reached from across the Tasman Sea in the east, was traversed from April to August 1770.*

PLATE 3.35 *(opposite, top)* A map of New Zealand *charted by James Cook during his first* Endeavour *voyage of 1768–1771. For the first time the entire coastline of New Zealand was circumnavigated and charted.*

PLATE 3.36 *(opposite, bottom)* Manuscript of A Chart of the passage between New Holland and New Guinea as seen in His Majesty's Ship Providence in 1792 *by Matthew Flinders. In the* Investigator *Flinders made the first scientific survey of large stretches of Australian coastline.*

Tasman made a second voyage two years later which allowed him to trace with greater precision the outline of Australia's northern shores. It was about this time that *Terra australis* became known as New Holland.

Dutch maps from the middle of the seventeenth century recorded the voyages and discoveries of the Dutch navigators. A map of 1650, *Pascaerte van de Zuydt-Zee*, attributed to Joan Blaeu of Amsterdam (see Chapter IV), showed the routes taken by Dutch navigators in the Pacific in the early years of the seventeenth century (Plate 9.13). Another chart, by the prominent Dutch publisher and chartmaker Pieter Goos, entitled *Oost Indien*, thought to have been issued as early as 1658, was possibly the first newly engraved map to show the Dutch discoveries in Australia down to the voyages of Tasman in 1642–1644 (Plate 9.11). This impressive nautical chart was used on board the vessels of the Dutch East India Company. A later chart, published in François Valentijn's *Oud- en Nieuw Oost-Indien* in 1726, depicts the voyages and discoveries of Tasman (Plate

3.31). Place-names and dates are given for various isolated stretches of the Australian coast as found by Dutch navigators up to 1644. Tasman's voyages were also illustrated on two untitled charts of the Indian Ocean attributed to Isaak de Graaf (Plate 3.32).

The English colonization of Australia

Sir Francis Drake (1540–1596) was the first British navigator to circumnavigate the world. Drake's pioneering voyage in the *Golden Hind* in 1577–1580 opened up new sea routes in the South Pacific. A silver medallion showing a map of the world (Plate 3.33) was struck in 1581 on Drake's return to England showing the course taken by the *Golden Hind*. It was, however, some 150 years after Drake's epic journey that Europeans began to cast their eyes eastwards in the direction of Australia with a view to exploration, settlement and colonization.

The English navigator James Cook (1728–1779) made two voyages of discovery to Australia and New Zealand in the ships under his command, *Endeavour*, *Resolution* and *Adventure*. Cook set off on his first expedition in the *Endeavour* in 1768. He landed at Botany Bay in 1770, taking possession of the Australian continent for Britain. He named the bay after the profusion of plants and flowers he found there. From April to August 1770 Cook traversed the east coast of Australia. Although *Endeavour* nearly floundered three times among the reefs, his charting of 3,200 kilometres of coastline in just four months resulted in remarkably accurate charts such as his chart of New South Wales (Plate 3.34).

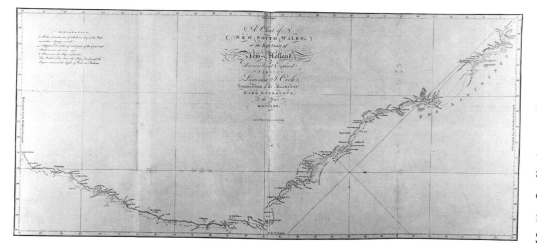

During his first *Endeavour* voyage of 1768–
1771 Cook also circumnavigated and charted the
coastline of New Zealand (Plate 3.35), occasionally venturing ashore to carry out triangulation
work. Close copies of Cook's chart were issued by
map publishers throughout Europe.

In 1802 the corvette *Investigator*, under the
command of Matthew Flinders, set sail for the
Pacific to explore the coastal regions of Tasmania
and eastern Australia. Flinders went on to explore
Australia's northeast coasts as far as the Gulf of
Carpentaria. Flinders made the first scientific
survey of large stretches of Australian coastline
prior to his arrest and imprisonment by the
French authorities at Mauritius in 1804. He
wrote an account of his voyage on his return to
England in 1810, *Voyage to Terra australis*, which
was published posthumously in 1814. The accom-
panying atlas contained many fine charts such as *A
Chart of the passage between New Holland and New
Guinea* . . . (Plate 3.36).

French explorations in Australia

Australia held considerable interest for the French
and they were the main competitors of the British
in the quest for colonial expansion in the southern
hemisphere. A French expedition under the command of Rear-Admiral Bruny d'Entrecasteaux in
1791 provided the data for the first scientific and
hydrographic exploration of the coasts of Tasmania and the marine maps of Beautemps-Beaupré,
father of modern hydrography. In 1800 Captain
Baudin was despatched by Napoleon Bonaparte to
investigate the lesser-known coasts of Australia,
from the Gulf of Carpentaria to Tasmania. Baudin
was accompanied by a scientific staff of twenty-
four experts. The aptly named ships *Géographe*
and *Naturaliste* set sail from Le Havre on 29
October 1800. The *Naturaliste* returned to Le
Havre in June 1803 with an impressive collection
of botanical and zoological specimens. The *Géographe* stayed on to finish mapping the southern and
western coasts of Australia.

References
1. *Descriptio insularum aquilonis.* Quoted in G. Jones, *The Norse Atlantic Saga*, 1964.
2. A. Cortesão, *The History of Portuguese Cartography* II, pages 120–121.
3. R.H. Fuson, *The Log of Christopher Columbus*, International Marine Publishing, page 9, 1987.
4. Richard Eden, English translation of Peter Martyr in *Decades of the New World*, 1555.

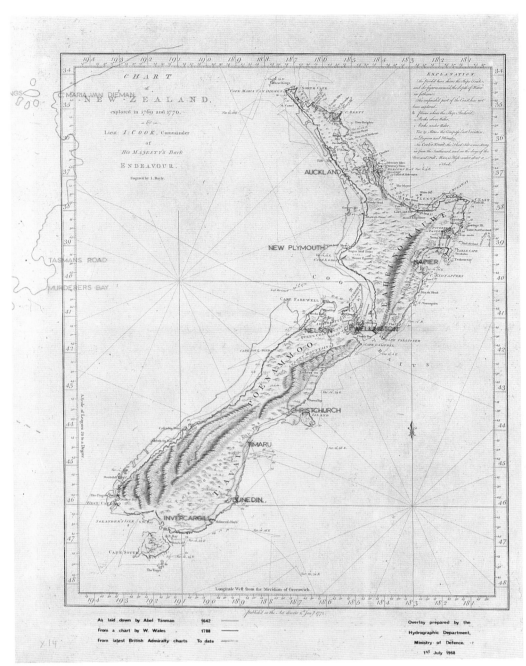

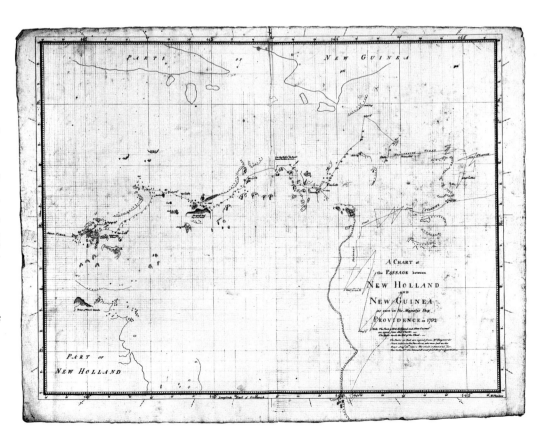

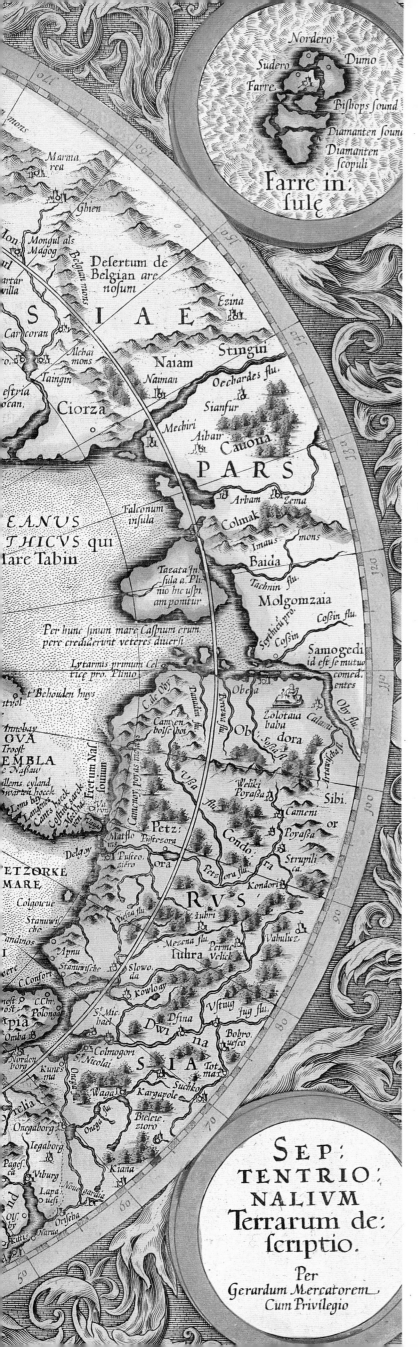

CHAPTER IV

THE DUTCH GOLDEN AGE

1500 – 1700 AD

FOLLOWING THE DISCOVERIES of the European explorers in the New World and the rapid spread of printing from the fifteenth century onwards, geographers and mapmakers in Europe were given a new impetus. The Renaissance period in western Europe is one of the most important times in the history of cartography. A map trade was established in most European countries. The Italians dominated mapmaking in the fifteenth century with the publication of Ptolemy's *Geography* in 1475 and its many subsequent editions (see Chapter V). In the late sixteenth century and throughout most of the seventeenth century, however, Gerard Mercator, Abraham Ortelius and the Blaeus ensured that the Netherlands was the centre of mapmaking in Europe.

The 'golden age' of mapmaking in the Netherlands occupied the greater part of the seventeenth century, but cartographic activity in this small corner of northwestern Europe certainly did not begin and end with that period. Far from it, for mapmakers in the Netherlands were active during the middle decades of the fifteenth century, producing many imposing maps.

PLATE 4.1 *Detail from* Septentrionalium terrarum descriptio *by Gerard Mercator, first issued in 1595. One of the few atlas maps compiled by Mercator himself, it is the first separate map of the Arctic. Mercator wrote to Dr John Dee in 1577 about the polar regions that 'there are many small rivers, some two, some one, some three kennings wide . . . called 'indrawing seas' because the current always flows northward so strongly that no wind can make a ship sail against it.'*

PLATE 4.2 An early print workshop *copper engraving, sixteenth century. Copper engraving was difficult, messy work, requiring the skills of a number of different people. The rolling press can be seen in the centre of the room; the finished maps are being hung up to dry.*

A particularly fine example is a large semi-pictorial map of part of Belgium, depicting the lower course of the River Scheldt from Rupelmonde to the North Sea, made in about 1468 at the orders of Charles the Bold, Duke of Burgundy, which was intended to indicate the bounds of the lands of the counts of Holland, the dukes of Brabant and the counts of Flanders. Another example, known as *De Sint Elizabethvloed van 1421* ('The Saint Elizabeth Flood of 1421') was attributed to the Master of Rhenen and has survived in the form of an anonymous fifteenth-century diptych now in the Rijksmuseum, Amsterdam. It gives an astonishing and highly detailed overview of the lands inundated in the western Netherlands not far from Dordrecht, from Gorinchem to Zevenbergen, in a manner which would be recalled in later generations in the series of perspective plans and views published by Braun and Hogenberg in the sixteenth and seventeenth centuries (see Chapter VIII).

Later, around the middle of the sixteenth century, booksellers, printers and publishers gradually began to adopt copper engraving as a medium for the illustration of books and broadsides (Plate 4.2), although woodcut techniques were not abandoned altogether. At the time, some of the best metal engravers were working in the

Netherlands in and around the great port city of Antwerp. It was here, in the commercial capital of western Europe, that guildsmen were producing prints and books of all kinds which were chiefly religious in nature. These publications were for sale both locally and in the Spanish possessions in the Americas and the Far East. Later they became available in the Jesuit missions in South and Central America and the Far East. All manner of specialities in the printing trade grew up in Antwerp, attracting practitioners from all over Europe: English, Italian, German, Portuguese and Spanish, as well as the merchants of the Hanseatic League. Indeed, by the 1560s, it was said that there were over 1,000 foreigners living and working within the city walls. An idea of the commercial activity and wealth of the city and its guilds can be gained from the following description by the German artist Albrecht Dürer (1471–1528), who visited Antwerp in 1520. He wrote in his diary a description of one of the many processions from the cathedral (the *Onze Lieve Vrouwekerk*) which took place at intervals throughout the year:

On the Sunday after Our Dear Lady's Assumption I saw the great Procession from the Church of Our Lady at Antwerpen, when the whole town of every craft and rank was assembled, each dressed in his best according to his rank. And all ranks and guilds had

PLATE 4.3 Method of triangulation *by Gemma Frisius, from* Libellus de locorum . . . an appendix to Cosmographicus liber *by Peter Apian, 1533. Gemma Frisius (1508–1555) was an astronomer, mathematician and doctor, and his work was of particular importance to cartography.*

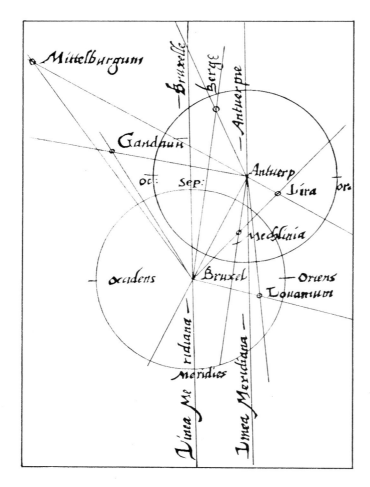

their signs, by which they might be known . . . There were the Goldsmiths, the Painters, the Masons, the Broderers, the Sculptors, the Fishermen, the Butchers, the Leatherers, the Clothmakers, the Bakers, the Cordwainers – indeed workmen of all kinds, and many craftsmen and dealers who work for their livelihood. Like the shopkeepers and merchants and their assistants of all kinds were there . . . all the religious orders and the members of some foundations, very devoutly, all in their different robes . . .[1]

Many of the tradesmen and guildsmen of the time would have been members of the Guild of St Luke, the guild for engravers, painters and similar craftsmen, which was highly organized in the Netherlands during the sixteenth century. The members were thoroughly trained, with high standards of craftsmanship. There were family dynasties where the elder members trained the juniors so that fathers and sons, uncles and cousins, brothers and relatives by marriage or partnership all mastered the same techniques – and, not infrequently, the same styles, designs and peculiarities. Guild members participated in common religious festivals and rites (such as that witnessed by Dürer) and contributed to a common fund, just like a modern mutual benefit society. Hours of work and ordinances were set down by the members, while the quality of the work produced was subject to the rigorous scrutiny of the wardens of the guild. Such, then, was the kind of professionalism found in the Netherlands at this time – in Antwerp in particular – and it seems natural that geographers, mapmakers and mapsellers would establish themselves in such a favourable environment, one which could almost inevitably guarantee a ready market for their products at home and abroad.

Elsewhere in Europe, particularly in the universities at Vienna, Nuremberg, Freiburg and Leuven, important advances were being made in the fields of science and mathematics, some of which were being reflected in cartography. The work of Gemma Frisius (1508–1555) is of particular importance to cartography. Frisius, born at Dokkum, was an astronomer, mathematician and lecturer in science and medicine at Leuven. He devised and described a concise method of triangulation which was published at Antwerp in 1533 under the title *Libellus de locorum describendorum*

ratione as an appendix to the *Cosmographicus liber* of Peter Apian. The text contained a diagram showing a triangulation established between Middelburg, Ghent and Brussels (Plate 4.3). It is most likely that the work was influenced in some degree by Sebastian Münster, who in 1528 had made a series of calculations for a detailed survey of Germany – *Erklärung des neuen Instruments der Sunnen, nach allen seinem scheyben und Cirkeln*, which was printed in that year at Oppenheim, near Frankfurt, by Jakob Kobel.

Jacob van Deventer

Quite early on in the sixteenth century mapmakers in the Netherlands 'began to make their influence felt, and the movement began that finally wrested supremacy in map production from Italy and transferred it to the Netherlands for a hundred years'.[2] One of the best known mapmakers of the time was Jacob Roelofs (c.1505–1575), better known as Jacob van Deventer after his native town. He achieved this position despite the fact that he wrote no work on surveying or mapmaking which became the textbook of successive mapmakers, and that his output was confined entirely to the Netherlands. Nevertheless, van Deventer was granted the title of Imperial Geographer in 1540 and became Royal Geographer in 1555. He studied at Leuven University from 1520 to about 1530 and, like his contemporary Gemma Frisius, obtained a degree in medicine

PLATE 4.4 Zelandicarum insularum *by Abraham Ortelius after Jacob van Deventer, copper engraving, c. 1570. Van Deventer is best known for his provincial maps and town plans of the Netherlands.*

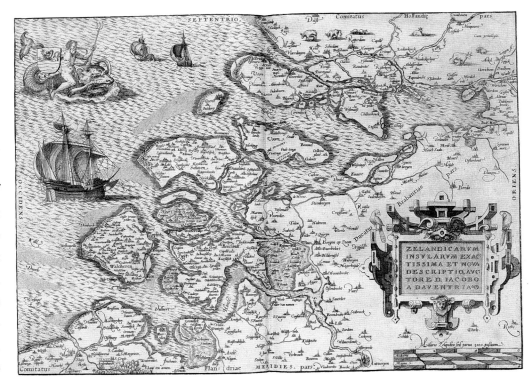

PLATE 4.5 Double portrait of Gerard Mercator *(left)* and Jodocus Hondius *(right)*, Amsterdam, 1620. This posthumous portrait of two of the most influential figures in the history of mapmaking was engraved for inclusion in the Mercator/Hondius series of atlases.

but went on to apply himself to the study of surveying. He is believed to have remained working at Leuven until 1542, when he removed to Mechelen, not far from Brussels.

In 1572 van Deventer had to flee to Cologne when the town of Mechelen was plundered by Spanish troops. He managed to take some of his maps and plans with him.

Van Deventer's talents appear to have been recognized early on in his career, for he received a commission to survey and map five provinces and regions of the Netherlands in 1530, and in 1536 presented his first map of the province of Brabant to the Council of Brabant at Brussels. This was followed over the next nine years by other maps, mostly now lost. These provincial maps became more widely known throughout Europe through their Italian versions issued by Lafreri, Tramezini and others a few years later and subsequently through versions issued by Ortelius in his *Theatrum* atlas from 1570 onwards. On the strength of his successes, van Deventer was commissioned to make a map of Delfland (part of the area of

Zuidholland between 's-Gravenhage and Rotterdam) in 1539; of the six copies delivered, sadly none has survived. There followed maps of several smaller districts. Van Deventer is, however, best known for his town plans of the Northern and Southern Netherlands which are discussed in Chapter VIII (see p.268–275).

Gerard Mercator

Of all the people involved in the history of mapmaking in the Netherlands, and indeed elsewhere, one name stands above all others, then as now. Gerard Mercator (1512–1594) was 'preeminent as a cartographer in whom geographical scholarship was allied to technical ability as mapdraughtsman and engraver' . . . a map-engraver of the next generation, Jodocus Hondius, singled out this combination of talents in his eulogy of Mercator, who [he wrote] "to his knowledge of geography and chronology added a quality exceedingly rare among scholars, a skill in drawings, engraving, and elegant illuminating".[3]

Mercator (Plate 4.5) is the most widely known figure in the history of cartography; his is a name recognized by anyone with even the most basic acquaintance with maps. Indeed, even so prominent a figure as Ortelius himself was to dub Mercator 'the Ptolemaeus of our century'. He was born Gerhard Kremer (Mercator being the Latinized form of the name) at Rupelmonde in Flanders, and went to study at Leuven in about 1535, gaining a master's degree and remaining there in profession until forced on account of religious persecution to flee to Duisburg in Germany in 1552. Mercator early on gained a considerable reputation as a maker of astronomical and mathematical instruments, working initially for Gemma Frisius in about 1536 and later on his own account. Between 1541 and 1551 he constructed large globes, for Charles V among others. His reputation spread far afield, a late example of which is illustrated by the beautiful gilt metal terrestrial and celestial globes which his workshop at Duisburg made for the Ottoman Sultan Murad III in 1579 modelled on the printed globe of 1541. These are still extant and were sold at Christie's in London in 1991.

Mercator made his first map in 1537, a map of Palestine engraved in copper. A year later, at the age of twenty-six, he constructed an untitled world map on a double-cordiform (heart-shaped) projection, modelled on a map by the French geographer Oronce Finé in 1531. A novel feature of Mercator's map is the separation of North America from Asia, contrary to the convention of the time, 'initiating a controversy as to the precise link between the two continents that was not to be fully resolved for over 200 years'.[4] Only two examples of this map are known today. Several years later, in 1550, a close copy of the original map was made and sold by Antonio Salamanca in Italy and a little later still was issued under the imprint of Antonio Lafreri.

Mercator's singular ability and aptitude as a maker of surveying and navigational instruments, his work as a land surveyor, and perhaps also the commendations he received for globe engraving in 1536 and 1537 led him to provide a solution to one of the problems concerning navigators of the time: that of the representation of loxodromes (lines of constant bearing) on charts.

During his years at Leuven, Mercator came to be regarded as the foremost European geographer of his day, having established himself as an authority on all matters of geography and cosmography at the imperial court. He came into contact with the work of the navigators, explorers and mapmakers of Portugal and Spain, and considered not only the representation of geographical subject matter on maps, but also the manner in which it was presented to the ultimate user, and the ease with which such documents could be read – a particular problem which we in the late twentieth century have still to resolve fully. His early treatise on lettering, the *Literarum Latinarum, quas Italicas, cusoriasque vocant, scribendarum ratio*, published at Antwerp in 1540, described how to write the italic (cursive) script and gave mapmakers a ready manual on the lettering of maps. This highly influential publication, illustrated with Mercator's own wood-blocks, provided a script which could be worked harmoniously yet still legibly into the overall design of a map or chart, but without pointless flourishes or ornament. Such embellishments 'must not seem to wind languidly and cautiously around as though they were broken down', he wrote at the very end of his manual.[5]

But Mercator's greatest achievements were yet to come, after he had removed to Duisburg in 1552. In 1544, for unrecorded reasons, Mercator was arrested and imprisoned on suspicion of

PLATE 4.6 *Terrestrial globe by Gerard Mercator, made at Leuven, 1541, and dedicated to Nicolaus Perrenot.*

heresy, while visiting the town of his birth. The university authorities at Leuven interceded on his behalf and Mercator was released after four months, whereupon he returned to his work at Leuven. In 1552 he left Leuven with his family and settled at Duisburg, no doubt because of the greater religious freedom and tolerance there, and also probably because he knew of the plans of the Duke of Jülich-Cleve-Berge to establish a university at Duisburg. Mercator was subsequently appointed cosmographer to Duke Wilhelm, and in 1563 became lecturer at the new Gymnasium (grammar school).

In 1554 Mercator published a large wall-map of Europe which did much to enhance his international reputation as a cartographer. No complete example of this map is known to have survived. (The only known copy is believed to have been destroyed at Breslau [Wrocław, in Poland] in 1945.) However, portions of the European map survive in the form of a remarkable little atlas, almost certainly made for Werner von Gymnich, a close friend of Mercator's. It came to light in Belgium in 1967 and was sold at a Sotheby's auction in London in 1979. In fact, not only portions of the Europe map survive in this 'atlas', but also portions of Mercator's map of the British Isles of 1564 and lesser portions of his great world map of 1569, together with two unique manuscript maps of parts of Italy, almost certainly by Mercator himself.[6] The European map was engraved in fifteen sheets, measuring some 1,320 by 1,590 mm overall, and was published at Duisburg. From the portions which do survive, it can be judged as a fine specimen of Mercator's engraving work, with lettering in the italic style which he had already done so much to popularize throughout Europe by means of the handbook he had produced in Antwerp fourteen years earlier.

The 1554 map of Europe was a remarkable achievement, establishing several improvements to the cartographic form of the continent, the most notable of which was the reduction of the longitudinal extent of the Mediterranean from Ptolemy's value of about 62° to a more accurate value (by modern standards) of about 53°. This was still some 10°30′ more than the modern value, but a considerable advance nevertheless. Mapmakers continued to accept Mercator's revised value for more than 150 years.

Mercator's latitudinal values were very accurate indeed, despite some errors creeping in towards the northern and eastern extremities. Mapmakers such as Mercator did not, of course, go out 'into the field' to gather survey data for maps such as that of Europe. Mercator was obliged to accept Ptolemy's position for Alexandria, but arrived at positions for other principal places by careful research and study of the best materials then available, such as itineraries and nautical charts, paying particular reference to relative directions provided by the best charts. These data would then be reconciled and co-ordinated with the known positions of principal places. Mercator was at pains to point out that he rejected the idea of using data gathered from the simultaneous observation of solar eclipses for the simple and (to us) obvious reason that simultaneous observations of eclipses were extremely difficult to achieve.

This sheds some light on the general methods of making maps of larger regions, of continental proportions, for it has been observed that maps 'depended largely upon the labour expended in the cartographer's office in attempting to reconcile a mass of disparate and often conflicting data'.[7] Beyond the confines of Europe, the only geographical features shown on maps which were even remotely reliable, as far as European mapmakers are concerned, were the coastlines, the lower courses of the larger rivers and perhaps the positioning of major landmarks – all features, in other words, which were obtained from sea and coastal charts. Knowledge of the interior beyond the immediate narrow coastal strips of large tracts of, say, Asia and West Africa, remained confused for the most part until well into the nineteenth century, until the arrival of explorers with reasonably accurate and reliable means to carry out extensive surveys.

Demand for Mercator's map of Europe seems to have been considerable, for a second edition was issued in 1572. The new edition of the map was improved and revised with additional information gleaned from English expeditions to Russia.[8] It is no doubt because of the harsh conditions under which this and similar large wall-maps were kept – unprotected and exposed to dampness, dust and dirt, seasonal temperature variations and so on – that so few maps intended for display purposes have survived, despite the fact that relatively large

numbers must have been printed. Indeed, according to the ledgers of the Antwerp publisher Christopher Plantin, no fewer than 868 copies of the Europe map, as issued in 1554 and revised in 1572, were sold between 1558 and 1576.[9]

In 1564, Mercator produced a large map of the British Isles, entitled *Angliae, Scotiae et Hiberniae nova descriptio*, measuring some 890 by 1290 mm and printed in eight sheets. The map shows the British Isles oriented with the west to the top, and the islands lying supine to the viewer. Little of the background to this map is known, but it is generally considered to have been based upon the draft map of the British Isles drawn by Lawrence Nowell, Dean of Lichfield, which is now in the British Library. Only two complete examples have survived, both of which are in libraries in

Italy, but the travelling atlas mentioned above contains five sheets made up from assembled portions of the British Isles map covering these islands, so that there exists a third, almost complete example of this outstanding opus of sixteenth-century mapmaking. It was a landmark in its own right, for it provided the basic outline of the British Isles which was followed by mapmakers for decades afterwards. Indeed, the general view of the British Isles which appears in Abraham Ortelius's *Theatrum* atlas gives an excellent impression, albeit reduced to folio atlas size, of how Mercator's large map looks. The 1564 map of the British Isles was not reissued, but it is of interest to note here that, in Mercator's own *Atlas* of 1595, the general map of the British Isles is taken from an altogether different source, the

PLATE 4.7 Europa *by Gerard Mercator, 1595. This may have been based on Mercator's earlier wall map of Europe which has not survived. It shows a clear water passage to the north of the landmass: the northeast sea passage that many explorers hoped would lead them to the East.*

PLATE 4.8
*Septentrionalium
terrarum descriptio by
Gerard Mercator, first
issued in 1595. One of the
few atlas maps compiled by
Mercator himself, it is the
first separate map of the
Arctic, drawing upon
materials as diverse as
Mercator's own world map
of 1569, the Ruysch map of
1507 and the fourteenth-
century* Inventio fortunata.

map of the English cartographer Christopher
Saxton (see p.162), issued in 1579, showing a
conventional north orientation.

By 1569, Mercator had already achieved a
considerable reputation, for although his previous
output had not been large, his works had been
acclaimed as outstanding. The achievement upon
which Mercator's posthumous reputation rests,
however, is his great world map of 1569, *Nova et
aucta orbis terrae descriptio ad usum navigantium
emendate accomodata*. The map was made upon the
'waxing latitudes' projection he devised for navigators which bears his name to this day. Only

three complete examples of this map are known to
have survived, plus a further small portion,
covering Greenland and Iceland, in the travelling
atlas discovered in 1967. The map is large,
measuring some 1,340 by 2,120 mm, and is
composed of twenty-one sheets. It had a threefold
purpose, as Mercator himself declared in one of
the several texts placed around the map: to be
useful to navigators (as explained in the title); to
represent the surface of the land as accurately as
possible; and to show the extent of the world as it
was known to classical geographers.

The Mercator projection was used on this map

for the first time. It is basically a cylindrical projection which allows lines drawn on a map constructed on this projection to appear as straight lines, like a grid. This means that any course plotted by navigators and pilots can also be drawn as a straight line connecting any two points, rather than in the form of an arc as in other projections. Even so, it was still some time before the projection came to be generally accepted, after the publication in 1599 of the mathematician Edward Wright's *Certaine errors in navigation*, which expounded and clarified the mathematical principles involved.

As with his other large maps, Mercator carefully studied all the materials currently available to him when compiling the world map. His sources included world maps by Ortelius and Gastaldi, regional maps of Africa by Gastaldi (1564), of Asia by Ortelius (1567), and of the Americas by Diego Gutierrez (*c.*1562) and Giovanni Battista Ramusio (1550–1559), together with Portuguese and Castilian charts, available accounts of voyages and discoveries, and the works of the classical geographers and medieval travellers. Mercator was also in correspondence with his friend, the Elizabethan scholar John Dee, concerning the possibility of the existence of a northwest passage to the Spice Islands (the East Indies), and investigated various theories as to the nature of the Arctic regions. For his continental outlines, Mercator departed from the ideas of Ptolemy. He recognized three large landmasses: the Old World of Europe, Asia and Africa; the New World of the Americas (which he called here *India nova*); and the great southern continent, called *Continens australis*. This latter landmass was derived from a classical belief that another continent existed in the southern hemisphere, as a balance or counterpart to the inhabited world of the northern hemisphere. Evidence for this belief seems also to have been based on a misreading of the accounts of the travellers Ludovico di Varthema and Marco Polo which concluded that continental lands, the hypothetical regions of *Beach* and *Lucach*, lay to the south of *Java Major* placed to the southeast of the East Indian Archipelago. To the west, Tierra del Fuego (seen by Magellan during his voyage nearly half a century earlier) was incorporated into the southern continent.

The representation of the Arctic is of particular interest, for Mercator devoted a special circular inset map to this region. He placed it at the lower left-hand corner because, owing to the nature of the projection used for the main body of the map, the polar regions could not be represented. As Mercator himself said 'our chart cannot be extended as far as the Pole, for the degrees of latitude would finally attain infinity'. This same inset was reproduced as a separate map in the *Atlas of 1595* – the first separate map devoted to the Arctic (Plate 4.8). The inset shows open water at the Pole itself, surrounded by a circular landmass divided into four roughly equal sections by 'inflowing seas'.

Mercator drew upon source material for the Arctic dating back to the fourteenth century. One of his principal sources was the *Inventio fortunata* of about 1364, which was attributed to Nicholas of Lynn, an English minorite friar from Oxford. The *Inventio fortunata* described the lands north of 54°N on the basis of a voyage which Nicholas is supposed to have made in 1360 'with an astrolabe'. It was the principal dissemination of the medieval Scandinavian view of the North, and was incorporated into Renaissance European geography and cartography. The *Inventio fortunata* commented, for example, that 'under the Arctic Pole is a magnetic rock thirty-three miles in circumference' – the *Rupes nigra* ('black rock') as shown on Mercator's inset. On the large islands and channels surrounding the Pole, the *Inventio fortunata* stated further that the *Rupes nigra* was 'surrounded by islands and depths into which the ocean flowed and was regurgitated'.

In a letter to John Dee, written in 1577, Mercator noted that 'there are many small rivers, some two, some one, some three *kennings* wide, more or less: and they are called "indrawing seas" because the current always flows so strongly that no wind can make a ship sail against it'.[10] This may, perhaps, be a reference to reported difficulties experienced by sailors in northern waters. It was through such channels in the Arctic that it was hoped to find northwest and northeast passages out to Cathay from Europe.

A little later, Francis Drake's plans for his circumnavigation in the 1570s envisaged the discovery and annexation of part of the southern continent of *Terra Australis*. His *Nova Albion* was located in the *Quivira Regnum* region of north-

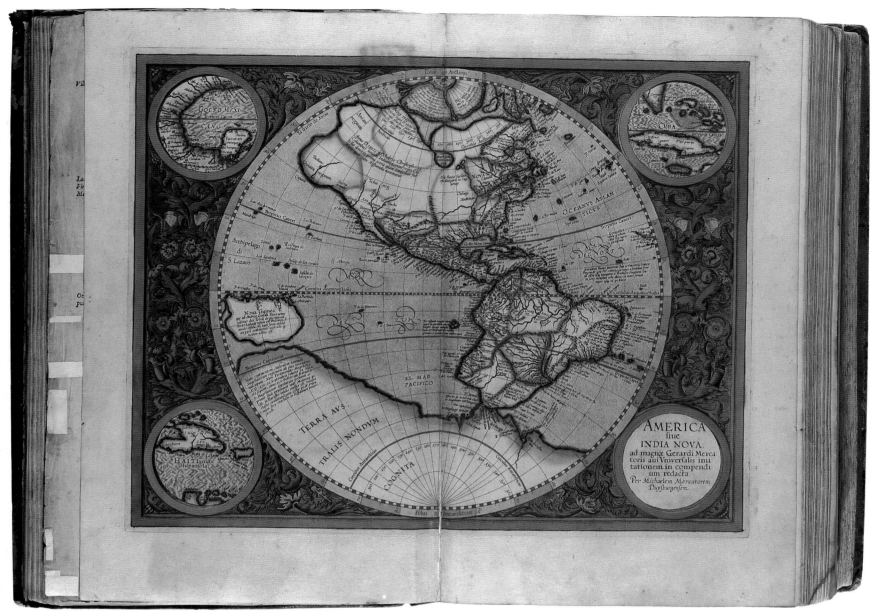

PLATE 4.9 America sive
India Nova *from* Atlas
sive cosmographicae
meditationes *by Michael
Mercator, Duisberg 1595,
with later editions at
Amsterdam, 1636. This is
the only known map to be
attributed to Michael
Mercator. The spandrel
insets show Cuba,
Hispaniola and the Gulf of
Mexico. At the bottom of the
map is a large unknown
land called* Terra
Australis.

western North America, conveniently located to
watch over the southern entrance to the hypothetical *El streto di Anian* which flowed from the
circumpolar Arctic waters into the northern
Pacific between Cathay and North America. During the 1640s, Abel Janszoon Tasman's circumnavigation of Australia was planned in order to
determine its relation to the supposed *Terra Australis*, a problem which continued to occupy and
intrigue the minds of geographers until Captain
James Cook finally settled the matter towards the
end of the eighteenth century. Directly or indirectly, therefore, Mercator's world map exercised a considerable influence on exploration long
after its initial appearance.

Mercator himself regarded his world map as
part of a co-ordinated programme of cartographical research. The map was intended to form the
basis of such research, and it was envisaged that
other sections were to deal with modern maps, the
maps accompanying his edition of Ptolemy (which
eventually appeared in 1578) and finally maps of

ancient geography – thus taking a universal view
of the creation, the heavens, the earth, the seas and
the history of the world. Towards this end, his
book *Chronologia* appeared in 1569. The preface
announced a work on geography to comprise the
work of Ptolemy augmented by a corpus of
modern maps. (The *Chronologia* found itself on
the Church's Index of forbidden works in 1603
because of its acknowledgement of the works of
heretics such as Martin Luther and its use of the
vulgate New Testament.) But the first portions of
the programme dealing with contemporary maps
did not appear until 1585 because of difficulties in
obtaining original materials of sufficiently good
quality, a lack of travel accounts and the problem
of finding competent engravers to reproduce maps.
Mercator was led to complain that progress on his
project was being held up because he and his
grandsons had to carry out the work themselves.
He also had, like many of his colleagues, to

(continued on page 101)

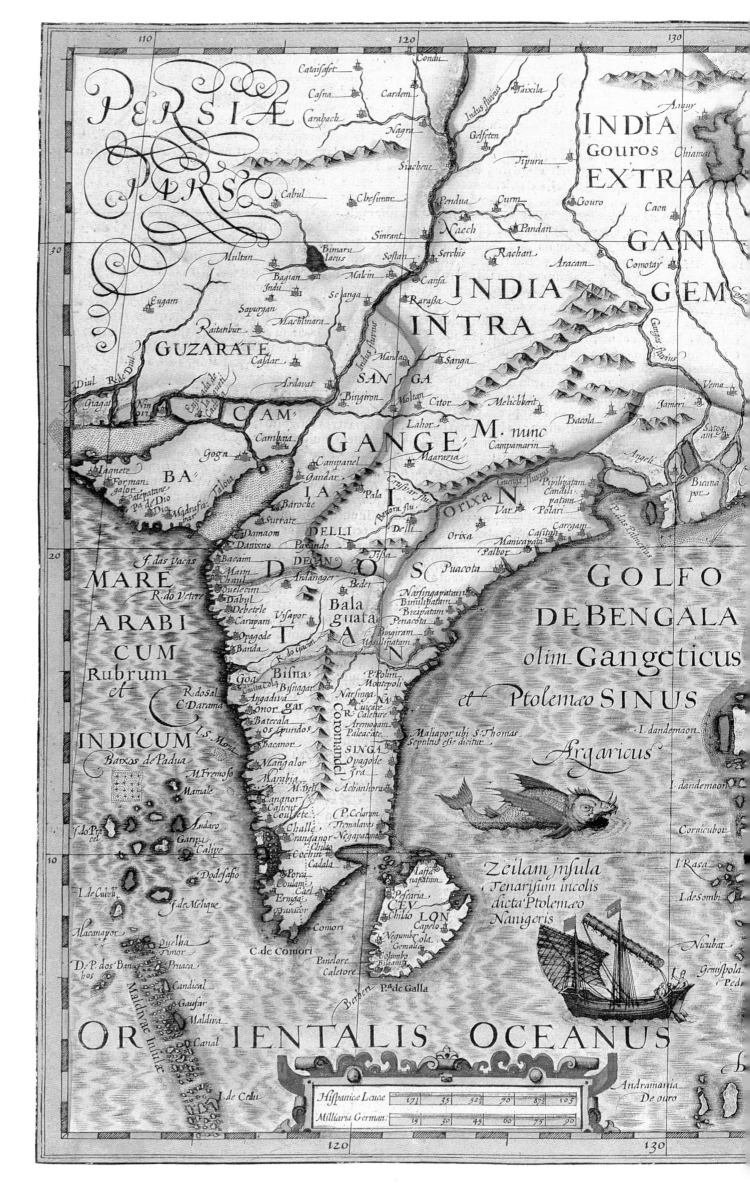

PLATE 4.11 India Orientalis *by Gerard Mercator and Jodocus Hondius, from* Atlas sive cosmographicae meditationes, *1606. Mercator's atlas saw the first use of the term 'atlas' applied to a collection of maps in book form.*

NDIOSA DESCRIPTIO

ori ac fautori summo, in veteris amicitię ac familiaritatis memoriā Rumoldus Mercator fieri curabat Aº. M.D.Lxxxvii.

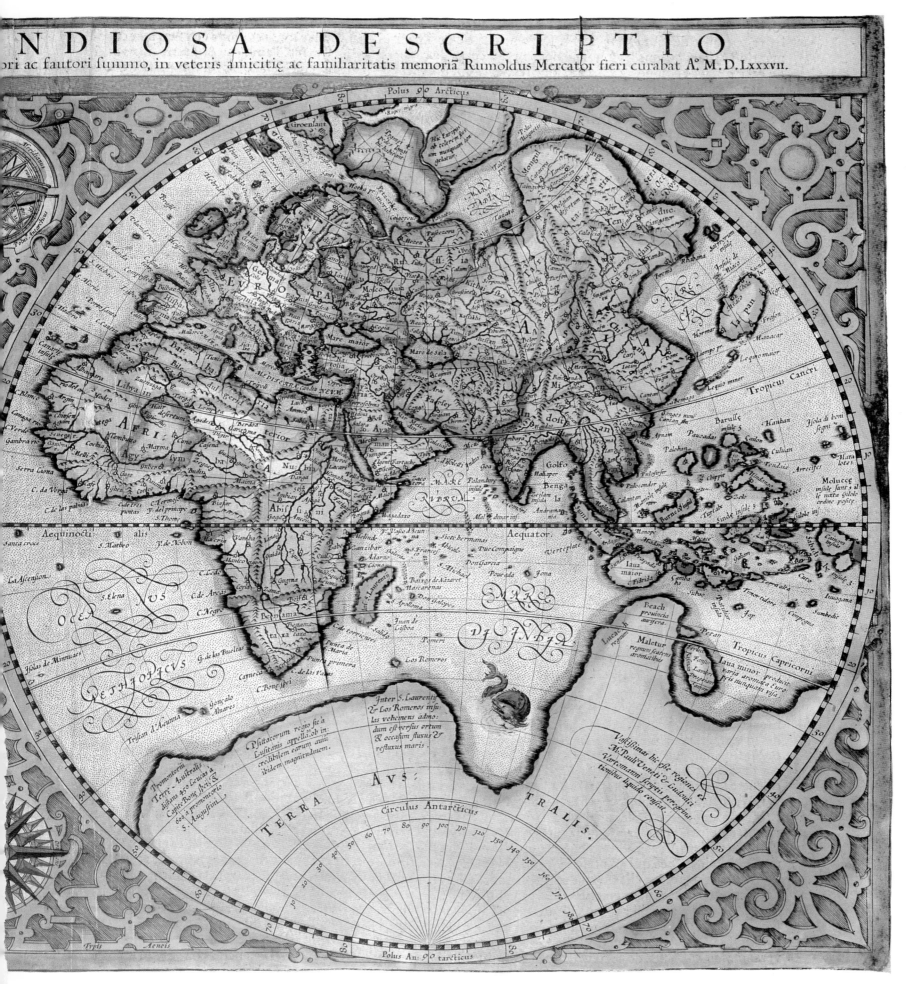

PLATE 4.10 *Orbis terrae compendiosa descriptio quam ex magna universali Gerardi Mercatoris . . . Aº. M.D. LXXXVII* by Rumold Mercator, copper engraving, *1587 and later. Rumold Mercator, grandson of Gerard Mercator, here acknowledges his grandfather's large world map of 1569 as his chief source. The map was published in editions of the* Atlas sive cosmographicae *until the 1630s.*

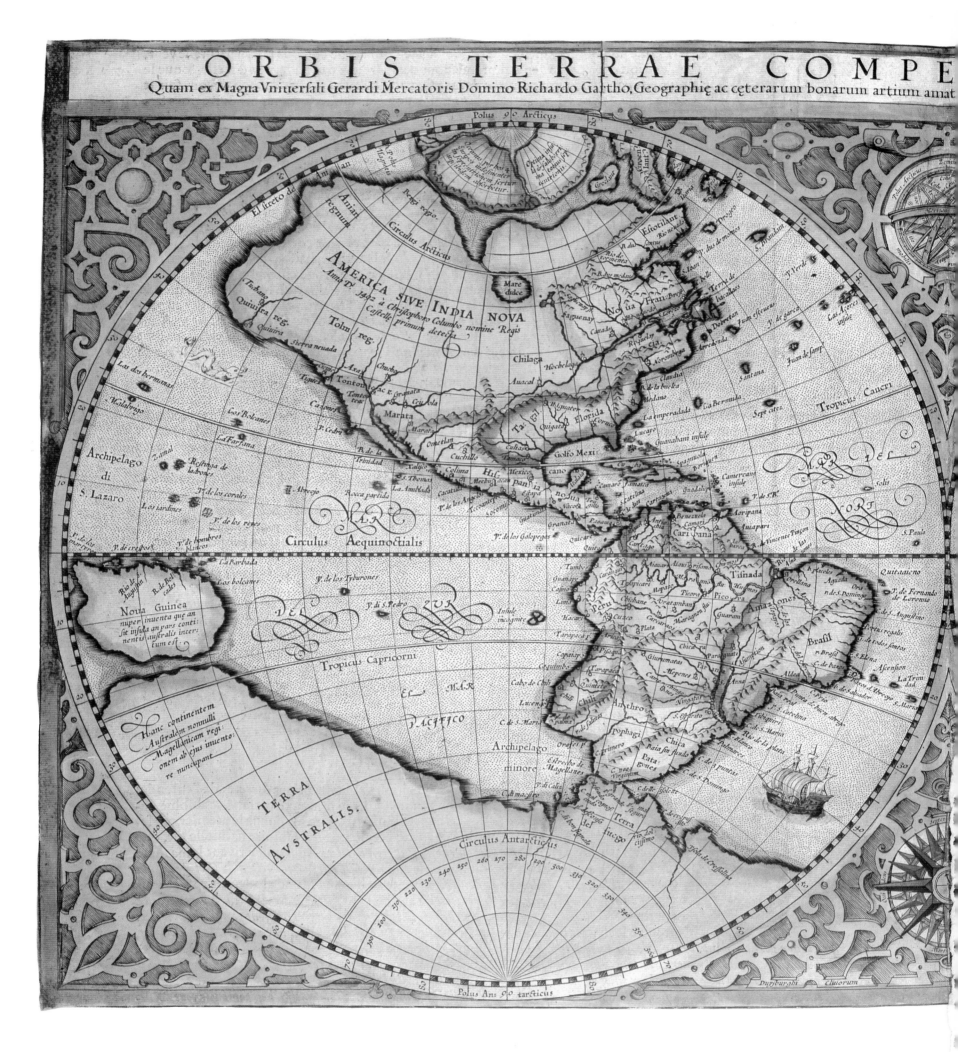

ORBIS TERRAE COMPE[

Quam ex Magna Vniuersali Gerardi Mercatoris Domino Richardo Gartho, Geographiæ ac cęterarum bonarum artium amat[

Polus 90 Arcticus

El streto de Anian

Anian regnum

Circulus Arcticus

AMERICA SIVE INDIA NOVA
Anno D. 1492 à Christophoro Columbo nomine Regis
Castellæ, primum detecta.

Mare dulce

Estotilant

Tropicus Cancri

Archipelago di S. Lazaro

MAR DEL

Circulus Aequinoctialis

MAR DEL SUR

Noua Guinea
nuper inuenta que an
sit insula an pars conti:
nentis australis incer:
tum est.

Peru

Brasil

Tropicus Capricorni

Hanc continentem
Australem nonnulli
Magellanicam regi:
onem ab ejus inuento:
re nuncupant.

EL MAR
PACIFICO

Archipelago minore

TERRA
AVSTRALIS.

Terra del fuego

Circulus Antarcticus

200 210 220 230 240 250 260 270 280 290 300 310 320 330 340 350

Polus Ant. 90 tarcticus

Duysburghi Cliuorum

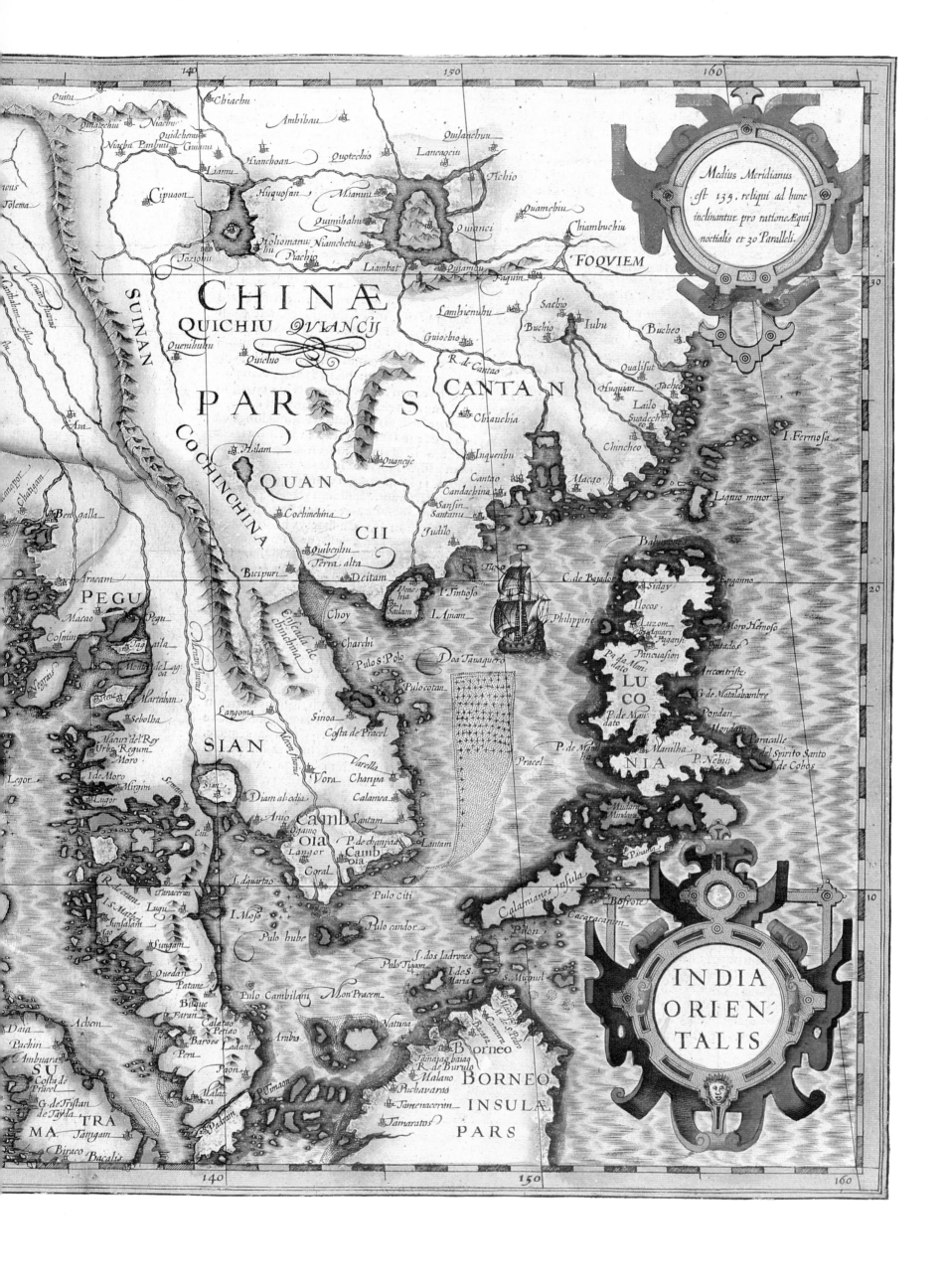

Quitu
Chiachu
Amihau
Omaizchiu Niachu
Quidchenu
Niachu Panhui Guiani
Hiancboan
Quotechio
Laneaociu
Achio
Quamchiu
Chiambuchiu
Liamu
Cipuaon
Huquofan
Mianuu
Quamchiu
Quianci
Holiomanu Niamchetu
Ioziohu Piachio
Liamhat
Quiamchu
Faquin
FOQVIEM

SUINAN

CHINÆ
QVICHIU QVIANCIS

Lamhienuhu
Saelio
Buchio   Iubu   Bucheo
Quenuhuhu
Guiocho
Quieluo
R. de Cantao
Qualifut
Sacheo
PAR   S
CANTAN
Huquian
Lailo
Suadech
Chauchia
Inquerihu
Chincheo

Hilam
CO
Quancije
Cantao
Macao
Liquio minor
QUAN
CHINCHINA
Cochmehina
Oandachina
I. Fermofa
Sanfin
Santanu
CII
Iudilo
Quibenhu
Terra. alta
Bicipuri
Deitam
Tuao
C. de Bajador
Balunione
Aracam
Done
hia
Sailaon
I. Sinthofo
Siday
PEGU
Ilocos
Engauno
Macao
Choy
L. Amam
Philippine
Luzom
Moro Hemofo
Cosnin
Pegu
Aquiari Piganh
Tagaila
Charchi
Paganh
Entados
Monte de Lag oa
Pancuafion
Reuc
Pulos Polo
Doa Tavaquero
Pa da Man
dato
Arcon trifte
Martaban
LU
G. de Matalahambre
Sebolha
Pulo cotan
CO
Sinoa
P. de Man
Pondan
Macur del Rey
dato
Urbs Regum
Costa de Pracel
Mondato
Moro
Langoma
P. de Man
Paracalle
I. de Moro Mirjim
Varella
ha
del Spirito Santo
SIAN
Vora
Charipa
Manilha
de Cobos
Legor
Sian
Diam ab odia
Calamea
Pracel
NIA
P. Nebui
Lugu
Cii
Anio
Camb
Lantam
I. Marec
Ogamo
OIA
Jurifalan
Tio
P. de chanpaa
Mudani
Sungam
Langor
Camb
Lantam
Mindano
I. Aquatio
Coral
oia
Pauana
Tanacerim
Pulo Citi
Calamianes Insula
Bofrion
R. de cinu.
I. Mofo
Pulo candor
Pilon
Cacaracarum
Quedan
Pulo hube
I. dos ladrones
Patane
Pulo Tipon
I. de S.
S. Miquel
Biique
Maria
Faran
Pulo Cambilan
Mon Pracem
Achem
Calatao
Petino
Daia
Baroes Ladant
Ambra
Nattuna
Pachin
Peru
Borneo
Ambuara
Paon
R. de Burulo
BORNEO
SU
Malacca
Malano
Costa de
P. Timaon
Puchavaras
INSULÆ
Pracel
G. de Tristan
Palpan
Tamenacerim
PARS
de Tayda
TRA
Tamaratos
MA Jangam
Biraco Bacalis

support himself by taking in other work as required. It was because Mercator was an original, rather than merely a reproductive engraver, that his work was slow in appearing. It also helps to explain his relatively small output.

Mercator was seventy-three years old when the first part of what was to become his *Atlas* was issued at Duisburg in 1585. This first part contained three sections, each with a separate title page, covering France (*Galliae tabulae geographicae*), the Low Countries (*Belgii Inferioris tabulae geographicae*), and Germany (*Germaniae tabulae geographicae*), containing fifty-one maps in all. Then, in 1589, the second part, entitled *Italiae, Sclavoniae et Graeciae tabulae geographice*, saw the light of day, covering Italy, the Balkans and Greece in twenty-two maps. The project lay unfinished at the time of Mercator's death in 1594, and it fell to his son Rumold to publish the third part, called *Atlantis pars altera*, the following year. It contained maps of the world and of four continents, as well as the rest of Europe, some thirty-four maps in all. The Latin sub-title of this third part, *Geographica nova totius mundi*, may be translated as 'The new geography of the whole world'. There was once a popular myth, thought to have originated in the seventeenth century, that the completion of the project was delayed because Mercator wished to avoid competition with the *Theatrum* of his friend Ortelius.

In the same year, 1595, Mercator's heirs issued the complete work, bearing the all-embracing general title *Atlas sive cosmographicae meditationes de fabrica mundi et fabricati figura*. This was the first use of the term *atlas* applied to a collection of maps in book form. The work had a long introductory text containing Mercator's 'cosmographical meditations on the creation and form of the earth'. The *Atlas* as it appeared in 1585 contained 107 maps, five of which were compiled by Rumold and two grandsons: a beautifully designed twin-hemispherical world map (on a projection more intelligible to the public than that devised for the 1569 world map) (Plate 4.10) and individual maps of the four continents derived from Gerard Mercator's earlier maps. The other twenty-nine maps in the *Atlas* were unpublished at the time of Mercator's death: sixteen covered the British Isles, the remainder the rest of Europe. A second, unaltered, edition appeared in 1602.

While demand for Mercator's works continued until the end of the sixteenth century, it seems that the *Atlas* was slow to sell at first, no doubt because many likely purchasers would already have possessed the work in its constituent parts when they were first published several years before. When the *Atlas* itself first appeared, it did not offer complete coverage of the world, and it was not until the plates were purchased from Mercator's heirs by the Amsterdam mapseller Jodocus Hondius, that thirty-seven further maps (covering the Iberian peninsula and parts of Africa, plus regional maps of Asia and the Americas) were added to make up some of the deficiency (Plates 4.11, 4.12). Following the first Hondius edition of the *Atlas* at Amsterdam, no fewer than forty-six editions, with text in Latin, French, German, Dutch and English, appeared up to 1659. The later editions were published by Hondius's successor Joannes Janssonius. As the years progressed, the editions of the *Atlas* became less recognisable as the work of Mercator and his heirs and more like the productions of the firms of Hondius and Janssonius. Finally, Mercator's *Atlas* was superseded by the atlas published by the firm of Blaeu, the earliest version of which was issued in 1630 (see below).

PLATE 4.12 Virginiae Item et Floridae Americae provinciarum *by Jodocus Hondius, copper engraving, Amsterdam, 1606 or later. An example of the kind of maps introduced by Hondius into his editions of Mercator's* Atlas. *Note the small insets, which are copied from the drawings of John White and Jacques Le Moyne after their illustrations to their travels in Florida.*

Abraham Ortelius

The most important contemporary of Mercator was undoubtedly Abraham Ortelius (1527–1598) (Plate 4.13), the begetter of the first uniformly conceived atlas of maps, the *Theatrum orbis terrarum* (Plates 4.14–16). Ortelius is first mentioned in 1547 in the enrolment records of the Guild of St Luke in Antwerp (see p.88–89) as an illuminator of maps. We know little of his early life and career, except that he was in business with his sister Anne (who died in 1600), engaged in the colouring and illuminating of maps, and that since 1554 at least, he had regularly attended the spring and autumn fairs at Frankfurt as a mapseller. Through these fairs, he made contact with visitors from all over Europe, particularly from Italy. Ortelius was a scholar and a craftsman, but not a practical surveyor like Mercator. In 1558 his name appears in the accounts of the firm of Plantin in Antwerp as *Abraham, peintre des cartes*.[11] His business seems to have been successful, allowing him to indulge his classical tastes and interests by forming an extensive library and a collection of antiquities. It was this interest which was to manifest itself in the *Parergon* – the comprehensive historical geographical supplement to his *Theatrum* atlas in later years (see below).

Ortelius travelled widely throughout western Europe and the British Isles and was fluent in several languages (Flemish, Latin, Greek, Italian, French, Spanish, German and English). His travels brought him a wide circle of learned correspondents and friends, among whom were such eminent men as Dr John Dee; William Camden, the English antiquary and historian; Richard Hakluyt, compiler and editor of a comprehensive collection of voyages and travels;

Humfray Lhuyd, the Welsh historian; and Mercator himself. Through such connections, Ortelius was able to amass much of his source material. Lhuyd is known to have sent him two maps of England and a map of Wales showing ancient and modern names, while Dr Dee wrote requesting information on his map of Asia (published in 1567) and Hakluyt wrote to ask Ortelius to publish material on North America with a potentially commercial eye on the English market.

Ortelius may well have begun collecting maps as early as 1561, when the merchant-adventurer Gillis Hooftman requested him to assemble a collection of maps of Europe, specifying in a letter that they must be convenient to handle and to use and that they must be 'not larger than a sheet of paper'. Hooftman's atlas is no longer in existence, but it comprised thirty-eight maps, thirty of which were printed in Rome (by Tramezini, Lafreri and others), the remainder in the Low Countries. Ortelius himself also issued a small number of maps in the same decade: for example, Asia (entitled *Asiae orbis partium maximae nova descriptio*, printed in eight sheets and measuring 1,015 by 1,450 mm) and a world map produced in 1564 (entitled *Nova totius terrarum orbis iuxta*

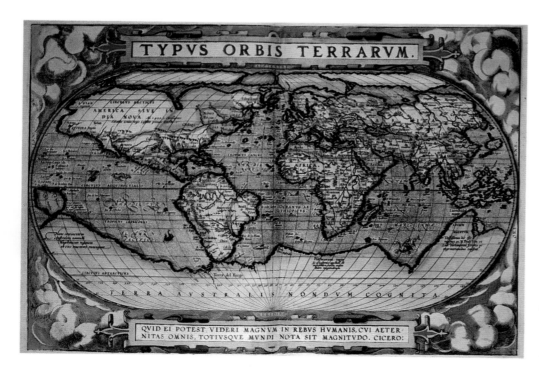

neotericorum traditiones descriptio, also in eight sheets, measuring 870 by 1,500 mm). In May 1570, the first edition of his famous atlas *Theatrum orbis terrarum* was published at Antwerp, containing seventy maps on fifty-three folio mapsheets, most of which had been engraved by Frans Hogenberg of Cologne. Sheets were not available for sale prior to the appearance of the finished work, since Ortelius conceived his *Theatrum* as a uniform atlas, not a mere collection of maps.

It is this conception which marks Ortelius as an innovator, for he was not an original cartographer – remember that only a handful of maps by him prior to 1570 are known, all of them derived from the works of others. Nevertheless, credit must be accorded to Ortelius, since he respected his sources. In his letters of instruction to his agents throughout Europe, he specified that he required the best maps available, and in the preliminary text matter to each edition of the *Theatrum* he printed a list of his source cartographers, the *Catalogus auctorum*. In the first edition, he named eighty-seven mapmakers. This list was added to in successive editions, so that by the time of the last revision of the list, in the posthumous edition of the *Theatrum* of 1601, no fewer than 183 names are cited. Indeed, we remain in Ortelius's debt, for were it not for the compilation of the *Catalogus auctorum*, the names of many sixteenth-century mapmakers would have been lost altogether.[12]

The *Theatrum* is considered to be the first modern atlas, 'compiled on principles laid down by its editor and not to satisfy the fancy of a customer'.[13] In modern publishing terms, it was a 'bestseller' for, in the first year of its existence, four editions were issued to meet demand. Furthermore, it remained in print, revised and expanded, until 1612, by which time competition from the Hondius editions of Mercator's *Atlas* had virtually taken over the atlas market. In all, forty-one editions of the *Theatrum* were published over its forty-year lifespan, a remarkable achievement even by modern publishing standards. In addition to the twenty-one Latin-text editions of the *Theatrum*, there were also two editions in Dutch, five in German, six in French, four in Spanish, two in Italian and one in English. By the time of Ortelius's death in 1598, five supplements, known as *Additamenta*, had been issued, adding 108 new maps, and several of the older

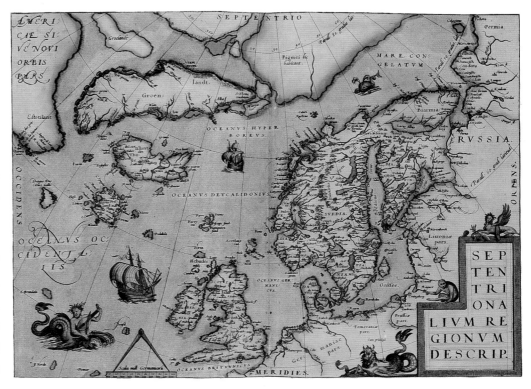

plates had either been altered, recut or replaced by more up-to-date plates.

The practice of issuing the *Additamenta* was novel, for it meant that it was not always necessary for owners of the atlas to purchase entirely new editions: sometimes owners would bind in the new maps into existing copies of the *Theatrum*, or merely place the *Additamentum* volume adjacent to the *Theatrum* on the shelf. The edition of the *Theatrum* following the appearance of an *Additamentum* would contain those new maps, with text, bound in the correct place in the atlas, the map numbering being altered accordingly. By this means, it is often possible to cite the date of an individual sheet from the atlas in the hands of a collector. This task has in recent years been made all the easier as a result of the labours of bibliographers and diligent researchers, such as Professor C. Koeman in the Netherlands.[14]

Ortelius was much interested in historical geography and later editions of the *Theatrum* contained a supplement called the *Parergon*, issued from 1592 onwards, which consisted of a series of maps of ancient geography compiled by Ortelius himself. It is an atlas in its own right, and copies are often found as individual volumes. Some of the maps were based on Ortelius's own work, such as those of the Roman Empire and of Ancient Egypt; others were compiled from maps and descriptions by other authorities, contemporary and classical. He even compiled (*c.*1596) an imaginary map of Utopia in the same format as all

PLATE 4.15
Septentrionalium regionum descriptio *by Abraham Ortelius, Antwerp, 1570 and later. Ortelius's standard atlas map of the Arctic, which remained in print for more than forty years.*

PLATE 4.16 *(right)*
America sive novi orbis,
nova descriptio *from*
Abraham Ortelius's
Theatrum orbis terrarum,
Antwerp, 1570. The blank
area in North America
illustrates the sparsity of
knowledge of the interior at
that time.

PLATE 4.17 *(below)*
Maris Pacifici . . . *by*
Abraham Ortelius,
Antwerp, 1589 and later.
One of the most striking and
popular of the maps in
Abraham Ortelius's
Theatrum *atlas, this is the*
first printed map devoted
to the Pacific Ocean. The
outstanding design is
complemented by the
strapwork cartouches typical
of Flemish ornamentation of
the period.

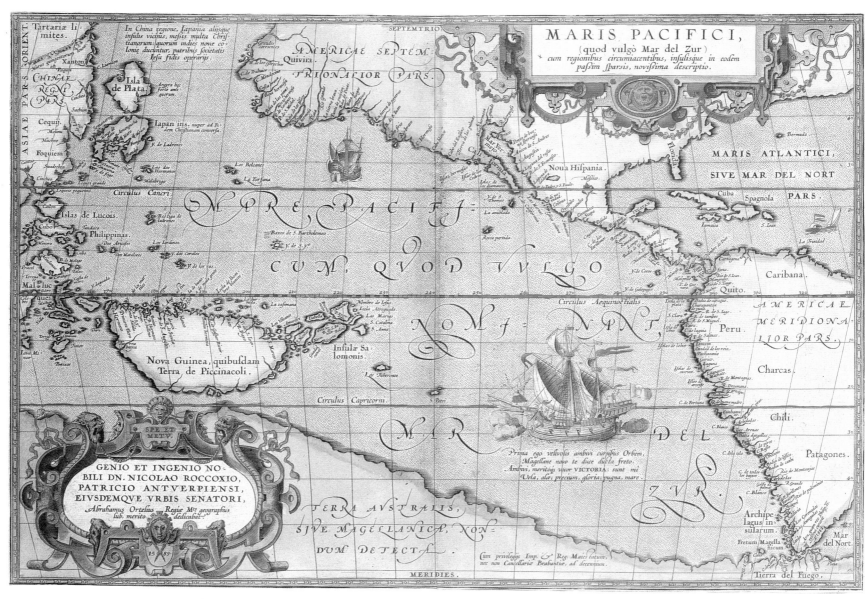

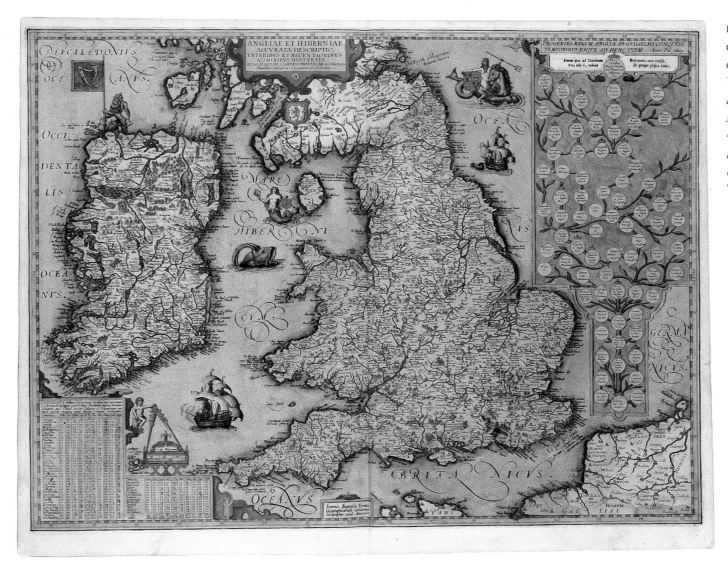

PLATE 4.18 Angliae et Hiberniae accurata descriptio *by Jan Baptist Vrients, Antwerp, 1606 and later, here shown in state II with altered wording in the panels of text. From later editions of Abraham Ortelius's* Theatrum *atlas.*

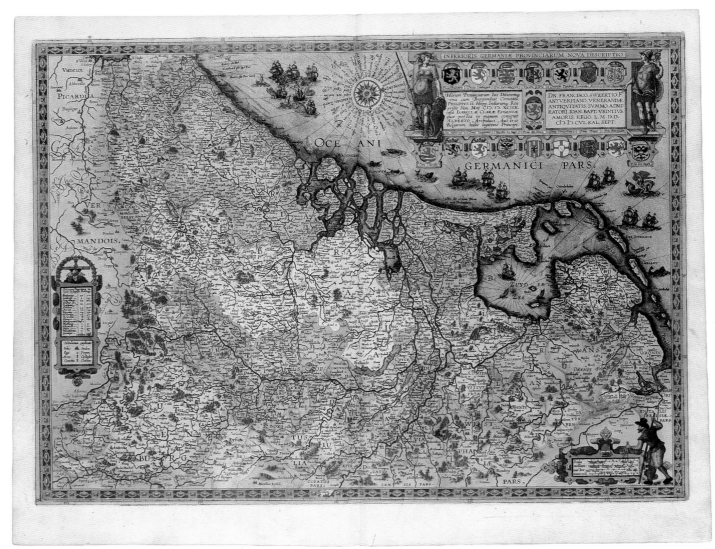

PLATE 4.19 Inferioris Germaniae provinciarum nova descriptio *by Jan Baptist Vrients, Antwerp, 1606 and later. From later editions of Abraham Ortelius's* Theatrum *atlas.*

PLATE 4.20 Dam Square, Amsterdam, *an oil painting by Jacob van der Ulft, 1659. At the time it was painted, the city was recognized as a prominent centre for the European map business.*

the maps of the *Theatrum* and *Parergon*. Only one example of this map is known, which came to light in the late 1970s.[15]

The *Theatrum orbis terrarum* atlas was not only popular and successful as an atlas, but it also established a new trend in publishing. As R.A. Skelton commented:

To 'engravers, illuminators and binders', as a contemporary records, Ortelius's enterprise brought prosperity, and until nearly 1600 the south Netherlands remained the centre of the map industry. Not only did the numerous and expanding editions of the *Theatrum* provide work for all kinds of craftsmen associated with the printing of maps and atlases; it also created a vogue for large cartographic projects. It is true that the finely engraved atlas of Gerard de Jode, the *Speculum orbis terrarum* published at Antwerp in 1578, was a commercial failure, stifled perhaps by the rivalry of Ortelius. Mercator's atlas, the first part of which was published in 1585, had been conceived many years earlier as part of a great treatise on creation; its success was due to Mercator's own reputation, and . . . it was engraved by Mercator and his family. But other grandiose collections . . . provided contracts in plenty for the family workshops of Flemish engravers at home or in exile; and their output, both in sheet- and atlas-maps, was immense.[16]

Many of these craftsmen worked abroad, exporting and making popular in their exile the

Flemish style of design and engraving. The brothers Remy and Frans Hogenberg, of Mechelen, settled and worked in London and Cologne respectively. Remy worked under the wing of Archbishop Parker at Lambeth, cutting several of the plates for Christopher Saxton's English county maps printed between 1574 and 1577 (see p.260–268). His brother Frans established himself as a type-cutter and founder (*lettergieter*) while continuing to carry out work for Ortelius, as well as his labours on the great *Civitates orbis terrarum* town plans project.

The era of the Blaeus

During the early years of the seventeenth century, Amsterdam was beginning to be recognized as a prominent centre of the map business in Europe. At this time it was becoming an established practice that pilots and navigators returning from their travels abroad should turn over their charts, together with any additions made as a result of their own observations, to an official mapmaker. Among the first of these was Pieter Plancius (1552–1622), who was appointed official cartographer to the *Vereenighde Oost-Indische Compagnie* in 1602. Plancius was an authority on the routes to the East, and prepared instructions for the second Dutch voyage to the East Indies in 1598. Two of Plancius's successors were Willem Janszoon Blaeu and his son Joan, in 1622 and 1638 respectively.

Little of the early history of the Blaeus has survived, fire and dispersal of their records having taken their inevitable toll over the years. Joan Blaeu was born at Alkmaar in Noord-Holland, in 1598 or early 1599. From his earliest days he was surrounded by scientific and navigational instruments since his father, Willem Janszoon Blaeu, had been keenly interested in mathematics and astronomy. To further this interest, Willem travelled to Denmark in 1594 to study under the renowned astronomer Tycho Brahe (1546–1601), becoming Brahe's assistant at his observatory, where he learned the art and science of instrument- and globe-making.

Willem Janszoon Blaeu returned to Alkmaar, and he and his family left in 1599 for Amsterdam, where he set up in business as a globe and scientific instrument maker. Capital and finance from overseas enterprise and the rising entrepreneurial

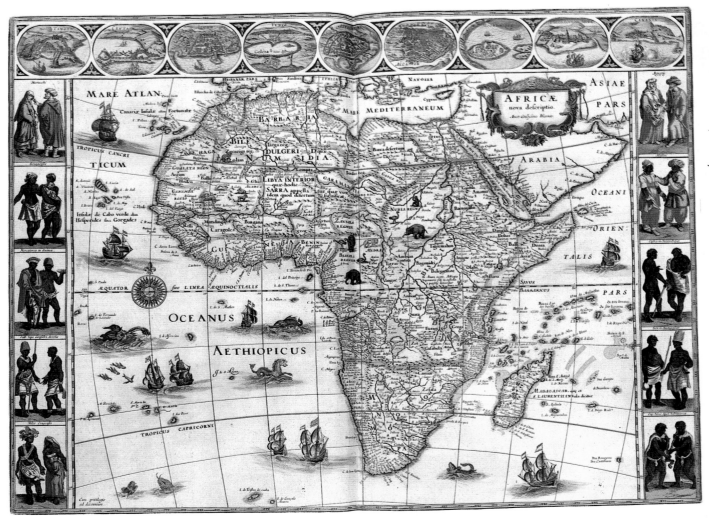

PLATE 4.21 *Africa nova descriptio by Willem Blaeu, Amsterdam, c. 1617. This map dates back to the early period of Blaeu's activity as a map publisher, although it appeared in Blaeu atlases from 1630 to the 1660s.*

classes in Amsterdam at this time provided the means to produce maps, atlases and globes on a large scale, none larger than the output of the firm of the Blaeus. In 1605, the family removed to an address 'op 't Water', which is now part of the west side of the Damrak in the centre of Amsterdam. Here, Willem Janszoon opened his shop and set up a printing press under the sign called *in de Vergulde Sonnewijzer* ('at the sign of the gilded sundial'), where works on navigation, astronomy, literature and theology were printed and sold. Willem Janszoon Blaeu's own religion is not known, but the few theological titles he issued from his press seem to indicate a certain tolerance of rival faiths. Joan Blaeu seems to have had some leanings towards Roman Catholicism in later years. Joan studied law at Leiden University, gaining a doctorate in 1620. After this date, very little is known of his life except that he married in 1634 and that, in 1651, Dr Blaeu (as he liked to style himself) was elected to the Council and Aldermen of Amsterdam, the first printer in the history of the city to hold such an office.

Joan Blaeu's name does not appear in connection with his life's work until around 1631, when he and his father collaborated on the first of what was to be a long and celebrated series of atlases. The partnership began in 1630 with the publication of an atlas entitled *Atlantis Appendix, sive pars altera . . . nunc primum editas*, containing sixty maps. At the time of writing, eight copies of this atlas are known: two are in the Netherlands, one in Germany, one in Belgium and three in England. The eighth – incomplete – atlas was sold in London in 1990. The title of the work is an allusion to the earlier atlas which had been published by Jodocus Hondius.

After the death of Hondius in 1629, Willem Janszoon Blaeu bought several of his map plates to add to his own small plate stock, with the intention of compiling and publishing an atlas of his own. In the preface to an early edition of his *Appendix* in 1631, he wrote:

Abraham Ortelius, the celebrated geographer of Philip II, king of Spain, made a *Theatrum Orbis Terrarum*, in which are maps of different parts of the world, some representing the ancient state of things, and others the modern. Whatever praise and thanks that incomparable man may have merited by this work, and with whatever appreciation the educated public may have received it, nevertheless this *Theatrum*

has its defects. Later the great mathematician Gerard
Mercator began to prepare, with tremendous labour
and at tremendous expense, the publication of his
Atlas, but death overtook him, so that he left his work
incompleted. By that its value is very considerably
decreased, because he was able to complete Europe
only (with the exception of Spain).[17]

Of the sixty maps in the first Blaeu atlas,
thirty-seven came directly from the Hondius plate
stock, a fact which did not escape either the notice
or the criticism of his rivals. Joannes Janssonius
(1588–1664) and Henricus Hondius (1597–
1651), brother and successor of Jodocus, who
called Blaeu's *Appendix* 'a hotch-potch of old
maps, which he [Blaeu] had altered, adapted, or
copied from their atlas'.[18] The Mercator–
Hondius *Atlas* had, in fact, dominated the Amsterdam and, in effect, the world map market
since the last full edition of Ortelius's *Theatrum* in

1612. Blaeu's use of the word *Appendix* or, later
on, *Atlantis Appendix*, was therefore an astute
commercial decision deliberately designed to link
his new work with a well-established and well-
respected work which was itself by then nearing
the end of its effective commercial life.

The first Blaeu atlas to bear the joint imprint of
father and son was the expanded *Appendix Theatri
A. Ortelii et Atlantis G. Mercatoris*, containing
ninety-eight maps and published in 1631 (Plates
4.21–24). The young sapling, as it were, was
already growing rapidly. The ambitions of the
Blaeus to produce a major world atlas were further
advanced in 1635 with the appearance of the
two-volume *Novus atlas* (or *Theatrum*), which
provided up to 208 maps. Four separate editions
in four different languages were published: German, Dutch, French and Latin. The newspaper
Nieuwstijdingen bij Jan van Hilten for 11 February
1634 recorded Blaeu's intentions as follows:

At Amsterdam are now printed in Willem Jansz. Blaeu's office, the great book of maps, or 'Atlas' in four languages: Latin, French, High German and Low German [i.e. Dutch]. The High German will appear towards Easter, the Low German and the French in the month of May, or early June at the latest, and the Latin shortly thereafter. All on very fine paper, entirely revised with newly engraved plates and new, wide-ranging descriptions.[19]

The rapid growth of the Blaeus' business thereafter meant that the premises 'op 't Water' had to be vacated in favour of a larger establishment at the nearby Bloemgracht. The publishing house remained here as the centre of the greater parts of the Blaeus' operations, which were described by Claude Joly in 1646, as 'l'imprimerie la plus plus belle de toute l'Europe'.[20]

A description by one Philip von Zesen, a German resident of some years' standing in Amsterdam, gives us a very good impression of the activity at such a publishing house:

. . . On the Bloemgracht, at the third bridge and third by-lane, stands the world-famous printing house of Mr. Joan Blaeu, councillor and alderman of this city. The establishment is equipped with nine presses for letterpress printing, called after the nine muses,

PLATE 4.23 *Detail of Asia noviter delineata by Willem Blaeu, Amsterdam, 1617 and later. This general map of Asia was first published in 1617 as a separate sheet and then included in the Blaeus' atlas series from 1630 to the 1660s.*

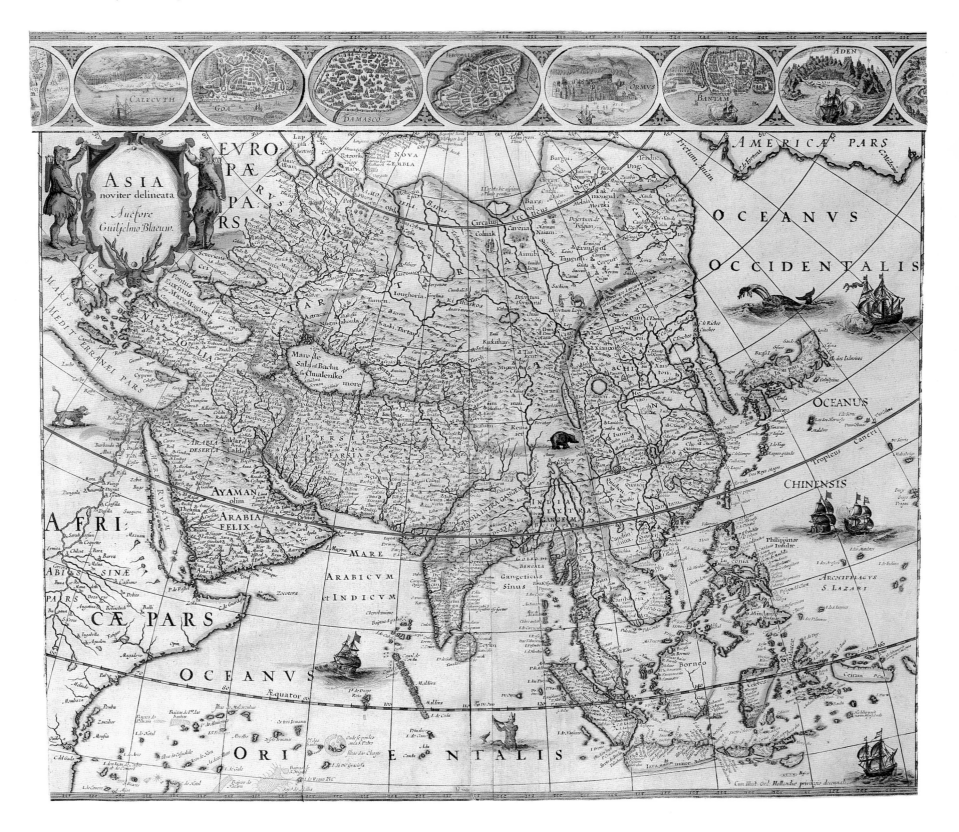

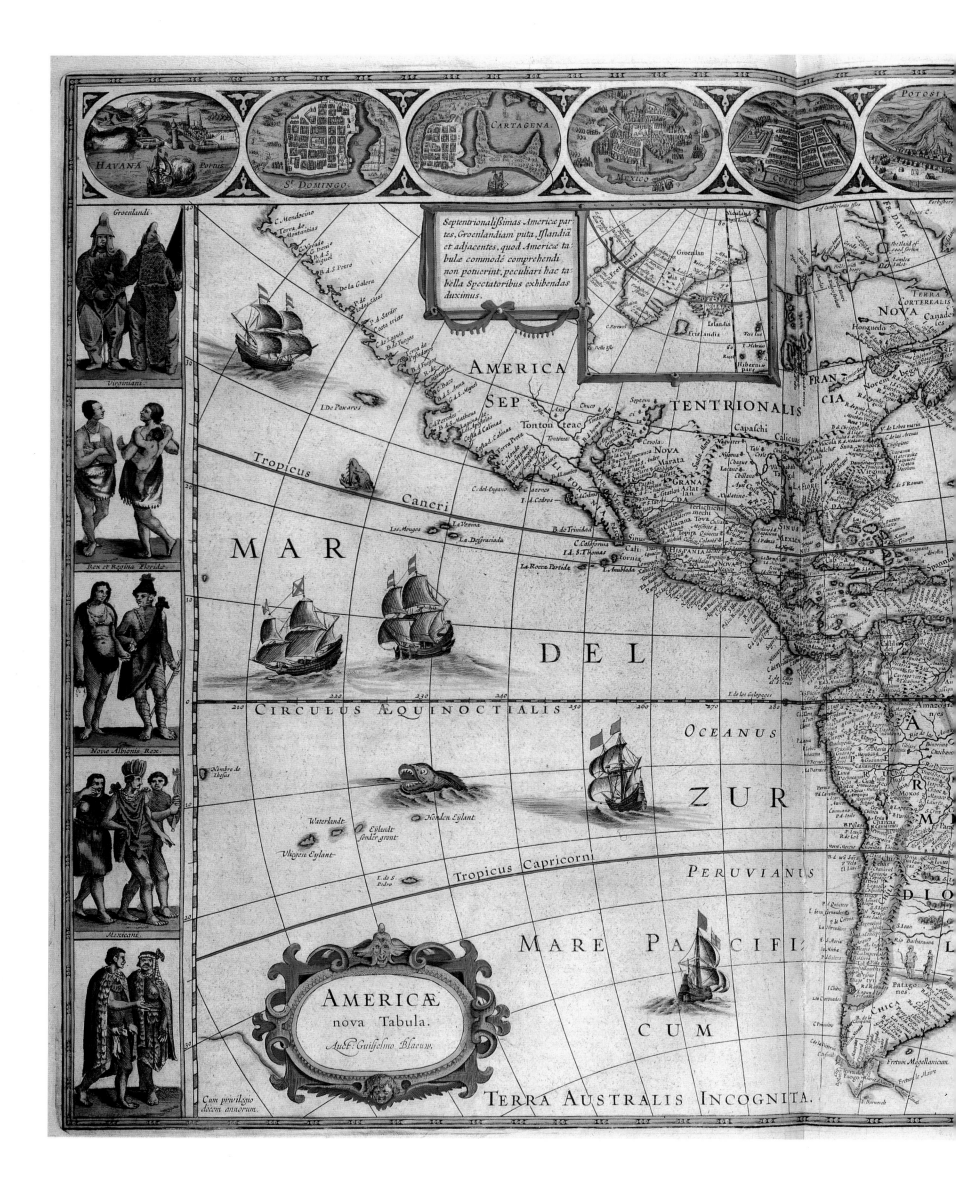

and six presses for printing copper-plates, and also with a type-foundry . . . The premises has a breadth of 75 ft and extends 135 ft. In front . . . is a room containing a number of cabinets in which are stored the plates which are used for the atlases, the Dutch and Walloon town atlases [i.e. the Townbooks of 1649, published in two volumes], and for the marine and other priceless books . . . Next door is the room where the copper-plates are printed . . . Then comes the printing office proper in a long gallery, well provided with windows on both sides. At the far end is a workroom where the type and other materials used in printing are kept. Before this room is a staircase leading to a room where on the next floor the corrector reads the proofs and revises and marks the errors made by the compositor. Here, too, there is a long ante-chamber or loft where, when the printing of the entire book is completed, the printed sheets are gathered into the order of appearance and also stored. At the very top . . . is the foundry where type for printing in several languages is cast . . .[21]

Willem Blaeu died in 1638, whereafter Joan took over the running of the firm's activities. He expanded the *Novus atlas* (Plate 4.26) from three volumes in 1640 to the celebrated *Atlas major*, in from nine to twelve tall folio volumes, depending on the language of the printed text, in 1662–1663 (Plate 4.28). Altogether, the *Atlas major* contained some 600 maps, and is thought to have been printed in an edition of 300 copies.

By the 1660s, such works as pilot-guides and sea-chart atlases (see Chapter IX) played a less important role in the output of the Blaeu publishing house. Other Amsterdam publishers, such as Pieter Goos or Hendrik Doncker, had taken over this work. Nevertheless, Joan Blaeu continued the tradition of making globes of all sizes and types. He also continued to issue wall-maps, for example the large world map of 1648 in twenty sheets, entitled *Nova totius terrarum orbis tabula*, on which the Dutch discoveries in the Antipodes were shown.

In this respect, Joan Blaeu received a considerable incentive to further the development of his

PLATE 4.24 America nova tabula *by Joan and Willem Blaeu, 1617–c. 1640. This was one of the longest lasting copper plates in Blaeu's* Atlas major. *Note the decorative border vignettes, including perspective plans or views of settlements in the Americas, as well as illustrations of native figures taken from the accounts of explorers of the time.*

PLATE 4.25 *Britannia prout divisa . . . by Willem Blaeu. This historical map of the British Isles first appeared in Blaeu's Atlas in 1645. It is almost identical to one issued by Blaeu's great rival, Joannes Janssonius. Blaeu based the ancient division of the kingdom on a map in John Speed's* Theatre of the Empire of Great Britaine. *The figures in the left-hand border represent Kent, Sussex, Wessex, Essex, Northumberland, East Anglia and Mercia, while on the right are scenes of historical incidents.*

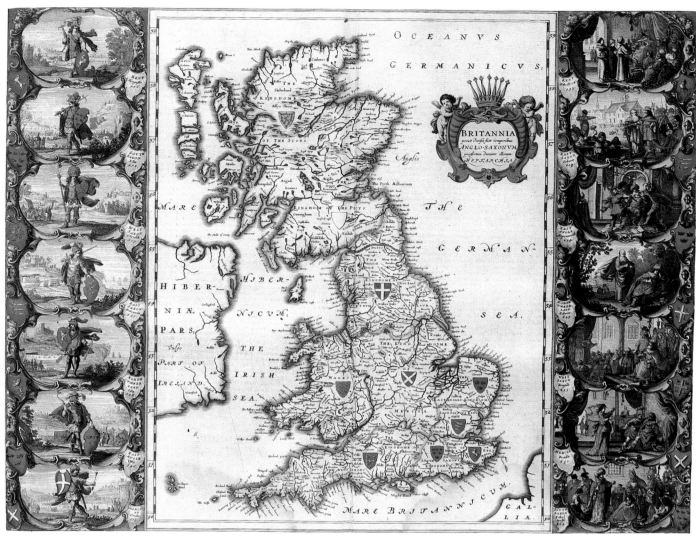

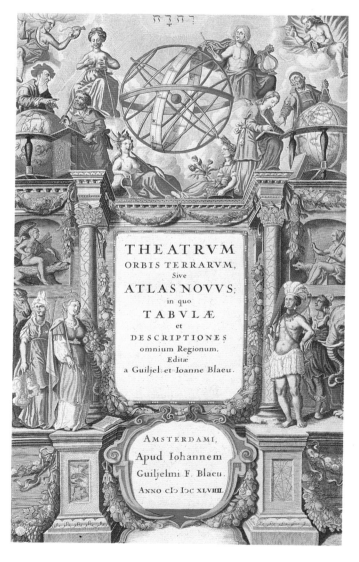

PLATE 4.26 *The title page to* Atlas novus *or* Theatrum orbis terrarum *by Willem and Joan Blaeu, Amsterdam, 1649. Four separate editions were published in German, French, Latin and Dutch from 1635 onwards.*

business, now that he was in sole charge. It was an incentive which emphasizes the fact that he was an extremely competent mapmaker. On the death of his father in 1638, Joan 'inherited' the appointment of official mapmaker to the *Vereenighde Oostindische Compagnie* (VOC), established in 1602 by the merger of several smaller pioneer trading companies in the East Indies. Since the VOC contributed in great measure to the wealth, prosperity and prestige of the United Netherlands, and in particular to Amsterdam, it is highly unlikely that Blaeu would have merited such an appointment had he been ill-organized and incompetent as a map publisher. He assumed the appointment in November 1638 with the duties of making manuscript charts and compiling sailing directions for the navigators and captains of the VOC, just as his predecessor Plancius had done half a century before.

Although Joan Blaeu incorporated up-to-date information on discoveries on his manuscript charts and his large wall-maps, he seems to have made relatively little use of the information at his disposal in the VOC archives for his atlases. His atlas maps of Asia and America date, for the most

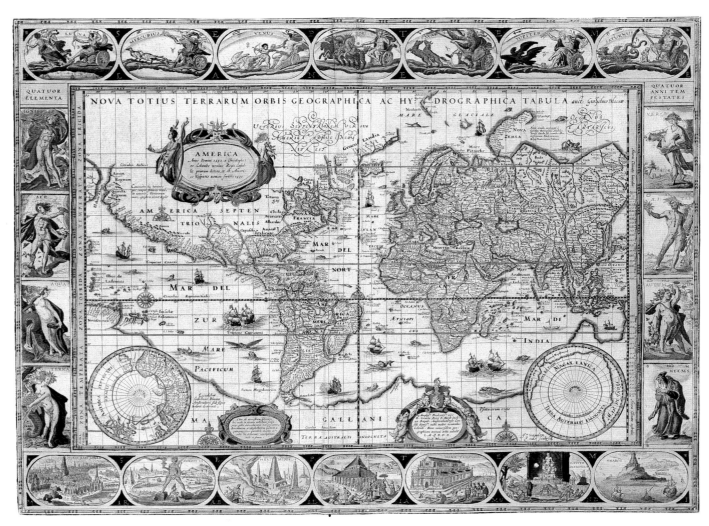

PLATE 4.27 *(left) A world atlas map on the Mercator projection by Willem Blaeu, copper engraving, Amsterdam, 1630 and later. Blaeu's map lasted as the standard view of the world until the 1660s. Note the allegorical decorations which symbolize the elements, the seasons and the continents.*

PLATE 4.28 *(below)* Nova et accuratissima totius terrarum *by Joan Blaeu, Amsterdam, c. 1662. This elegant double hemisphere world map was published in the* Atlas major *from 1662 to 1672. California is shown as an island. The astronomers, Tycho Brahe and Galileo appear at top right and top left respectively.*

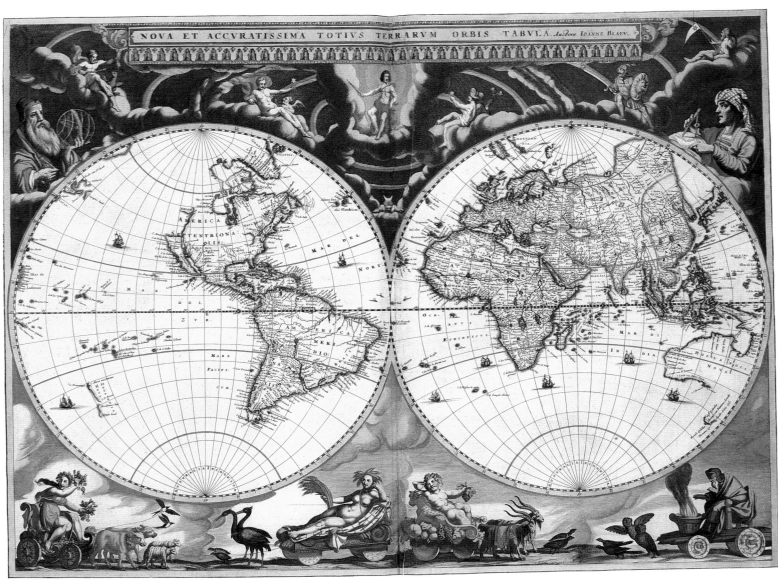

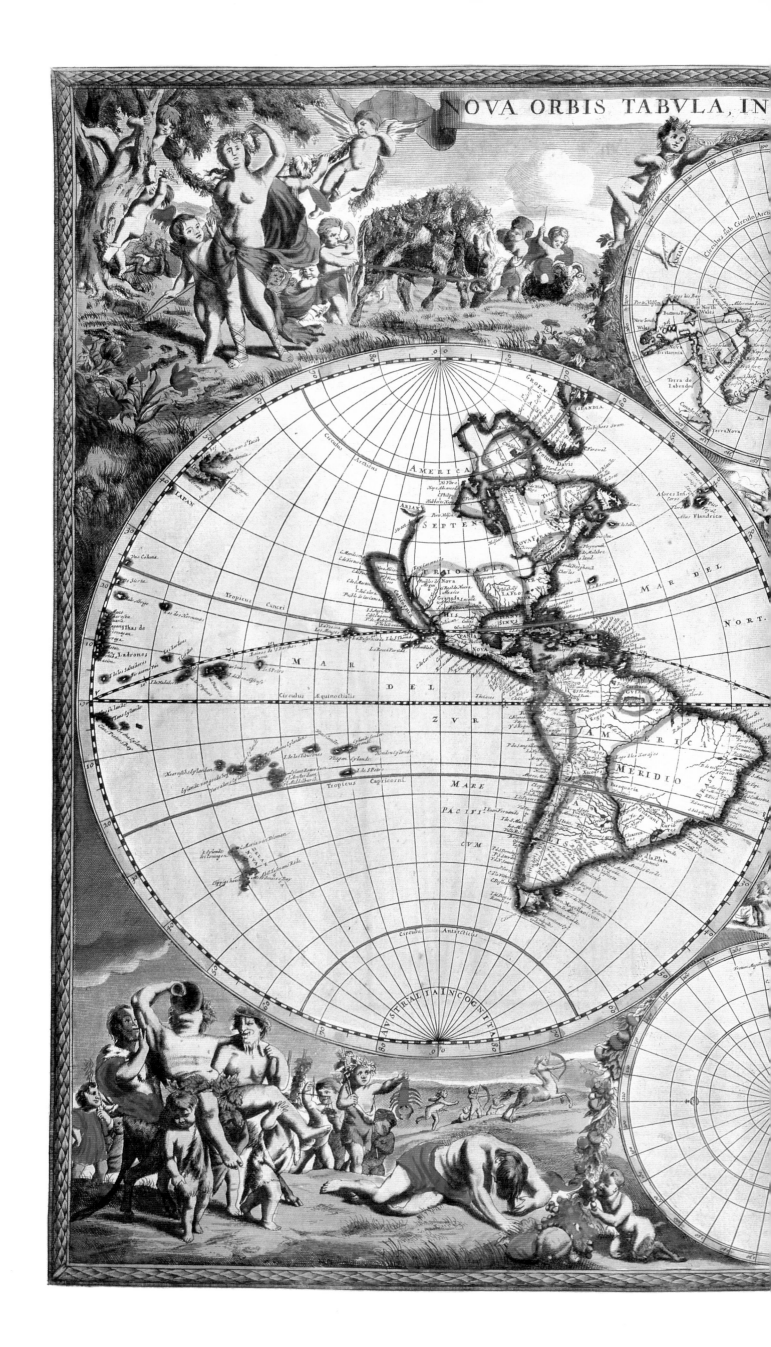

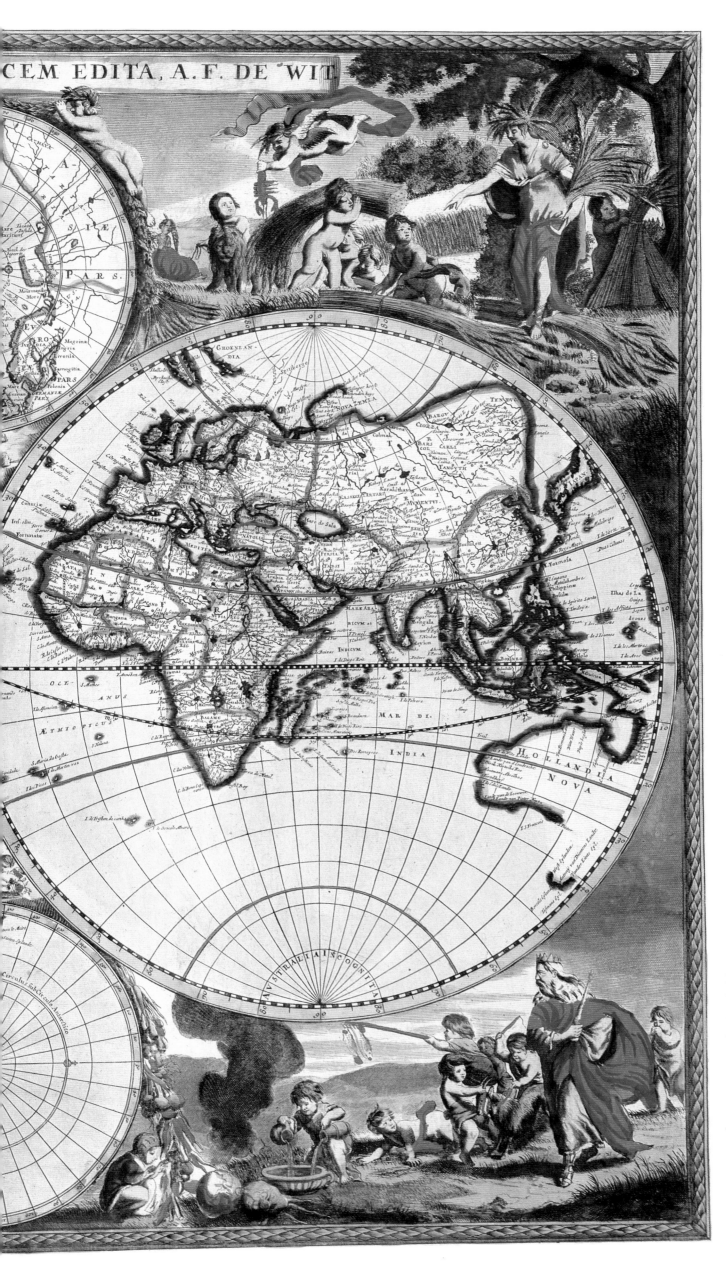

PLATE 4.29 *Nova orbis tabula in lucem edita by Frederick de Wit* c. *1675. An earlier state of the map exists without the cherubs in the centre and the decorative border. Frederick de Wit bought some of the Blaeu family copperplates when they were disposed of by auction in about 1694.*

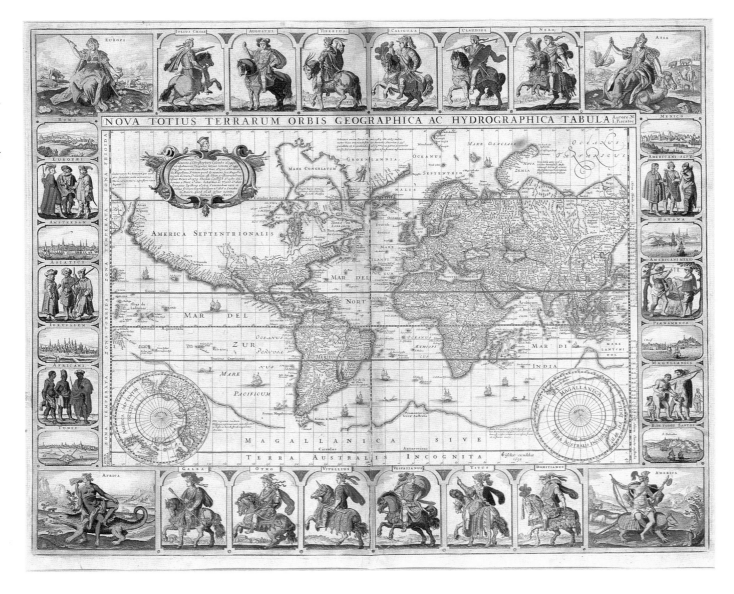

part, from about 1635. The discoveries of Abel
Janszoon Tasman in Tasmania, New Zealand and
Australia in 1642–1644 were indeed incorporated
in his wall map of the world in 1648, but the
relevant maps in the *Novus atlas* were never
revised as such. Furthermore, although his fellow
map publishers such as Hendrik Doncker and
Pieter van Alphen did incorporate relatively recent information in their sea atlases, Blaeu did not
– or perhaps could not – take advantage of his
privileged position in the VOC in order to issue
such an atlas to match his other publications. This
helps to explain why many surviving sets of the
Atlas major are complemented by a sea atlas,
bound uniformly, by one or another of his publishing rivals, or occasionally a copy of Andreas
Cellarius's *Atlas coelestis; seu Harmonia macrocosmica* of 1660, published by Blaeu's arch-rival
Joannes Janssonius.

Most of the surviving copies of the *Atlas major*
are bound in what might be called a 'standard'
vellum gilt binding. Wealthy clients, however,
could specify a commissioned binding in morocco

or even velvet, embellished with family crests for
display purposes. Such work was carried out by
the famous Amsterdam binder Albert Magnus,
who flourished from the 1660s to 1680. As it
appears that Blaeu had no bindery on his premises,
it is likely that Magnus bound copies in the
'standard' binding. Colour was also an important
consideration. Blaeu's atlases could be had plain
(that is, without added colouring), but many
clients buying the works for display at home
preferred their copies illuminated with rich hand-
colouring and gold highlighting. This of course
was more expensive, and there were several
afzetters (artists) who specialised in this work, just
as Ortelius had done a century before. Blaeu's atlas
was the most expensive printed book available in
the seventeenth century. His catalogue issued in
1670 quoted prices for the twelve-volume French-
text edition of the *Atlas major* at 450 florins for a
coloured set, and 350 florins for a plain set, the
charges including the vellum binding. In 1992,
a set of the Dutch-text edition of the atlas, together
with the Townbooks of the Netherlands, was sold

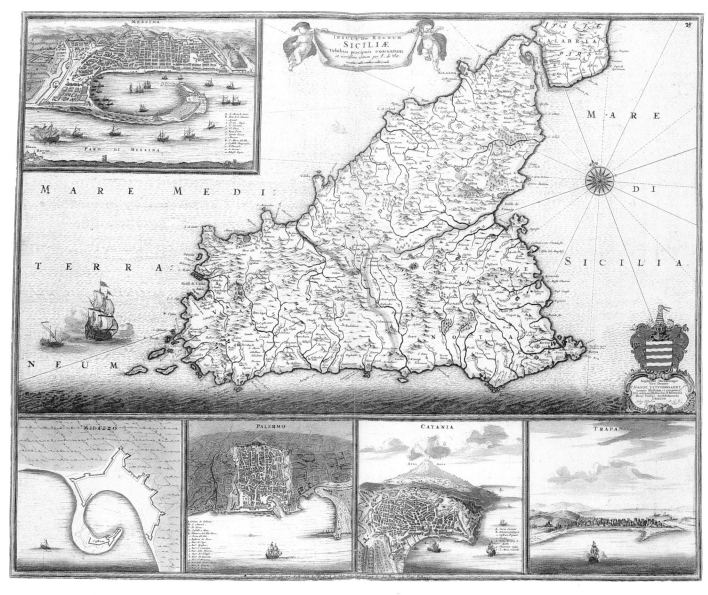

PLATE 4.31 *Siciliae by Frederick de Wit, c. 1670. De Wit was one of the most prominent and successful map engravers and publishers in Amsterdam. His work was notable for the quality of the engraving and colouring.*

at Sotheby's for £180,000 (see Chapter VIII).

Blaeu's premises were virtually destroyed by a fire in February 1672, after which the printing establishment was forced to close. Even so, his atlases and maps remained in demand. Many of the plates were rescued and these, together with unsold sets of the atlases and other books in Blaeu's stock, were sold by public auction after Joan Blaeu's death. Many of the plates were bought by Amsterdam publishers, for example Abraham Wolfgang, who was in partnership with the booksellers Boom, van Waesberghen en van Someren. Following Wolfgang's death in 1694, the plates of Blaeu's atlas which still survived were disposed of, again by auction, to the publishers Pieter Mortier (who bought the plates of the Italian Townbooks) and Frederick de Wit (who bought the Netherlands' Townbook plates). The fate of the atlas map plates is not known, although occasionally one still finds a composite atlas, compiled in Amsterdam or in Germany in the early eighteenth century, containing impressions of a few of the Blaeu plates.

References

1. *Albrecht Dürer: Diary of his Journey to the Netherlands 1520–1521*, pages 60–61, 1971.
2. R.V. Tooley, *Maps and Map-Makers*, page 29, 1949.
3. R.A. Skelton, *Decorative Printed Maps*, page 45, 1964.
4. R.W. Shirley, *The Mapping of the World*, page 84, 1983.
5. Quoted in A.S. Osley, *Mercator*, page 174, 1969.
6. See Sotheby's catalogue, sale 13 March 1979; also P.N. Scott and J.J.S. Goss, 'Important Mercator "Discovery" Under The Hammer', in *The Map Collector*, 6, 1979, pages 27–35.
7. G.R. Crone, *Maps and their Makers*, page 76, 1956.
8. H. Averdunk and J. Müller-Reinhard, *Gerhard Mercator und die Geographen unter seinen Nachkommen*, reprint edition, pages 53–61, 1979.
9. R.A. Skelton, *op. cit.*, page 45.
10. Quoted in E.G.R. Taylor, 'A Letter Dated 1577 From Mercator To John Dee', in *Imago Mundi XIII*, pages 56–68, 1956.
11. P.H. Meurer, *Fontes Cartographici Orteliani*, page 18, 1991.
12. P.H. Meurer, *op. cit.*, pages 43–50.
13. R.A. Skelton, *op. cit.*, page 46.
14. See Professor Koeman's series *Atlantes neerlandici*, published in five volumes from 1967–1972 and a supplementary sixth volume published in 1984.
15. C. Kruyfhooft, 'A Recent Discovery: Utopia By Abraham Ortelius', in *The Map Collector* 16, pages 10–14, 1981.
16. R.A. Skelton, *op. cit.*, page 46.
17. Quoted in J.H. Keuning, 'Blaeu's *Atlas*', in *Imago Mundi XIV*, page 76, 1959.
18. J.H. Keuning, *op. cit.*, page 77.
19. Quoted in M.M. Kleerkoper and W.P. van Stockum, *De Boekhandel te Amsterdam, vnl. in de 17e eeuw*, page 1152, 1914–1916.
20. Claude Joly, *Voyage fait à Münster*, page 116, 1670.
21. Philip von Zesen, *Beschreibung der Stadt Amsterdam*, 1664, quoted in J.J.S. Goss, *Blaeu's the Grand Atlas of the Seventeenth-Century World*, page 11, 1990.

...aces in the Citie observed by Alphabetical letters.
...nitye Colledge.   O. Sainct Gyles.
...ges Colledge.   P. Magdalen Colledge.
...re Hall   Q. Emanuell Colledge.
...us Colledge.   R. Christes Colledge.
...ct Iohns Colledge.   S. Sainct Andrew.
...ct Sepulchre.   T. Iesus Colledge.
...holowes in § Iury   V. Quenes Colledge.
...nct Michael   W. Sainct Botolphe
...itye Church   X. Pembrok Hall
...ct Edward   Y. Peter house.
...nct Benets.   Z. Sainct Clement.
...pus Christi Coll: 1. Litle Sainct Maries.
...nct Peters.   2. The Castle.

Pembrok Hall
Orchard

S. Thomas lees

SHIRE   Trokenhole

Crowland   WISBICH
Dowsdale

Thorney   The new leame
                                    Waterfe

Eldernall   GIRVII. or
                                    W

Whittlesey
Whittlesey Dike

Peter-   THE ILE OF
burgh   Dud

Whittlesey
Mere

Yaxley   Vg Mere   Rasey
Tokeworth   Mere

Stilton   Holme

Cunnyngton

PART   OF   Ramsey
                     Bury

Wistow   Sutton

HVNTING: Somersham
                        Bluntsham
                 Woodhurst   Erith
                                    Erith C

Huntingdon St Iues Holywel
                              Ouse flu
                              Willingham
Godmanchester Hemingfordes Fenny draton No
                              Swavse
TON   Begars busshe Cunnyngto Lowlworth
                                    Hoggin
SHIRE   Offordes   PAPWORTH Dry dra
              Graveley Papworth annes
                      Papworth euered Knapwell
              Toseland Yelding Madinaley
                      Elsworth HY: Childersley
Wintering ham Elsley Boxworth Hard wich
              St Neot Croxton
                              STOW Toste
              Gransdē Buene HV: Caucote
              ma   Caxton   Euersden § pua
PARTE   Stow Kingston Euersden ma
OF   Waresley   Gramsden pua
       Tetworth   Wimple
                    WETHERLEE
OF   Gamlingay   HV: Oxwell
                        Great East
                        Harley Arrington Walim
BEDFORD Potton St George Crawden
              Cokinghatley Clopton
                    Tadlow   Wendye
                    Biglewade Whaddon
                    Dunton Shengye ARNINGFORD
                              Basingborne
SHIRE Henxworth Gilden morden Abbington
       Steeple   HVN:
              morde HVN Lylyngton
                    PART

CHAPTER V

THE MAPMAKING TRADITION

1500 – 1800 AD

THE NETHERLANDS DOMINATED mapmaking in Europe for the greater part of the sixteenth and seventeenth centuries. Elsewhere in Europe, however, a map trade was developing simultaneously in many other countries and, in particular, in Italy, Germany, France and England. The European influence spread to the Far East, to China and Japan, where some impressive local and world maps were produced during the Renaissance period.

Prior to the appearance of Abraham Ortelius's *Theatrum orbis terrarum* (see p.102) in 1570, printed maps had been dominated for almost a century by the influence of Ptolemy's *Geography*. Generally speaking, manuscript maps and charts were improved and altered with each new edition. However, this was not so, as a rule, when subsequent editions of printed maps or charts were produced. Printed maps were not revised in the same way because the publishers were often less critical of source materials than the makers of manuscript maps and charts and, in addition, it was more difficult to make changes as the printing plates or blocks would have to be altered or re-engraved. Anachronisms persisted in printed editions, often for many years, or even decades, long after the errors they depicted had been disproved. The 'California as an island' myth (see Chapter XI) is a classic example.

PLATE 5.1 *Detail of* Cambridgeshire *by John Speed, from his* Theatre of the Empire of Great Britaine, *1611. The coats-of-arms are of the colleges and also 'of all such princes of noble men as have heretofore borne the honorable tytles & dignities of the Earldome of Cambridge.'*

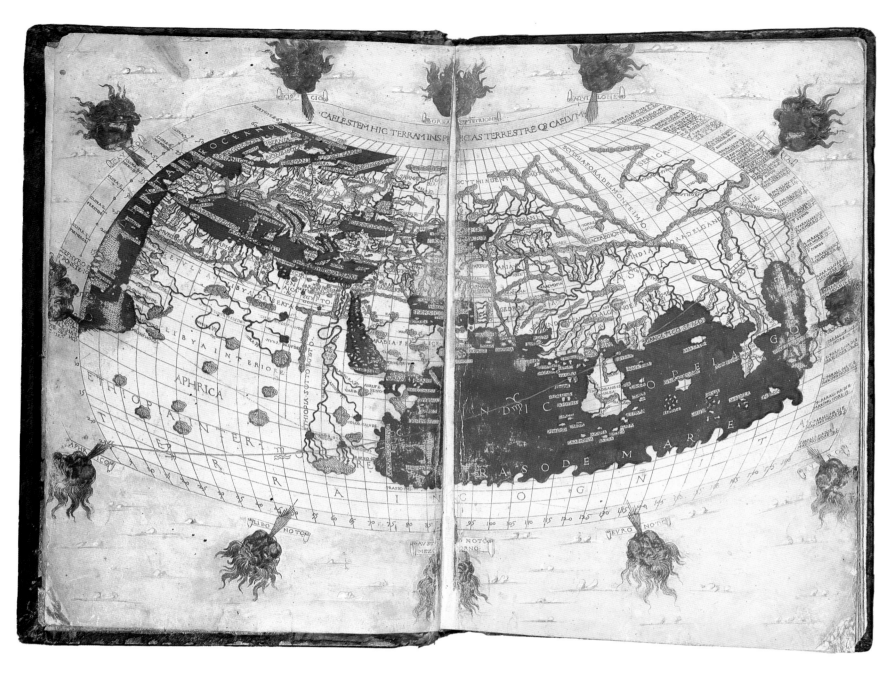

PLATE 5.2 *A Ptolemaic map of the world by Francesco Berlinghieri, Florence, 1482. This map was prepared for inclusion in Berlinghieri's* Geographia – *a description of the world in Italian verse derived from Classical and contemporary sources.*

The text of the *Geography*, as conceived by Ptolemy (*c.* AD 90–168), was written some time between the years AD 127 and 155. However, little is known of the fate of the book for about a thousand years until some surviving Greek manuscripts, written at the Vatopedi monastery during the fourteenth century, were brought into Italy some time before 1400 at the decline of the Byzantine empire. The monks' version of the *Geography* is the oldest extant manuscript copy of Ptolemy's work, and one of these manuscripts is now kept in the British Library in London. The Greek text was translated into Latin by 1409 and the maps were redrawn in Italy by about 1460.

Ptolemy's *Geography* consisted of eight books covering the general principles of mapmaking. Long tables of towns and other items such as physical features were included, accompanied by co-ordinates of latitude and longitude. The maps, all contained in Book VIII, included twenty-six of the regions of the known world (ten of the regions of Europe, four of North Africa and twelve of the regions of Asia), plus a world map, together with brief descriptive texts.

The first printed edition of the *Geography* comprised the text only and was issued in 1475. The Bologna edition, appearing two years later, was the first illustrated edition of Ptolemy. 'Modern' maps (usually recognized by the wording *tabula moderna* added to their titles, to distinguish them from the classical or Ptolemaic maps, appeared after 1482. The maps were redrawn by a German resident at Florence, known by the sobriquet Donnus Nicolaus Germanus (or 'Master Nicholas the German'). The very earliest illustrated editions (Bologna 1477; Rome 1478; Florence *c.*1482 (Plates 5.2, 5.3) included only Ptolemaic maps, essentially to illustrate the text. These maps were printed from engraved copper plates. However, an edition was published at Ulm

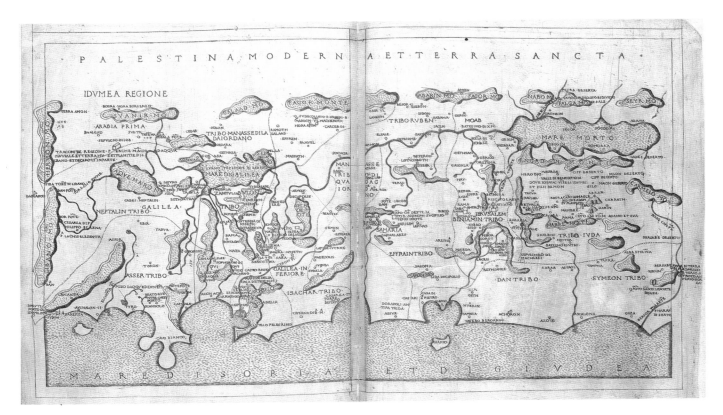

PLATES 5.3, 5.4 *(left and below) Two versions of* Palestina moderna et Terra Sancta *from the rare Florence edition of Ptolemy by Francesco Berlinghieri, copper engraving,* c. 1482. *It was based on Petrus Vesconte's map first drawn in* c. 1320. *Many place and feature names are easily recognizable today. Note how differently the same map can appear when coloured.*

in Germany in 1482 (and reprinted in 1486), containing the same suite of maps, but printed from woodblocks (Plates 5.5, 5.6).

It has never been clear, and debate continues even now, how much of Ptolemy's own work survived in the *Geography* in the form in which it was brought to the West and subsequently edited and revised. Indeed, it is still not known whether Ptolemy himself ever drew *any* maps to illustrate his text. It should be noted that all of the editors of

the *Geography* during the Renaissance combined a respect for Ptolemy's authority with an increasing awareness of the 'modern' world. The text would almost certainly have been amended to include 'modern' maps, indices, new symbols, signs, etc, to fit in with contemporary practice and techniques. Such was the authority of Ptolemy that by the end of the sixteenth century thirty-one editions in Latin or Italian, with maps, had appeared in print, latterly alongside the atlases of Abraham

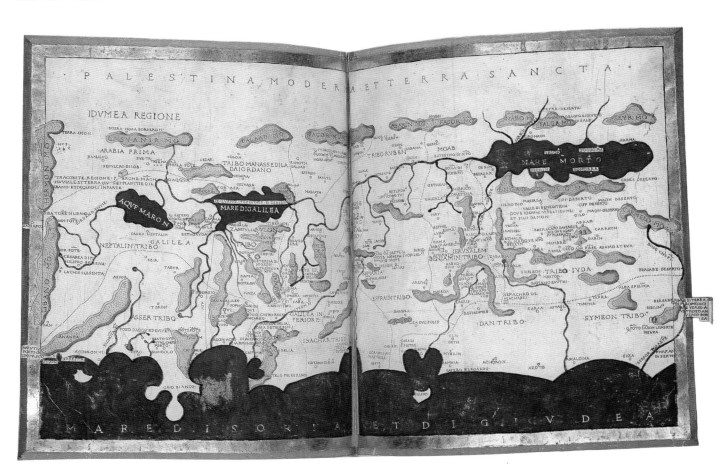

PLATES 5.5, 5.6 *(right and below) Arabia from the Ulm edition of Ptolemy, woodcut, 1482 (right) and the later edition, 1486 (below). The Ulm Ptolemy was the first atlas with woodcut maps and the first to be printed in Germany. The 1482 edition (right) is in the rich royal blue colouring characteristic of this edition.*

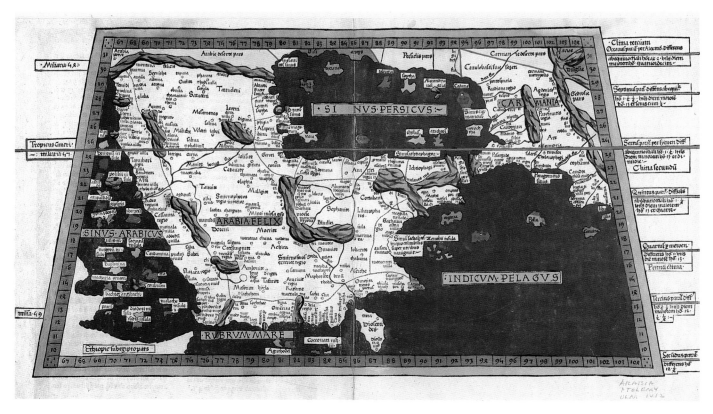

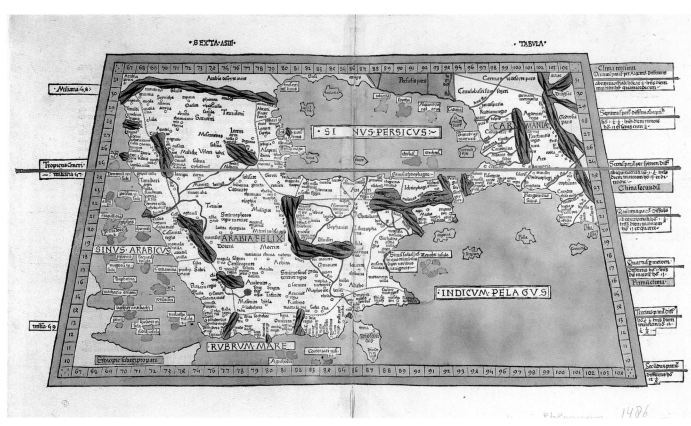

Ortelius, Gerard Mercator and the numerous collected atlases issued in Italy.

The Old World of Ptolemy was rapidly being extended by the European discovery and exploration of the Americas – the New World. From the first recorded toe-hold of Columbus in 1492 the outline of the landmass of North and South America emerged from the ocean, in recognizable form on printed maps, within the span of only fifty years. Contrast this with the two or three millennia that it took for the revelation of the Old World. For the first time in recorded history, the unveiling of a continent was, as a modern commentator might put it, a 'media event'.

The exploration of the New World and the exploitation of the sea route to India and the East Indies gave geographers a new impetus, but it did not devalue Ptolemy's achievement. Geographers and mapmakers appended their newly acquired knowledge onto the stock, as it were, of Ptolemy, dividing the globe into hemispheres. An increasing number of 'modern' maps was added to the

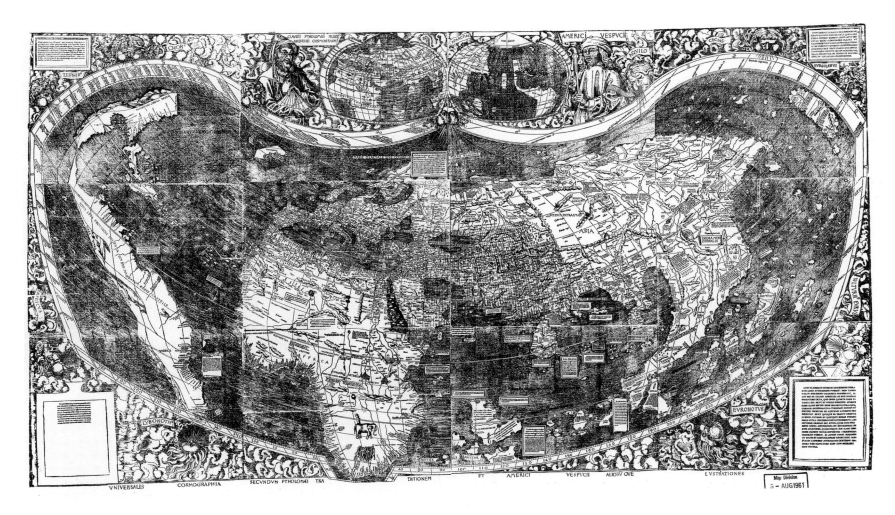

original body of twenty-seven maps, which were themselves often extensively redrawn or revised.

The Ptolemaic Old World and the western New World found their main expression in the great world map by Martin Waldseemüller. His *Universalis cosmographia secundum Ptholomaei traditionem et Americi Vespucci alioru[m]que lustrationes*, dated 1507 and printed at Strasbourg, was made according to the tradition of Ptolemy and included the voyages of Amerigo Vespucci and others (Plate 5.7). In compiling this map, Waldseemüller may have been aware of the Henricus Martellus map of the Old World, drawn in about 1490, showing Africa based on the Portuguese voyages, with a redrawing of Cathay, or China, after the travels of Marco Polo. In the New World, credit is given to Amerigo Vespucci's voyages in 1499–1502, while Columbus is but briefly mentioned in connection with his discovery of the Trinidad group in 1498.

Newfoundland is represented after the voyages of Corte Real in 1500–1501, while North and South America are divided by a very narrow strait on the main map but, curiously, joined in the same location by a slender isthmus on one of the smaller inset maps. This anomaly, and the well-defined peninsula just north of Cuba, apparently reflect the continuing uncertainty of the nature of this part of the New World – remember that Columbus himself had always maintained that he had found China. With the benefit of hindsight, it is obvious that Waldseemüller's map had its limitations, but from the outset it was acknowledged as the cartographic masterpiece it surely is, and many mapmakers in the decades to come placed great reliance on his work.

The editions of Ptolemy's Geography

The Bologna edition (folio, 1477), containing twenty-six copper-engraved maps, was the first engraved atlas. This edition used the 1406 translation into Latin by Jacopo d'Agnolo (known as Angelus), corrected and amended by Filippo Beroaldo and edited by Angelo Vadius.

The Rome edition (folio, 1478) again used the d'Agnolo translation, with corrections and improvements by Domitius Calderini. This edition contained twenty-seven copper-engraved maps which were reprinted in 1490 by Pietro de Turre, then in late 1507 by Bernardinus Venetus de Vitalibus, with the addition of seven 'modern' maps, including Scandinavia, Central and Eastern Europe and Palestine. A further reprint was

PLATE 5.7 *The large world map by Martin Waldseemüller, woodcut, dated 1507. Although 1000 copies are said to have been printed, only one example now survives (this reproduction is taken from a facsimile).*

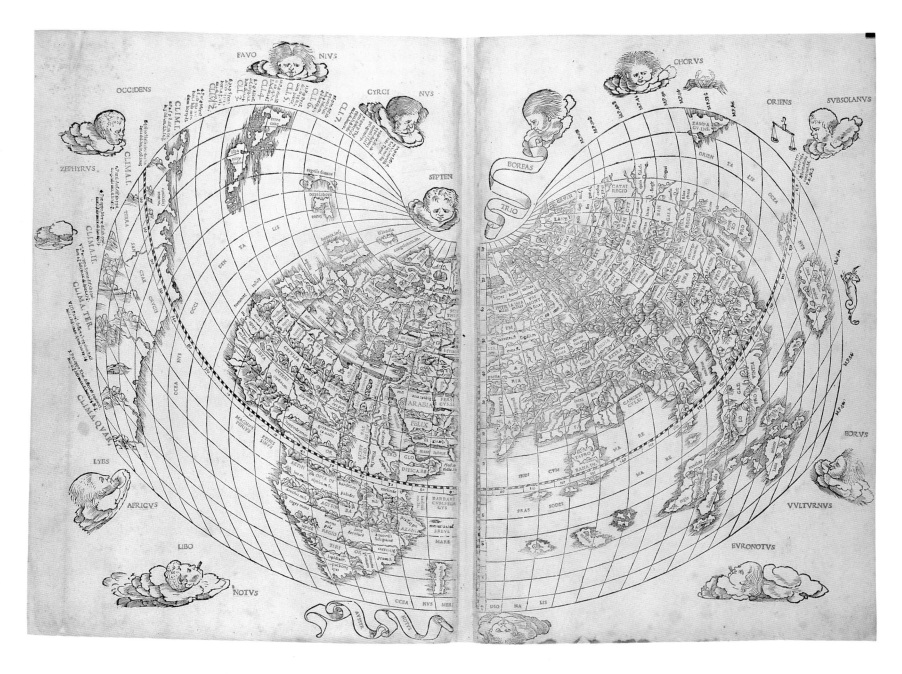

issued in the first half of 1508, with an account of
the New World written by Marco Beneventano
and a further 'modern' map, the celebrated fan-
shaped world map by Johannes Ruysch (Plate
3.19). This is the first map in an edition of
Ptolemy to show any part of the New World.

Further technical advances were introduced
with the edition printed at Venice in 1511 by
Jacobus Pentius de Leucho. This edition contained
twenty-eight woodcut maps, each printed in two
colours, in this case red and black. It also included
a cordiform (heart-shaped) world map, which
showed the eastern part of South America, Cuba,
Hispaniola and Labrador, and in the east the
whole of the Far Eastern coastline of Asia (Plate
5.8). Although the maps in this edition were
newly made and edited by Bernardus Sylvanus,
they contain virtually no geographical advances,
and they were not reprinted. Examples printed on
vellum are known to have existed.

Soon after, in 1513, there appeared from the
printing-press of Johannes Schott at Strasbourg
the most important edition of Ptolemy's Geography,
containing many new regional maps. Twenty new
maps based on contemporary knowledge were
included in addition to the traditional body of
twenty-seven maps of the Ptolemaic world. Schott's
edition was produced under the superintendence
of the geographer Martin Waldseemüller of
St Dié. This edition of Ptolemy is, in effect, the
first modern atlas. It was also noted for the multi-
coloured printed map of Lotharingia (Lorraine in
France), the first of its kind (Plate 5.9). The
edition was reprinted in 1520, using the same
woodcut blocks (with the exception of the map of
Switzerland, which for this edition was recut in a
much simplified form).

In 1522, another edition of the Geography was
printed in Strasbourg, this time by Johannes
Gruninger. The number of woodcut maps was

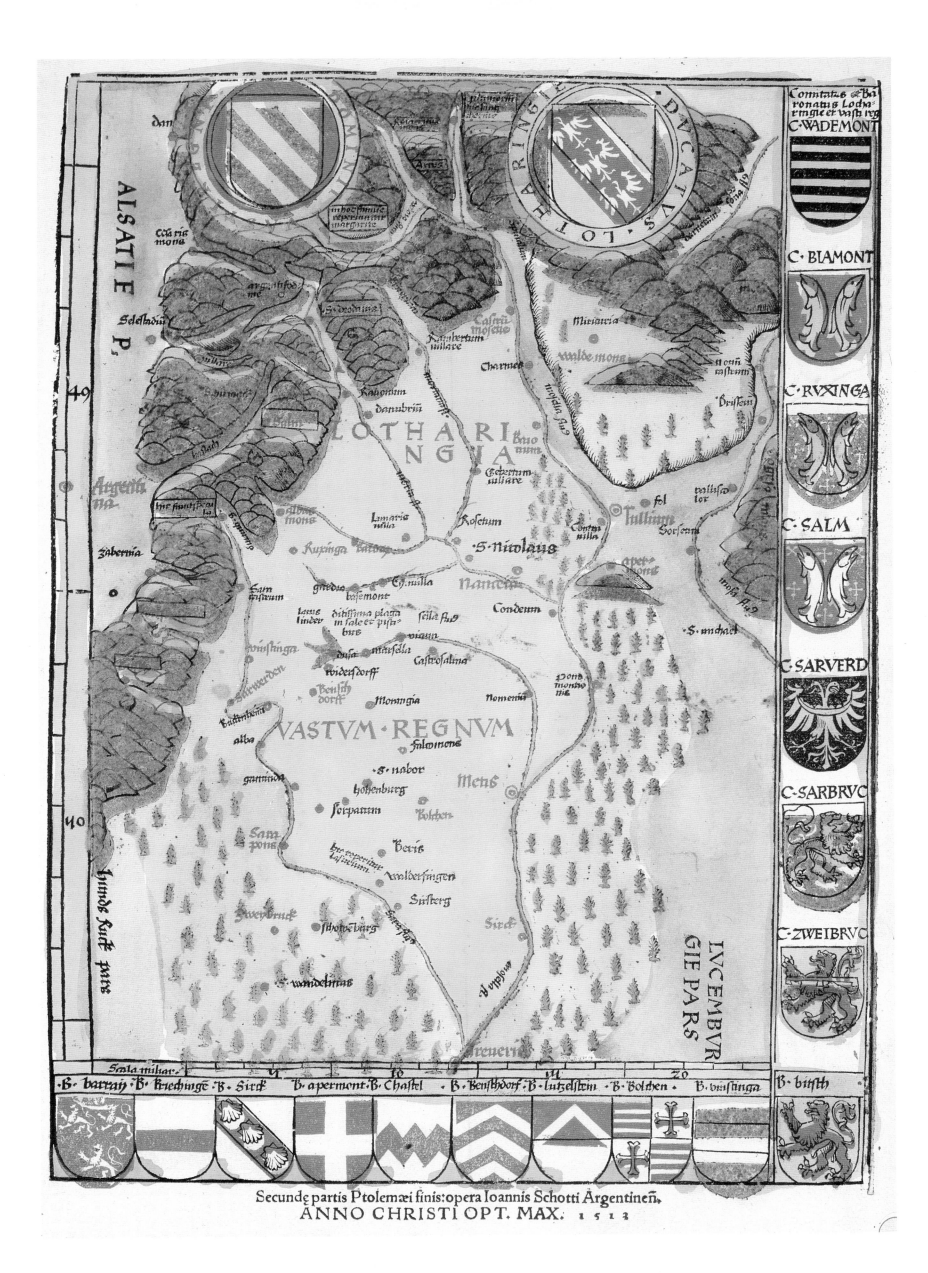

ALSATIE P₅

49

40

Ingunde Rick pars

DOMINIVM DE

DVCATVS·LOTHARINGIE

in hoc simile reperiuntur margarite

LOTHA·RI·NGIA

buonum

VASTVM·REGNVM

Mens

LVCEMBVRGIE PARS

Comitatus et Baronatus Lotha ringie et vast reg C·WADEMONT

C·BIAMONT

C·RVXINGA

C·SALM

C·SARVERD

C·SARBRVC

C·ZWEIBRVC

·B·barray··B·kriechinge··B·Sirck· ·B·apermont··B·Chastel· ·B·Benshdorf··B·lutzelstein· ·B·Bolchen· ·B·vinsinga B·bitsth

Secundę partis Ptolemæi finis:opera Ioannis Schotti Argentineñ.
ANNO CHRISTI OPT. MAX. 1513

125

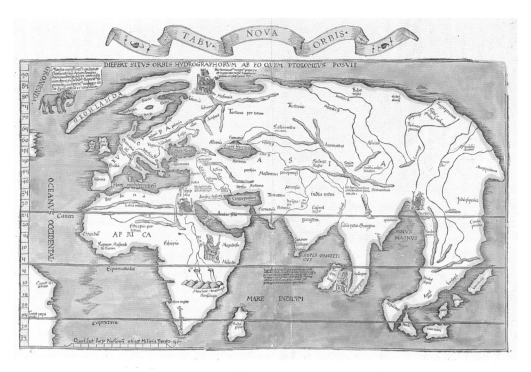

PLATE 5.10 *(above)*
*Tabu[la] nova orbis by
Martin Waldseemüller/
Laurent Fries, Strasbourg,
1522; this issue Lyon, 1535
and later. This impressive
woodcut map shows the
general conception of the
world in the sixteenth
century. It is a reduced
version of Waldseemüller's
map of 1513 in his edition
of Ptolemy's* Geography.

PLATE 5.11 *(opposite,
top)* Universalis tabula
iuxta Ptolemeum *by
Gerard Mercator, Cologne,
1578. Mercator spent a
good deal of his time revising
Ptolemy's* Geography, *and
this map of the world is one
of the finest Ptolemaic maps
available. Mercator
engraved the copperplate,
which was re-used for over
150 years.*

reduced from those in the previous two editions,
while three new maps were compiled and cut for
this printing: a world map by Laurens Fries (Plate
5.10), and two modern maps of southeast Asia and
of the Far East respectively, giving a total of fifty
maps in all. In 1525, Gruninger reprinted these
maps with the text retranslated by the geographer
Wilibald Pirckheimer of Nuremberg.

The maps were again reprinted in 1535, at
Lyon, by Melchior and Gaspar Trechsel with a
text edited by Michael Servetus. It was this edition
which is said to have been ordered to be destroyed
by burning on the orders of Jean Calvin. Servetus
had gone back to manuscript and to early printed
editions of the text in order to correct or delete
errors which had crept in over the years. Unfortunately, a passage relating to Palestine (stating, on
the basis of thirteenth- and fourteenth-century
travellers' accounts, that it was not the fertile land
of milk and honey as claimed in the Bible) was
overlooked and was used as evidence against
Servetus when he was executed at the stake for
heresy in 1553. Several examples of this edition
have survived. A further printing of the fifty
maps was made at Vienne in eastern France by
Trechsel in 1541.

An important edition appeared at Basel in
1540, printed by Heinrich Petri. It was edited by
the scholar Sebastian Münster, mathematician,
geographer and professor at Basel University. He
also compiled a highly influential encyclopaedic
work, entitled *Cosmographia universalis*, which
first appeared in 1544 and contained forty-eight

woodcut maps. Münster was among the first
editors of a published geographical text to quote or
acknowledge his sources and authorities. The same
maps were used in the parallel editions of the
Cosmographia (to 1578) and Ptolemy (to 1552)
over several years. Münster's maps became the
most influential general and regional maps until
the first appearance of Ortelius's *Theatrum orbis
terrarum* in 1570.

A new *octavo*, or pocket-format, edition of the
Geography, now translated into Italian, appeared at
Venice in 1548. It was printed by Niccolo Bascar-
ini and contained sixty copper-engraved maps
designed by the Italian mapmaker Giacomo Gastaldi. They were based in part on the maps in
Münster's edition, but several of the maps were
entirely new, including a map of New Spain, a
separate map of South America and modern world
maps. Although this edition was not reprinted, the
maps were adopted and copied by other Italian
editors and publishers of Ptolemy in the latter half
of the sixteenth century.

The first of these derivatives was issued by
Vincenzo Valgrisi at Venice in 1561. The text was
again in Italian and was translated by Girolamo
Ruscelli. The edition was illustrated with sixty-
four elegantly designed copper-engraved maps,
slightly enlarged from the 1548 edition. Among
the several 'modern' maps was a twin-
hemispherical world map, the first of its kind used
in an atlas, adapted from a map published by
Gastaldi some years earlier. This version of
Ptolemy was reprinted four times in thirteen years
(in 1562 by Valgrisi, twice in 1564 by Giordano
Ziletti – in Latin and Italian, and in 1574 with the
addition of a new map of the environs of Rome).
The maps were reworked for a further edition,
now with sixty-nine maps, published at Venice by
the heirs of Melchior Sessa in 1598–1599.

One of the most beautiful and visually pleasing
of all the sixteenth-century editions of Ptolemy
must surely be that issued at Cologne in 1578 by
Godfried Kempen. The twenty-eight maps, after
Ptolemy, were engraved by Gerard Mercator and
considered by many to be among his finest work.
Indeed, such was their excellence that seven further
editions of Mercator's plates were issued up to
1730, albeit much altered and partly re-engraved.
The world map in this edition is one of the finest
of all Ptolemaic maps available (Plate 5.11).

Then, in 1596 there appeared at Venice yet another new edition, issued by Giovanni and Giorgio Galignani. It had sixty-four copper-engraved maps by Girolamo Porro and the text was edited by the famous Italian geographer Giovanni Antonio Magini. The new maps in this edition made up a reduced-format version of part of Mercator's recently published *Atlas*.

The small, but growing, number of contemporary maps added to many of the editions of Ptolemy during the sixteenth century probably gave rise to the idea of issuing atlases composed entirely of maps based on new geographical knowledge. The so-called printed or 'assembled to order' atlases published in Italy started this trend, which culminated in 1570 with the publication of Ortelius's lasting monument, the *Theatrum orbis terrarum*. Naturally, geographers would continue to pay homage to Ptolemy in one form or another for a long time. Indeed, the layout and ordering of the maps in many of today's atlases is a distant echo of Ptolemy's *Geography*, in that many atlases (certainly those published in Europe) still follow the order of regions set out two millennia ago, with the Americas and Australasia coming towards the end of the maps. In fact, the very first atlas devoted to the Americas, compiled by Cornelis van Wytfliet in 1597, was conceived as a supplement to Ptolemy's *Geography*. This fact was acknowledged by van Wytfliet in its very title – *Descriptionis Ptolemaicae augmentum*.

During the seventeenth century, although the influence of Ptolemy's view of the world diminished, his work continued to be printed by various atlas publishers, mostly in the Netherlands, as an historical adjunct to atlases compiled from contemporary geographical knowledge. The plates of Mercator's edition were reworked and reprinted in historical atlases, much as we today would consult an historical atlas for information on the ancient world, to compare with an atlas of the modern world.

Editions published in the eighteenth and nineteenth centuries can only have had an historical value. Even now, facsimile editions of Ptolemy are available, often published with detailed introductory texts, such as those issued in Amsterdam during the 1960s and 1970s by Theatrum Orbis Terrarum Ltd. These facsimile editions often give a valuable insight into the mapmaking and print-

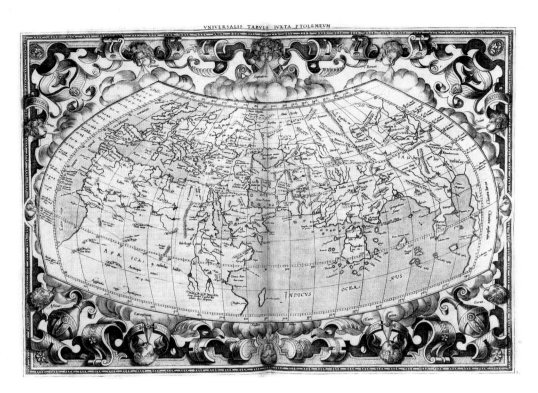

ing trades at the time of the original editions and many atlas collectors value these and regard them with almost as much pleasure as the originals upon which they are based.

Italy, from Sonetti to Cassini

Italian books of maps called *isolari*, or island books, covering the island groups of the eastern Mediterranean, had been published as early as 1485. Bartolommeo dalli Sonetti's *Isolario*, published in Venice in that year, contained charts and maps based on actual observation by trained and practised navigators (Plate 9.2). The minor tradition of island books continued for a century and

PLATE 5.12 *Central Europe, covering the Baltic to Venice and from Flanders to the Black Sea, by Francesco Rosselli, copper engraving, probably printed at Florence, c. 1492.*

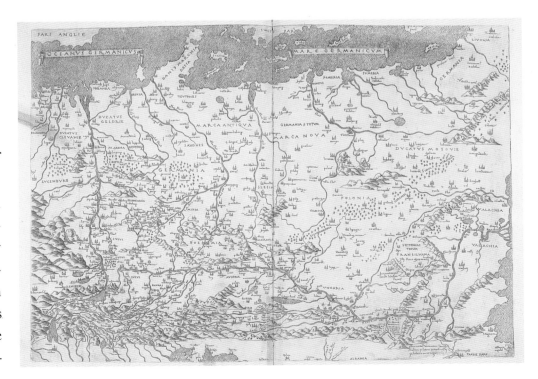

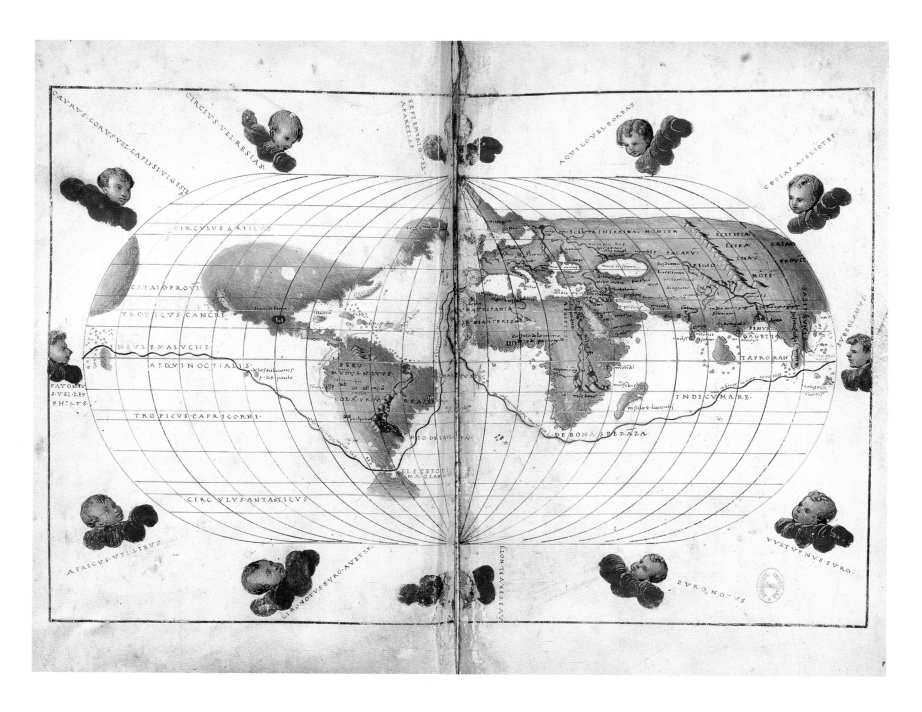

PLATE 5.13 *Manuscript world map from a portolan atlas by Battista Agnese, 1543. The map shows the route of Magellan's circumnavigation in 1519–1522. Some sixty-five atlases by the Genoese mapmaker Agnese are still extant – testimony to the high regard with which his work has been held for centuries.*

PLATE 5.14 *(opposite, top)* Spain *by Vincentus Corsulensis, Venice, 1551. This is the only known copy of this large six-sheet wall map, measuring 960 × 930 mm. It comes from the so-called* Doria Atlas, *named after the Genoese family.*

more. Benedetto Bordone's popular *Isolario*, containing miniature woodcut maps, was published in 1528 and was followed by Giovanni Francesco Camocio's *Isole famose*, containing copper-engraved maps. Highly attractive miniatures were inset into the text of Tomaso Porcacchi da Castiglione's *L'isole più famose del mondo*, published in 1572 and reissued several times with additional maps. This latter title took the concept of an island book to its logical extreme, for it considered the world, from individual Greek islands to whole continents, as a series of islands.

However, the notion of a book of printed maps based on current geographical knowledge did not take root until some time after the appearance of Ptolemy's *Geography*. The geographer Livio Sanuto of Venice prepared a project for a series of geographical texts with detailed descriptions of the world and maps based on contemporary know-

ledge. Regrettably, however, his *Geografia* never proceeded beyond the first volume, which described the continent of Africa, and which has been referred to as 'an admirable summary of sixteenth-century knowledge of the continent'.

In fact, it is not known who originated the idea of assembling loose maps as collections. Few available printed maps were of a format suitable for binding into a folio-sized volume, so they were usually folded down to size. Many smaller maps were inlaid or margined to size by the simple expedient of pasting strips of paper to their outer edges. For us, several centuries after the event, this practice has had a felicitous consequence in that examples of more than 600 different sixteenth-century Italian maps have been preserved, often in excellent condition. In contrast, relatively few maps from north of the Alps have survived in an unrestored state. Mapmakers in such commercial centres of the time as Nuremberg in Bavaria had been issuing printed road maps and large, multiple-sheet regional maps for purposes of display. Consequently, although a few examples, such as Philipp Apian's map of Bavaria, the *Bairische Landtafeln* (Plate 6.10), issued at Ingolstadt in 1568, are known, very few of these maps have survived. On occasion this practice of assembling maps into atlases has meant that the Italian mapmakers have left for us today sometimes the only evidence of original maps, now lost, from north of the Alps. Such maps were copied in Venice, Rome and in other Italian cities, although not always with an acknowledgement of the work of the original mapmaker.

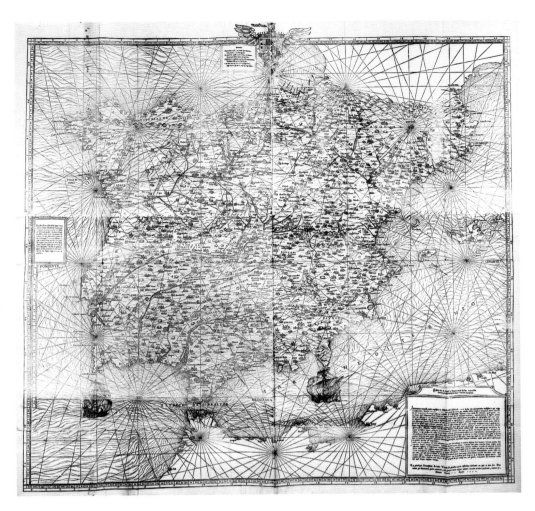

Sometimes, however, the maps in these Italian atlases were anything up to thirty years old by the time they were assembled. One famous example is the so-called 'Doria Atlas' (named for the Genoese noble family, among whom was the admiral Andrea Doria, who saved the fleet of the Emperor Charles V from destruction at Algiers in 1541). The Doria Atlas was probably assembled in about 1570. It contains 105 maps ranging in date from 1535 to the middle 1560s. Since some of the maps in the atlas show signs of plate wear, it is likely that several of them enjoyed a long existence in print. The atlas was sold at auction in London in 1980 and is now in a private collection. Records do exist from these times, such as a catalogue of the Frankfurt Book Fair, issued in 1573, which lists printed maps available from the stocks of various mapsellers, a few of which are dated before 1565 but none before 1560.

The Roman mapmakers

Perhaps the best known of all the sixteenth-century Italian practitioners was Antonio Lafreri (1512–1577). He was born at Besançon in the French province of Burgundy and was known originally as Antoine du Pérac Lafréry, but changed his name when he emigrated to Rome in about 1540. He set up in business in Rome as a map- and printseller, first in partnership with Antonio Salamanca (c. 1500–1562), a bookseller, map- and print-engraver, and then in his own right from 1563 until his death in 1577. Other contemporaries included Claudio Duchetti (Lafreri's nephew born Claude Duchet in 1554) and Michele Tramezini (fl. 1539–1562). The latter

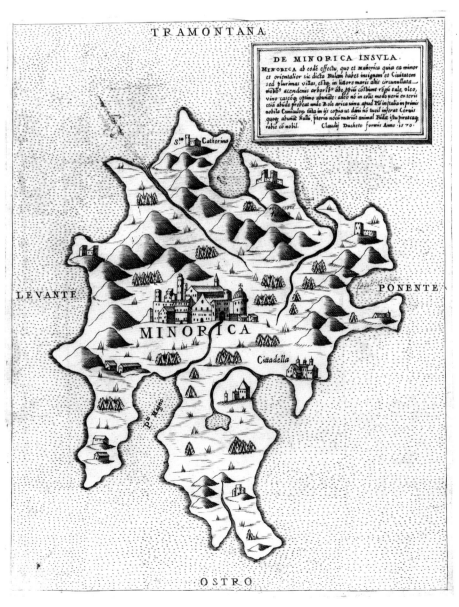

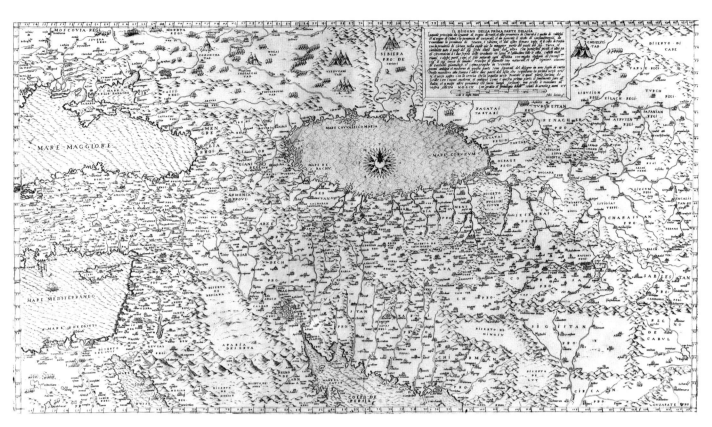

had two workshops, one in partnership with his brother Francesco in Rome, the other in Venice.

These workshops produced many fine regional maps during the 1550s and 1560s (Plate 5.15). In 1558 the workshops issued a map of Scandinavia, *Septentrionalium regionum Svetiae, Gothiae Norvegiae Daniae et terratum adiacentium recens exacta-q[ue] descriptio*, which was a reduced version of an earlier nine-sheet map by the Dutch mapmaker and mariner Cornelis Anthoniszoon printed in 1543. Also in 1558 they published a map of the Low Countries provinces of Friesland, *Frisiae antiovissimae* [sic] *trans Rhenum Provinc[ia] et adiacentium regionum nova et exacta descriptio*, which was a condensed version of a map compiled in 1545 by another, better-known, Dutch mapmaker, Jacob van Deventer. A map of Spain, *Nova totius Hispaniae descriptio*, was issued in 1559 after the map compiled by the Neapolitan architect, artist and mapmaker Pirro Ligorio. A large twelve-sheet plan of ancient Rome was published in 1561 and entitled *Antiquae urbis imago . . . effigies antiquae Romae* (again, after Pirro Ligorio, and issued by Michele and Francesco Tramezini in partnership).

Some of the atlases assembled in Rome around 1570 bear an engraved title-page with the wording *Geografia. Tavole moderne di geografia de la maggior parte del mondo di diversi autori raccolte et messe secondo l'ordine di Tolomeo con i disegni di molta citta et fortezze di diverse provintie stampate in rame con studio et diligenza in Roma*. The name of Lafreri is frequently associated with such a title (although no name is placed in the Rome imprint), and over the years such Italian atlases have been given the generic name of 'Lafreri atlases'.[1] Lafreri actually printed a list of the maps offered for sale at his establishment in Rome in about 1573, which at one time led to the belief that all such atlases emanated from the Lafreri workshop. We now know that this view was mistaken since the Venetian traders, Camocio and Forlani (see below) among them, were doing likewise.

Venetian craftsmen

Venice, like Rome, was a thriving centre of map engraving and printing at this time. Among the most important Venetian practitioners was Giovanni Francesco Camocio (*fl.* 1558–1575) who is well known for several separate regional maps, as well as a small number of atlases of the *isolario* type. These atlases, published during the 1560s and 1570s, were at first printed in loose sheets or assembled to order, but were later issued as more or less uniform collections of maps together with a title-page. Between 1570 and 1575, Camocio issued several *isolari*, bearing the imprint *alla libraria del segno di S. Marco*. A number of these *isolari* concentrate on the widespread military activity that took place in the Mediterranean between the state of Venice and the Turkish Empire in 1570–1573.

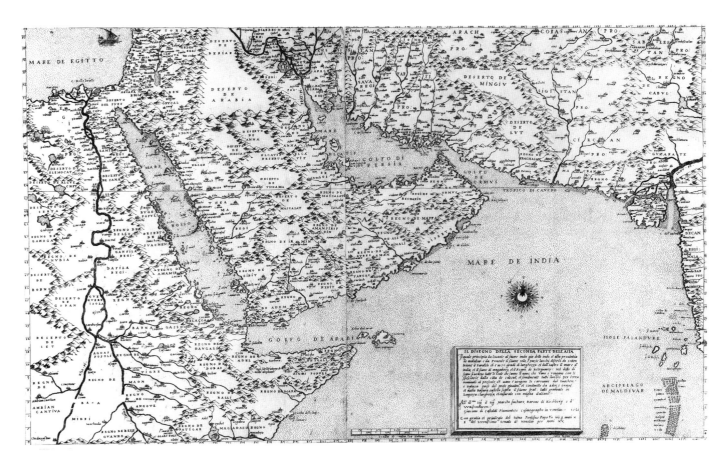

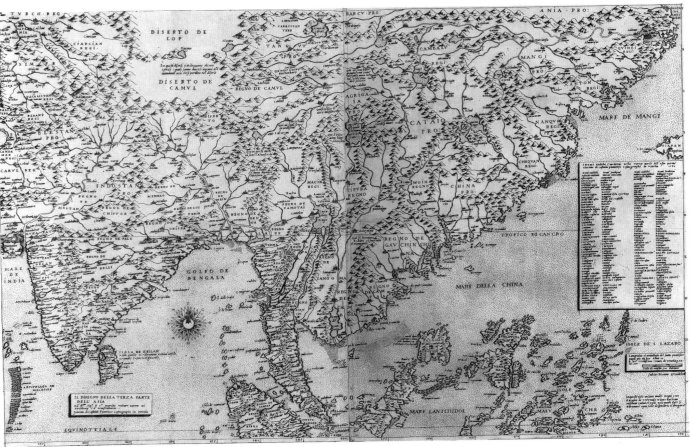

The relatively large numbers of surviving examples of such atlases suggests that they were issued as illustrated history books – like their near contemporaries from north of the Alps, the *Geschichtsblätter* (publications illustrating historical events) put out by Frans Hogenberg, which describe the horrors of the Spanish Fury in the Netherlands. The victory of the Venetian fleet over the Ottoman navy at the Battle of Lepanto in 1571 ensured that large quantities of prints, maps and plans were issued in the years afterward to celebrate the Christian victory: indeed, a keen collector could assemble a large collection of maps and views relating to this one event alone.

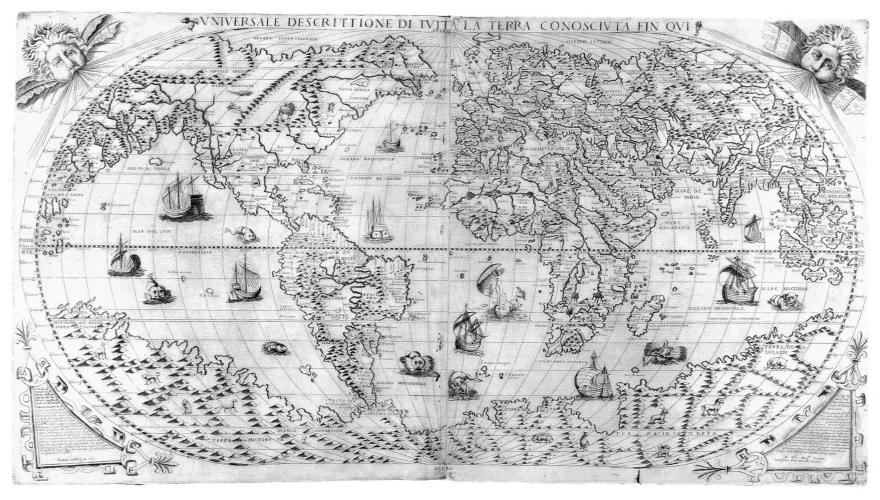

UNIVERSALE DESCRITTIONE DI TUTTA LA TERRA CONOSCIUTA FIN QUI

PLATE 5.17 *(above)*
World map on an oval
projection, Universale
descrittione di tutta la
terra conosciuta fin qui,
by Paolo Forlani, copper
engraving, Venice, 1565.
A close copy of Giacomo
Gastaldi's map of 1546.

PLATE 5.18 *(opposite,*
top) Cosmographia
universalis ab Orontio
olim descripta *by Giovanni*
Cimerlino, Verona or
Venice, 1566. This
beautiful engraving, in a
perfect heart shape,
acknowledges the cordiform
map by Oronce Finé of
1534 as its source. The map
is found in many Italian
assembled-to-order atlases.

PLATE 5.19 *(opposite,*
bottom) Carta Maritima di
Tutto l'Arcipelago *from*
Specchio del mare *by*
Francesco Maria Levanto,
copper engraving, Genoa,
1664. An almost exact copy
of a contemporary Dutch
chart.

Most of the Italian output of this period is distinguished by the fineness of the engraving work – often severe, occasionally devoid of the decorative features so often associated with old maps, but almost invariably elegant and with carefully controlled lettering. Most of the maps depicting Italy and its regions were based on original surveys, but those of countries north of the Alps and beyond copied the work of foreign mapmakers, sometimes almost exactly, at other times on reduced scales. The maps of Giacomo Gastaldi (*c.*1500–1565) – already mentioned in connection with his pocket-sized edition of Ptolemy in 1548 – included detailed regional maps of Italy, but also large, multiple-sheet maps of the continents, such as Asia in eight sheets (*Il disegno* or *La descrittione*), issued over the years 1559–1561; a huge nine-sheet woodcut map of the world (*Cosmographia universalis et exactissima iuxta postremam neotericorum traditionem, c.*1561); and a large map of Africa, also in eight sheets (*Il disegno della geografia moderna de tutta la parte dell'Africa*), issued by the Venetian engraver and publisher Fabio Licinio in 1564. Maps such as Gastaldi's were to influence northern European atlas publishers in the latter part of the century (see below).

One of the most prolific Venetian map engravers and publishers of the time was Paolo Forlani (*fl.*1560–1574). He is known to have placed his imprint on at least eighty different maps and prints and over forty town views, and no doubt sold a great many more (Plate 5.17). Copious as the output of Forlani and his contemporaries may have been, it was also uneven from a geographical point of view. It was largely determined by the requirements of expanding markets, both in Italy and elsewhere in Europe. Thus, the stock of printed maps for sale at a printshop was replenished not only by fresh impressions from the plate stocks to hand, but also from prints and plates bought in from other sources – perhaps because of the bankruptcy of a fellow engraver or mapseller, or perhaps in response to a request from a client to make up a collection of maps and prints for assembly as an atlas. As a result of this interchange of maps and plates between engravers and sellers it is often difficult to attribute precisely a given subject to a particular workshop. (See the bibliographical study of Forlani for further details of this practice.[2])

It can be seen, therefore, that the prototype of the book of maps which we describe today as an atlas stems from Italian inspiration. From the

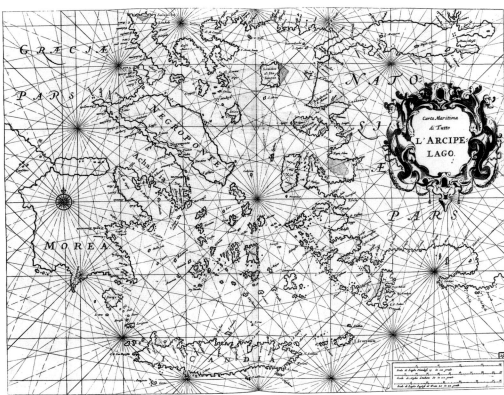

relatively large number (about seventy) of such atlases which have survived or are catalogued, it appears that there was some system in the Italian ordering of maps. A standard order of arrangement was adopted, that of the classical order of Ptolemy, beginning with the world and going on to Europe, then Africa, then Asia and finally, after their discovery, the Americas.

The decline of Italian mapmaking

However, this flowering of activity in the 1560s and 1570s actually marked the start of the decline of Italy's dominance of the map trade in the sixteenth century. While it was a period of considerable prosperity in Italy, and in particular in Venice following the victory at Lepanto, several factors were undermining the edifice of supremacy. Not the least of these was the gradual shift of the western world's centre of economic gravity away from the Mediterranean to trade routes into the Far East, northern Europe and across to the Americas. Another factor was the rise of mercantilism in the Low Countries, emphasizing the fact that the Venetian defeat of the Ottoman fleet in 1571 was indeed a late stroke. All this meant that much first-hand information about the world and its activities beyond the enclosed Mediterranean was being denied to Italy.

The year 1570 is a turning point in the story of mapmaking, for this was when Abraham Ortelius published his pivotal *Theatrum orbis terrarum*, the first uniformly conceived atlas of maps. In the following decades, pre-eminence in mapmaking shifted gradually to the Netherlands, and more specifically to Antwerp (see Chapter IV). Of course, this is not to suggest that mapmaking in Italy ceased altogether, although the decline in the quality of their maps was rapid, and Italian work remained significantly inferior to that which was produced in northern Europe for more than a century. In 1620, the first regional atlas of Italy was issued, Giovanni Antonio Magini's *Italia*, which contained sixty general and regional maps. Work on this atlas was begun long before 1600, but it was not published until 1620, three years after Magini's death. It was edited by his son Fabio, and many of the maps were engraved by the Englishman Benjamin Wright. Several of the maps in Magini's atlas were engraved in a style which rather coarsely imitates the then current Flemish strapwork designs familiar from maps and prints produced north of the Alps. (Strapwork originated from designs of interwoven and interlaced straps of leather with their ends curling.) Then, in 1646–1647, there appeared at Florence that most remarkable of marine atlases, *Dell'arcano del mare*, by the expatriate Englishman Sir Robert Dudley (Plates 9.15 and 9.16). A second edition, augmented and corrected, was brought out in 1661, after Dudley's death. Another Italian marine atlas from this period was the *Specchio del mare* by the navigator Francesco Maria Levanto, published at Genoa in 1664 (Plate 5.19). Only the first part of this atlas, covering the Mediterranean, was published; but it is presumed that Levanto's atlas would have continued along the lines of the Dutch atlases, since contemporary Dutch marine atlases were the model. A later edition of Levanto's atlas formed one of several parts of the large *Atlante veneto* of Vincenzo Maria Coronelli, of Venice.

The Franciscan friar Vincenzo Maria Coronelli (1650–1718) (cosmographer to the Most Serene Republic of Venice) founded the world's first formally organized geographical society, the *Accademia cosmografica degli argonauti*, in Venice in 1680. His copious output included globes, charts, atlases, geographies and travel guides, but his atlases are today Coronelli's main claim to fame among collectors. The *Atlante veneto*, issued from 1690 to 1701, ran to some thirteen volumes (fourteen or more if the Levanto *Specchio* marine atlas is included) and comprised island books, several volumes of a general world atlas and a cosmography. The collation of copies can vary considerably, so much so that it is sometimes extremely difficult to state a standard collation. The *Atlante veneto* contained 300–400 maps and charts, and some examples have fine plates depicting a variety of subjects (for example, vessels of the merchant and fighting marine of the European maritime powers and portraits of the doges of Venice, prominent persons in Venetian history and fellow geographers). While much of Coronelli's output tends to be derivative, his maps are often highly decorative, large in size and almost overfilled with detail (Plate 5.20).

The eighteenth century was another low period for Italian mapmaking, with only a few highlights, such as the fine *Atlas universel* issued at Venice by P. Santini in 1776, based on the atlas of the same name published in France by the Roberts de Vaugondy. The *Atlante novissimo* of Antonio Zatta, also of Venice, was issued in four volumes between 1775 and 1785 (Plate 5.22). Among the many fine maps in this atlas are the first published map of New Zealand (based on the discoveries of Captain James Cook) and a rendering of the great map of the British colonies in North America by John Mitchell, first published in London in 1755. Two other notable Italians made their mark during this period. The painter, engraver and publisher Giovanni Maria Cassini produced his four-volume *Nuovo atlante geografico* atlas in Rome between 1792 and 1801 which contained maps of the newly discovered parts of the Americas and the

(continued on page 140)

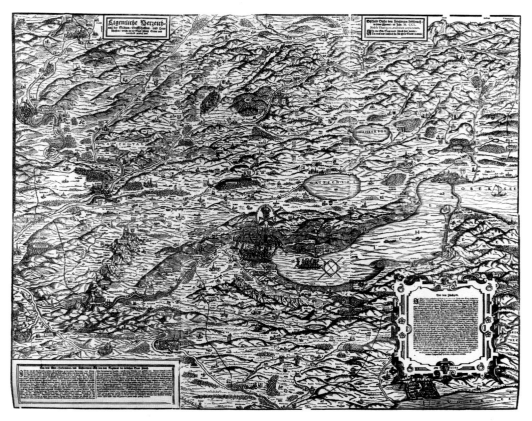

PLATE 5.24 Eigentliche
Verzeichnuss der Städten,
Graffschafften, und
Herrschafften, welche in
der Stadt Zürich-grebiet
und Landschafft gehörig
sind *by Jos Murer,
woodcut, 1566. Orientated
northeast to the top, a fine
early example of the
technique of perspective
applied to cartography.*

Pacific, such as Hawaii, Tahiti and Alaska. All the
maps had decorative cartouches which were sometimes the most attractive parts of the maps (Plate
5.21). Giovanni-Antonio Rizzi-Zannoni issued a
maritime atlas entitled *Atlante marittimo delle due
Sicile* in 1793, and numerous separately published
maps in the finest decorative and artistic tradition
(Plate 5.23). A particularly fine example is a
remarkable map of the environs of Naples, *Carta
dei littorale di Napoli*, from 1794, showing,
among other things, Vesuvius in sharp and detailed relief. The whole is enclosed within an
elaborate border and has a cartouche that must
surely have been inspired by the many beautiful
etchings of the Etruscan, Greek and Roman
antiquities in the collection of the British envoy to
Naples, Sir William Hamilton (husband of the
notorious Lady Hamilton, who ran off with Lord
Nelson), published by Pierre-François Hugues
d'Hancarville at Naples during the late 1760s.

Northern Europe

While there was some cartographic activity in
Germany during the sixteenth and seventeenth
centuries, it was on nothing like the scale of that
found in Italy or in the Netherlands. Editions of
Ptolemy were issued from presses in Germany
from an early date, and men such as Johann
Schöner, who was born at Karlstadt, in 1477 and
settled at Nuremberg in 1504, establishing a

significant reputation as a German globemaker
between 1515 and 1533.

A small but active school of cartography was
established in Cologne during the sixteenth century. Prominent figures included Caspar Vopell
(1511–1564), professor of mathematics, who
made a world map in 1545 printed in twelve
sheets. No copies now exist, save for a Venetian
derivative printed in 1558 with the title *Nova et
integra universalisque orbis totius iuxta Germanam
neotericorum traditionem descriptio*, and a further
derivative issued at Antwerp in 1570. Vopell also
issued a large map of the Rhine in five sheets in
1555, and a large map of Europe in the same year.

One of the best-known works published from
Cologne at this time was the *Theatrum Terrae
Sanctae*, an encyclopaedic work describing Palestine compiled by Christiaan van Adrichom
(1533–1585), which was illustrated with twelve
fine general and regional maps. It was first published in 1590 and went through many editions. A
particularly famous work, containing one of the
best known of all caricature maps, the *Leo Belgicus*
(see Chapter XI), was also published in Cologne
by Michael Eitzinger (c.1530–1598).

Among the expatriate cartographers working in
Cologne at the time was the French-born Jean
Matal (c.1520–1597), otherwise known as Johannes Metellus, who issued an atlas in parts from
1594 onwards. The complete version, containing
261 maps (the most comprehensive atlas of its
kind at the time), appeared in 1602, and was
probably completed by Mathias Quad (see below)
after Matal's death.

But perhaps the best known Cologne mapmaker, apart from Braun or Hogenberg (see Chapter
VIII), of the late sixteenth and early seventeenth
centuries is Maththias Quad (1557–1613), geographer, humanist and engraver. Along with the
printer and bookseller Johann Bussemecher, Quad
began issuing small-format atlases, largely derived from the works of Mercator, Ortelius, and,
in the case of the maps of the Americas, Wytfliet.
Examples of atlases issued by Quad are *Europae
totius orbis terrarum* (1592); *Geographisch Handtbuch* (1600); and *Fasciculus geographicus* (1508);
all of which seemed to have been issued in small
numbers. Quad himself ran foul of the Church
authorities in Cologne in 1600 and for a time was
not permitted to issue any new material.

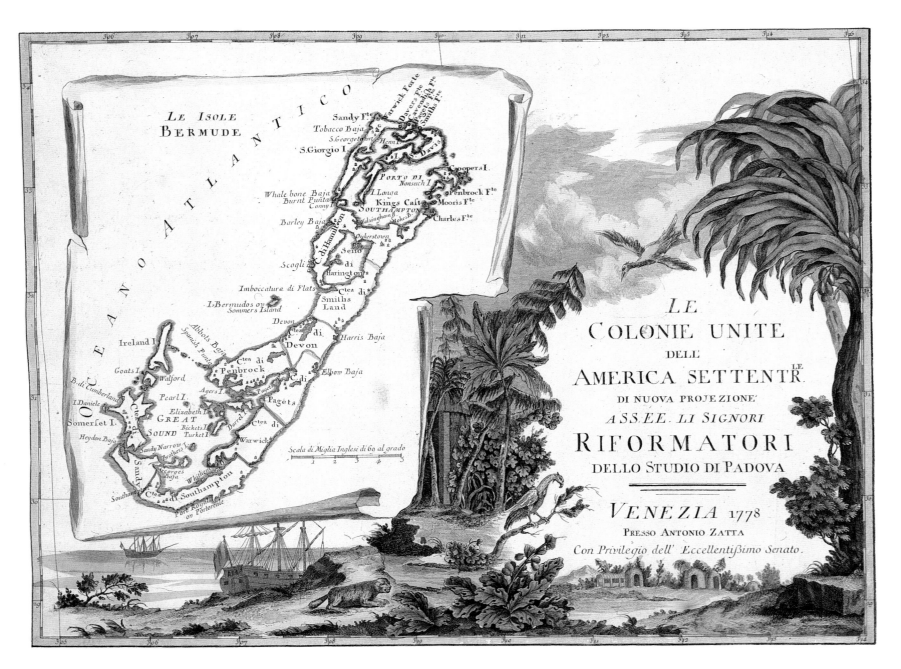

LE ISOLE
BERMUDE

OCEANO ATLANTICO

Sandy F.te
Tobacco Baja
S.Georgetown
S.Giorgio I.
Warwick Forte
Davers p.ta
Paget's p.ta
Smith's F.te
Henn
Davis
Cooper I.
PORTO DI
Nonsuch I.
Whale bone Baja
Burnt Punta
Conny
I.Longa
Kings Cast
Penbrock F.te
Mooris F.te
Barley Baja
C.di Hamilton
Walsingham
Moke B.
SOUTHAMPTON
Charles F.te
Oukerstown
Seno
di
Harington's
Scogli
Imboccatura di Flats
C.tea di
Smiths
Land
I.Bermudos ov
Sommer's Island
Devon
C.tea di
Devon
Harris Baja
Ireland I.
Abbots Baja
Spanish Punta
C.tea di
Penbrock
Elbow Baja
Goats I.
Walsford
Pearl I.
Agers I.
Paget
C.di
Paget's
B.di Cumberland
I.Daniele
Elizabeth I.
Rickets I.
Turket I.
Dorral
C.tea di
Warwick
Somerset I.
GREAT
SOUND
Heydon Baja
Sandy Narrow
Brothers
S.Georges
Baja
Whiboits
Southampton
C.tea di Southampton
Port Royal
ov Portroyale

Scala di Miglia Inglesi di 60 al grado
1 2 3 4 5

LE
COLONIE UNITE
DELL
AMERICA SETTENTR.LE
DI NUOVA PROJEZIONE
ASS.EE. LI SIGNORI
RIFORMATORI
DELLO STUDIO DI PADOVA

VENEZIA 1778
PRESSO ANTONIO ZATTA
Con Privilegio dell' Eccellentissimo Senato.

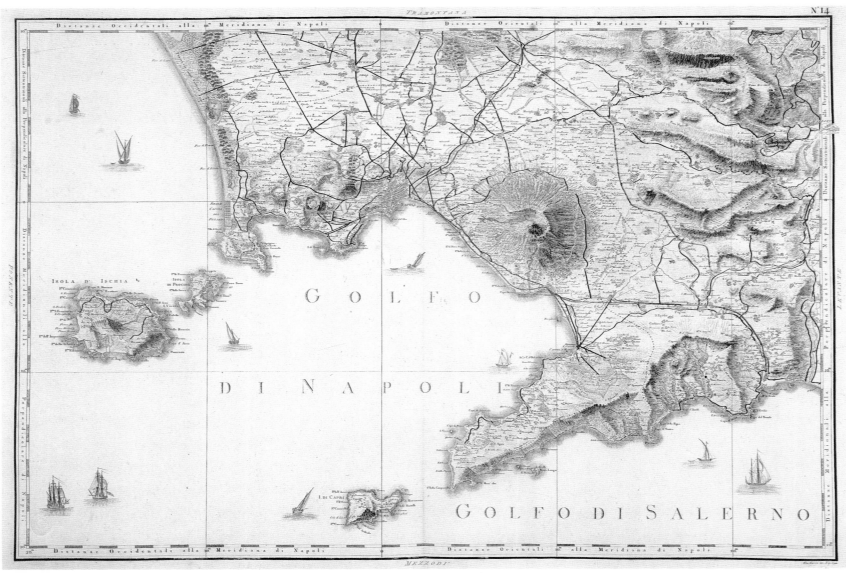

TRAMONTANA
N.14
Distanze Occidentali alla m. Meridiana di Napoli
Distanze Orientali m. alla Meridiana di Napoli

ISOLA D' ISCHIA
ISOLA DI PROCIDA

GOLFO

DI NAPOLI

I. DI CAPRI

GOLFO DI SALERNO

Distanze Occidentali alla m. Meridiana di Napoli
Distanze Orientali m. alla Meridiana di Napoli
MEZZODI

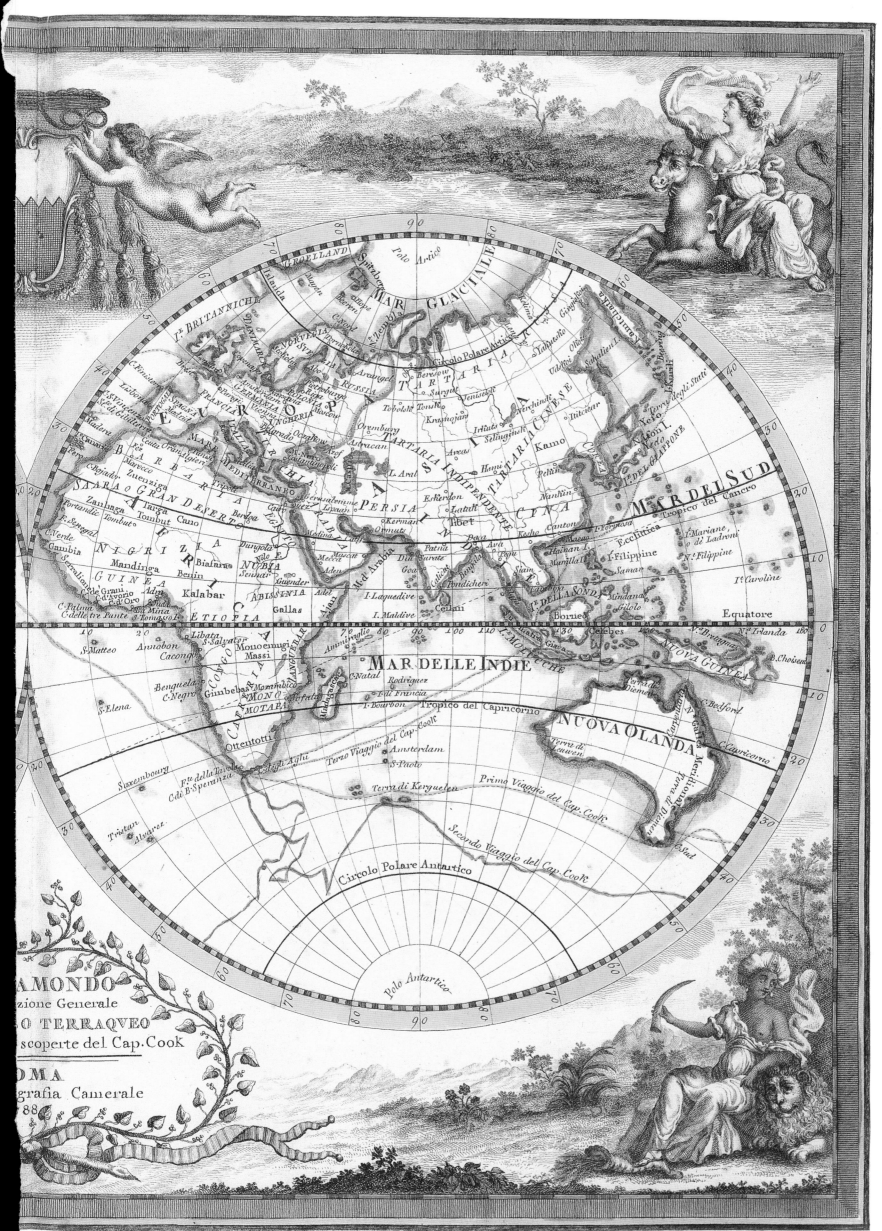

MAPPAMONDO
...zione Generale
...O TERRAQVEO
...scoperte del Cap. Cook

...OMA
...grafia Camerale
...88

Giº Mª Cassini Somª inc.

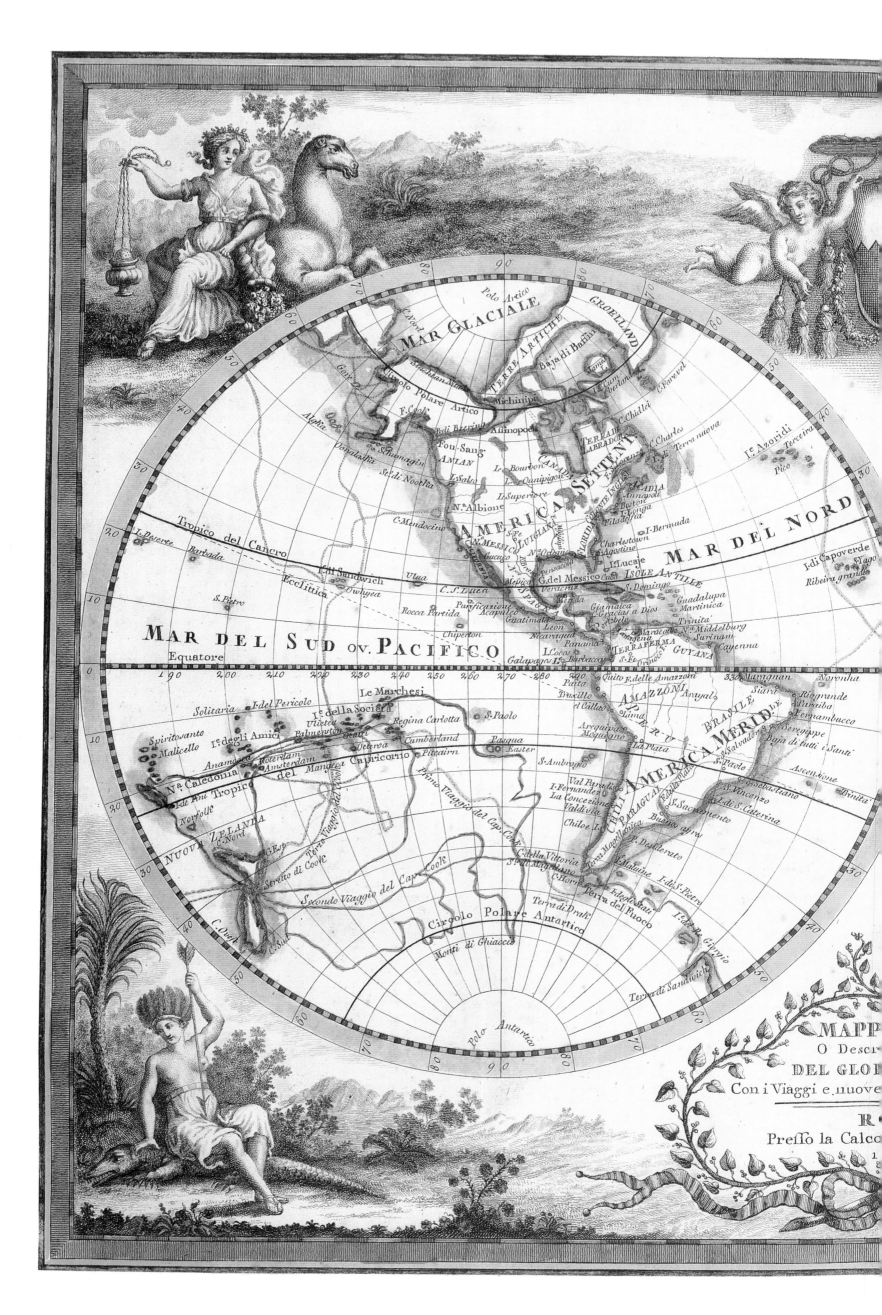

MAR GLACIALE GROENLAND

Polo Artico

C.Nord

TERRE ARTICHE

Baja di Baffin

Circolo Polare Artico

Michinipi

Assinopoels

F.di Bering

Fou-Sang

F.Cook

B.di Bering

TERRE DI LABRADOR

C.Chidlei

C.Charles

C.Farewel

Terranuova

I.e Azoridi

Terceira

Pico

Algku

Donalaska

Schumagin

Sct.di Nootka

I.Salo

Le Bourbon

L.Ounipigon

I.Superiore

AMERICA SETTENT.

Na.Albione

CANADA

FIUME INGLESE

Quebec

Boston

I.Longa

Filadelfia

Beaufort

Annapoli

ACADIA

C.Mendocino

Tropico del Cancro

Ecclittica

I.e di Sandwich

Ulua

I.Deserte

Barbada

S.Pietro

C.S.Luca

Owhyea

Rocca Partida

Purificazione

Chiperton

N.MESSICO

Mexico

Veracruz

S.Fe

Acapulco

Guatimala

Leon

LUISIANA

Pensacola

FLORIDA

N.Orleans

S.Agostino

Charlestown

I.Bermuda

I.Lucaje

Cuba

ISOLE ANTILLE

S.Domingo

I.di Capoverde

S.Jago

Ribeira grande

MAR DEL NORD

Guadalupa

Martinica

Giamaica

Gracias a Dios

Portobelo

Trinita

Nicaragua

Panama

Cartagena

Maracaibo

Na.Middelburg

Surinam

Barbacoa

TERRAFERMA

S.Fe Orinoco

Cayenna

GUYANA

MAR DEL SUD ov. PACIFICO

Equatore

L.Cocos

Galapagos I.

Quito

F.delle Amazzoni

Plata

Brasilio

Maranan

Noronha

Siarà

Riogrande

Paraiba

Fernambucco

190   200   210   220   230   240   250   260   270   280

330

AMAZZONI

Solitaria   I.del Pericolo

Le Marchesi

I.e della Società

Regina Carlotta

S.Paolo

Lima

Callao

PERU

BRASILE

Areguipa

Moquano

La Plata

S.Salvador

S.Paolo

Baja di tutti i Santi

Spiritosanto

I.degli Amici

Palmerston

Otaitù

Oteroa

Cumberland

Pasqua

S.Ambrogio

AMERICA MERID.le

Seregippe

Ascensione

Malicello

Anamoca

Roterdam

Amsterdam

Geati

Pitcairn

Easter

Val Paradiso

I.Fernandez

CHILI

PARAGUAY

S.Sebastiano

S.Vincenzo

Trinita

Na.Caledonia

La Concezione

La Plata

Valdivia

Buenos ayres

Ld.S.Caterina

S.Sacramento

Tropico del Capricorno

Primo Viaggio del Cap. Cook

Chiloe I.

Terra Magellanica

P.Desiderato

I.de Pini

Norfolk

Secondo Viaggio del Cap. Cook

C.della Vittoria

Stretto di Magellano

C.Horn

I.Maluine

F.di S.Pietro

NUOVA ZELANDA

C.Nord

C.Est

Terzo Viaggio del Cap. Cook

Terra di Drake

Isole Statì

Stretto di Cook

Terra del Fuoco

C.di Giprnio

C.Ouest

C.Sud

Terra di Sandwich

Circolo Polare Antartico

Monti di Ghiaccio

Polo Antartico

MAPP

O Descr

DEL GLOB

Con i Viaggi e nuove

R

Presso la Calco

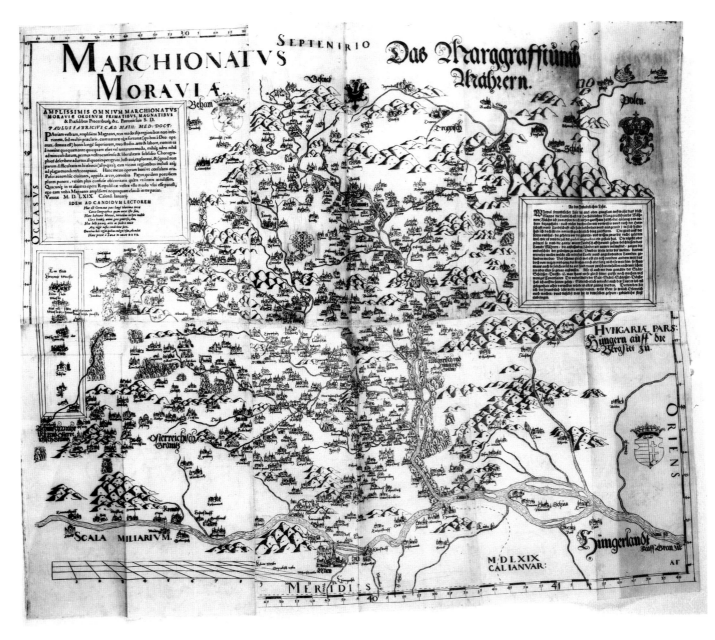

PLATE 5.25
Marchionatus Moravia *by*
Paulus Fabricius, Venice,
1569. This is the first
modern map of Moravia —
only two other copies of this
map are known. It is
included in the famous
Doria Atlas and is also a
wall map on six sheets
measuring 830 × 976 mm.
Fabricius was a professor of
astronomy in Vienna.

Homann and his heirs

During the seventeenth century, Germany produced relatively little of cartographic importance. Mapmaking in the empire at this time was largely dependent upon the products of the Dutch publishing houses. The maps and atlases of Hondius, Blaeu and Janssonius all enjoyed wide popularity in Germany, since they were translated into German specifically to supply that market, through the great book fairs at Frankfurt and Leipzig. Nevertheless, some maps were published in Germany in this period. The most noteworthy are the publications of the Merian family, who issued long series of illustrated topographies of the regions of Germany and other parts of Europe. The maps that the Merians produced were often copied from Blaeu, in reduced form, and were accompanied by many fine town plans, views and folding panoramas (see Chapter VIII).

The opening years of the eighteenth century saw a revival of map publishing in Germany, largely

PLATE 5.26 Johann
Baptist Homann (*1663–*
1725) engraved by W.
Winter. Homann, a
Lutheran, played an
important part in the
revival of map publishing in
Germany at the start of the
eighteenth century. After his
death in 1725 his business
was continued under the
name Homann's Heirs.

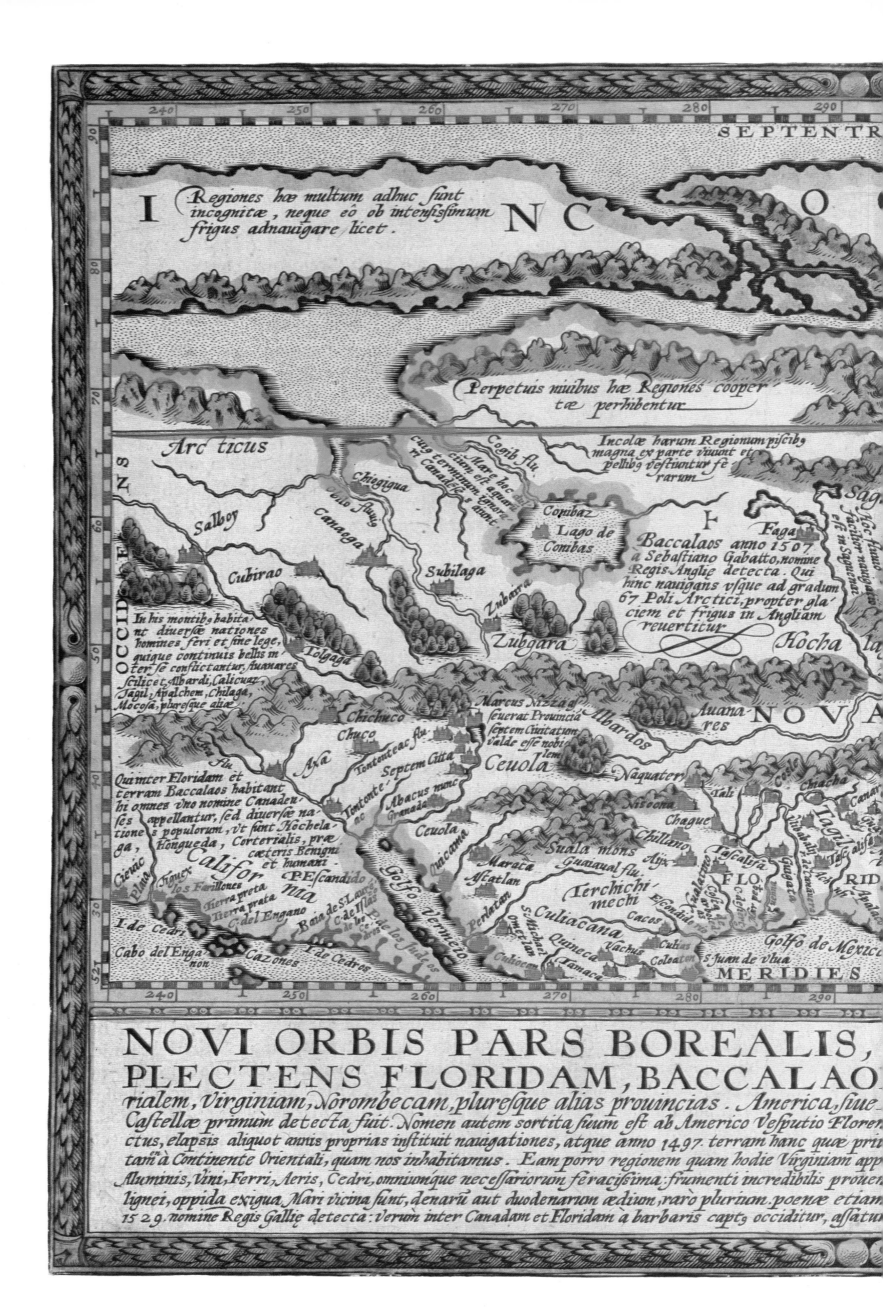

I Regiones hæ multum adhuc sunt
incognitæ, neque eô ob intensissimum
frigus adnauigare licet.

NC O

Perpetuis niuibus hæ Regiones cooper
tæ perhibentur

Arcticus

Incolæ harum Regionum piscibꝫ
magna ex parte viuunt et
pellibꝫ vestiuntur fe
rarum

Chiegigua

Cogib flu.

Mare hoc dul
cium est aqua
ri termunum ignora
ri Canadenses auont

Salboy

Canaega

Cubirao

Copibaz
Lago de
Combas

Subilaga

Zubara

Baccalaos anno 1507
a Sebastiano Gabatto, nomine
Regis Angliæ detecta. Qui
hinc nauigans vsque ad gradum
67 Poli Arctici, propter gla
ciem et frigus in Angliam
reuertitur

Faga

Sag

In his montibꝫ habita
nt diuersæ nationes
homines feri et sine lege,
quique continuis bellis in
ter se conflictantur, suanares
scilicet, Albardi, Calicuas,
Sagil, Aualchem, Chilaga,
Mocosa, pluresque aliæ

Tolgaga

Zubgara

Hocha

Chichieco
Chuco

Aña

Marcus Nizza
seuerat Prouinciã
septem Ciuitatium
valde esse nobi
lem

Albardos

Auana
res

NOVA

Tontonteac flu.

Aña flu.

Qui inter Floridam et
terram Baccalaos habitant
hi omnes vno nomine Canaden
ses appellantur, sed diuersæ na
tione s populorum, vt sunt Hochela
ga, Hongueda, Corterialis, præ
cæteris Benigni
et humani

Septem Citta

Tontonte
ac

Abacus nunc
Granada

Ceuola

Naquateri

Tali

Coele

chacha

Nitocha

Chague

Chillano

Ceuola

Quicama

Suala mõs
Guaiaual flu.

Alix

Tascalista

FLO

RID

Caliaca

Figuez

los Farillones

Tierra prota

Tierra prata

C. del Engano

Califor
nia

P. Escandido

Maraca
Aftatlan

Perlatan

Culiacana

S. Michael
omerian

Ierchichi
mechi

Cacos

Quineca

El candido

Apatlan

Colida

Colioan

FLO
detta

I. de Cedri

Baia de S. Laure

C. de Illas

Vachus

Culias

Golfo de Mexico

Cabo del Enga
non

Cazones

I. de Cedros

Ede los Jud
es

de los Re
es

Golfo
Vermeio

Culioem

Quneca

Tamaca

Culias
Coloatan

S. Juan de Vlua

NOVI ORBIS PARS BOREALIS,
PLECTENS FLORIDAM, BACCALAO
rialem, Virginiam, Norombecam, pluresque alias prouincias. America, siue
Castellæ primùm detecta fuit. Nomen autem sortita suum est ab Americo Vesputio Floren
ctus, elapsis aliquot annis proprias instituit nauigationes, atque anno 1497. terram hanc quæ pri
tam à Continente Orientali, quam nos inhabitamus. Eam porro regionem quam hodie Virginiam app
Aluminis, Vini, Ferri, Aeris, Cedri, omniumque necessariorum feracissima: frumenti incredibilis prouen
lignei, oppida exigua. Mari vicina sunt, denarû aut duodenarum ædium, rarò plurium, poenæ etiam
1529. nomine Regis Galliæ detecta: Verùm inter Canadam et Floridam à barbaris captꝫ occiditur, assatu

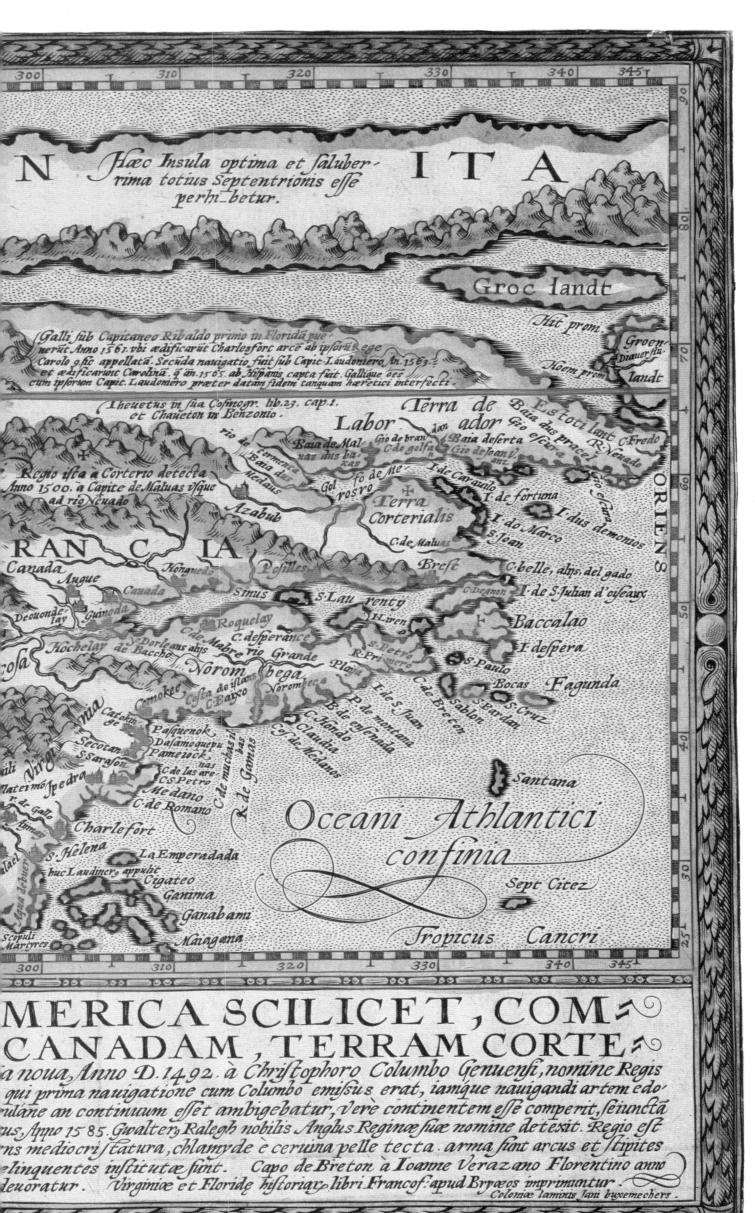

Map labels (as they appear):

N · ITA

Hæc Insula optima et saluber-
rima totius Septentrionis esse
perhibetur.

Groc Iandt

Galli sub Capitaneo Ribaldo primo in Floridã pue-
nerũt Anno 1561. vbi ædificarũt Charlesfort arcê ab ipsorũ ege
Carolo 9.sic appellatã. Secũda nauigatio fuit sub Capit. Laudoniero An. 1563.
et ædificarunt Carolinã. q̃ an. 1565. ab Hispanis capta fuit. Gallique oes
cum ipsorum Capit. Laudoniero præter datam fidem tanquam hæretici interfecti.

Hit prom.

Groen-
Diauers stu.
landt

Koem prom.

Theuetus in sua Cosmogr. lib.23. cap.1.
et Chaueton in Benzonio.

Terra de
Labor dam ador
Baia dus pract.
Estoti landt · C. Fredo

Baia de Mal-
nas dus ba-
xas

Gio de bran
C. do golfo
Baia deserta
Gio de soani

Gio escura
R. Nouado
Gio escura

rio de Formenta
Baia dus
Medaus

Regio ista a Corterio detecta
Anno 1500. a Capite de Maluas vsque
ad rio Neuado

Azabuk

Golfo de me
rosro
I. de Caruaio

Terra
Corterialis

I. de fortuna
I. dus demonios

C. de Maluas

I. do Marco
S. Ioan

RAN CIA

Honguedo

Posilles

Brest
C. belle, alijs, del gado

Canada
Augue

Canada

Sinus
S. Lau renty
C. Degnon
I. de S. Iulian d'oiseaux

Deouonde-
lay Guinoda

Roquelay
I. Liren

F
Baccalao

Hochelar
Sy. Dorle ans alijs
de Bacche
C. de Mabre
C. desperance
rio
Grande
S. Petro
R. Primero
I. despera

cosa

Norom bega
Comokee
Costa de islas
C. Bayxo
Norombeca
Playa

C. de Breton
S. Paulo
Bocas
S. Cruz
Fagunda

nia
Cataku-
ge
B. de esfrenada
I. de S. Iuan
P. de montana
Sablon
S. Bardan

Virgi
Secotan
S. sarason
Pasquenok
Dalamoquepu
Pameiock
nas

C. de las are-
Cs. Petro
C. de muchas il-
las

C. Hondo
C. de Medanos
Claudia

Santana

Platei mô
r. de Gallo
Agnian
Medano
C. de Romano
R. de Gamas

Oceani Athlantici
confinia

Charlefort

S. Helena
La Emperadada
huc Laudiner appulit
Cigateo
Ganima

Sept. Citez

Scopuli
Martyres
Ganabami
Maiagona

Tropicus Cancri

ORIENS

PLATE 5.27 Novi orbis
pars borealis, America
Scilicet *by Mathias Quad,
Cologne, 1600 and later.
This is a general map of
North America, one of the
earliest available, which
was based on a now rare
map by Cornelis de Jode of
Antwerp, published in
1593. Quad's version was
published in his atlas, the*
Geographisch Handtbuch.

MERICA SCILICET, COM-
CANADAM, TERRAM CORTE-

a noua, Anno D. 1492. a Christophoro Columbo Genuensi, nomine Regis
qui prima nauigatione cum Columbo emissus erat, iamque nauigandi artem edo-
rulane an continuum esset ambigebatur, Verè continentem esse comperit, seiunctã
us, Anno 1585. Gwalter Ralegh nobilis Anglus Reginæ suæ nomine detexit. Regio est
ns mediocri statura, chlamyde è ceruina pelle tecta. arma sunt arcus et stipites
linquentes institutæ sunt. Capo de Breton a Ioanne Verazano Florentino anno
deuoratur. Virginiæ et Floridæ historiæ libri Francof: apud Bryæos imprimuntur.
Coloniæ laminis Ioñ buxemechers.

through the efforts of Johann Baptist Homann
(1663–1724) (Plate 5.26), who founded a large
publishing house in Nuremberg in 1702. The
'Officina Homanniana', as it became known,
continued in business until 1813. Trained as an
engraver, Homann worked during the 1690s for
map publishers in Amsterdam. His first atlas
appeared in 1707, with maps mostly derived from
Dutch and French models. Between 1702 and
1715 Homann engraved about one hundred
maps, generally on the same format. Relief was
depicted by pictorial representation, rather like
'molehills', and towns were shown either by
conventional symbols or, in the case of the large
settlements, by miniature plans (Plate 5.28).

Nearly all of Homann's maps were undated, so
that it is often the case that older maps are found
together with more recent ones in the same atlas,
all with the same imprint. It can be very difficult
to date individual Homann maps, despite the fact
that he was appointed Geographer to the Holy
Roman Emperor in 1715, entitling him to append
that title to his name. In many of his firm's larger
composite atlases (which could contain over 200
maps and town plans) examples are found of
1720s maps, some with the imperial appellation,
and some without it.

The Homann firm was extremely successful in
its activities, for Homann's commercial organization allowed him to build up a large stock of
plates, some bought from Dutch publishers, and
to sell his products at prices lower than those of
rival French and Dutch publishers. His maps are
easily recognizable by their style of engraving:
obviously descended from Dutch maps, but engraved with a heavier hand and with bolder
lettering. They frequently included large and
decorative title cartouches, which often incorporate vignettes of towns, occupations or other
features held to be representative of the region
shown on the map. These decorative devices were
most often left uncoloured, any colour added to
the maps being in the form of heavy washes.
These washes, usually in yellows, reds and greens,
were applied to the geographical detail of the map,
sometimes imparting a rather heavy appearance.
Often, medallion portraits of kings and emperors,
or their coats of arms, were included, offering

(continued on page 148)

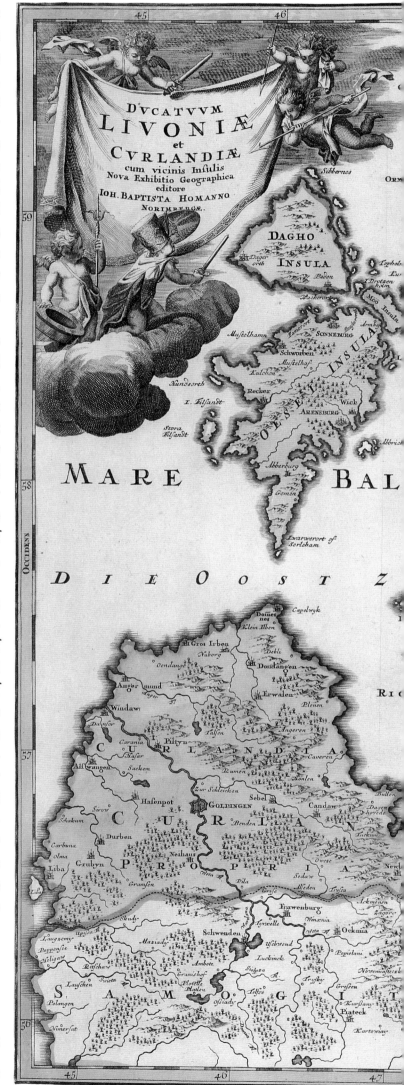

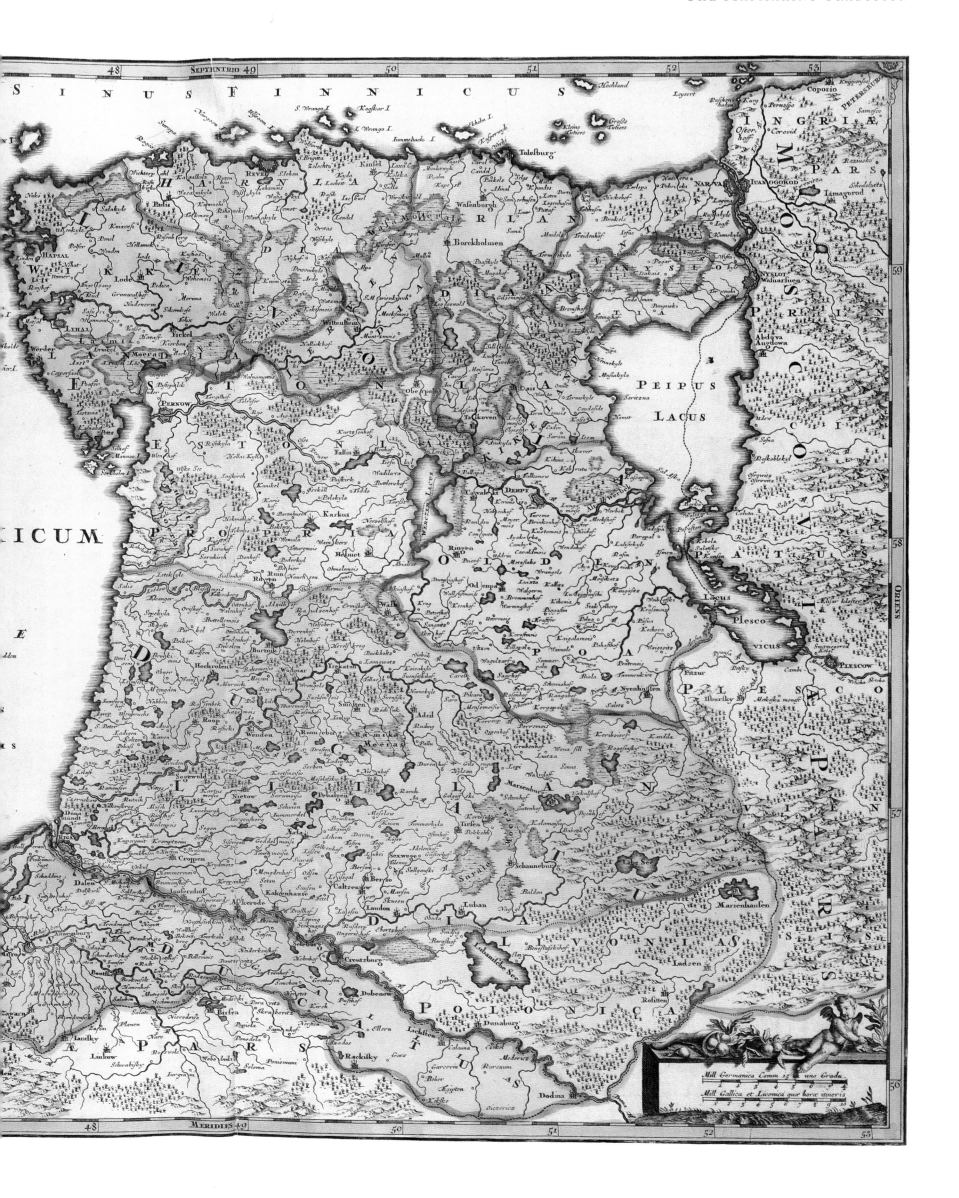

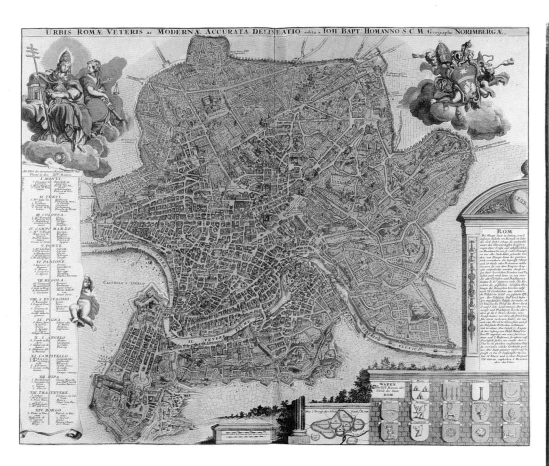

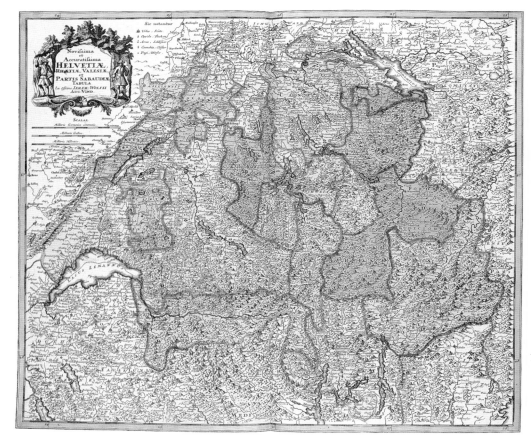

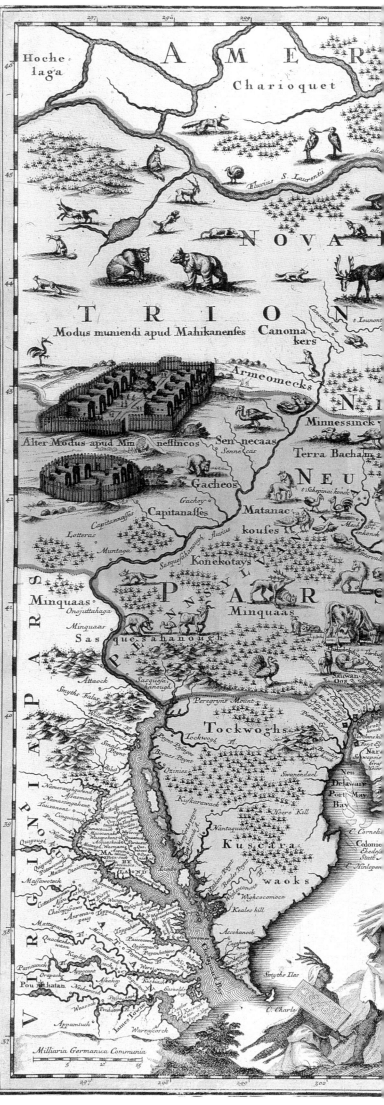

PLATE 5.29 *(top)* Urbis Romae veteris et moderna accurata delineata *by J.B. Homann, c. 1720 and later. This is one of several town plans included in editions of the* Grosser *atlas and composite atlases issued by the Nuremberg firm over several years.*

PLATE 5.30 *(above)* Novissima et accuratissima Helvetia *by Jeremias Wolff, c. 1530. Wolff (1663–1724) was a map engraver working in Augsburg. Many of his maps were distributed in eighteenth-century composite atlases.*

PLATE 5.31 *(right)* Recens edita totius Novi Belgii in America Septentrionali *by Georg Matthäus Seutter/T.C. Lotter, 1730 and c. 1760. This is the first Lotter issue of Seutter's map of New England, with an inset view of New York.*

HELVETIAE PAGI seu CANTONES. XIII. OHRT der EIDGENOSSSCHAFT. 1. ZÜ
1. S. GALLEN ABT. 2. S. GALLEN STATT. 3. PÜNDTEN. 4. WALLIS. 5. MULHAUSEN. 6. BIEL. 7. NEUBURG. NI
THAL. adscitis Abbatiscellanis Tigurinis, Bernensibus, Lucernensibus, Uriis, Suitensibus, Suboylvanis, Tugiensibus, Glaronensibus, qui VII
BE. 5. GRANSON. Uriorum, Suitensium et Subsylvanorum sunt 1. BELLINZONA. 2. RIVIERA, 3. VALLEBREGNIA. PALENS

PLATE 5.32 *(above)*
Ducatus Slesvicensis by
Georg Matthäus Seutter,
1750. A map of
Scandinavia by the Seutter
family, who were the rival
map publishers in Germany
to the Homanns. Matthäus
Seutter the elder had been
apprenticed to Johann
Baptist Homann in 1697
and his maps bear a strong
resemblance to those of his
master.

PLATE 5.33 *(opposite, top*
and bottom) Helvetiae pagi
sive cantones XIII *by*
Johann Jakob Scheuchzer,
1711. This large four-sheet
map of Switzerland is seen
here in a very close copy
from a composite Dutch
atlas issued in Amsterdam in
the 1730s and 1740s. It is
also a fine demonstration of
Dutch colouring of the
eighteenth century at its best.

possible clues as to the date of publication. However, in many cases, these details can be misleading and sometimes confusing.

Nevertheless, Homann restored the status of cartography in Germany, and his heirs continued the business, calling themselves *Homann'sche Erben* or *Heredites Homannianae* (Homann's Heirs). Nuremberg became a leading centre for geographical publication of all kinds. In addition to atlases, such as the *Neuer Atlas*, *Grosser Atlas* and *Atlas Maior*, recalling, of course, the title of the last great Blaeu atlas – the Homann firm also issued detailed regional atlases and maps intended for publication in travel books. A number of educational and scientific atlases were issued in the mid-eighteenth century, illustrating texts on map-making and surveying, as well as smaller-format school atlases. All the country and feature names were omitted from the school atlases, the intention being that the student should insert names as they were learned. Homann's Heirs also issued German versions of maps published in France and England, their engravers often copying the original information with remarkable fidelity.

The firm of Seutter

Late in the eighteenth century, in Augsburg, the firm established by Georg Matthäus Seutter the elder (1768–1757) produced a large number of atlases and maps in competition with Homann's Heirs. Seutter himself had been apprenticed to Homann in 1697 and his maps were often derived

ERN. 3. LUCERN. 4. URI. 5. SCHWEIZ. 6. UNDERWALDEN. 7. ZUG. 8. GLARUS. 9. BASEL. 10. FREIBURG. 11. SOLOTHURN. 12. SCHAFFHAUSEN. 13. APPENZELL. CONFOEDERATI. ZUGEWANDTE OHRT
8. GENFF GENEVE. 9. BISCHOFF BASEL Tegurinis, Lucernensibus, Urijs, Suicensibus, Subsylvanis, Tugensibus, Glaronensibus, qui vn. Cantones veteres, vn alte Ohrt vulgo vocantur, parent 1. THURGEU, adscritis in criminalibus Bernensibus, Friburgensibus, et Solodorensibus. 2. SARGANS. 3. FREYEAMPTER. 4. RHEIN
rum nōie veniunt, paret BADEN. Graffsch. XII. prim. Canton. jurisdiction. agnoscunt Praefectura Transalpina. 1. LAUIS, LUGANO. 2. LUGGARUS, LOCARNO. 3. MENDRIS. 4. MEINTHAL. Bernensium et Friburgensium Dominio subsunt 1. MURTEN. 2. SCHWARZENBURG. 3. ESCHALENS. 4. OR
utiorum et Glaronensium GASTER. CASTRARHAETICA. Sui juris sunti. RAPERSCHWEIL. 2. ENGELBERG. 3. GERSAU.

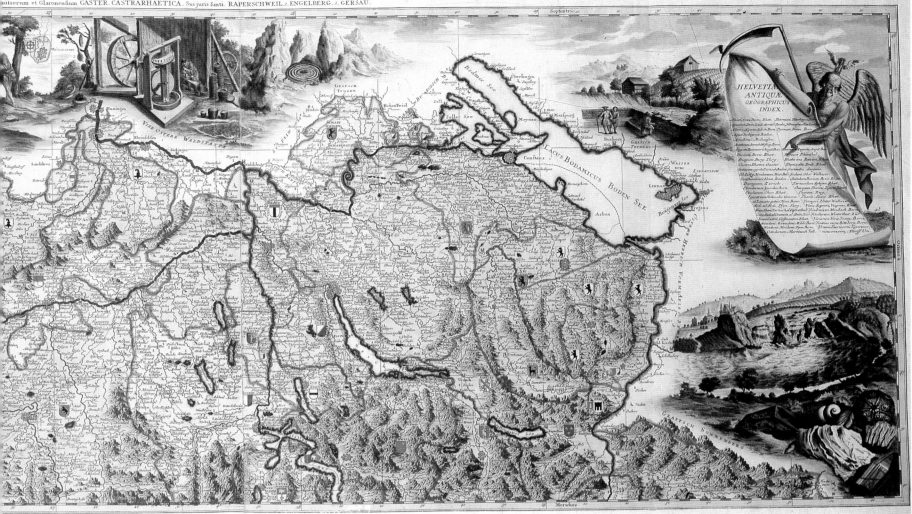

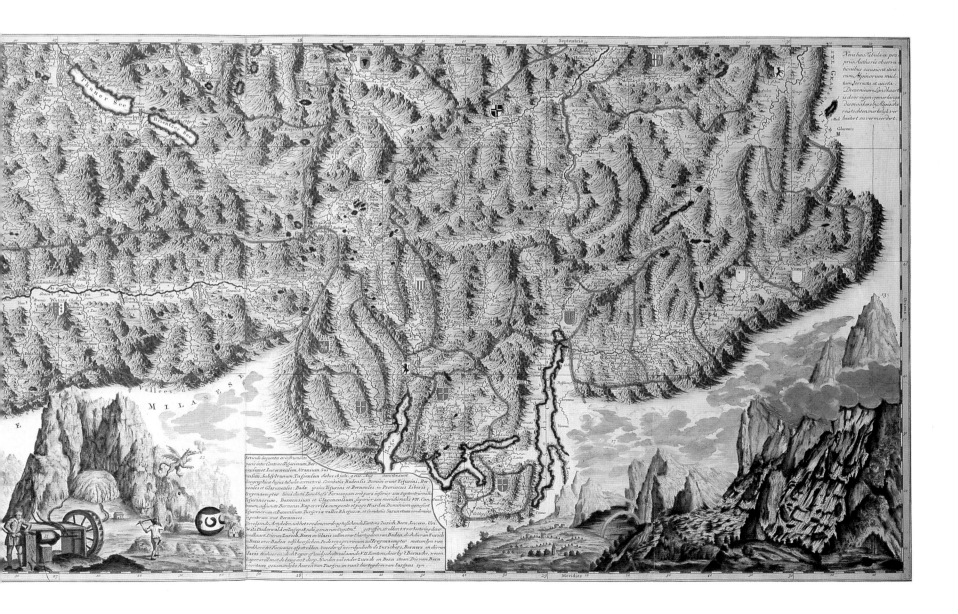

PLATE 5.34 Archiducatus Austriae Superioris descriptio facta Anno *1667* by Georg Matthäus Vischer, Augsburg, *1669* and later. Printed from twelve plates, this is an impressive example of a separately published regional map, depicting relief by means of hill-shading.

from the same source materials as those of the Homanns. Seutter used a similar style of bold colour washes, but the engraving was done in a heavier manner (Plates 5.31, 5.32). Some very fine large composite atlases containing town plans were issued by Seutter and his heirs, such as his *Atlas novus* of 1730 and the *Atlas minor* of 1740 (see Chapter VIII). Seutter established a branch of his publishing business in Vienna in the 1730s.

France from Finé to d'Anville

Map publishing and organized atlas cartography in France developed comparatively late, towards the end of the sixteenth century. Single maps did occasionally appear, such as the double-cordiform world map of Oronce Finé (1494–1555), *Nova, et integra universi orbis descriptio*. Finé's map was first issued in 1531 and was subsequently used, in

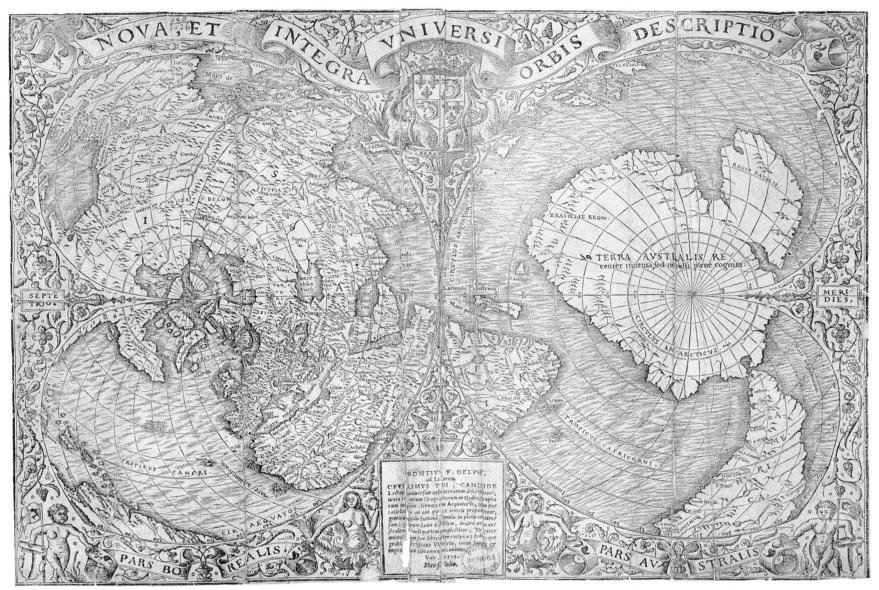

various states, to illustrate notable books (Plate 3.35). Finé had also prepared a single-cordiform world map in 1519, but this was not published until 1534. Only two copies survive. This map is better known via Peter Apian's version, published in Germany in 1530. The independent business in maps and charts, however, was slow in branching off from the book trade in France; many surveys, maps and charts remained as manuscripts for a long time before being reproduced by means of engravings or woodcuts. Sometimes they were not copied at all or, more frequently, they were copied by publishers elsewhere first, in Italy or in the Netherlands. Among such mapmakers were Jean Jolivet (fl. 1545–1569), geographer to François I, who made large maps of Normandy and Berry in 1545, and a large general map of France in four sheets in 1560 entitled *Nouvelle description des Gaules, avec les confins Dalemagne et Italye*. The only known copy of this map survived until 1945 at Breslau (Wroclaw), in Poland, but it is also known through Ortelius's *Theatrum* atlas version, and later printings of the original blocks.

André Thevet (1502–1590), a franciscan friar and geographer, travelled widely and later made maps of the world and the continents. He also published an important history of French colonization activities in the Americas in 1558, under the title *France antarctique*. Gilles Bouleau de Bouillon (c. 1510–1563) made numerous regional maps of France which were taken up by Italian publishers or communicated to Ortelius for inclusion in the *Theatrum*, such as *Nova et exactissima Sabaudiae ducat. descriptio 1556*, printed in two sheets. Jacques Surhon and his son, Jean, issued maps of Namur (1555) and of Vermandois (1558) which have come down to us, again, through the medium of Ortelius's *Theatrum*.

Le théâtre françoys

It was not until 1594 that the first atlas of France was produced: *Le théâtre françoys*, compiled by Maurice Bouguereau (who died the same year), a bookseller of Tours. At that time Tours was the seat of the French court and a place of shelter for many Parisian booksellers and printers during the

PLATE 5.35 Nova, et integra universi orbis descriptio *by Oronce Finé, woodcut, Paris, first issued in 1531. When first published, in an edition of Johann Huttich and Simon Grynaeus's* Novus orbis regionum *in 1532, this double cordiform map was considerably in advance of other maps, although North America is shown to be firmly part of Asia.*

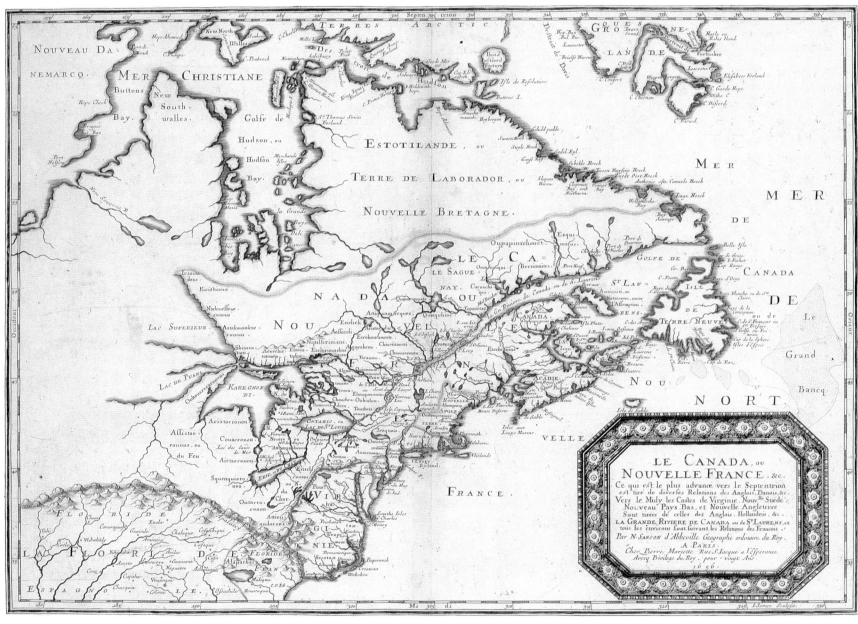

bitter civil wars known as the Wars of Religion. From the title of Bouguereau's atlas, it can be assumed that he had Ortelius's atlas in mind. The maps were engraved by Gabriel Tavernier, himself an exile, this time from Antwerp, who seems to have been acquainted with Ortelius. *Le théâtre françoys* forms the basis of all subsequent regional atlases of France and contains the first printed maps of several French provinces and regions. It contained up to three general maps of France followed by fifteen regional or provincial maps. This rather emphasized the fact that at this time there was no strong central government in France, still less political stability, for France achieved this much later than England. Consequently, no uniform survey of the country could be commissioned by authority, and Bouguereau's atlas was, therefore, probably issued in only a small number of copies in and around Tours.

In the early part of the seventeenth century, Bouguereau's map plates were acquired by Jean le Clerc (1560–1621). Le Clerc reissued the maps three times (in 1619, 1620 and 1621), under the title *Théâtre géographique du royaume de France*, by which time the maps had increased to forty-nine in number. After his death, the plates passed to Le Clerc's heirs who reissued the atlas a further three times. Jean Boisseau (*fl.* 1637–1658) subsequently reissued the atlas in 1642 under the title *Théâtre des Gaules*, this time with seventy-five maps. Boisseau, incidentally, held the royal appointment for colouring maps. In 1657, Melchior Tavernier (brother of Gabriel) issued the maps in his own atlas which bore the same title as that of Boisseau, but which contained as many as ninety-five maps. Many of these were either reprinted or copied from existing Dutch maps.

The French school

Under Louis XIV, France achieved a measure of political stability. As a result, an independent French map business began to develop and flourish, one which would eventually rival and supersede that of Amsterdam:

Mapmaking, in common with fine and applied arts generally, enjoyed royal patronage and was harnessed to the service of the State; and cartography of the seventeenth and eighteenth centuries in France had an 'official' character scarcely known in other countries.[3]

The founder of the French 'school' was Nicolas Sanson d'Abbeville (1600–1667), *géographe ordinaire du roi*, who issued a map of France as early as 1629. His first atlas appeared in 1654, with another appearing in parts in 1658 under the title *Cartes générales de toutes les parties du monde*. The latter contained about 113 maps. The maps of the Sanson family (Nicolas the younger, who died in 1648; Guillaume, who died in 1703; and Adrien, who died in 1708) are characterized by their often very handsome neoclassical and baroque designs, in common with much French graphic art of the time (Plates 5.36, 5.37). Quite individual in design, with 'wholly French elegance in the drawing of their detail and the character of their lettering',[4] the Sanson maps achieved popularity outside France as well, and were much copied by Dutch, English and German mapmakers for many years, well into the eighteenth century.

The Sanson plates were acquired by Alexis Hubert Jaillot (1632–1712), head of a long-running family printing establishment, who re-engraved the maps on a larger, grander and altogether more elaborate scale for his *Atlas*

PLATE 5.38 *(above) A rare monumental world map by Nicolas Jaugeon, copper engraving, 1688. A pictorial encyclopaedia.*

PLATE 5.36 *(opposite, top)* Le Nouveau Mexique et La Floride *by Nicholas Sanson d'Abbeville, Paris, 1656. Janson's map is the first printed French atlas map to emphasize California and New Mexico; it became a model for maps showing California as an island.*

PLATE 5.37 *(opposite, bottom)* Le Canada, ou Nouvelle France *by Nicholas Sanson d'Abbeville, 1656 and later. This map is the most influential record of the French establishments in North America in the middle of the seventeenth century.*

153

nouveau which appeared in 1689. Jaillot's atlas was very closely copied by the Amsterdam publisher Pieter Mortier in 1696, and later by others, so that these maps were still being included in atlases until the middle of the eighteenth century (Plates 5.39, 5.40). Jaillot produced in addition a magnificent atlas of sea charts in 1693 under the title *Neptune françois ou atlas nouveau des cartes marines*. The *Neptune françois* later formed the embryo of the series of charts and atlases issued by Jacques-Nicolas Bellin (see Chapter IX).

The scholarly work of d'Anville

Jean Baptiste Bourguignon d'Anville (1697–1782) was a scholar who worked mostly with written materials; he was also an editor who designed new maps by collecting and collating information from as many varied sources as possible. D'Anville's particular forte was the assessment and integration of data derived from older sources, which he correlated with more up-to-date materials in the belief that there was still much of value to be gained from consulting older maps, documents and texts. He was meticulous in his attention to detail, revising and re-issuing maps as new data became available, and he also relied upon an extensive network of correspondents to keep him informed of, and supplied with, new maps and information, in much the same manner that Mercator and Ortelius had done in the late sixteenth century. Some of the more important maps were published with a detailed memoir on his compilation methods and a critical assessment of the documents and sources used. One example is the *Mémoir sur la carte de l'Empire ottoman* (Paris, 1747), a slim little volume which was nevertheless comprehensive in scope.

D'Anville's working life was spent in and around Paris; apparently he never ventured beyond the immediate environs of the city. He assembled a large collection of maps, numbering nearly 9,000 items in all, which was acquired by the French government not long before his death. Prior to this important acquisition, government departments maintained their own small, disparate collections of reference materials which were often not available for use by other departments or offices. The king also had his own collection, but this was a private rather than a public archive. It was due largely to the efforts of one of the royal librarians, Jean Denis Barbié du Bocage (a pupil of d'Anville in earlier years), that the collection of his erstwhile tutor was eventually bought by the government for the Ministry of Foreign Affairs for the use of diplomats. This collection subsequently passed from the Ministry to the Bibliothèque Nationale in 1924.

D'Anville acquired an international reputation for his careful work, many of his maps being copied by other publishers abroad, particularly in England and Germany. D'Anville was in fact the last, and perhaps the greatest, of those who, since the Renaissance, had followed this procedure, and he probably carried it as far as possible. He was one of the first to study the works of oriental writers for details on the countries of the east. Further approach to accuracy could be attained only from exploration and actual survey of the continental interiors.[5] D'Anville's historical research resulted in the publication of numerous historical maps and atlases, the best known being the many editions of *A Complete Body of Ancient Geography*, from 1757 onwards.

Recognition of d'Anville's methods came early on from the Society of Jesus, better known as the Jesuits. They entrusted him with the preparation, for wider publication, of their surveys of the provinces of the Chinese Empire. The Jesuits had been working on these since the seventeenth century, and one of their members, Jean-Baptiste Regis, had been specializing in the Kangxi empire between 1708 and 1716. Regis had also issued an atlas of maps in Peking in 1718. These maps were based for the most part upon astronomical observations, while others were simpler route surveys. It was from these maps, or rather from their western versions, that Europeans gained their accurate conception of the geography of the interior of China and Korea.

With the aid of the Chinese surveys, d'Anville was able to compile a general map of the Chinese Empire to accompany a description of China by Jean-Baptiste du Halde, entitled *Description géographique, historique, chronologique, politique, et physique de l'empire de la Chine et de la Tartarie chinoise*. This work was issued in Paris in 1735, in four folio volumes, and is probably the most celebrated of all eighteenth-century works on China. The survey was compiled from published and unpublished writings and research by seventeen Jesuits and illustrated with forty-six maps and plans by d'Anville. The same maps were also issued in atlas form in Amsterdam two years later, under the title *Nouvel atlas de la Chine, de la Tartarie Chinoise et du Thibet: contenant les cartes générales & particulières de ces pays, ainsi que la carte du Royaume de Corée*. There was also a London edition, issued by Emanuel Bowen between 1738 and 1741. In this atlas of China, d'Anville acted as a compiler. His map of Italy, *l'Italie*, published in 1743, showed the results of his study of historical sources in the shape of Roman itineraries and measures of route length. The overall accuracy of his work was borne out by geodetic observations done some years later.

D'Anville also made important new maps of the continents in several sheets: *Amérique septentrionale* in 1746; *Amérique méridionale* in 1748; *Afrique* in 1749; *Carte d'Asie* in 1751–1753; *Europe* in 1754–1760; and a large twin-hemispherical world map in 1761. There was also a large, accurate map of Louisiana, *Carte de la Louisiane*, issued in 1752. (Louisiana was then a vastly more extended area than that now covered by the modern state of Louisiana.) Unlike most contemporary maps of continental outlines, d'Anville's treatment of the interiors presented considerable improvements on anything which had gone before. Prior to the publication of his map of Africa in 1749, knowledge of the interior was based largely on either fantasy, Ptolemy, or the map of Gastaldi issued in 1564. (This last was in turn derived from accounts written by a Moorish traveller and published in Rome some years before.) D'Anville removed all traces of myth and fantasy and published a map which remained the best of its kind until the interior of Africa was explored and colonized by European powers in the nineteenth century. The same may also be said of his *Carte de l'Ethiopie*, issued in 1727, which was based on Portuguese Jesuit sources. The map showed the Blue Nile rising in Lake Tana and reduced the southern course of the White Nile. Similarly, d'Anville's map of India, issued in 1752, proved to be the best of its kind of the subcontinent, prior to the publication of Major Rennell's surveys (Chapter VII).

Several of d'Anville's large maps were issued in atlas form in 1761, with numerous revisions and amendments appearing at frequent intervals. His

maps continued to be accepted as authoritative until well into the nineteenth century, testimony to his own principle, expressed in the spirit of the Age of Enlightenment, of eliminating falsehoods in the service of knowledge. This principle was carried on by d'Anville's son-in-law, the cartographer Philippe Buache (1700–1773), who became noted for his theoretical mapmaking (for example, his famous series of maps of the American Northwest, made in 1753 for the Diderot-d'Alembert *Encyclopédie*).

(continued on page 161)

PLATE 5.39 *The right hand sheet of* Théâtre de la guerre en Espagne et en Portugal *by Pieter Mortier, Amsterdam, c. 1710. An attractive map of the Iberian peninsula, which was included in the Sanson/Jaillot atlas dedicated to King Charles II of Spain in commemoration of the Spanish War of Succession.*

LE GRAND
TEATRE DE LA GUERRE
EN ITALIE
Dressé sur les Mémoires des plus Habiles Ingénieurs Suivant les Armées
Presenté à SON ALTESSE Serenissime
LE PRINCE EUGENE DE SAVOYE

LA VILLE DE CREMONE

MER DE GÊNES

MER MÉDITERRANÉE

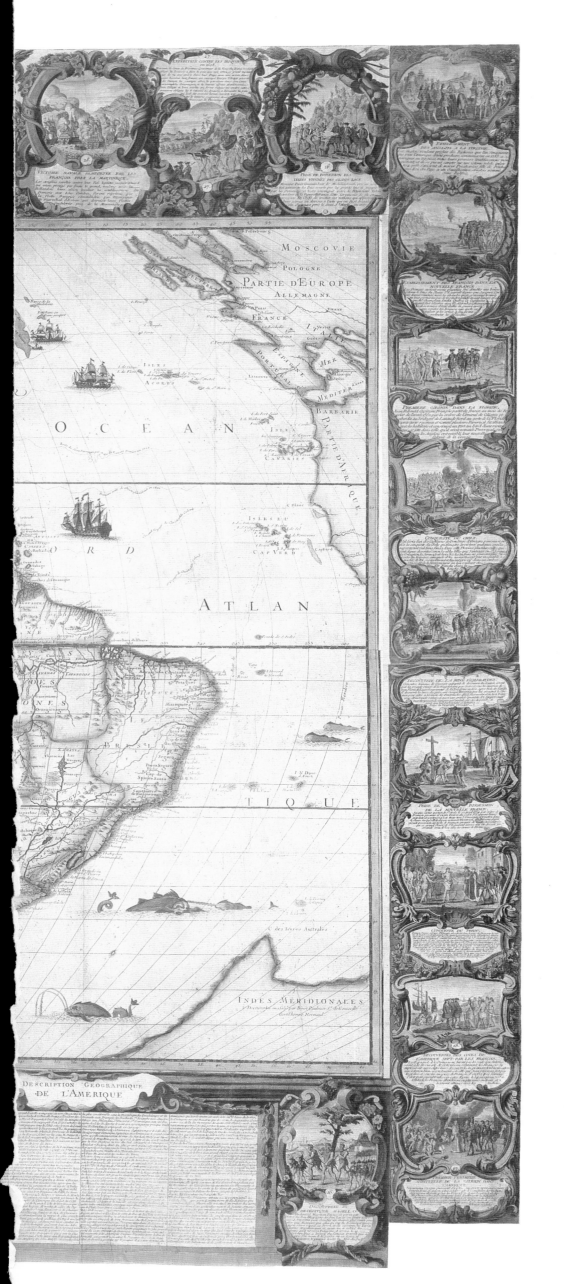

PLATE 5.40 *(far left)* Grand Théâtre de la guerre en Italie *by Pieter Mortier, Amsterdam, c. 1710. This is part of a large four-sheet map of the theatre of war in Savoy and Piedmont. Such maps could be sold separately as wall-maps or used in composite atlases. Note the rich colouring of the vignette.*

PLATE 5.41 *(left)* L'Amerique *by J.B. Nolin, c. 1720. This large French wall map measuring 137 × 121 cm (54 × 47.5 in.) would have originally hung on wooden bars. The map itself is surrounded by thirty decorative border scenes depicting various stages in the history of the Americas. The title cartouche includes a dedication to Louis XV. Wall maps were designed for both educational and decorative purposes during this period.*

PLATE 5.42 *(overleaf)* A general description of England and Ireland with ye costes adioyning *by Laurence Nowell, c. 1564. This is a small map depicting Shakespeare's homeland as it appeared to his contemporaries at around the time of his birth. It was a landmark in the history of the mapping of Britain, and once belonged to Queen Elizabeth I's favourite minister, Lord Burghley.*

A general description
of England & Ireland
with ye costes adioy-
ninge:

OC. GERMANICVS

Mare Gallicum

England, from Saxton to Green

Early English history was highlighted by important mapmaking achievements. The thirteenth-century Hereford *Mappamundi* was undoubtedly an early masterpiece of English mapmaking. The earliest separate maps of the British Isles, depicting an itinerary from Dover to London and to Newcastle, were also drawn in the thirteenth century and were attributed to Matthew Paris of St Albans. Another early extant map is the so-called 'Gough Map' drawn some time between 1350 and 1370, showing the main roads and the coastal outline of England with remarkable accuracy. (The map is now in the Bodleian Library, Oxford.) The eighteenth-century antiquarian Richard Gough (1735–1809) was led to comment that 'the greatest merit of this map is that it may justly boast itself the first among us wherein the roads and distances are laid down'. The

PLATE 5.43 *(left)*
Britania insula *by George Lily, Venice, 1562. This is the first map of the British Isles to be printed from a copperplate.*

PLATE 5.44 *(below)*
Map of Devonshire *by Christopher Saxton, 1575.* Saxton's Atlas of England and Wales *embodied the earliest systematic topographical survey of the two nations. It was not only the first English atlas in the modern sense of the word, but also the earliest uniform national atlas produced by any country. Saxton, who was born in Yorkshire, is known as the father of English cartography.*

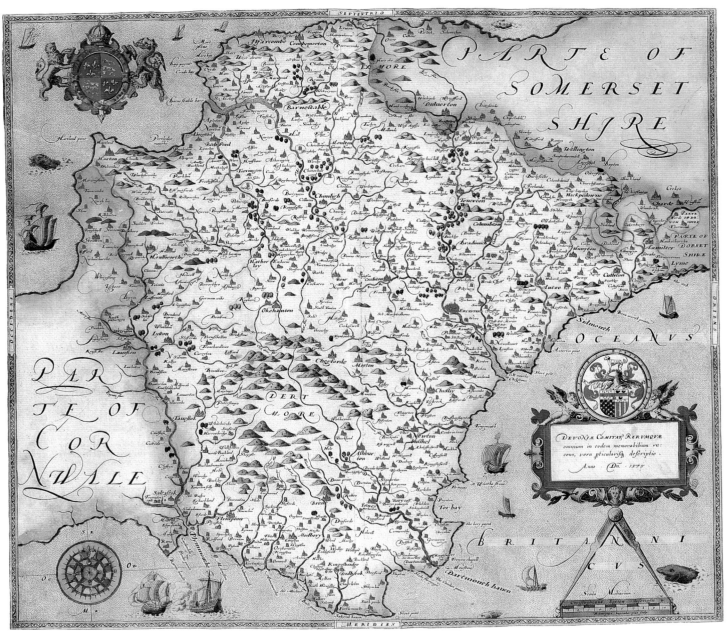

influence of the map continued to make its presence felt, even 200 years later, in the maps of Sebastian Münster and George Lily: the latter's *Britanniae insulae* was issued in 1546 (Plate 5.43) in Rome during Lily's exile there.

Christopher Saxton

The friend and correspondent of Gerard Mercator, Laurence Nowell, Dean of Lichfield, also made a manuscript map of the British Isles (Plate 5.42). In 1563, he wrote to his patron Sir William Cecil (later Lord Burghley), Secretary of State to Elizabeth I, complaining of the inaccuracy of general maps of England and proposing a design for constructing a series of maps of all the counties, and requesting the financial support and encouragement of Cecil. The proposal came to nought, but his friend Thomas Seckford secured the support of Cecil and the Privy Council for a survey of the counties of England and Wales, to be carried out by Christopher Saxton (*c*.1542–1611), the 'Father of English Cartography'. Such support was born of the need to secure the defence of the kingdom against enemies at home and abroad, and in 1575 the Privy Council ordered that Saxton be 'assisted in all places where he shall come for the view of mete places to describe certen counties in Cartes being thereunto appointed by her Mat^es bill under her Signet'. A further order was issued in 1576 for the survey of Wales, and Saxton was awarded grants of land and rents. It was also ordered that Cecil was to receive proofs of each map as it was engraved and printed.

Saxton's surveys were carried out in the remarkably short space of five years, between 1574 and 1579, resulting in some thirty-five maps (Plates 5.44, 5.45). The survey work would probably have begun in East Anglia, the south and southwest, carrying on through the Midlands to northern England, thence to Wales and the Marches. The privilege to print the maps was granted in 1577 for ten years, and the maps were issued in an atlas in 1579, together with a finely engraved frontispiece portrait of the sovereign, Elizabeth I. This atlas was the first national survey of England to be published in the British Isles.

At the time, English copper-plate engraving was still very much in its formative stages, and the technique was being learned by Englishmen from craftsmen from the Netherlands. Indeed, of the thirty-six plates in Saxton's atlas, fourteen were engraved by Flemish or Dutch craftsmen and eight by English engravers, all reflecting the style of design and lettering then prevalent across the

PLATE 5.45 Map of Cornwall *by Christopher Saxton, 1576. This was first published as a separate map and later incorporated into Saxton's famous* Atlas of England and Wales. *The copperplate was engraved by Lenaert Terwoot of Antwerp and its decoration is a particularly fine example of the ornate style of the Flemish school, with fish, flowers, birds, galleons and sea monsters. The Latin title is surmounted by the Tudor arms of Elizabeth I supported by the lion and the Wessex dragon, which symbolize her patronage of the atlas.*

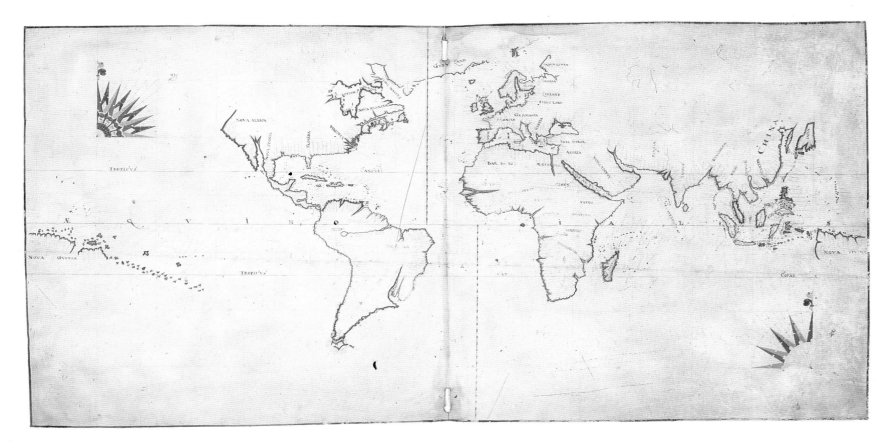

North Sea. The maps met with immediate acclaim from Saxton's contemporaries, being easy to read, uncrowded by superfluous detail and showing towns, parks and forests, and county boundaries, but not roads. They became a popular symbol of national unity. William Harrison wrote that one 'could see England set forth in several shires after the same manner as Ortelius hath dealt with other countries of the main, to the great benefit of our nation'; he went on to pronounce them 'to be perfect and exact'.[6]

Reprints of Saxton's maps followed, largely unaltered, for several years up to about 1600. The later printings included additional preliminary leaves and indices, as well as a revised frontispiece. Demand for maps during the English Civil War led to Saxton's maps being republished in 1645 by William Web, with the heraldry suitably altered or deleted. Web's edition is now rare. Subsequent editions followed around 1683 and 1689, by the London printer and bookseller Philip Lea. The latter showed roads added after a survey of the post- and crossroads of England and Wales by John Ogilby in the 1670s. Other editions followed around 1720, 1749 and 1770, by which time the plates were so worn, or had been so extensively retouched and recut, that they were barely recognizable as Saxton's maps.

In 1583, Saxton constructed a large wall-map of England and Wales, engraved and printed on twenty sheets, at the expense of his patron Thomas Seckford. This map, like the county maps, was reprinted many times and in several different formats, both as a large wall-map and as a small pocket road atlas. Examples were still being sold, heavily 'corrected', as late as 1795.

John Norden

Saxton was followed by other surveyors and mapmakers, all hoping for patronage and financial support for surveys of county maps. The project of John Norden (1548–1625), estate surveyor and lawyer, met with little success. Norden worked for years on a scheme (or 'chorography', in other words, a regional geography) to describe the counties of England, illustrated with maps, in a form suitable for the traveller. The work was intended to make good deficiencies Norden had found both in Saxton's maps and in the text of Camden's *Britannia* (published, unillustrated, in 1585). At first, Norden received support from William Cecil and the Privy Council, but he was unable to continue his project owing to lack of funds. Only a few of the small *quarto* volumes (or chorographical descriptions) projected were published, under the general title *Speculum Britanniae*: Middlesex in 1593 (reprinted in 1723); Herefordshire in 1598 (reprinted in 1723 also); Cornwall remained in manuscript and was printed only in 1728 without maps; Essex also remained in

PLATE 5.46 *An untitled world map on a Mercator-type projection, drawn on vellum, England, c. 1615–1618. The so-called Northumberland world map is a rare example of an English chart from the Jacobean period which may have been drawn by, or inspired by, the mathematician Edward Wright (c. 1558–1615).*

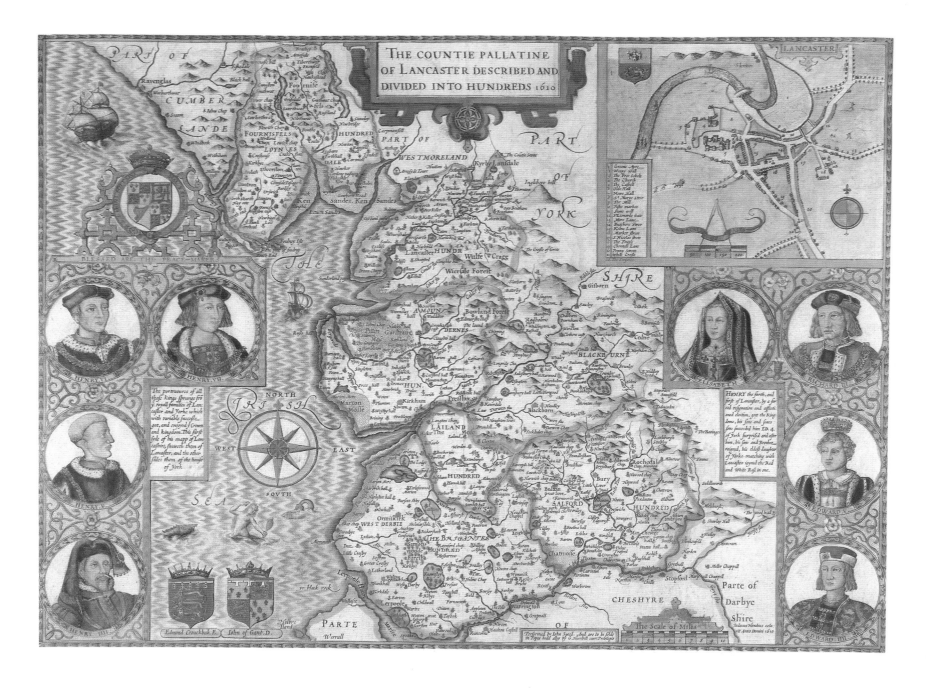

PLATE 5.47 The Countie Pallatine of Lancaster described *by John Speed, copper engraving, London, 1611 and later. This beautiful and decorative map of Lancashire is taken from Speed's famous atlas* Theatre of the Empire of Great Britaine.

PLATE 5.48 *(opposite)* Cambridgeshire *by John Speed, London, 1611 and later. This is another map from Speed's* Theatre of the Empire of Great Britaine.

manuscript and was printed only in 1840. Norden left other unfinished maps and surveys when he died in 1625.

An important innovation for English mapmaking was Norden's introduction of a map reference grid and keys to the symbols used. These features were not new among certain European mapmakers, but they were introduced by Norden as practical aids to the map user. The careful manner in which he carried out his surveys ensured that some of his maps and manuscripts remained authoritative for a century afterwards.

John Speed

Mention the subject of English county maps to collectors, and the name of John Speed will almost certainly come to mind. Speed (1552–1629), antiquary and tailor, is justly celebrated for his *Theatre of the Empire of Great Britaine* which was first published in 1611–1612 (note here the use of

the word 'theatre', following Ortelius once again, in the title). The work was intended to accompany a history of the British Isles, for which Speed began collecting materials during the mid-1590s. It was the first printed atlas of the British Isles, and was divided into separate books for England, Wales, Scotland and Ireland (Plates 5.47, 5.48).

The *Theatre* dominated the seventeenth-century map market in England, going through many reprints and additions. Foreign maps were added in 1627–1631, and it was augmented in 1676 with additional foreign maps. It also formed the basis of Dutch atlases containing British county maps, such as those of Blaeu and Janssonius in the 1640s and later. Speed's maps were still being reprinted during the eighteenth century, by which time, like those of Saxton, they must have had mere curiosity value. Speed based his maps, for the most part, on those of Saxton or Norden, frankly admitting that 'I have put my sickle into

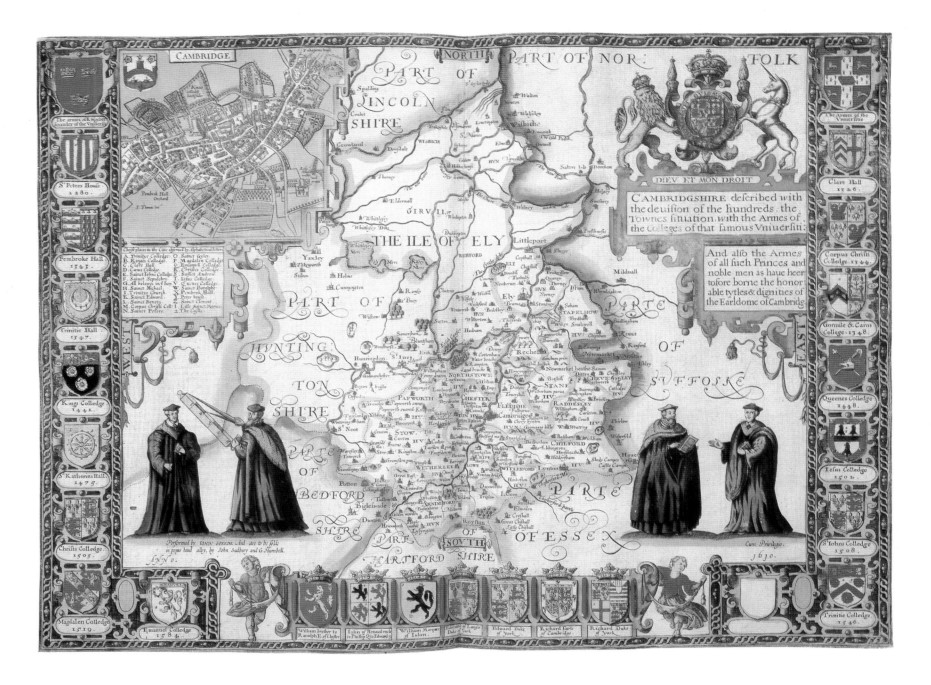

other mens corne'. An important innovation in Speed's maps was the inclusion of inset town plans (Plates 5.47, 5.48). Speed compiled more than seventy plans of 'cities and shiretowns', the greater part of which were based, very probably, on first-hand observation.

Speed is not recorded as having sought the patronage or financial support of a private bene-factor; instead, the atlas represented the consider-able investment of the partnership of John Sud-bury and George Humble of London. The atlas proved to be a commercial success, and was produced in large quantities, if the number of copies which appear on the market even now is any judge. The plates were engraved for the most part by Jodocus Hondius of Amsterdam, the work commencing in about 1605:

Both Speed and his publishers must have felt that so substantial a task called for the experience and indust-

rial organization of a Dutch firm, and the maps for *Theatre* without doubt owe their success to Hondius's skill in the invention of picturesque decorative detail and in framing a coherent design from the heter-ogeneous drafts furnished by Speed.[7]

These decorative features included portraits, costume designs, vignettes of buildings, pictures of coins and antiquities, and heraldry – all the things, in fact, which would have interested the acquisitive mind of the antiquary.

Some editions of Speed's atlas were published between 1611–1612 and 1676. In 1627, Speed's publishers added a foreign supplement, the first of its kind published in England. It was entitled *A Prospect of the most Famous Parts of the World* and was reprinted several times with the *Theatre* to 1676 (Plates 5.50, 5.51). Speed's publishers issued the so-called 'miniature Speed' pocket atlas which in reality had nothing to do with Speed at

PLATE 5.49 *(overleaf)* Britain as it was devided in the tyme of the Englishe–Saxons especially during their Heptarchy *by John Speed, engraved by Jodocus Hondius, London, 1611–1612. From Speed's* Theatre of the Empire of Great Britaine. *The vignettes on the left depict the aspiring Saxon kings and the ones on the right show the conversion of the Saxon kings to Christianity.*

BRITAIN
As it was devided
in the tyme of the Englishe
Saxons especially during
their Heptarchy

POTENS · TERRA · ARMIS · ANIMOSIVINI

Performed by Iohn Speede & are
to be sold by Iohn Sudbury & Georg
Humble in Popes head alley at London

THE GER

MAYN

SEA

THE BRITISH OCEAN

THE PICTES WAL

BERNICIA

Deira

KINGDOME OF

Cleve Land

THE KINGDOME OF

MERCIA

EAST ANGLES KINGDOM

EAST SAXONS KING

DOME

London

KINGDOME OF

KENT

KINGDOME OF SOUTH SAXONS

Wight I.

GALLIA

ETHELBERT

ANNO 595

SEBERT

ANNO 604

ERPEN WALD

ANNO 624

EDWIN

ANNO 627

KENGILS

ANNO 635

PEADA

ANNO 650

ETHEL WOLFE

ANNO 662

KENT

EAST SAXON

EAST ANGLE

NORTH UMBER LAND

WEST SAXON

MERCIA

SOUTH SAXON

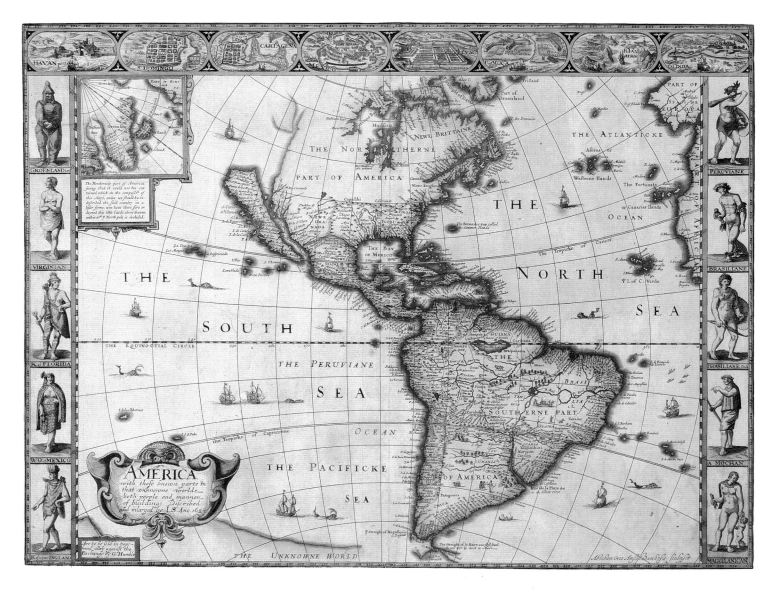

PLATE 5.50 (above)
America by John Speed,
engraved by Abraham Goos
and published by George
Humble, London, 1626.
This map was issued in
editions of Speed's Prospect
atlas from 1627 onwards.
California appears as an
island and the mythical
islands of Frisland and
Brasil are still to be found
in the North Sea.

PLATE 5.51 (right) The
kingdome of China by
John Speed, from his
Prospect atlas, 1627 and
later.

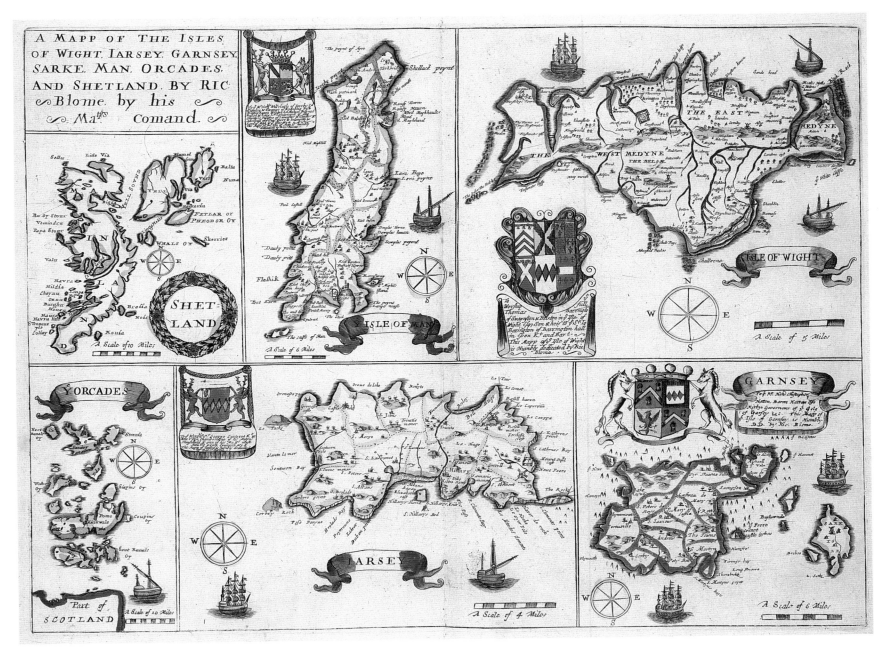

all. The atlas was based on a series of miniature maps issued by the Dutch mapmaker Pieter van den Keere (1571–1646), and was intended to capitalize on the success of Speed's folio atlas. It was called *England Wales Scotland and Ireland described and abridgd*, adding as a commercial catch-all the wording 'from a farr larger volume done by John Speed'. Foreign maps, reduced from Speed's *Prospect*, were added in 1646.

Other seventeenth-century English maps

In parallel with the Speed atlas, Dutch publishers added maps of the British counties and regions to their own atlases throughout the seventeenth century, all of which were adapted from Speed's maps. Also, throughout the seventeenth century, publishers reissued William Camden's *Britannia*, with sets of county maps inserted as illustrations. The best of these were the maps engraved by William Kip (who died in 1635) for the 1607

Latin-text edition; these were reprinted in 1610 and 1637 with the text translated into English. Later in the century, Robert Morden produced a series of maps to illustrate Edmund Gibson's translation and revision of Camden's work. These maps appeared in 1695, and were among the earliest English county maps to show roads. They were taken from John Ogilby's survey, published in 1675 as *Britannia*, which contained road maps designed in strip form on a uniform scale of one inch to one mile.

John Ogilby (1600–1676), geographer, historian and 'Master of the King's Revels', was responsible for a series of fine descriptive volumes, illustrated with maps and engravings, which were intended to describe the whole world. These were, for the most part, English translations of the works of Montanus, and covered Africa, America, China and Japan, with materials added from English sources (Plate 5.53).

PLATE 5.52 A Mapp of the Isles of Wight, Iarsey, Garnsey, Sarke, Man, Oraces and Shetland *by Richard Blome, c. 1683. Blome was a heraldic writer and cartographer working during the second half of the seventeenth century. He copied his maps from the work of others, but made no attempt to hide his sources. One of his best known works was the* Britannia, *based on maps by John Speed.*

PLATE 5.53 *(right)* Nova
Virginia tabula *by John
Ogilby, 1671–1672. This
general map of Virginia, a
careful reduction of John
Smith's landmark map of
Virginia, made in 1612,
appeared in both Arnold
Montanus's* Nieuwe en
Onbekende Weereld *and
in John Ogilby's* America.
*John Ogilby was an
Englishman who had a
variety of careers before
becoming a surveyor and
cartographer late in life.*

An abortive project for another English world atlas, in twelve volumes, by Moses Pitt (who died in 1696) failed after four volumes had been published in 1680–1683. This atlas was almost entirely compiled from old plates acquired from the plate stock of Joannes Janssonius. Pitt worked in partnership with Janssonius's heirs and Stevin Swart, giving a reprise to many of the plates which Janssonius had acquired over the years, some of them going back as far as the stocks that were used for Mercator's *Atlas*.

A growing dissatisfaction

In England during the early years of the eighteenth century mapmaking had fallen into a dire state of affairs. Certainly, there were several competent mapmakers active at this time: Robert Morden (fl. 1669–1703), best known for his issues of William Camden's *Britannia* with its maps of the English counties; John Senex (fl. 1702–1740) whose *New General Atlas* was published in 1721, containing well-crafted maps of the known world; and Herman Moll (fl. c.1678–1732), a prolific *emigré* mapmaker whose output included several atlases, both general and regional, as well as many maps specifically for collections of travels and voyages (Plate 5.54).

But in British mapmaking in general there was little in the way of innovation or improvement, and 'cartographers were failing dismally to keep pace with the requirements of students and readers'.[8] At the same time interest in the outside world was steadily increasing. Large numbers of collections of travel accounts were being produced in London. Many of these were either abridgements or English translations of earlier Dutch, French or German writers and travellers, with occasionally a translation of Arab accounts of the Levant and beyond. Although the great dependence on the output of the Amsterdam publishers, in particular for sea charts and maps of distant countries, was by now greatly declining, many British mapmakers had little to offer the interested public. They contented themselves with merely reissuing maps from plate stocks bought in from earlier practitioners in the trade in Britain and abroad. The best examples of this practice are the continuing reissues of the old Christopher Saxton plates of the 1570s, which were still being printed off in the middle years of the eighteenth century;

the same applies to the maps of John Speed. Such products can only have had a certain curiosity value, perhaps in the same way that publishers were still printing versions of the maps used to illustrate Ptolemy's *Geography*.

John Green, the pseudonym of the Irish-born mapmaker Braddock Mead (c.1668–1757) himself commented: 'For want of encouragement, chart as well as mapmaking, is fallen into the hands of the engravers, whose Skill consists in supplying the print-sellers with their productions in the most expeditious manner and at the lowest rates'.[9] Great progress had already been made in France by the Sansons, father and son, by d'Anville and by Guillaume de l'Isle; and in England John Green was to pave the way for further much-needed reforms in cartography.

Early cartographic reforms

As is often the case with scientific advances, the way to progress was seen on the horizon long before the difficulties underfoot were cleared away. For example, owing to the problems of accurately determining the longitude and latitude of certain places and physical features, it was becoming increasingly difficult to reconcile the often conflicting reports of travellers and navigators, and to correlate their routes and itineraries. In some countries, a town or city may have had three or four quite different names, or an island may have been known by different names according to the nationality of the voyager who was describing it – to say nothing of the difficulties which European travellers often experienced in rendering non-European place-names.

The new methods of John Green

G.R. Crone notes that the early eighteenth-century attitude towards the then prevailing state of mapmaking was well illustrated in an anonymous work published in 1717 entitled *The Construction of Maps and Globes*. (It was attributed to 'a certain Mead', perhaps alluding to John Green's real name, Braddock Mead.) In the work there is an appendix, 'being a seasonable Enquiry into Maps, Books of Geography and Travel. Intermix'd with some necessary Cautions, Helps and Directions for future Map-makers, Geographers, and Travellers'. The author of the work claims that 'The Atlases of negligent and unskilful

PLATE 5.54 (*opposite bottom*) North America *by Herman Moll, London, 1720 and later. In 1718 the Frenchman Guillaume de l'Isle had published his* Carte de la Louisiane, *which showed French claims encompassing the whole of trans-Appalachian North America. Here, Herman Moll presents his counterblast by reducing French Louisiana to south of the Ohio river and pressing English claims in Canada by labelling Labrador as New Britain. Moll was a Dutch engraver who came to London in the late seventeenth century.*

Geographers, had long since made something of this kind necessary, in order to put a stop to those spurious Maps and incorrect Books which were daily published by them, and continu'd more and more to involve Geography in Error and Contempt.'

The author further complains that mapmakers never credit their sources or authorities for any improvements or alterations incorporated into their works; that they neglect charts, or 'Wagoners', in delineating coastlines; that they generally omit roads ('What can a Man learn from a multitude of Places, confusedly scatter'd? Like a Traveller in a Pathless Wood, he is at a loss which way to guide himself'); that towns are commonly misplaced, and that unsuitable projections and various initial meridians are employed.

Aware that the reason for the low state of cartography also rested in part with the traveller, the author's advice to him is comprehensive: he should: (1) provide himself with a 'true going

Watch' and note the differences of time at the places he passes through ('No Travellers as yet has been so curious as this comes to'); (2) collect all details of the route from a member of his company; (3) check the various estimates of the length of the stages 'by the Rate he travels at'; (4) observe 'with a Compass, as near he can, the Course he travels, or the Bearings of Places one from another'; (5) enquire into all the rivers he crosses; (6) make drawings of towns, ruins, and 'all other Curiosities of Art and Nature'; (7) 'He should, above all things, take the Latitude of Places. How easie wou'd it be for a Traveller, ever and anon, to make an Observation with an Instrument, which he might carry in his Pocket, that wou'd take the Latitude within ten Minutes at most'; (8) 'He shou'd draw a Map of his Travels, if he can conveniently, on the Spot; for who so fit to do it as the Traveller himself?'; (9) while residing at the metropolis of any foreign kingdom, 'he shou'd consult the Geographers and their Maps, if they have any'; (10) and finally 'let him observe the Eclipses of the Moon and Planets, particularly of *Jupiter*, by his Satellites, as often as he has an Opportunity'.[10]

Geographers were often accused of giving faulty descriptions of countries because of their uncritical approach to their sources. Area dimensions were quoted from old texts which had themselves been derived from antiquated maps, without checking whether or not these accounts had been based on actual observation. Classical texts were often quoted from extracts or abridgements rather than from the original works. Little attempt was made to reconcile place-names found in such old sources, and there was rarely any evidence that any attempt had been made to co-ordinate between such texts and the maps that were chosen to illustrate them.

Crone notes further that John Green's cartographical output was to be summarised thus:

(1) The distinguishing on the map of places the position of which had been astronomically determined ('A line drawn under the Name of a place denotes the latitude being observed and two lines both the Lat[itude] and Longitude'). Green insists that this method was his own . . . (2) The provision of a table of authorities on each map, so that some idea of its reliability might be formed. This he carried out consistently. (3) The provision of an explanatory table

of geographical terms occurring on the maps of foreign countries.[11]

In such a manner, Green lamented the poor state into which the science and practice of mapmaking had fallen into the hands of engravers and others who copied each other's work without discrimination; those 'ignorant or mercenary Hands', who happened to come into the fortunate possession of original materials, jealously concealed the fact from their rivals. He attributed this to the 'little Esteem, or rather great Contempt, that Maps are [held] in here'. During his active career, he did much to rectify this situation himself, especially during the years that he was employed by Thomas Jefferys in London. Both men were disciples of the meticulous methods of the great French mapmaker Jean d'Anville.

Geographical names

For his day, Green had a remarkably advanced view on the collation of information and the correct presentation of it on maps or in travel books. He was in a sense anticipating the work of the present-day Permanent Committee on Geographical Names. A particular instance is his striving for the correct English rendering of foreign place-names. His translation and editing of the text to the encyclopaedic *Description géographique, historique, chronologique, politique, et physique de l'empire de la Chine et de la Tartarie chinoise*, compiled by the French Jesuit Jean-Baptiste du Halde and published in four folio volumes in 1735, is a case in point. In his translation Green introduced a conventional alphabet for rendering names into acceptable English forms, giving a Chinese syllabary in English, Portuguese and French transcriptions. His translation appeared in two volumes, published in 1738–1731, under the title *A Description of the Empire of China and Chinese Tartary . . . with Notes Geographical, Historical, and Critical, and other Improvements, particularly in the Maps*. These maps included redrawings of some of d'Anville's maps with several place-names inserted – omitted from the French versions – while others were subjected to a critical examination.

In general, Green's work demonstrated an admiration for d'Anville's work. Nevertheless, he did on occasion engage in controversy with his

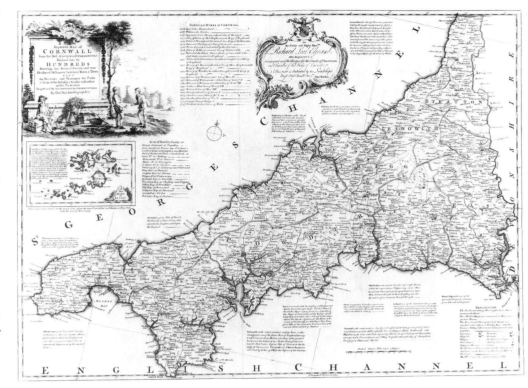

French colleagues, but he was appreciative of the work being done in France, keeping in touch with progress there. He approved of the establishment of the French Dépôt de la Marine, complaining that a similar body had not been established in Britain to improve the lamentable state of nautical chartmaking in his own country. Green made known his complaints in the introductory text to a collection of voyages and travels issued by Thomas Astley, the *New General Collection of Voyages and Travels* (1745–1747).

In truth, he [Green] was somewhat in advance of his times: the public demand was for narratives of exploration and adventure, not for minutely critical dissertations on Chinese geography, the identity of obscure Eastern cities, or the correct rendering of foreign place names. These circumstances account for the relatively small success which attended his efforts . . . It must also be remembered that Green's work was done just before the great general improvement in the technique of astronomical observation, particularly in the determination of longitude, which made possible, for example, the highly accurate surveys of Capt. James Cook, so that his services to cartography were naturally soon forgotten when there was no lack of accurate material at the disposal of cartographers. Nevertheless, Green deserves to be remembered for breaking away from the old unreformed cartography, and for perceiving clearly, and following as far as existing data permitted, the methods upon which modern cartography was to be established.[12]

PLATE 5.56 A New Improved Map of Cornwall *from* The Large English Atlas *by Emanuel Bowen and Thomas Kitchin, copper engraving, 1750 and later. The most impressive atlas map of the county made in the eighteenth century.*

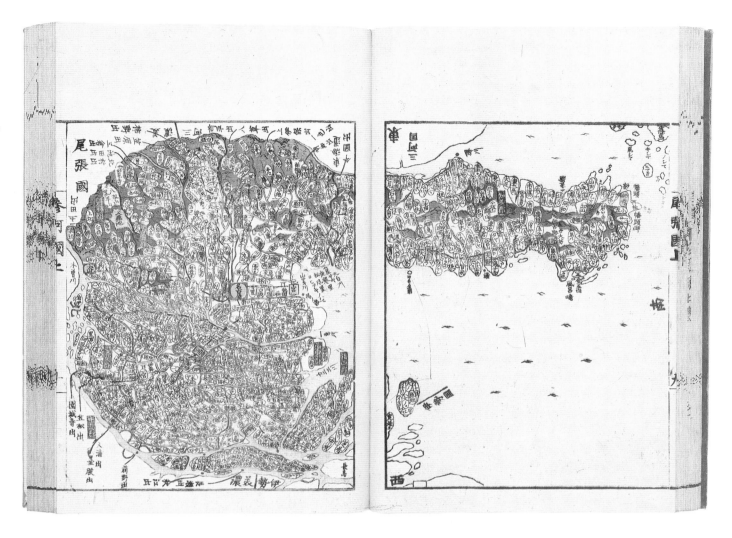

Japan

European maps greatly influenced Japanese cartography in the early seventeenth century. From an early stage, Japan used sophisticated methods of surveying. The first topographical surveys of the country were made in 1605 and some of the later surveys, from the early nineteenth century, are still in use today. However, from 1643 onwards, the Japanese government imposed a policy of deliberate isolation, effectively writing off Japan from all other countries. No one was allowed to leave the country, and the building of large ships was also prohibited. This naturally had the effect of halting progress on existing maps of foreign lands and seas. The ban was eventually lifted in the late eighteenth century but, in the meantime, the Japanese mapmakers poured their talents into producing maps of their own country. Some of these were outstandingly attractive works such as those by Ishikawa Toshiyaki, who made some exquisite maps and town plans around the start of the eighteenth century. Nagakubo Genshu was known for his map of all Japan. He is also accredited as the first Japanese to incorporate the use of parallels and meridians into his work.

The first printed maps of the country, made from woodcuts, appeared in the seventeenth century. Early examples of these fairly unusual works are still collected by map enthusiasts today.

China

From the sixteenth to the eighteenth centuries, Chinese cartography was influenced by developments in Europe. The most important maps of the time were produced by Jesuits in China.

Father Matteo Ricci (1552–1610), who arrived at Macao in 1583, was the first Jesuit to enter China. No other person from the West has had such an influence upon that country. Ricci was the first to introduce western science into China and the first to penetrate Peking. He is known to have compiled three world maps, the first of which, made some time during 1584 as a Chinese version of a European map, has not survived. Ricci's second map was made in 1600 and again no copies have survived. His third map, published in 1602, was designed to fit a large folding screen, measuring some 3.65 by 1.82 metres, comprising six panels, and five examples are known to have survived (Plate 5.60). In an almost apologetic note on the map Ricci stated: 'I should have made a globe, but because it was an inconvenient form for a map I was obliged to convert the sphere into two dimensions and turn circles into lines'. The map itself was made on an oval projection which follows broadly that given by Abraham Ortelius in his 1570 *Theatrum orbis terrarum* world map, with the important distinction that Ricci places China near the centre of his map.

One of the most celebrated of all eighteenth-century works on China, *Description géographique, historique, chronologique, politique, et physique de l'empire de la Chine et de la tartarie chinoise*, by Jean-Baptiste du Halde, with maps based on Jesuit surveys, is discussed in detail on page 154.

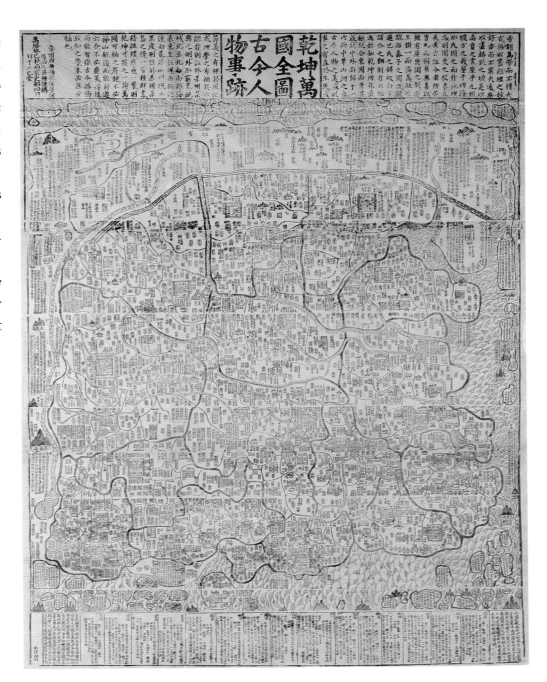

References

1. A.E. Nordenskiöld, *Facsimile Atlas to the Early History of Cartography*, Stockholm, 1889.

2. D. Woodward, *The Maps and Prints of Paolo Forlani: A Descriptive Bibliography*, 1990.

3. R.A. Skelton, *Decorative Printed Maps*, page 67; see also H.G. Fordham, *Studies in Carto-Bibliography*, pages 128–166, 1914.

4. R.A. Skelton, *op. cit.*, page 67.

5. G.R. Crone, 'John Green. Notes On A Neglected Eighteenth Century Geographer And Cartographer'. In *Imago Mundi* VI, page 89, 1949.

6. William Harrison, *Description of England*, 1577.

7. R.A. Skelton, *op. cit.*, page 54.

8. G.R. Crone, *op. cit.*, page 86.

9. G.R. Crone, *op cit*.

10. G.R. Crone, *op. cit.*, page 86.

11. G.R. Crone, *op cit*, page 87.

12. G.R. Crone, *op cit*, pages 87–88.

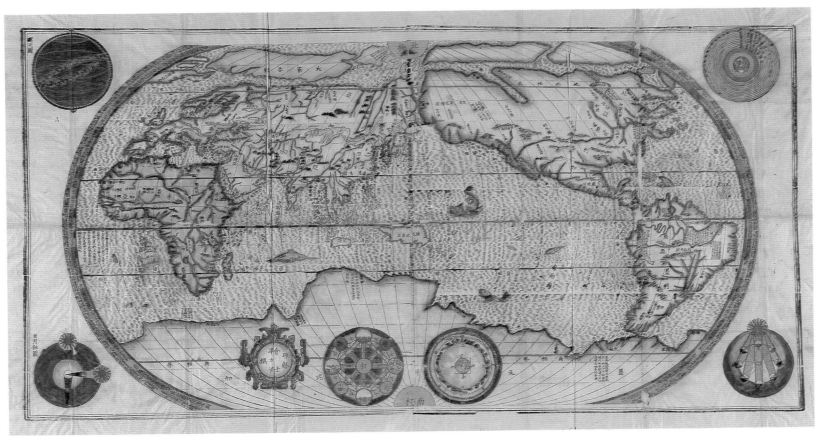

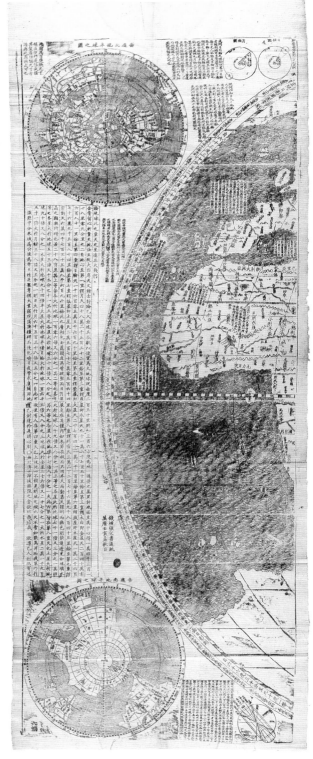
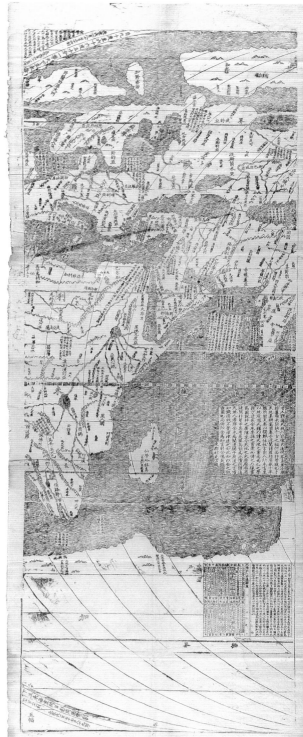
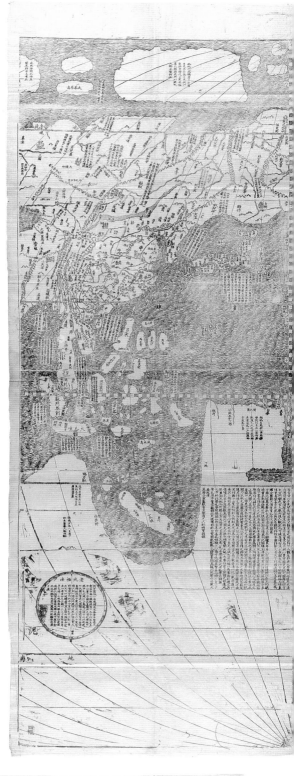

PLATE 5.61 *(right) Map of the Middle Kingdom [Zhongguo Tu] by Michal Piotr Boym SJ, (a Polish Jesuit working in China), manuscript on paper, Rome, c. 1652. A rare surviving example of a Jesuit manuscript map, brought back to Europe for the purpose of disseminating information to the West.*

PLATE 5.62 *(far right) An anonymous Chinese map of Guangzhou (Canton) province, woodblock on native paper, c. 1739. This unique example shows internal administrative divisions and distances.*

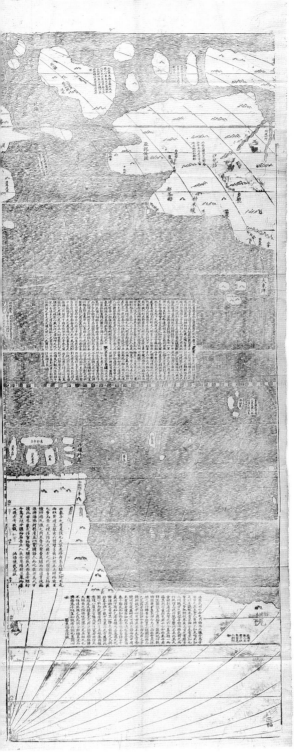

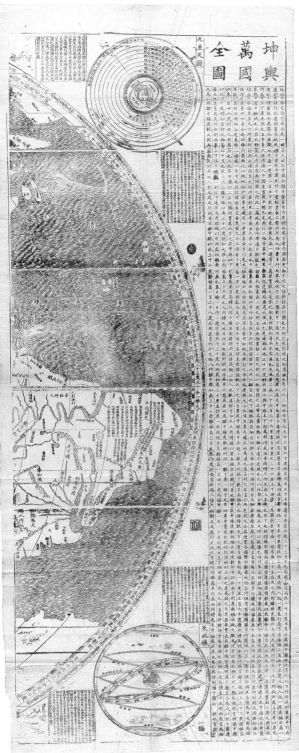

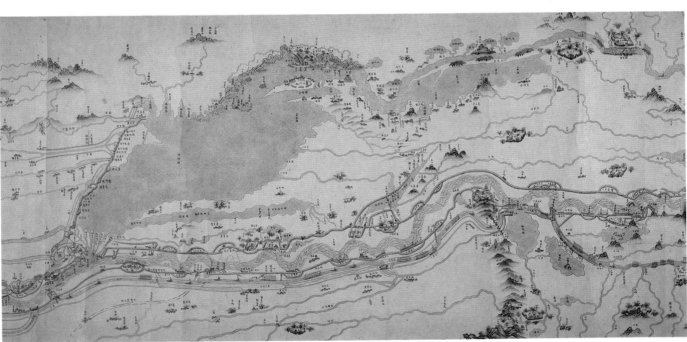

PLATE 5.63 *(left) Part of a scroll map of the Grand Canal in eastern central China dating from the late eighteenth or early nineteenth century. This section shows Jiangsu province, north of Nanjing. The canal, which was begun in the fourth century BC and extended in the thirteenth century AD, is more than 1170 kilometres in length.*

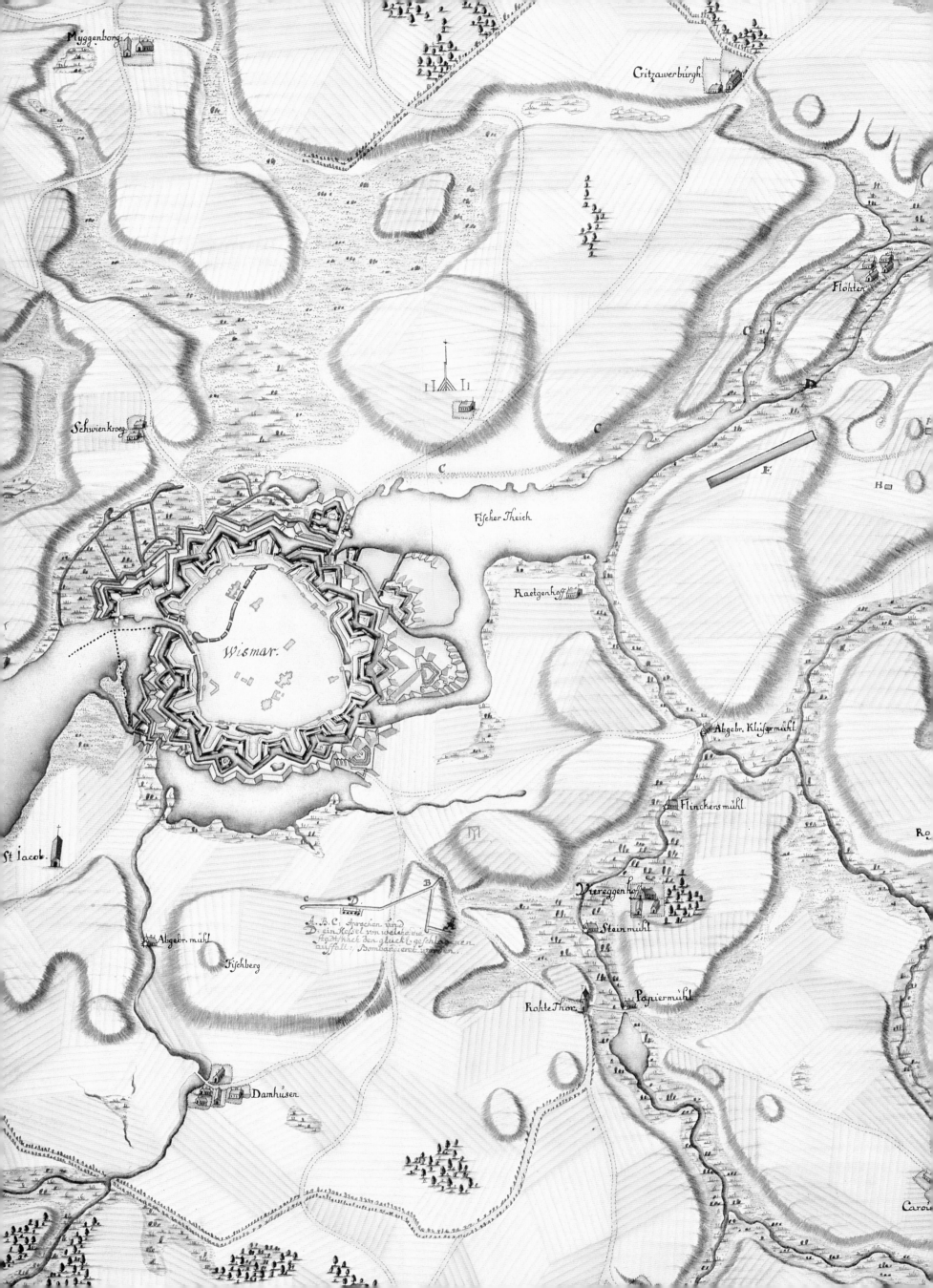

Myggenborg

Critzawerburgh

Flöhten

Schwienkroeg

Fischer Theich

C

C

E

H

Raetgenhoff

Wismar.

Abgebr. Klistermühl

Flinchersmühl

St. Iacob.

B

Rogeggenhoff

C   D

A. B. C. Sprechen und
D. ein Kessel von welchen die
Stadt nach den glücklich geschlagenen
aufsoll, Bombardieret werden.

Steinmühl

Abgebr. mühl

Fischberg

Papiermühl

Rohte Thor

Damhüsen

Carou

CHAPTER VI

THE REFORM OF CARTOGRAPHY

1700 – 1850 AD

THE SCIENTIFIC CLIMATE of the eighteenth century stimulated change in a number of fields, including cartography which underwent quite radical reform. The advances in mathematics and astronomy formulated by Sir Isaac Newton (1642–1727) came to fruition. The motions of the planets and other heavenly bodies were calculated and marked out so that predictions could be set out accurately for long periods ahead. With the aid of lunar tables, the method of determining longitude to within one degree of accuracy was perfected according to formulae described by Newton. Improvements in the instruments used to carry out such work contributed greatly to such achievements of accuracy. The mathematician, astronomer and instrument maker John Hadley (1682–1744) brought out an improved version of the quadrant which used reflecting mirrors, and accurate readings were obtained by the use of the vernier scale. Jesse Ramsden (1735–1800) perfected his Great Theodolite (Plate 6.7), a surveying instrument for measuring horizontal and vertical angles. As a result of the introduction of these new precision instruments cartographers were now able to carry out accurate triangular surveys.

PLATE 6.1 *Detail from* Plan von die Situation und Vestung Wismar *by Heinrich von Scheele, manuscript in inks and colours, c. 1712. Note how the skilful use of watercolours can give a strong relief effect to the mapping of river valleys and uplands.*

The nearly perfect clock

At the start of the eighteenth century, work was urgently being carried out to develop a sea-going timepiece. Early clocks, broadly speaking, were of two kinds: large, non-portable timepieces driven by a falling weight, and smaller, portable instruments such as table clocks and watches, driven by a coiled spring.

Robert Hooke (1635–1703), astronomer, mathematician and experimenter, had developed an interest in portable timepieces for use at sea in the late seventeenth century. After considerable labour and research, Hooke produced a report in which he professed disillusionment at the prospect of ever designing such an instrument. He wrote:

All I could obtain was a Catalogue of Difficulties, *first* in the doing of it, *secondly* in the bringing of it into publick use, *thirdly*, in making advantage of it. Difficulties were proposed from the alteration of *Climates, Airs, heats* and *colds*, temperature of *Springs*, the nature of *Vibrations*, the wearing of Materials, the

motion of the Ship, and divers others . . . it would be difficult to bring [such a timepiece] to use, for Sea-men know their way already to any Port.

He also noted that 'No King or State would pay a farthing' as a reward for anyone finding the best means to determine longitude.[1] In 1664, Hooke delivered a lecture to the Royal Society on the application of springs to the balance of a watch in order to render the movement more even, expressing his idea, simply, as *Ut tensio, sic vis* (As is tension, so is force). This principle was later taken up in Hooke's law (beloved by generations of schoolchildren) in which he announced in 1678 that the force exerted by a spring is directly proportional to the extent to which it is tensioned.

The first timepiece developed specifically for use on board ship was made by the Dutch mathematician, astronomer and physicist Christiaan Huyghens (1629–1695) in 1656 (Plate 6.2). In Huyghens' timepiece, the escapement was governed by a pendulum instead of a spring balance. But, unless it was used in a flat calm, the device was useless, for when it was tossed around in rough weather – the norm rather than the exception in Dutch waters – it ran unevenly or gave up altogether. As Brown observed, however:

. . . by 1715 every physical principal and mechanical part that would have to be incorporated in an accurate timekeeper was understood by watchmakers. All that remained was to bridge the gap between a good clock and one that was nearly perfect. It was that half degree of longitude, that two minutes of time, which meant the difference between conquest and failure, the difference between £20,000 and just another timekeeper.[2]

John Harrison's great achievement

The quest for the 'nearly perfect' clock was the life work of John Harrison (1693–1776), the Yorkshire-born clockmaker, mathematician and instrument maker (Plate 6.3). Harrison interested himself in the mechanisms of clocks and watches from an early age, completing his first 'regulator', or grandfather clock, in 1715 when he was aged twenty-two. It incorporated an improved pendulum-controlled movement which, over a period of fourteen years, neither gained nor lost more than a second. In 1714, Parliament published notice of a reward of £20,000 'to such

PLATE 6.2 *The pendulum clock invented by Christiaan Huyghens (1629–1695), a Dutch mathematician, in 1656. Huyghens's clock was the first accurate timepiece designed specifically for use on board ship. However, as it was a pendulum instrument, as the section shows, unless it was used on a flat calm ocean, it proved virtually useless.*

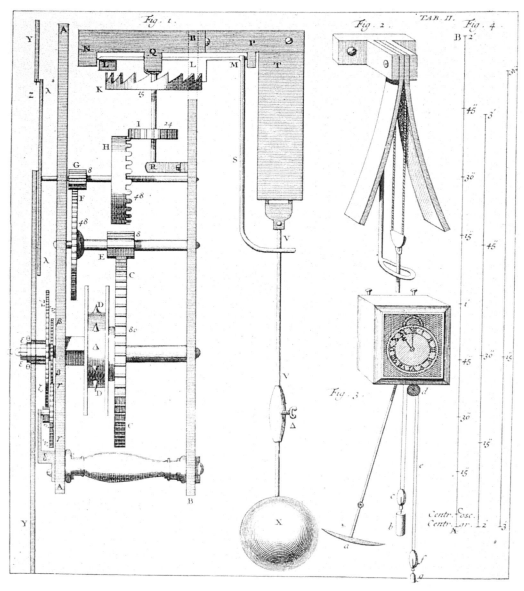

noted that 'Mr. John Harrison produced a new invented machine, in the nature of clockwork, whereby he proposes to keep time at sea with more exactness than by any other instrument or method hitherto contrived . . .', noting also that Harrison proposed to construct a second, smaller, improved and less cumbersome clock, voting him £500 to help defray his expenses. In fact 'Number Two', finished in 1739, turned out to be heavier than the first clock and Harrison decided to test it himself, under extreme conditions. It never went to sea because by the time it was ready, England found itself at war once more with Spain; certainly the Admiralty had no desire to present the Spanish *real armada* with any opportunity to seize the instrument as war booty in the event of capture.

Early in 1741, Harrison announced to the Board that he had commenced work on a third clock, far superior to 'Number One' and 'Number Two'. He was awarded a further £500 by the Board towards his expenses. Despite his initial optimism that he could have the new clock ready

PLATE 6.3 *(left) A portrait of John Harrison (1693–1776) who devoted much of his working life to the quest for the 'nearly perfect clock'. At his elbow can be seen his 'Number Four' timepiece of 1759 which won him the parliamentary prize of £20,000 for solving the problem of longitude at sea. (From* The Gallery of Portraits, *Volume V, London, 1835.)*

PLATE 6.4 *(below) The beautiful 'Number Four' chronometer made by John Harrison in 1759, which solved the problem of determining longitude at sea. The timepiece was spring-driven and measured 127 mm across.*

person or persons as shall discover the Longitude', but it was not until 1728 that Harrison went to London with drawings of the marine clock that he hoped to construct, seeking financial support from the Board of Longitude. On the advice of the Astronomer Royal, Dr Edmond Halley (1656–1742), he discussed his ideas with the horologist George Graham, who offered to loan Harrison the funds to build his clock. The labour occupied him for some seven years, his 'Number One', as he named the clock, being completed in 1735. The device weighed some seventy-two pounds and was worked by two balances connected by wires running over brass arcs so that their motions were opposed. Any effect on one caused by the motion of a ship at sea would therefore be counteracted by the other. 'Number One' was examined by members of the Royal Society, who awarded it a certificate stating that the clock promised a degree of accuracy sufficient to meet the conditions laid down by the Parliamentary reward offer.

A trial at sea was arranged in 1736, Harrison sailing to Lisbon on board HMS *Centurion*. Trials proved successful, showing the conventional navigation methods of the ship's master to be out by more than one degree at the Lizard on the return voyage in comparison with Harrison's computations with his device which gave a one-degree or twenty-six-mile margin of error. In 1737, the minutes of the Board of Longitude

for sea trials in two years, Harrison suffered delays and difficulties in the perfection of anti-friction devices in the balances, so that when 'Number Three' was announced as ready for trials in 1746, the machine still weighed a little over forty-five kilograms. The Board continued to vote Harrison funds, while the Royal Society awarded Harrison its Copley medal, the highest honour which it could bestow.

Even before any sea trial of 'Number Three', Harrison began work on a 'Number Four' in 1757. This new clock was somewhat larger than a pocket chronometer, with an intricate mechanism designed without sacrificing accuracy. It was a device 'which by reason alike of its beauty, its accuracy, and its historical interest, must take pride of place as the most famous chronometer that ever has been or ever will be made'; it was finished by 1759.[3] 'Number Four' was much smaller and less cumbersome than its three predecessors,

rather resembling a large pendant watch about 125 mm in diameter (Plate 6.4). It was the culmination of half a century of 'self-denial, unremitting toil, and ceaseless concentration'. Harrison was justly proud of his achievement:

I think I may make so bold to say, that there is neither any other Mechanical or Mathematical thing in the World that is more beautiful or curious in texture than this my watch or Time-keeper for the Longitude . . . and I heartily thank Almighty God that I have lived so long, as in some measure to complete it.[4]

A further two years were spent in checking and adjusting 'Number Four' before Harrison reported to the Board, in March 1761, that it was ready for a sea trial. In October of that year, Harrison's son William, embarked aboard HMS *Deptford*, Jamaica bound. Harrison himself, now aged sixty-eight, had decided not to risk the long sea voyage. The Board of Longitude had already arranged to have the longitude of Jamaica determined scientifically by observation of the satellites of Jupiter, but as the season was well advanced, they decided eventually to take the best previously established reckoning. Local time at Portsmouth and Jamaica was to be determined by taking equal solar altitudes by instrumental observation. The differences were to be compared against readings of 'Number Four'. On arrival at Jamaica, 'Number Four' was found to be just five seconds slow, giving an error of longitude of a mere one-and-a-quarter nautical miles. By the time it was brought back to Plymouth after some five months of heat, cold and variable weather conditions, the clock had a total error equivalent of only twenty-eight and a half nautical miles, quite within the limit of half a degree that had been laid down in the original Act of Parliament of 1714 and qualifying Harrison for the reward of £20,000.

The money did not arrive immediately, for there were disputes at official levels to be overcome, and a new trial was ordered, this time out to Barbados. Harrison was also required to submit all his drawings, as well as the first three timepieces, for scrutiny by the Board. Two further instruments were requested, 'Number Five' being finished in 1770 after three years' work. By now, Harrison was seventy-eight years old and his powers were beginning to fail him. Nevertheless, he had King George III as an ally in his cause to

PLATE 6.5 *A typical selection of instruments used by surveyors and navigators in the eighteenth and nineteenth centuries: compass, sextant, tables, dividers and glasses.*

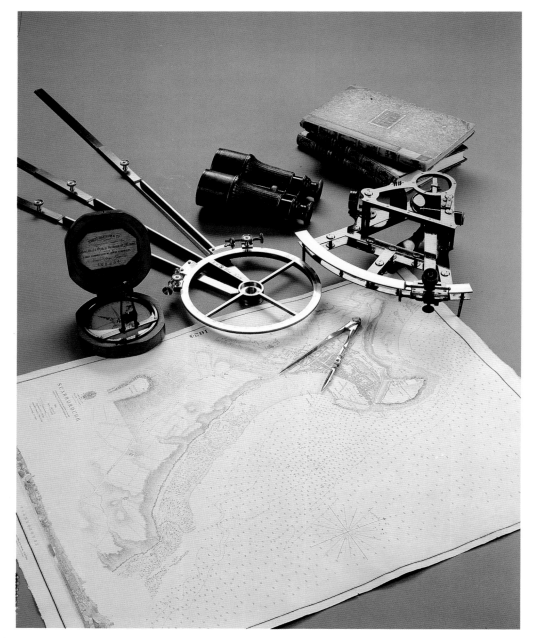

Pantometria, published in London in 1571 after an instrument that had been constructed two years previously by Humphrey Cole.

Perhaps the best known example of the theodolite is that of Jesse Ramsden (1735–1800) (Plate 6.6), of Halifax, who in 1763 invented a graduating engine, by means of which the brass circle of a surveying instrument could be accurately divided. Prior to Ramsden's invention, it had been extremely difficult to construct a precision instrument properly. When it was perfected, his celebrated Great Theodolite (which was commissioned in 1784) comprised: a horizontal circle almost one metre in diameter divided by dots into sectors of ten minutes of arc; two micrometer microscopes for reading off the circle, and angles to tenths of seconds; also, a telescopic sight moving freely in the plane of the instrument (Plate 6.7). Ramsden's instrument was heavy and cumbersome, weighing just over ninety kilograms and it had to be

PLATE 6.6 *(left) Jesse Ramsden (1735–1800) with his graduating engine, by means of which he was able to divide the brass circle of his celebrated Great Theodolite.*

PLATE 6.7 *(below) Jesse Ramsden's Great Theodolite of 1784. It was a most efficient instrument and was in the service of the Ordnance Survey for more than sixty years. The device weighed some 90.72 kg and required a special vehicle for transportation.*

claim his reward. After hearing the case from start to finish, the King declared 'By God, Harrison, I'll see you righted!' and Harrison circulated a broadside, *The Case of Mr. John Harrison*, to publicize his claims to the full reward. Parliament drew up the necessary money bill, to which George gave his assent, and Harrison finally received payment allowing him to live in comfort the few remaining years until his death in 1776.

A version of Harrison's successful instrument was carried by Captain James Cook on his second and third voyages (between 1772 and 1779), giving extremely accurate results.

The theodolite

The new and improved instruments of the time were used initially for navigation or for hydrographic surveying. Explorers relied much on the sextant (which, with its precision-divided scales, was a considerable improvement on the earlier quadrant) and on the chronometer for their surveys and position-finding. Another instrument which saw refinement during this period was the theodolite, which had evolved from a sixteenth-century instrument called the *polymetrum*, invented in 1512 by Martin Waldseemüller. The first known theodolite as it might be recognized today was that described by Leonard Digges in his

universalis and an edition of Ptolemy, proposed a map based on the triangulation of the whole of the German empire, thereby anticipating the triangulation survey of France by some two centuries. The technique was also used for Philipp Apian's large map of Bavaria, first published in 1568 (Plate 6.10), and for the astronomer Tycho Brahe's map of the island of Ven in Denmark in 1596. In the sixteenth century, Italian military engineers used the principles of triangulation to measure distances and elevations in fortifications.

Triangulation involves measuring a base-line and then constructing away from that line so that the lengths of the sides can be determined, simply but accurately, by trigonometry. By using church steeples or specially constructed towers or scaffolds for taking sight readings, surveyors could extend networks of triangles over long distances from a single base (Plate 6.9). The first man to complete a triangulation survey of a substantial area was the mathematician and geographer Willebrord Snel van Roijen (1580–1626), who had invented a quadrant to measure the angular distances of the planets. He measured an arc of meridian in 1615 in *Rijnlandsche roeden* and described his methods in his *Eratosthenes batavus, de terrae ambitus vera quantitate*, published at Leiden in 1617. His calculations, however, were lengthy and on close scrutiny open to error.

PLATE 6.8 *(above) Early surveying methods in the mid-sixteenth century, showing the use of sundials, quadrants and the cross-staff. (From* Rudimenta mathematica *by Sebastian Münster, Basel, 1551.)*

transported in a special four-wheeled vehicle. Nevertheless, the theodolite was a most efficient instrument, remaining in use for some sixty-six years, and the refined and much smaller device in use today is its direct descendant. It was used by William Roy in the connection of the triangulation networks of England and France in 1790, in the Great Trigonometrical Survey of Great Britain, and ten years later in 1800 was shipped to India for the triangulation survey of the subcontinent.

Triangulation

The technique of triangulation, so vital a part of surveying, was used as far back as the early sixteenth century. Gemma Frisius, the Belgian mathematician, published a manual on the subject in 1533 entitled *Libellus de locorum describendorum ratione* (Plate 4.3). Less than twenty years later, Sebastian Münster, compiler of the *Cosmographia*

PLATE 6.9 *(right) An early-sixteenth-century demonstration of the basic principles of triangulation in surveying, here to determine the distance to a church. (From* Instrumentorum mechanicorum *by Lieven Hulsius, Frankfurt-am-Main, 1605.)*

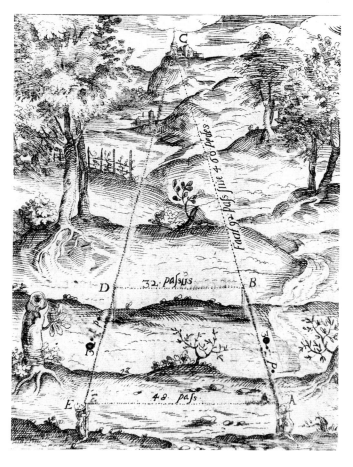

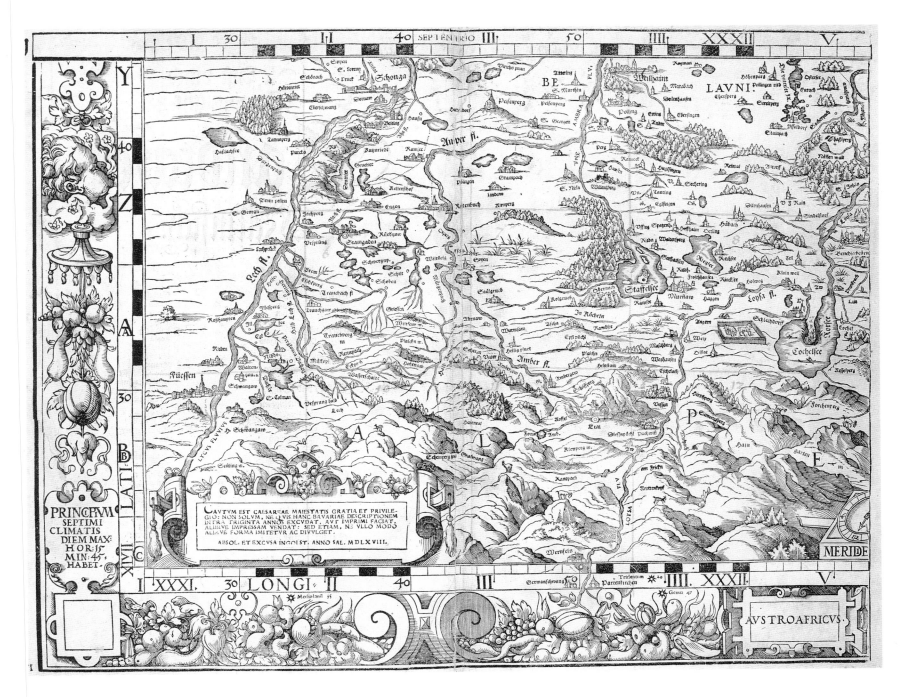

PLATE 6.10 Bavaria *by Philipp Apian, 1568 and later. Apian was one of the first to produce a map using the technique of triangulation. This map is also a fine early example of a separately published regional survey.*

It was not until the dissemination of logarithmic tables, first devised by John Napier (1550–1617) and refined by Edward Wright, Edmund Gunter and Henry Briggs between 1615 and 1628, that tedious calculations by multiplication and division were replaced by the much simpler use of addition and subtraction. But although new and improved instruments and techniques were now available to surveyors, their use was far from widespread. Leonard Digges' theodolite, for example, although described in 1571, did not become significant until the mid-eighteenth century. In 1631, Pierre Vernier made a device for reading off linear scale divisions, but this was not incorporated into surveying instruments for about a hundred years. Melchisedec Thevenot's invention of that very simple but effective device, the bubble spirit level in 1666, lay forgotten for half a century and William Gascoigne's micrometer was

similarly neglected for more than twenty years.

These delays could, of course, be attributed to the very high cost of making such instruments, the lack of suitably refined techniques to make them, the lack of qualified craftsmen and users and perhaps a lack of demand. Whatever the reason, although the technique of triangulation was to become indispensable for accurate large-scale topographical mapping, it was curiously slow in being taken up for general use. It was not until 1739–1744 that the technique of triangulation was applied to an area as large as France.

France: the first survey

In 1668, Jean-Baptiste Colbert (1619–1683), the royal financial adviser to Louis XIV, sought ways of obtaining accurate maps of France. Ambitious in affairs of state, he exercised his considerable powers by establishing a navy and by founding the *Académie Royale des Sciences* in 1666 (Plates 6.11, 6.12). The outstanding problem was the finding of longitude at sea, for accurate clocks like Harrison's, able to measure differences of time, were not yet available. In Colbert's day, the relationship between astronomical observation and cartography was well understood, but before the true size and form of France could be known, the size and shape of the earth itself had to be determined. To this end, Colbert requested the members of the *Académie* to devise and recommend methods of producing more accurate maps of the kingdom of Louis XIV. In recognition of his work on the

accurate determination of longitude, Colbert had offered the Italian Giovanni Domenico Cassini (1625–1712), professor of astronomy at the university of Bologna, membership of the *Académie* in 1665. Best known for his work on the movements of the four major satellites of Jupiter, the tables known as the *Ephemerides* published for the year 1668, Cassini had made Galileo's findings on that subject more easily accessible to navigators. Cassini settled in Paris in 1669, changing his name to Jean Dominique when he acquired French citizenship in 1673. As part of his dowry on the occasion of his marriage he acquired the Château de Thury.

The avowed purpose of founding the *Académie* was the correction and improvement of maps and nautical charts. During 1668–1669 the *savants* of the *Académie* set up tests for various techniques of mapping in the environs of Paris, under the direction of Gilles de Riberval and Jean Picard (1620–1682). Picard was already well known for having made and perfected several astronomical instruments and he particularly wanted to obtain an accurate reading of the circumference of the earth by taking careful measurements of an arc of meridian. The first serious attempt at such a measurement had been made by Willebrord Snel van Roijen (1580–1626), the Dutch geographer and mathematician. By using a quadrant with a radius of 700 mm and a semicircle with a radius of 500 mm, he ran a triangulation between Alkmaar and Bergen op Zoom in the west of the Netherlands in 1615–1616. His work, however, seems to have lain forgotten by Dutch mapmakers; certainly his name is very rarely mentioned on seventeenth-century maps of the Netherlands, and none of the seventeenth-century Dutch mapmakers are known to have used his data as the basis for a map. Pioneers, like prophets, often go unregarded in their own countries and this was the case with Snel, for it was the French who took up his work with serious intent. A map by Guillaume de l'Isle (1675–1726), entitled *Provinces Unies des Pays Bas*, was issued in 1705 (Plate 6.13) with the legend: *Tirée des cartes les plus correctes rectifiées par les observations géométriques de Snellius et par celles que Cassini y a faites en dernier lieu.*[5]

Picard surveyed a base-line running approximately north–south between two points, on the road from Paris to Fontainebleau between the mill

PLATE 6.11 *The commemorative medal for the establishment of the* Académie Royale des Sciences *under the auspices of Louis XIV of France in 1666. It was under the aegis of the* Académie *that France began the reform of cartography by instigating the first national uniform topographical survey.*

at Villejuif and the pavilion at Juvisy. He was assisted by Cassini, using a newly assembled instrument. In 1669–1670 Picard measured thirteen triangles by this means from a base-line of 5,663 *toises* (that is, 11,037 metres, one *toise* being approximately 1.95 metres). Later, greatly pleased by the progress of his work, the *Académie* permitted Picard to spend several months in Denmark in 1671–1672 comparing data obtained by the great astronomer Tycho Brahe with new data to be obtained by Cassini in Paris. Such visits, beyond as well as within France, became a regular feature in the careers of those members of the *Académie* who were engaged on cartographic work. Both Picard and Cassini travelled extensively throughout France during the 1670s.

After the early researches on the meridian had been carried out, the *Académie* resolved to apply the new methods and techniques to the construction of an entirely new map of France. Louis XIV granted his approval for the project in 1679 and Picard, with other surveyors, among them Philippe de la Hire (1640–1718) (Plate 6.15), known for his globular projection, was sent to survey the coasts in order to co-ordinate fieldwork with existing charts. Starting in the north at Nantes and Brest, they established that existing maps and charts were so inaccurate that Brest, for example, was placed thirty leagues too far west on them. The following year they made their way south to Bayonne, Bordeaux and Royan on the Biscay coast. In 1681 they travelled north again along the Channel coast. In 1682 the areas around Saint Malo, Caen, Calais and Dunkirk were covered. Picard held that a coastal survey was only the first step towards the completion of the map of the entire territory of France and presented a memorandum on the subject to the *Académie*. He realized that those parts of France which had been surveyed were often separated by regions as yet uncovered, sometimes by considerable distances. Thus, Picard needed to find a way to link the surveys. To this end, he proposed that the length and breadth of the country be determined first, allowing more detailed field surveys to be fitted into a framework devised from a network of triangles covering all of France. He proposed to start with a chain running from Dunkirk in the north to Perpignan in the south, following approximately the meridian of Paris. Such a chain would permit the even more accurate measurement of the length of a degree, and other chains could be easily added along the land frontiers and coasts.

The work of the Cassinis

Unfortunately, Picard did not live to see his proposals bear fruit, for he died in October 1682. Work on the continuation of the project was entrusted to Cassini, who had shared the task with Picard. Cassini proposed that two teams, one in the south, the other in the north, should work simultaneously toward each other – Cassini's team southwards and La Hire's team northwards. About a year after the death of Picard, however, French cartography was dealt another blow by the death of Jean-Baptiste Colbert in 1683. The survey of France had barely begun, and there was everything still to achieve. Cartography had been strongly supported under Colbert, but under François Le Tellier, his successor as patron-

PLATE 6.12 *An engraving by Dufloz of 1730 depicting* Louis XIV visiting the Musée de l'Histoire Naturelle *and the* Académie. *Some of the products of cartographic reform can be seen in the foreground – maps, plans and instruments for the* Observatoire *currently under construction.*

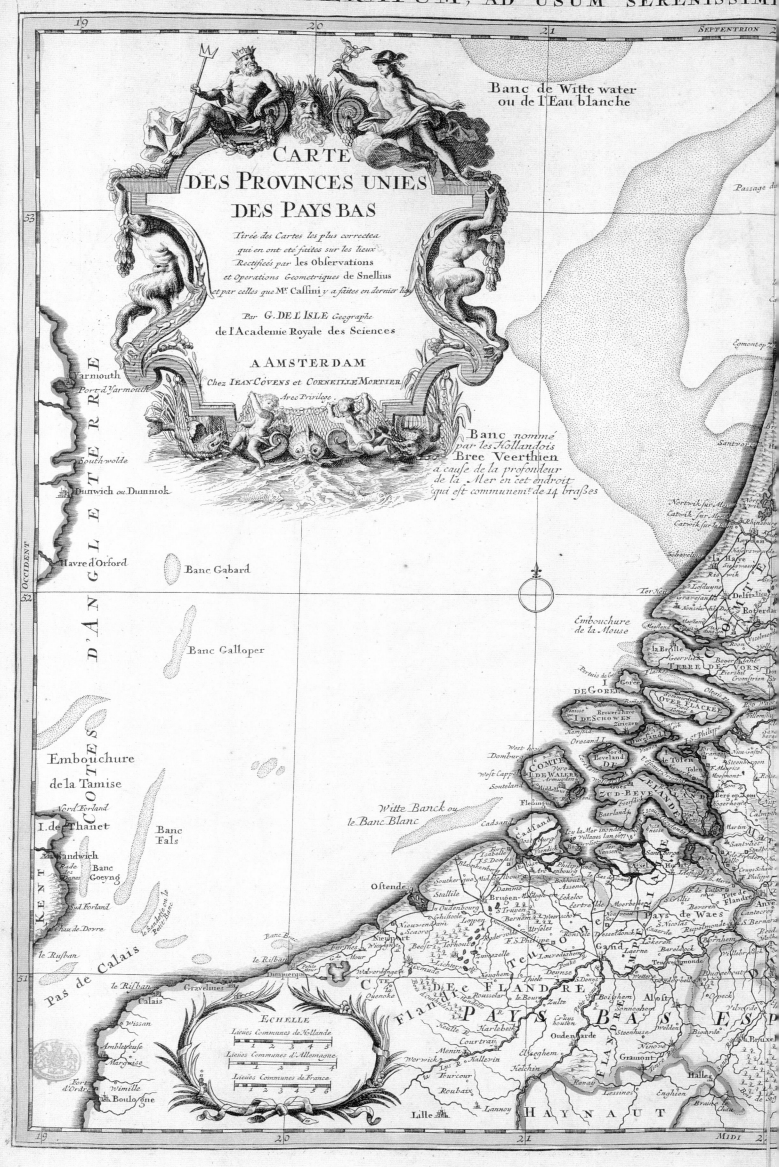

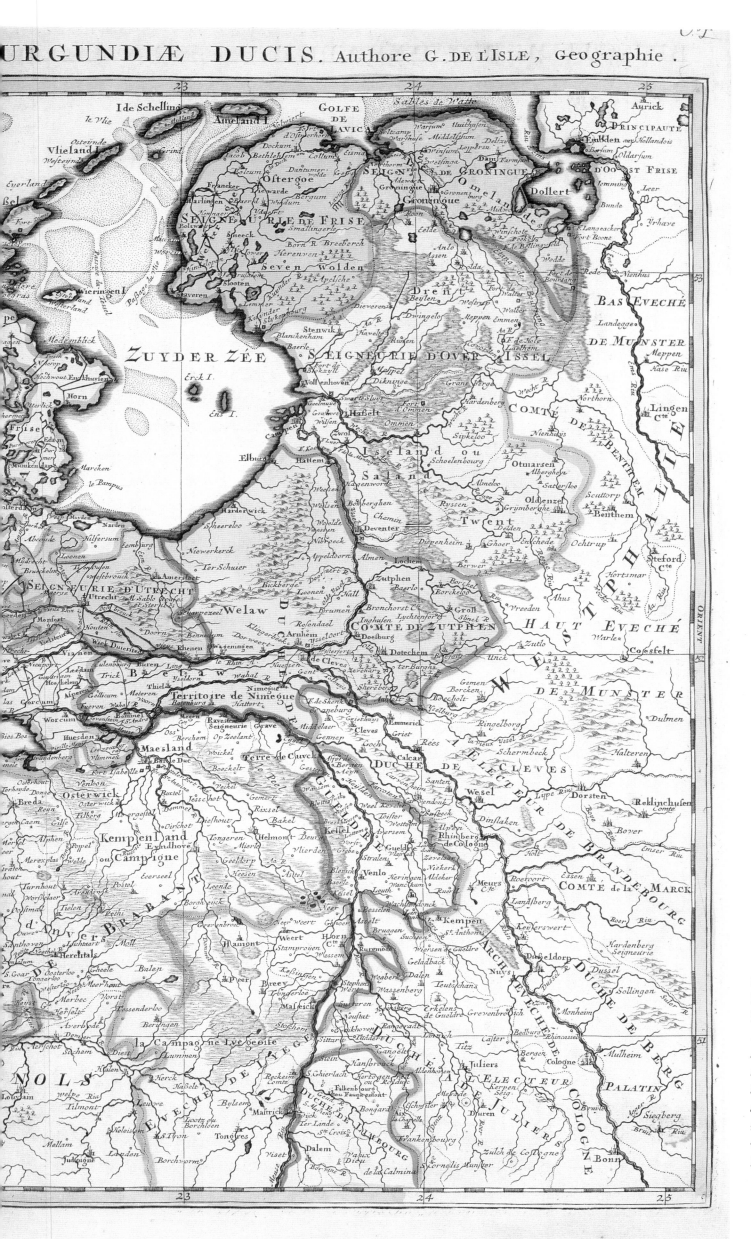

URGUNDIÆ DUCIS. Authore G. DE L'ISLE, Geographie.

PLATE 6.13 Carte des
Provinces Unies des Pays
Bas *by Guillaume de l'Isle,
1705 and later (here in an
Amsterdam edition). De
l'Isle's map claims to be
based on the maps corrected
according to the geometrical
methods of Willebrord Snel
van Roijen and Giovanni
Domenico Cassini.*

PLATE 6.14 Carte de
France corrigée par
ordre du Roy sur les
observations de Messrs. de
l'Académie des Sciences *by
Philippe de la Hire, 1693
and later. This version
appeared in the* Académie's
Mémoires *of 1729. When
Louis XIV saw the new
corrected outline of the
coasts, he reflected that the
survey had cost him more
territory than a war.*

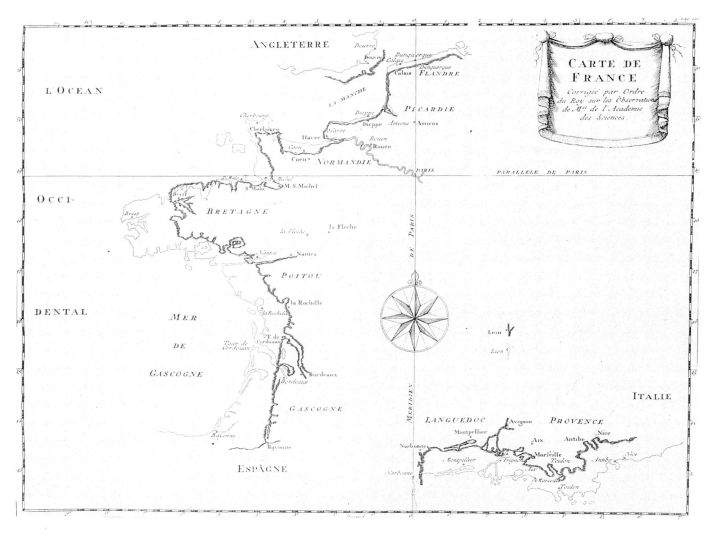

PLATE 6.15 *Philippe de
la Hire (1640–1718),
mathematician, inventor of
a globular map projection,
and surveyor for the*
Académie.

minister of the *Académie*, matters were different. By the end of 1683, the chain reached only as far as the Massif Central. Le Tellier died in 1691 and Cassini's hopes were raised once more, but, because France was again at war, little interest was shown – the irony being, of course, that the need for an accurate survey of any country is at no time more urgent than during wartime:

As a royal body, the *Académie* could pursue such work vigorously if that was the will of the king and of its patron-minister; but if they opposed such activities, which required so many men and so much money, there was little the academicians could do on their own to advance the project.[6]

Despite the apparent apathy of the *Académie*, an outline map of France was published in 1693, based on the manuscript compiled by La Hire nine years before, embodying the results of the coastal surveys thus far. The published map, proudly entitled *Carte de France corrigée par ordre du Roy-sur les observations de Messrs. de l'Académie des Sciences*, showed the older, traditional outline of the coasts (based on a general map of Sanson) in a thin, unshaded line, and the new, corrected outline in a heavier, shaded line (Plate 6.14). The

general result was to shift the western (Breton) extremity of France one-and-a-half degrees of longitude to the east relative to the Paris meridian (the meridian being shown, incidentally, for the first time on a printed map), and the southern, Mediterranean coastline about half a degree of latitude to the north, relative to the latitude of Paris. Sanson's outline gave France an area of 31,657 square leagues; the new *Académie* outline a figure of only 25,386 square leagues. When it was shown to Louis XIV, the sight of the new map is said to have caused the king to remark that the survey had cost more territory than if he had fought a disastrous military campaign.

After some further delays, fieldwork along the Paris meridian at last resumed in 1700. Cassini was now joined by his son Jacques (1677–1756) and reached a point near the Spanish frontier, at Collioure, in 1701. Yet again, progress was interrupted, this time by the War of the Spanish Succession, which broke out in 1701 and dragged on until 1713. Cassini the elder died in 1712, aged eighty-six, before work could once again be resumed. Louis XIV himself died in 1715, but fieldwork was resumed once more in 1718 by Jacques Cassini and de la Hire, so that the chain begun by Picard thirty-nine years before was finally completed. In the resumed survey, twenty-eight triangles were run from Paris to Dunkerque. Cassini's report, *De la grandeur et la figure de la terre*, was published in 1720 and passed judgement on the existing maps of France, comparing them for accuracy in determining the correct positions of cities and natural features. Cassini's work brought to an end the first stages in the construction of the modern map of France and with it the realization that: 'men, institutions, and money – far more than ideas – regulated the rate of progress. The national map survey had been launched in France under Colbert by people who perhaps underestimated the effort, time, and money that this venture required'.[7] Cassini's calculations of the length of a degree, published in the report, gave a value of 59,960 *toises*.

Cartographic survey work in France lay dormant until the 1730s. Jacques Cassini advocated the complete triangulation of France, realizing that attempts to fit haphazard surveys to the Paris meridian were doomed to failure. Now, with his own son, César-François Cassini de Thury (1714–1784) (Plate 6.19), he took up the reins once more in 1733. The backbone of the triangulation thus advocated was the verified meridian of Paris, along which at intervals of 60,000 *toises* (that is, about one degree of latitude), perpendiculars were carried geometrically to the east and west. The positions of towns and prominent natural features were determined from these perpendiculars. This, essentially, is the origin of the map projection still known by Cassini's name. Cassini's projection was widely adopted in later years by other mapping agencies, including the Ordnance Survey in Great Britain. On it the scale is correct along straight lines perpendicular to the meridian and the distance along a great circle through the position which intersects that meridian at right angles.

It was realized during the 1730s that the various departments of the government were pulling against each other so far as the need for accurate mapping was concerned, with the result that existing efforts were critically under-financed and were at the mercy of inadequate control. The army was mapping sections of the land frontier and the fortification engineers also set up their own mapping department. In 1720, the *Dépôt de la marine* had been set up to service the charting

requirements of the Navy and other mariners. It was fortunate that the responsibility for continuing work on the triangulation survey fell to Cassini. The very name, and the dynasty begun by the elder Cassini, created a sense of permanence. The survey could be continued as long as the sons wished to engage themselves in such painstaking work. Fortunately, this proved to be the case.

It was equally fortunate that Louis XV had studied geography under Guillaume de l'Isle and that he was a keen amateur scientist. The King was therefore easily persuaded to give his support to the continuation of the great project. In 1733, Jacques Cassini read a paper to the *Académie* summarizing progress to date. In his paper Cassini stated that more triangles had to be surveyed and that the length of a degree had to be verified before any map could be published as a result of the triangulation surveys. Nevertheless, many observations had been made throughout the country, and the latitude and longitude of many places had been redetermined. In addition to the 'new' outline map of France and a set of reasonably accurate charts of the French Atlantic coast, there was also a new topographical map of Paris and its environs, the large nine-sheet *Carte particulière des environs de Paris, par Messrs. de l'Académie royale*

PLATE 6.16 Carte de France *from* Mémoires de l'Académie des Sciences, *1718. The map illustrates the triangulation network used in order to determine accurately the meridian of Paris.*

des Sciences en 1674. The map was engraved in 1678 by F. de la Pointe from the drawings of the draughtsman David du Vivier at a scale of 1:86,400. The engraving, too, represented an innovation in methods and techniques. Hachures were used for the first time to indicate relief, for example, in place of the then still conventional method of using 'molehills'.

In June 1733, Cassini and his assistants began survey work on a line perpendicular to the Paris meridian. Special pyramids about 1.2 metres wide and about 2.4 metres high, or occasionally special structures such as scaffolds, were erected every ten kilometres or so if there were no prominent landmarks suitable for use as surveying stations. Problems were posed by forests, for sightings were rendered impossible by thick stands of trees.

PLATE 6.17 *Illustration showing the measurement of the Paris meridian from a base-line, from* Discours du méridien *by Jacques Cassini, 1749.*

DISCOURS
PRELIMINAIRE·

Expofition des Opérations faites pour vérifier la ligne Meridienne de Paris, & pour déterminer la grandeur des degrés terreftres, compris entre les paralleles qui traverfent la France.

TOUTES les tentatives qui ont été faites par ordre du Roi, tant en France, que dans les différentes parties du Monde, pour déterminer la grandeur & la figure de la Terre, font affez juger combien cette recherche eft importante pour la perfection de l'Aftronomie, de la Géographie & de la Navigation, indépendamment des connoiffances que l'on peut en retirer pour le progrès de la Phyfique.

ON avoit d'abord fuppofé la Terre fphérique ; & dans

In order to circumvent this, the surveyors chose to follow the course of the Loire. In so doing, they obtained valuable data for the engineers who were working on projects to regulate the flow of the river by means of dykes and embankments.

Eventually, Saint Malo on the Channel coast was reached, making the connection of the triangulation there with Picard's earlier work. On completion of this line, a degree of longitude was taken measured by astronomical observations of the satellites of Jupiter, deriving a value of 36,670 *toises.* However, this was found to be 1,037 *toises* short of the value determined for a truly spherical earth. In other words, degrees of latitude appeared to diminish in length towards the poles, more so in fact than on a perfect sphere. In late 1733, a team of surveyors made ready to continue the line of triangles eastwards towards Strasbourg, the work being completed the following year. Another measurement of a degree produced the same result as on the Saint Malo line, and it was then that Louis XV gave the order for a decisive experiment to be undertaken to determine for certain the true shape of the earth.

To this end, two expeditions were sent out from France to survey two arcs of meridian: the first as close as possible to the equator, the second as reasonably near the North Pole as possible. In 1735, the equatorial expedition began work on the survey of an arc between Tarqui and Cotchesqui in Peru, from a base-line near Quito in Ecuador. The work occupied some ten years, under difficult conditions. The second expedition (from 1734 to 1737) surveyed an arc near the Gulf of Bothnia, under conditions equally as difficult as those experienced in South America. The surveyors were obliged, because of the difficult ice conditions, to run their stations from Torneå in Sweden northwards to a high point near Pello in Finland. The results of both these expeditions proved that the earth is flattened at the poles rather than elongated and therefore not a perfect sphere. The values of a degree nearer the Equator were given as 56,746 *toises* (110,598 kilometres) and near the pole as 56,749 *toises* (110,604 kilometres).

In the meantime, the Cassini survey in France was continued to Brest on the northwest coast in 1735, followed by another line to the west in 1736. This new survey showed, among other things, that the coastal charts of the Atlantic shoreline of France which were published in the current edition of *Le neptune françois* were still far from perfect. In order to obtain yet more data, a second chain of triangles was run in 1737 through Cherbourg, Nantes and Bayonne. At the same time, another team surveyed the Channel coast to Dunkirk. In 1738 the parties commenced a chain of triangles across the southern frontier, from Bayonne on the Biscay coast to Antibes on the Mediterranean coast. Later, while one team re-surveyed the meridian of Paris, completing the task by 1740, the other took charge of the eastern frontier survey, beginning at Nice and closing near Metz in the northeast of France in the late summer of 1740. Normandy and Brittany had been completed in 1739, so that now, after some eight years of painstaking surveying, the whole of France was enclosed by an uninterrupted chain of 400 principal triangles surveyed from eighteen bases. Thus the framework that had been advocated by Picard so many decades before was finally finished, and a proper foundation for a large-scale national map was at last in place. By the time the Cassinis completed their work in 1744 there were 800 triangles from nineteen bases. All that remained were the smaller, less accessible places, where suspicion of strangers was common. This is quite understandable, for normally the only strangers venturing into these remote areas were official tax collectors, priests and sometimes itinerant peddlers. Like Christopher Saxton many years before in England, the Cassini teams of surveyors carried letters of authority obliging landowners and administrators to render them all the assistance and co-operation that was requested of them.

The first cartographic results of these arduous years of surveying work appeared in 1744, in the form of a single-sheet outline map of France showing the lines of triangulation covering nearly all of the country save for the aforementioned least accessible parts. The map, on a scale of 1:1,800,000, was engraved by Guillaume Dheulland and entitled *Nouvelle carte qui comprend les principaux triangles qui servent de fondement à la description géométrique de la France*. A more complete map, in eighteen sheets, was presented to the *Académie* by Cassini de Thury in 1745. Based on additional surveys carried out between 1740 and 1745, these eighteen sheets formed a large map at a scale of 1:878,000, containing the 800 triangles

from the nineteen bases. Cassini de Thury was at pains to point out that, although it was an outline map showing triangulations, many towns and cities were located, as well as smaller places, châteaux and important landmarks — all shown geometrically for the first time in France.

The story of the survey of France certainly does not end here, for Cassini de Thury began work on a more detailed survey which would take over forty years to complete. In 1746, he travelled to Flanders (the Austrian Netherlands) to make another triangulation survey. This one would tie into the main French triangulation in connection with a topographical survey being carried out by parties of army engineers in the Schelde valley in

PLATE 6.18 *An illustration of the Paris meridian survey showing how observations were taken in varying terrains, from* Discours du méridien *by Jacques Cassini, 1749.*

LA MERIDIENNE DE PARIS,
VERIFIÉE
PAR DE NOUVELLES OBSERVATIONS.

JUSQU'ICI nous avons confidéré la Meridienne de l'Obfervatoire comme divifée en quatre parties, dont la fomme auroit été égale à toute fon étendue, fi tous les arcs que nous avons mefurés, avoient été fous le même Meridien.

Cette divifion étoit néceffaire pour le plan que nous nous étions propofés, de comparer la grandeur de plufieurs degrés confécutifs, & de déterminer ainfi avec plus de précifion, la grandeur & la figure de la Terre.

Préfentement que ce premier Objet eft rempli, nous confidererons la Meridienne par rapport à la Carte générale du

PLATE 6.19 *Portrait of César-François Cassini de Thury (1714–1784), who continued the triangulation work for the first great survey of France.*

the Oudenaarde, Dendermonde and Aalst region. The results sufficiently impressed Louis XV for the king to commission Cassini de Thury to draw up a plan for a large-scale detailed topographical survey of the kingdom. Work was begun in 1747 at a cost of 40,000 *livres* a year. The project became known as the *Carte de Cassini*, and with good reason, for it was Cassini de Thury above all others, who kept the survey alive and progressing against the odds. In 1756, government funding for the project was withdrawn, ostensibly on the grounds of heavy military expenditure. Cassini de Thury thereupon assumed the entire responsibility for the survey, managing to find a group of financiers and capitalists who agreed to underwrite the costs of the map in return for some proprietary interest in its eventual publication. Other funding for the project came from the administrations of the various provincial States-General, who saw and appreciated the value of accurate topographical mapping of their respective regions. Cassini de Thury died in 1784, but on his death, nearly all of the project had been completed. Only parts of Normandy and Brittany in the north of the country remained to be finished, and final completion eventually came in 1789 under the leadership of Cassini de Thury's son, Jacques-Dominique Cassini (1748–1845).

On completion, the *Carte de Cassini* consisted of 182 sheets (each a uniform 555 mm by 880 mm), drawn at a uniform scale of 1:86,400. It was the most ambitious mapping project yet attempted and achieved by one country. The work was available in atlas form, bound in one or more large folio volumes and preceded by an introductory note — the *Avertissement, ou introduction à la carte générale et particulière de France*. The *Carte de Cassini* was also available mounted and cut up as folding map sheets in slipcases. Slipcases made to resemble books were especially popular, as maps covering substantial parts of the country could thus be carried in a convenient format. Visually, the map was based on du Vivier's 1678 map of the Paris region, clearly engraved and imparting a generally clean and uncrowded appearance. The major routes were emphasized, the larger towns and cities shown by miniature plans, and the smaller settlements indicated by a variety of conventional symbols. Additional features such as churches, priories, monasteries, châteaux, mills and other

PLATE 6.20 *(opposite) The general index map from* Carte de France *by Jacques Cassini, 1747. The map shows the primary triangulation network established by Cassini and his team of surveyors, indicating the disposition of the 182 sheets in the series as published. The series was available either as a large folio atlas or as folding maps sold in slip-cases.*

structures were depicted, and forests were also carefully drawn. The names of local landowners and proprietors and the local gentry and other dignitaries were also included.

However, the map had one shortcoming in its depiction of relief compared to modern topographical mapping. In areas of flatter relief, rivers were shown as flowing in narrow valleys with their borders hatched. Only isolated elevations were shown, so that the general effect in some areas resembled a vast plateau dissected by deep canyons representing the river valleys. In more mountainous areas, the relief took on a tiered effect, with ridges appearing as narrow white bands enclosed by perpendicular lines of shading, resembling long, hairy caterpillars. A satisfactory form of depicting relief on a map, using data derived from accurate observation, was not devised until many years later.

Such defects notwithstanding, the map remains one of the most remarkable monuments in the history of mapmaking. It was, and quite rightly so, a matter of national pride:

As a publishing venture it has few peers in the history of cartography. Even today people admire the quality of engraving and enjoy looking at the features of France two centuries ago; it is one of the best-known artifacts of the eighteenth century. But in the eighteenth century its reputation as a scientific document took precedence over its graphic qualities. Few people then purchased sheets and still fewer bought complete editions, yet many were aware of its existence. People who never saw even a portion of the Cassini survey nonetheless knew that France had been mapped in unprecedented detail and accuracy. The Cassini map represented the conquest of space through measurement. . . . Its most lasting impact on cartography was perhaps the proof it gave by example, that such a vast enterprise could be undertaken and successfully concluded. Consider the difference between attitudes toward mapping in the 1670s and 1740s. In the first instance mapmaking projects were launched by people who underestimated the effort, time, and money they would require. In the second instance they were promoted by people who knew full well what difficulties they might confront but were not intimidated by the prospect. The very challenge was all the more worthwhile in their eyes for being so great.[8]

(continued on page 199)

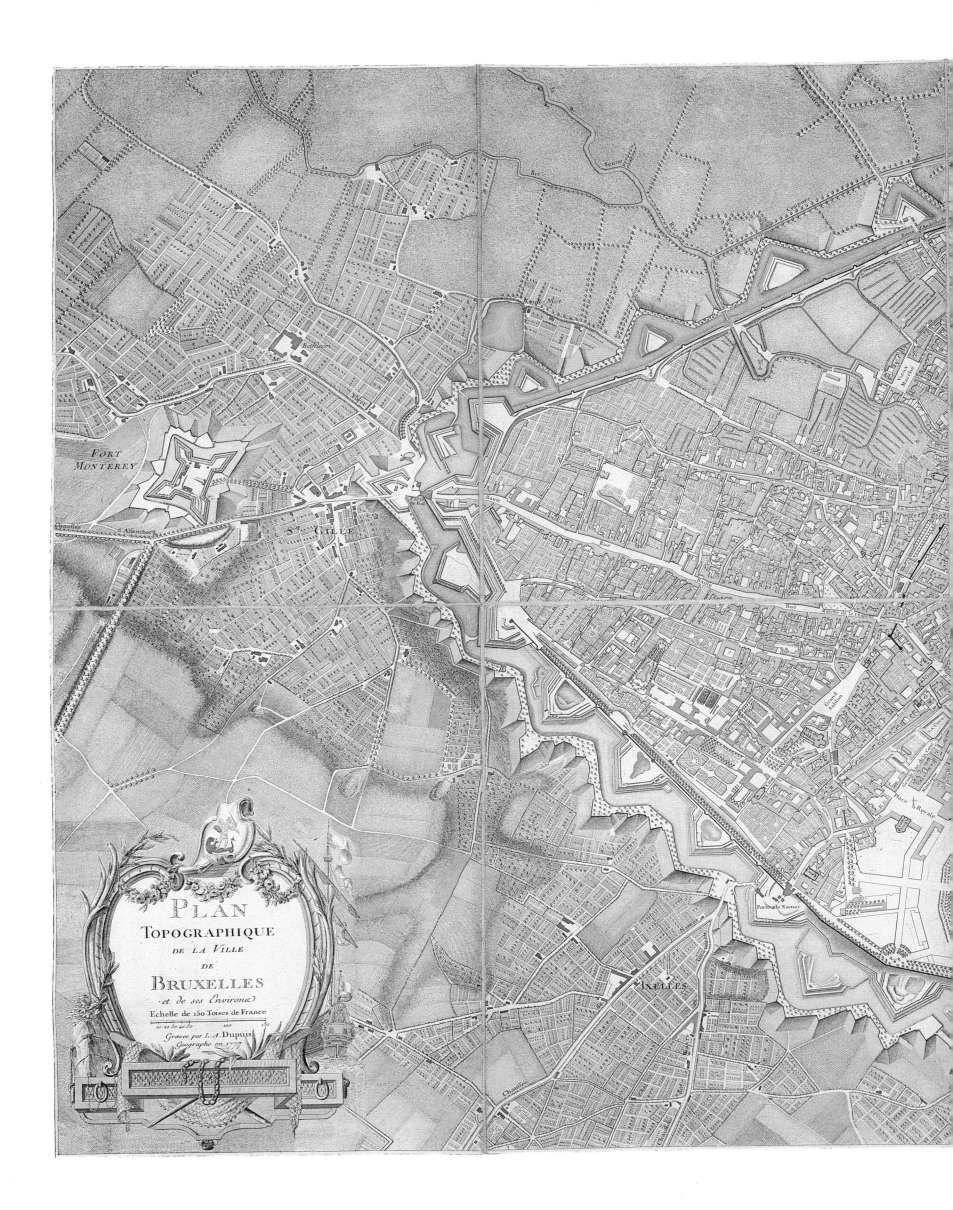

FORT
MONTEREY

St. GILLE

PLAN
TOPOGRAPHIQUE
DE LA VILLE
DE
BRUXELLES
et de ses Environs
Echelle de 150 Toises de France
10. 20. 30. 40. 50   100   150
Gravée par L. A. Dupuis
Geographe en 1777

IXELLES

Porte de Namur

Place Royale

Grand Sablon

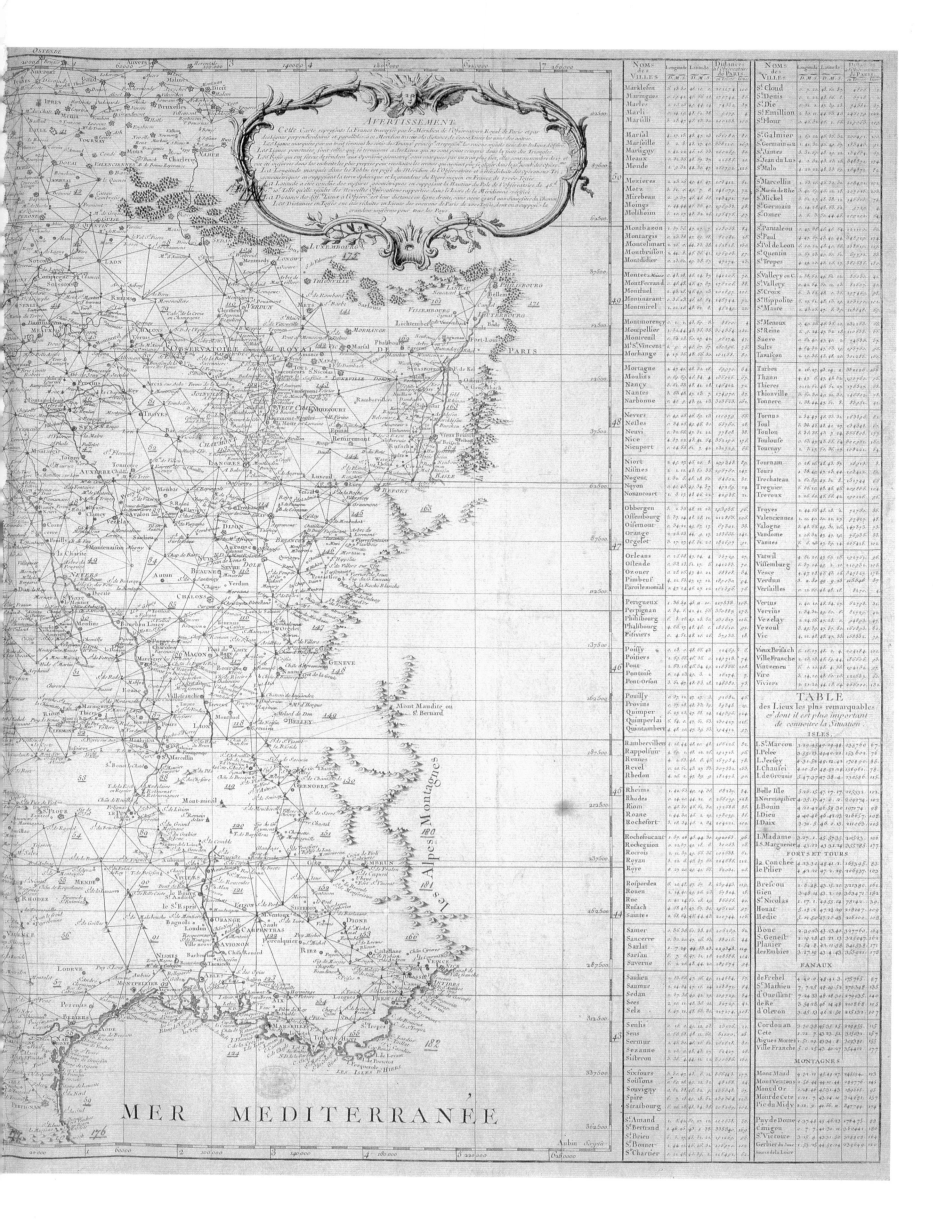

MER MÉDITERRANÉE

LA MANCHE

OCEAN

Monts Pirennees

NOUVELLE CARTE
Qui Comprend
les principaux Triangles qui servent de
Fondement a la Description Geometrique
de la
FRANCE
Levée par ordre du Roy.
Par Messrs Maraldi & Cassini de Thury,
de l'Académie Royale
des Sciences.
Année 1744.

ECHELLE

Longitude Occidentale

The Austrian Empire

Cassini's *Carte de France* is of historical importance because it was the first general topographical map of a country based on extensive triangulation and topographical field surveys. The military and civil value of the survey was not lost upon the rulers and governments of neighbouring European nations and, in particular, the Austrians. The Austrian Empire consisted of a number of geographically scattered territories in Europe comprising many different ethnic groups in Lombardy, Piedmont, Transylvania and the border territories along the southern frontier with the Turkish Empire, Bohemia, Bukovina and elsewhere. The Austrians were well aware that the possibility of an uprising was never very far away in the empire.

The Austrian Netherlands

The Cassini surveys provided the inspiration for those of the neighbouring Austrian Netherlands (more or less the area covered by present-day Belgium). Under the leadership of Count Joseph Johann von Ferraris (1726–1814), a detailed topographical survey was begun. The work was carried out between 1771 and 1777 by Ferraris's students at the *École Mathématique du Corps d'Artillerie* at Mechelen. Plane table methods were used for the survey and the work was prepared in manuscript in 275 sheets. For final publication, however, the country was covered in twenty-five sheets, on the scale of the Cassini map (1:86,400). Ferraris gave his survey the title: *Carte chorographique des Pays-Bas autrichiennes dédiée à leurs Majestés impériales et royales par le comte de Ferraris, Lieutenant-général de leurs armées.* The map's fine engraving was by L.A. Dupuis and others, who were working under the direction of Jean Baptiste Pierre Tardieu.

The twenty-five sheets of the published version include: a detailed key of conventional symbols; a dedication to, and portrait of, the Emperor Joseph II; a sheet index; and an index diagram (showing to the user how the map could be joined together to make one large wall-map if desired). Sheet XXI is a finely detailed plan of Brussels, entitled *Plan topographique de la Ville de Bruxelles* (Plate 6.21). In less than a decade, Belgium (that is, the area of the Netherlands now called Belgium) acquired an outstanding topographical map. It is also of importance for the cartographical history of the southern provinces of the modern Netherlands.

The Ferraris survey was tied to the Cassini's triangulation of France, carried out between 1741 and 1748, but only at the southwestern extremity of Flanders near Dunkirk, just across the French frontier. It was not tied to the French triangulation farther east, except for sections along the frontier which were linked by polygons rather than by triangles; the greater part of the survey, away from the French frontier, was not controlled by triangulation.[9] Nevertheless, this first detailed survey of the area of northern Europe now covered by modern Belgium was, and remains, a highly regarded topographical map.

In fact, since the large scale of the original manuscript survey allowed a considerable degree of detail to be included on the 275 sheets, the Ferraris survey of Belgium may justly be considered as a cadastral survey rather than a straightforward topographical survey. (A cadastral map is in essence a map which delineates property boundaries, specifically parcels of land within a given administrative division, with added information concerning location, area and value for inland revenue or other government fiscal purposes. Early estate maps may be considered as cadastral maps for this reason. Surveys of this nature culminated in the great *Cadastre napoléonien* ordered by Napoléon I in 1807 as the national cadastral map of France.)

Later surveys of the Austrian Empire

Under Ferraris a survey of Mecklenburg-Strelitz in nine sheets was completed in 1780, and a similar one of Mecklenburg-Schwerin in sixteen sheets in 1788. Elsewhere in the Austrian Empire, surveys of variable quality and accuracy were put in hand or were already under way in Silesia, Bohemia and Moravia. Later, surveys in the Austrian lands in Transylvania, Lombardy and the Tyrol were begun. In the latter case, the resultant map was issued in twenty-three sheets in 1769–1774, with an extension into the neighbouring Vorarlberg following in 1783.

The triangulations of Austria and northern Italy were intended to tie into the French system based on the meridian of Paris. As a result, maps were published in Milan in 1796. In a complex multiethnic, polyglot empire such as that of Austria, the

PLATE 6.21 *(opposite)* Plan topographique de la Ville de Bruxelles *by Louis-André Dupuis, copper engraving, 1777. This plan is a sheet from the celebrated* Ferraris Carte chorographique des Pays-Bas autrichiennes. *Note the remains of the old city wall and new parks and squares which had begun to be laid out. Northwest is at the top.*

need for accurate mapping for military use in the event of conflict, rebellion or civil war was obvious. By 1787 the emperor of the time, Joseph II (who reigned from 1765–1790), had made sure that every province of his far-flung, diverse empire was mapped in some form or another. Needless to say, there was as yet little uniformity or continuity between the different provincial surveys; and certainly no general topographical map. Under Franz II (the last Holy Roman Emperor, who reigned from 1792 until 1806 — when the empire ceased to exist — continuing as Franz I of Austria until his death in 1835), such a survey was finally commissioned, the General Staff issuing maps between 1792 and about 1800.

If the work of mapping France under the auspices of the great Cassini survey had been a difficult task, that of Austria was certainly no less so. In Lombardy in northern Italy a triangulation network was tied to the Piedmont network and extended to the Adriatic shores, the maps beginning to appear between 1814 and 1839. This may have been too late for use during the Napoleonic wars, but at least it provided the basis for future surveys. The first survey of the Austrian Empire was finished by 1860, thereby completing a project begun a century earlier in 1762 at the orders of Maria-Theresa, towards the end of her reign. The work continued throughout the intervening years, despite the disruptions and turmoil brought about by the wars and campaigns of the Napoleonic era.

The British Isles surveyed

As we have seen, England was at the forefront of designing instruments and developing techniques to help the progress of cartography. It is surprising, therefore, that England was not the first country to be fully surveyed. Cartographers and surveyors in England were at least as well placed as their French counterparts to make progress in the practical application of mathematics and trigonometry to their art. However, the indifference of many of their colleagues and the inadequate funding — where it existed at all — stultified their efforts. Despite the greater attention given to estate surveys (largely commissioned by an increasingly wealthy land-owning class), to the problems of navigation and to improved instruc-

tion in mathematics, triangulation surveys were no more in evidence in England than in the Netherlands in the 1620s. To be sure, there were ambitious plans for a new survey of England mooted by members of the Royal Society (founded in 1662 as a forum for scientists who were keen to improve and promote scientific knowledge), but neither that august body nor the Royal Observatory at Greenwich (founded in 1675) was able to offer financial support. Not even the Astronomer Royal, the great Dr Edmond Halley (1656–1742) was able to sway opinion in this respect.

Perhaps the right people were not yet available to exploit such advances, but in later years, when the French made great progress, the English for their part made no efforts at all. This was particularly surprising as, under continuing threat of war from Europe, the English needed accurate maps at least as much as the French. In 1664, in his *Telluris theoria*, Thomas Burnet wrote this plea:

I do not doubt, but that it would be of very good use to have *natural* Maps of the Earth . . . Our common Maps I call *Civil*, which note habited and cultivated: But natural Maps leave out all that, and represent the Earth as it would be if there were not an Inhabitant upon it, nor ever had been; the Skeleton of the Earth, as I may so say, with the site of all its parts. Methinks also every Prince should have such a Draught of his Country and Dominions, to see how the ground lies in the several parts of them, which highest, which lowest; what respect they have to one another, and to the Sea; how the Rivers flow, and why; how the Mountains lie, how Heaths, and how the Marches. Such a Map or Survey would be useful both in time of War and Peace, and many good observations might be made by it, not only as to Natural History and Philosophy, but also in order to the perfect improvement of a Country.[10]

Almost inevitably, no government initiatives were taken, any efforts to improve mapmaking being made on an informal basis with the collaboration from time to time of the country's men of science. As J.W. Konvitz commented recently:

Given the lack of demonstrable achievement, innovation in cartography no doubt appeared risky. The examples of bold projects that failed would have deterred others. Cartography needed consistent, visionary leadership, the co-operation of many talented and well-trained professionals, and a lot of money. In France, the government under Louis XIV and Colbert began to provide leadership that brought results.[11]

Military surveys

During the first half of the eighteenth century, considerable progress in topographical mapping had been made by the military surveyors trained at the Royal Military Academy, founded by Royal Warrant in 1741 at Woolwich, to the southeast of London. These surveyors passed to the Corps of Engineers, a department of the Board of Ordnance, with particular responsibility for the care and maintenance of fortifications and the defence of the realm. Naturally, such a responsibility involved the compilation of detailed maps, plans and surveys. It was set down that the functions of the Chief Engineer were:

. . . to be well-skilled in all parts of the Mathematicks, more particularly in Stereometry [the measure of three dimensions], Altemetry [the measurement of altitudes] and Geodoesia [the measurement of the shape of the earth]. To take Distances, Heights, Depths, Surveys of Land, Measure of solid Bodies, and to cut any part of ground to a proportion given; . . . and to be perfect in Architecture, civil and military, . . . to draw and design the situation of any

place, in their due Prospects, Uprights, and Perspective; . . . To keep perfect draughts of . . . Fortifications, Forts, and Fortresses of Our Kingdom, their situation, figure and profile, . . . To make Plots or Models of all manner of Fortification, both Forts or Camps, commanded by Us to be erected for Our Service . . .[12]

Over the years, the corps developed mathematical surveying to a degree of refinement comparable with that being undertaken in France by means of base-lines and primary triangles. Details were filled in from secondary triangles, either by eye or by the use of plane table methods. Officers and civilian members of the service undertook the first systematic survey of a large area of the country, the Military Survey of Scotland, between 1747 and 1755. It was begun by Colonel David Watson (who died a few years later, in 1762), but is now permanently associated with the name of the Scottish surveyor William Roy (1726–1790).

The work of William Roy

The survey of Scotland was not, however, based on triangulation. Rather, it was a military reconnaissance, undertaken as a rapid response survey following the outbreak of rebellion. It was used to map roads, settlements and the major physical

PLATE 6.22 *The surveyor's waywiser, an instrument used for measuring distances in miles, giving a distance reading according to the revolution of the large wheel. The modern pocket version used for measuring distances on a map works on exactly the same principle.*

PLATE 6.23 *William Roy conducting a survey near Loch Rannoch, as part of his military survey of Scotland in 1745–1755. Six parties of surveyors worked in the field under Roy's direction, each of which comprised a surveyor and six men: one to carry the theodolite, two to measure each chain for the fore and back stations, and one man to act as a batman.*

features of Scotland for use during likely military operations. In 1785, William Roy wrote:

The rise and progress of the rebellion . . . convinced Government of what infinite importance it would be to the State that a country, so very inaccessible by nature, should be thoroughly explored and laid open, by establishing military posts in its inmost recesses, and carrying roads of communication to its remotest parts. With a view to the commencement of arrangements of this sort, a body of infantry was encamped at Fort Augustus in 1747 . . . at which camp my much-respected friend, the late Lieutenant-General Watson, then Deputy Quarter-Master General in North Britain . . . first conceived the idea of making a map of the Highlands. As Assistant Quarter-Master, it fell to my lot to begin, and afterwards to have a considerable share in, the execution of that map; which being . . . meant at first to be confined to the Highlands only, was nevertheless at last extended to the Lowlands; and thus

made general in what related to the mainland of Scotland, the islands . . . not having been surveyed.

Although this work, which is still in . . . an unfinished state, possessed considerable merit, and perfectly answered the purpose for which it was originally intended; yet having been carried out with instruments of the common, or even inferior kind, and the sum allowed for it being inadequate to the execution of so great a design in the best manner, it is rather to be considered as a magnificent military sketch, than a very accurate map of a country. It would, however, have been completed, and many of its imperfections no doubt remedied; but the breaking out of the war of 1755 prevented both, by furnishing service of other kind for those who had been employed upon it.[13]

From 1747 to 1749, the survey was carried out by Roy himself, still a young man and apparently the only trained surveyor engaged in fieldwork.

Although he was not at the time in the Army at all, he was attached to the Quartermaster's Department as a civilian assistant, working with the military. He did not receive a commission until 1756, shortly after the outbreak of the Seven Years' War, when he was nearly thirty years old. Indeed, it is not certain whether he received his cartographic training as a civilian or in the service of the Board of Ordnance. From 1749 until the completion of the survey in 1755, six parties of surveyors were working in the field under Roy's direction (Plate 6.23). Each of these parties comprised a surveyor and six men: one to carry the theodolite, two to measure with the chain for the fore and back stations, and the remaining man to act as batman or factotum. In addition to theodolites, the surveyors used surveying compasses called 'circumferenters' and chains, from over ten to just under thirteen metres long. No observations for latitude and longitude were taken, nor are these indicated on the finished sheets. The sheets of the survey were oriented to magnetic north and were drawn at a scale of one inch to 1,000 yards (or 1:36,000), a scale which was never again used for official maps in Britain.

The finished survey was never printed, but reductions were engraved and published in Roy's *Military Antiquities*, published in 1774. Each surveyor kept a field book, in which were recorded station angles, measurements and intersections, and a sketch book in which to delineate 'the face of the country'. Unfortunately, none of these has survived. Detail was filled by eye or by intersection from the measured lines. The finished map was thus built up from a series of route surveys (a method used some years later in a survey of the Indian subcontinent), with speed taking preference over accuracy, as inclement weather conditions in winter rendered fieldwork difficult if not impossible. Relief was boldly depicted by a combination of hill-shading and crude hachuring in the direction of the slope. Rivers were shown in blue, roads in brown, and settlements in red. Woodland and forests were represented by green tree symbols, parallel hatching depicted cultivated land, and stippling was used for sands and shallows.

For some forty or so years following Roy's completion of the Military Survey in Scotland, little interest was taken in the maps. They had been placed on deposit in the Royal Library in 1761, where they were stored and occasionally consulted. There they remained, almost forgotten, until Aaron Arrowsmith (1750–1823) learned of their existence in 1805 and sought permission to use them as source materials for a new map of Scotland which he was preparing for the 'Parliamentary Commission for making roads and building bridges in the Highlands of Scotland'. In this compilation, Arrowsmith also made use of over sixty observations for latitude, nautical charts of the Western Isles, local surveys and estate maps loaned by the local landowners. Published in 1807 in four large sheets, at a scale of 1:253,440, the map was entitled *Map of Scotland constructed from original materials obtained under the authority of the Parliamentary Commissioners making roads and building bridges in the Highlands of Scotland*. It remained the standard map of the country for over forty years, during which time it underwent several reissues and revisions, until the Ordnance Survey finally completed its primary triangulation of the country late in the 1840s.

Roy maintained his interest in surveying throughout his active career. As early as 1760–1762 he advocated the establishment of a triangulation for the whole of the British Isles, incorporating the work done previously in the survey of Scotland. Many years later he wrote:

On the conclusion of the peace in 1763 (which ended the Seven Years' War), it came for the first time under the consideration of government, to make a general survey of the whole island at the public cost . . . whereof the direction was to have been committed to my charge . . . by extending the great triangles quite to the northern extremity of the island, and filling them in from the original map.[14]

Such a survey was to result in maps at a scale of one inch to one mile (1:63,360), based on accurate triangulation – in other words, the basic idea for what was to become the Ordnance Survey some forty years later. At the time, no further progress on the idea was made, no doubt – as ever – on grounds of cost.

In 1766 Roy raised the matter again. In the previous year he had been appointed Surveyor-General of Coasts and Engineer for making and directing Military Surveys in Great Britain. He was directed: 'to inspect, survey and make Reports from time to time of the state of the Coasts and Districts of the Country adjacent to the Coasts of this Kingdom and Islands thereunto belonging', encompassing fortifications as well as mapping tasks. In Roy's view, maps were fundamental to his profession, and he submitted a scheme to George III (1738–1820) in which it was proposed to make use of the new county surveys being published by private proprietors and mapmakers. These were being issued, or were in active preparation, at the one inch scale or larger. Roy commented that:

There are already good Surveys made by different people, of . . . Middlesex, Hertfordshire, Berkshire, Hampshire, Dorsetshire, Devonshire, Hertfordshire

and Shropshire, . . . Sussex, . . . Cornwall, . . . Surrey, . . . Kent, Bedfordshire, Buckinghamshire, Oxfordshire, Northamptonshire, Huntingdonshire, Worcestershire, Cumberland & the Bishopric of Durham, are carrying on in the same manner, . . . Such a number of Counties being already either surveyed or Surveying, it is not to be doubted, but that in time, the others will likewise be done.[15]

As though foreshadowing the establishment of the Ordnance Survey, Roy proposed the measurement of an arc of meridian to assist in the accurate determination of latitudes and longitudes and to provide information on the figure of the earth. In the same proposition to George III he stated: 'In carrying on the Serieses [sic] of Triangles, it would be useful to trace one grand Meridian line, thro' the whole extent of the Island, marked by Obelisks from distance to distance like that thro' France'.[16] At the time, military surveyors were otherwise occupied, but Roy continued to advocate the establishment of a survey to publish a map on the one inch scale right up to the time of his death in 1790. His suggestion was that the survey should be based upon a proper, scientific triangulation of the whole country, beginning with the measurement of a base six or eight miles in length located in open, level country, such as Cambridgeshire, from which principal and secondary triangles could be extended. In addition, 'only proper persons' were to be employed, 'furnished with good Instruments', and they were to observe 'Serieses of Triangles along the Coast, and along the remarkable Ridges of Hills and principal Rivers'. In this way 'the Situations of all the material points would be truly fixed with regard to one another, and thence the Great Outlines of the Country would be truly determined'.[17]

With such interests, and with his association with the Royal Society, it was perhaps inevitable that Roy should be charged with the operations which connected the Royal Observatory at Greenwich with the meridian of Paris by triangulation. As early as 1783, César François Cassini de Thury had proposed a co-operative venture between France and England. In October of that year, the Comte d'Adhémar, French ambassador to Great Britain, presented to Charles James Fox a copy of an essay entitled *Sur la jonction de Douvres à Londres* written by Cassini de Thury. The essay

PLATE 6.24 *A typical late-eighteenth-century instrument-maker's trade-card, illustrating several of his wares, including a small telescope, a plane-table, a waywiser, a sextant, a theodolite and a globe.*

described the advantages of collaboration between the observatories of Paris and Greenwich, for the purpose of precisely measuring the difference in latitude and longitude at the two establishments. At the time, there was an apparent discrepancy of some eleven seconds of arc for the longitude and some fifteen seconds of arc for the latitude. The text of the essay was referred to the Royal Society and Cassini's proposals were received by that august body with somewhat mixed feelings, particularly with regard to the supposed error in the position of the Greenwich Observatory. Nevertheless, the President of the Royal Society, Sir Joseph Banks (1743–1820), approached William Roy, who had been promoted to major-general, to undertake the survey.

For the purpose, Roy proposed the measurement of a base-line, five miles (8.0465 km) in length, on Hounslow Heath, then still in the open and flat countryside to the west of London. A chain of triangles was carried thence to Dover, where the link with the French triangulation was made. On 21 August 1784, a summer Saturday afternoon, the line was measured in the presence of George III, Sir Joseph Banks and other luminaries of the Royal Society in an almost carnival atmosphere. The details of the event were recorded minutely in the *Philosophical Transactions*: how the line was measured three times – firstly,

with a one hundred-foot (thirty metre) chain made by Jesse Ramsden; secondly, with seasoned twenty-foot (6.1-metre) deal rods; and thirdly, with rods of glass tubing. All of these measuring devices had been checked against a standard, in this case a finely divided brass scale graduated to be read by vernier scales down to one thousandth of an inch (0.0256 mm). The actual linear measurements were carried out according to rigorous procedures to ensure accuracy. As a check on linear expansion and contraction of the measuring equipment, temperature and humidity changes were constantly monitored. The measurements were finally completed eleven days later, and Roy was able to announce that the base measured was 27,404.0137 feet (8,352.743 metres), corrected to sea level after 'throwing out some useless decimals', as Roy put it.

Despite the rapid progress which Roy had made in the measurement of the Hounslow Heath base, the observations for carrying the triangulation to the Kent coast were not to begin until the summer of 1787, a delay of three years which was a matter of great disappointment to Roy. The main reason for the delay was the need to design and build instruments specifically for the project. In 1784, Roy had ordered a theodolite from Jesse Ramsden, the instrument which became known as the 'Great Theodolite' (Plate 6.7). It was a combination of a

PLATE 6.25 *A map of the Channel survey from the* Philosophical Transactions *of the Royal Society (Volume LXXX) for 1790. The triangles spanning the Channel were the largest ever attempted. The survey revealed that England was badly mapped, and encouraged the establishment of the Ordnance Survey.*

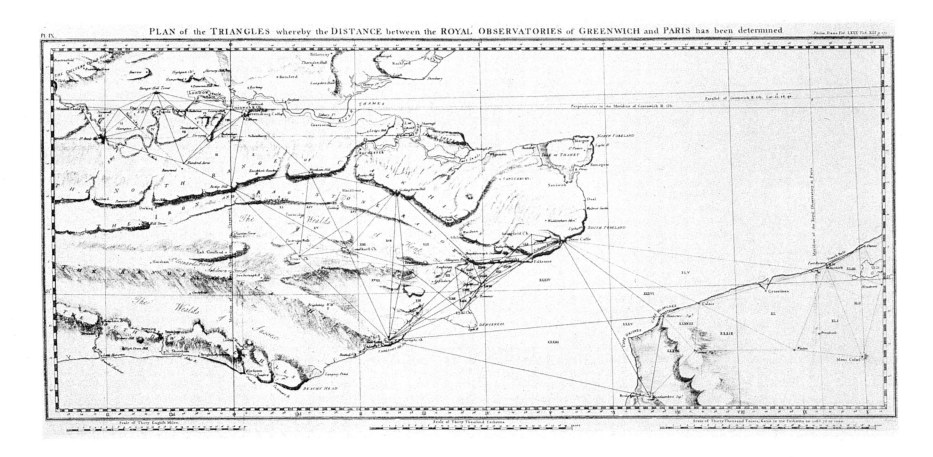

PLAN of the TRIANGLES whereby the DISTANCE between the ROYAL OBSERVATORIES of GREENWICH and PARIS has been determined

PLATE 6.26 *Portrait of the Duke of Richmond, Master General of His Majesty's Ordnance, by Romney. The Duke of Richmond obtained the royal assent for the continuation of the general survey of Great Britain started by William Roy.*

transit telescope for taking vertical angles and a graduated brass circle fitted with a telescope for taking horizontal angles down to fractions of a second of arc. During 1786 Roy, now sixty years old and in increasingly poor health, wrote in frustration at the total lack of progress that was being made:

It will be yet some days before Ramsden can possibly finish the Division and after that the semicircle for the uppermost telescope is to divide, the levels to adjust, and a number of other small things to do, all of which require time . . . . It is hard upon me to have this operation hanging over my head for another year, without any fault of mine: But with such a man as Ramsden there is no help for it.[18]

Ramsden's theodolite was finally delivered to Roy in July 1787, the end of the month witnessing its establishment on the end of the Hounslow Heath base. Despite the delays and frustrations, which were largely of Ramsden's making, Roy was fulsome in his praise for the instrument:

[It is] a great theodolet, rendered extremely perfect; having this advantage in particular, which common theodolets have not, that its transit telescope can be nicely adjusted by inversion on its supports; that is to say, it can be turned upside down, in the same manner that transit-instruments are, in fixed observatories.[19]

Weighing just over ninety kilograms it was a fine precision machine, a work of craftsmanship. Thereafter matters proceeded at a considerably more rapid pace. Roy had compiled a map of the intended disposition of the triangles, 19.32 to 28.98 kilometres to a side, from Greenwich to the Kent coast and from coast to coast across the Channel, and the series on the French side in the vicinity of Calais and Dunkirk, with an eye to possible future surveys.

At Dover, the French were represented by three members of the *Académie* – Jacques-Dominique Cassini (the fourth member of the Cassini dynasty), Pierre-François Méchain and Adrien Marie Legendre – who stayed until the final details of the operation had been worked out. It was decided by the French and the British to use white lights and reflector lamps for the signals on either side of the Channel, the actual observations being made on clear, calm nights.

The connection with the French triangulation

was finally achieved at two stations on either side of the Channel – at Dover Castle and Fairlight Head on the English side, and at Cap Blancnez and Montlambert on the French side – on 17 October 1787: 'thereby to establish for ever the triangular connection between the two countries', as Roy wrote (Plate 6.25).[20]

The operation conducted by Roy and his surveying parties was the first co-operative venture of its kind carried out on British soil, and the triangulation exposed many errors on even the best maps of England then available. To the end of his life – Roy died in 1790 – he continued to press on in his efforts to launch a general survey of Great Britain, maintaining that it would be a pity to make redundant the expensive instruments and the body of trained surveyors alike. In his last paper, published posthumously, Roy wrote:

. . . the writer of this account cannot but help consider it as being incumbent on him to recommend that the trigonometrical operation, so successfully begun, should certainly be continued, and gradually extended over the whole island. Compared with the greatness of the object, the annual expence to the publick would be a mere trifle . . . . The honour of the nation is concerned in having at least as good a map of this as of any other country.[21]

William Roy's epitaph was the splendid One-Inch series of the Ordnance Survey.

The Ordnance Survey

Shortly after William Roy's death in 1790, the Duke of Richmond, Master-General of the Board of Ordnance, obtained the Royal assent for the continuation of the survey (Plate 6.26). Richmond had recently acquired a Ramsden theodolite as a result of his interest in mapping. During the 1780s, he had been influential in securing men and equipment for Roy, and he was anxious to ensure that the idea of a national survey had not died with Roy, being mindful of the possible threat of war with France. Richmond considered it prudent to have all such mapping and surveying activities retained in the military while France was in a state of revolution. Thus from 1791 the Trigonometrical Survey of Great Britain, as it was known, became a military project without outside support. The Board of Ordnance was continued as the Ordnance Survey, with the rôle of the Royal Society in surveying and mapping activities coming to an end altogether. This marked the effective transfer of scientific aims to primarily military objectives. As Harley and O'Donoghue comment:

By the end of the eighteenth century Britain was accustomed to waging war abroad and her military leaders . . . were learning the lesson that adequate military intelligence required systematic geographical knowledge of the theatre of conflict. They were equally convinced that 'if government must have such a knowledge of the enemy's country, it is still more requisite that it should know its own'. Both defensive and offensive warfare required the same cartographic information and it is in this light that the Board of Ordnance reformulated the national role of the Trigonometrical Survey. Under their management it was 'to ascertain by a correct trigonometrical operation, the situation of all Head-lands upon the Channel, Eminences, and the remarkable objects throughout the Country, thereby preparing correct materials for a geographical description of it'.[22]

The Duke of Richmond had commissioned surveys of his estates in Sussex. To this end he employed two trained local surveyors, Thomas Yeakell the elder and William Gardner. They were at the time engaged in the compilation of a large-scale county map of Sussex, *An actual Topographical Survey of the County of Sussex* (Plate 6.27), at a scale of two inches to one mile (1:31,680). However, only four sheets of this survey were published, between 1778 and 1782; the map was never completed, for through the good offices of the duke, Yeakell and Gardner both obtained important positions at the Ordnance office in London.

From the beginning, the cartographers of the Ordnance Survey were under some influence, directly or indirectly, of the general style of the private county mapmakers of the eighteenth century. The Yeakell and Gardner map was republished by William Faden in 1795, this time at the one-inch scale (1:63,360), having been completed

(continued on page 213)

PLATE 6.27 An actual Topographical Survey of the County of Sussex *by Thomas Yeakell and William Gardner, issued in four sheets, 1778–1783. Here may be seen the close resemblance of such private surveys to the early editions of the Ordnance Survey maps and vice versa.*

PLATE 6.28 *(opposite)*
*Chromolithographs by
Charles Donovan of
nineteenth-century Ordnance
surveyors, pictured both in
the field and outside the
Academy at Woolwich. Top:
the Royal Sappers and
Miners, 1837. Bottom: the
Royal Engineers, 1887.*

PLATE 6.29 *(left) Part of
the Ordnance Survey One-
Inch map of Sussex. The
map bears a close
resemblance to private
surveys such as those of
Yeakell and Gardner.*

by Thomas Gream. The connection between the private mapmakers and the new Ordnance Survey mapmakers may also be illustrated by the fact that the Sussex map, in its Faden issue, was the first published map based on data obtained from the Trigonometrical Survey.

Work on the national survey began, for strategic reasons, in Kent and the southern part of Essex facing north Kent across the Thames estuary, using the data from Roy's triangulation. Officers of the Royal Artillery, trained at the Royal Military Academy at Woolwich, were chosen to conduct the survey under the leadership of Lieutenant-Colonel Edward Williams, assisted by Captain William Mudge (1762–1820). They were assisted by a civilian, Isaac Dalby (1744–1824), later professor of mathematics at Woolwich. The detailed plans of strategic areas were supplied by the Royal Engineers. Williams died in 1798 and was succeeded by Mudge, now promoted to the rank of major. In 1805, a Corps of Royal Military Surveyors and Draughtsmen was created, its complement trained by and for the Ordnance Survey. As a result, surveying methods were standardized and considerably improved. Although the Corps was disbanded in 1817, it was re-established a few years later, in 1823, by Major Thomas Frederick Colby (1784–1852), who was chief executive of the Ordnance Survey from 1809, and served as Director-General from 1820 to 1848. In 1824 the military connection was further enhanced when the Corps became the 13th (Survey) Company of the Royal Engineers.

As the work of the Survey got under way, a certain amount of suspicion and friction among the general public was almost inevitable. Ever since the days of the first great fiscal survey of the country undertaken in the years following the Norman Conquest of England in 1066 surveyors had been subject to prejudice and suspicion. Landowners would deny access to their property, and on occasion men of the Survey would avoid trouble by skirting round estates. However, not long after the first sheets of the Ordnance map became available to the interested public in 1801 (the Mudge map of Kent), it was realized that here were better maps than anything published hitherto. Influential landowners and other citizens organized groups to request that their counties or districts be mapped straight away, out of turn if

necessary, even offering a guarantee to purchase a number of finished copies if the Survey would undertake to come into their areas without delay. This appears to have been motivated not, unfortunately, by a sense of public-spiritedness, but more by a sense of self-interest. The landowners were hoping to have their property surveyed quickly and partly out of government expense, so that marshy areas could then be easily identified and drained for profit. The Ordnance Survey took on civilian surveyors and the mapping of many scattered areas was contracted out (Plate 6.30).

The Russian Empire surveyed

In the Russian Empire no organized attempt to survey the vast tracts which extended from the Baltic shores in the west to the Pacific coast of Siberia in the east was made until 1720, during the reign of Tsar Peter I ('Peter the Great') (reigned 1682–1725). In that year he issued an order for thirty 'geometers' from the Russian Navy to be sent into the provinces to prepare surveys, maps and detailed geographical and topographical descriptions. Six years later, Tsarina Catherine I ordered all maps previously prepared to be transferred to the Academy of Sciences for verification and revision.

It was at about this time that the two de l'Isle brothers – Joseph-Nicolas (1688–1768) and Louis de l'Isle de la Croyère (who died in 1741) – were in St Petersburg and were placed in charge of the Russian surveys. For his work Joseph-Nicolas was paid the handsome salary of 1,800 roubles a year. In addition to setting up a School of Astronomy, the de l'Isles created a Geographical Department at the Academy in 1735 (or, rather, the Geographical Department was accorded official status, having been in a state of semi-official existence for some time). This, to some extent, took care of their regular complaints about the lack of facilities and technical assistance. It also meant that the small band of trained geodesists assigned to the Frenchmen could be drafted to assist with the completion of a project for a general survey atlas and a detailed general map of the empire. A Russian world atlas, with twenty-seven maps, was completed by 1737: the *Atlas sochinenniy k pol'ze i upotrebleniyu yunoshestva i vsekh chitateley vedomosty i istoricheskikh knig* ('Atlas compiled for the

PLATE 6.30 *(opposite) A survey of Glenelg, c. 1872, from the* Ordnance Survey of Scotland. *The Ordnance Survey One-Inch map series of Great Britain, first issued in 1801, provided the basis for British topographical mapping for more than one hundred years.*

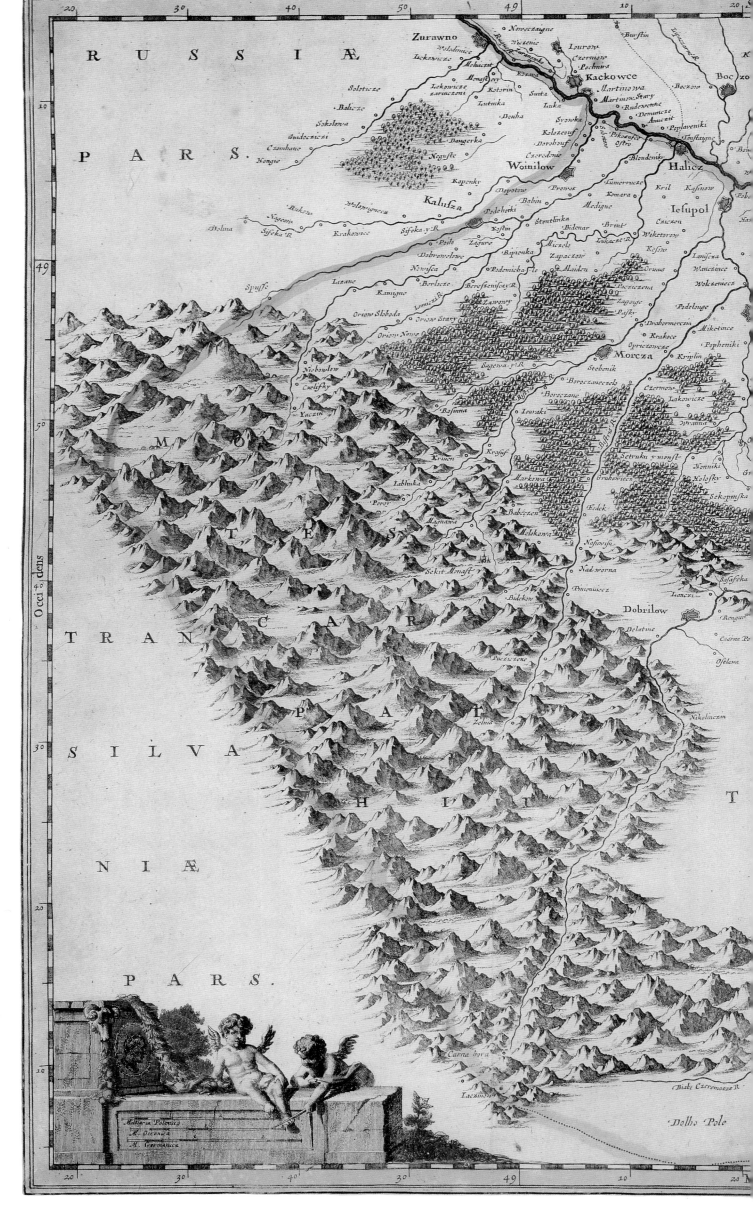

PLATE 6.31 Ukrainae
pars *by Guillaume
Levasseur de Beauplan,
1600, which is found in
some copies of Joan Blaeu's*
Atlas major *of 1662.
Levasseur de Beauplan spent
seventeen years in Russia
and Poland, founding
settlements and colonies and
carrying out military
surveys.*

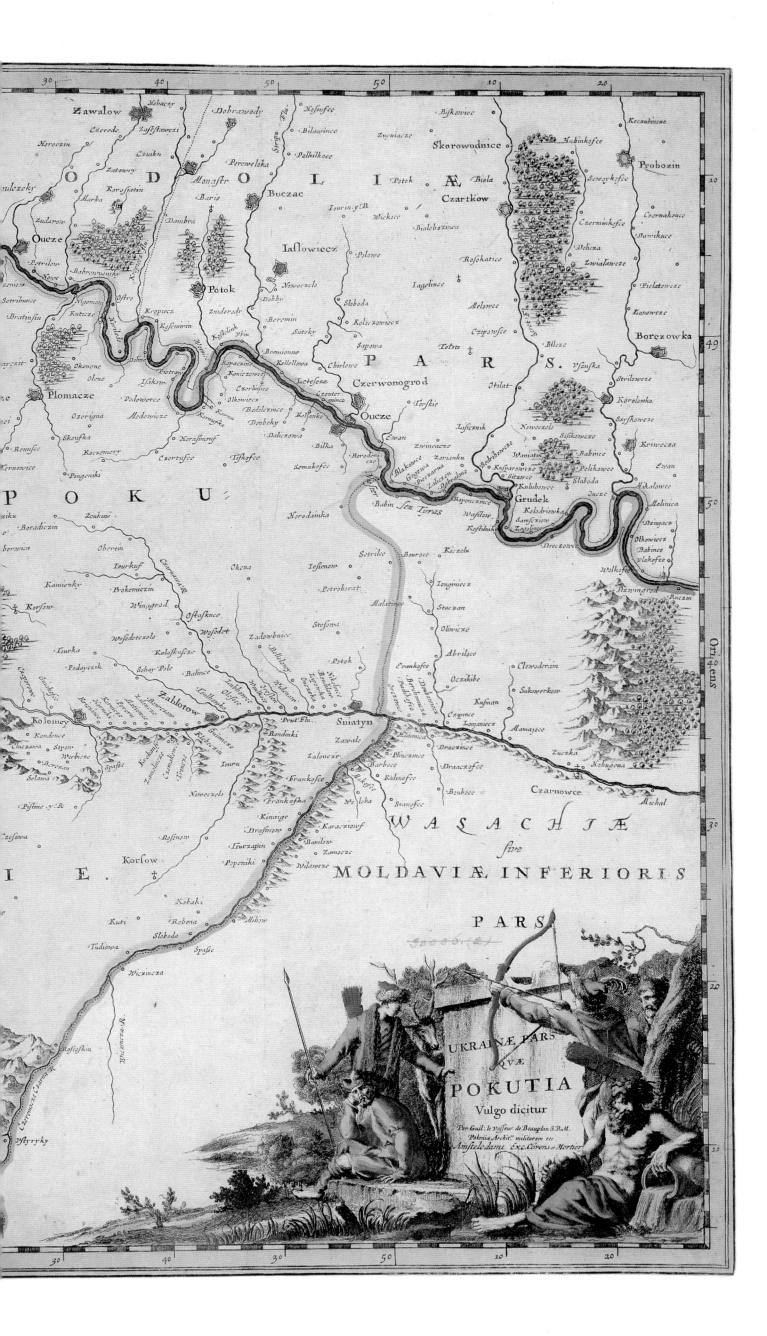

benefit and use of youth and of all readers of the new and historical books').[23]

However, it was an atlas of the Russian Empire, the *Atlas Rossiyskoy* (or *Atlas russicus*, as it is more widely known), which placed Russian mapping before the wider public, both in Russia itself and in Western Europe (Plates 6.35, 6.36). The atlas was published by the Academy in 1745, with nineteen detailed regional maps and a large general map of the empire, with editions containing brief texts, in Russian, Latin, French or German. In this famous work, thirteen maps cover European Russia at a uniform scale of 1:1,527,000 and the remaining six maps cover nearly all of Asiatic Russia except for the extreme northeast at the Chukchi peninsula and those parts in what was until recently known as Soviet Central Asia. With the publication of the *Atlas russicus*, for the first time virtually the whole Russian empire was laid down in a uniform series of maps. Building on the foundations laid down by the de l'Isles, surveyors went out to all parts of the

Empire, taking observations to obtain accurate positions of the larger towns and physical features of the areas around them.

The leading learned societies of Europe greeted the *Atlas russicus* with praise – and some criticism of its shortcomings. The compilers had themselves called for improvements, stressing that the limited time and facilities at the disposal of the cartographers had precluded the use of much of the scientific data brought back from earlier Academy expeditions into Siberia. D'Anville, as part of a detailed critique, produced an *Atlas russicus* in which he stated that 'no one could expect an atlas to include all the desirable material for otherwise no atlas would ever be put out'.[24]

In 1745, Joseph-Nicholas de l'Isle's contract in Russia expired: a new one was prepared, but he never signed it. After a further two years, he left Russia with an annual pension, having undertaken to promote the work of the Academy abroad. However, when he returned to Paris, having put some distance between himself and his erstwhile

PLATE 6.32 *(right)* Nieuwe, en seer accurate caert vande Doorgravinge om met schepen uyt de revier de Don of Tanais . . . *by Cornelis Cruys, one of the charts from the* Nieuw Pas-kaart Boek, behelsende de Groote Rivier Don of Tanais, *Amsterdam, Hendrik Donker, c. 1705.*

PLATE 6.33 *(opposite, top)* Nova descriptio geographica Tartariae magna *by Philipp Johann von Strahlenberg, 1730. This is one of the most important eighteenth-century Russian survey maps of Siberia.*

PLATE 6.34 *(opposite, bottom)* Imperii Russici tabula generalis [Generalnaya karta o rossiyskoy imperii] *by Ivan Kirilov, copper engraving, 1734. This map was prepared for an atlas of the Russian Empire.*

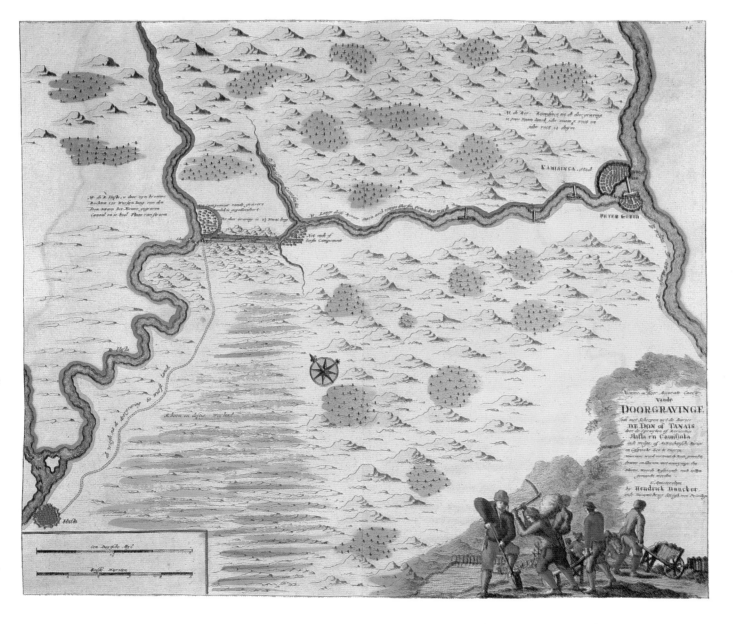

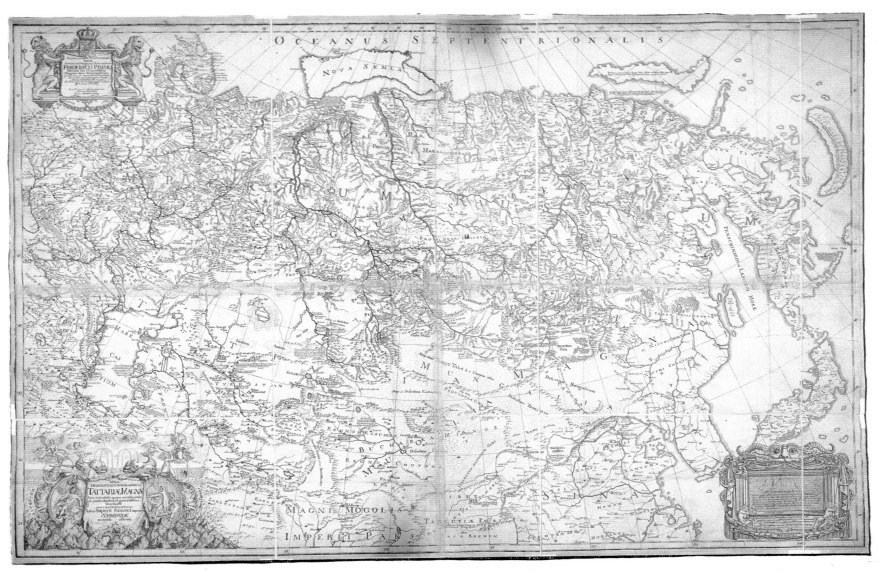

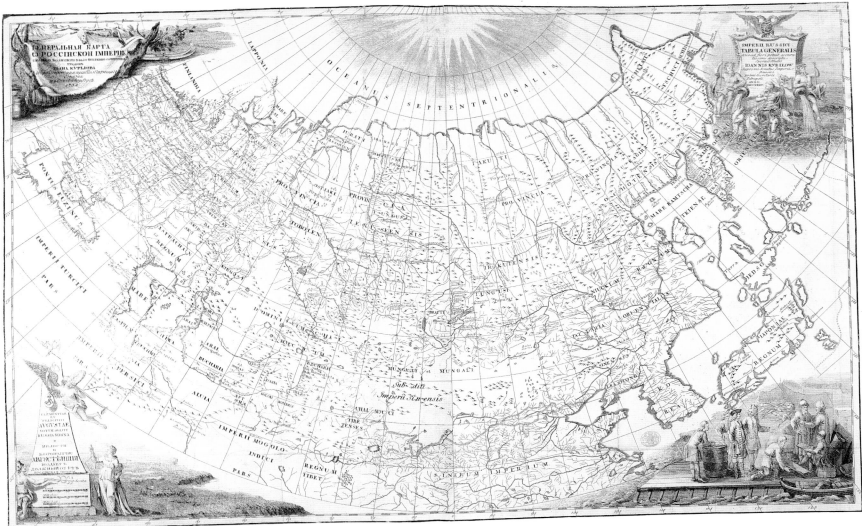

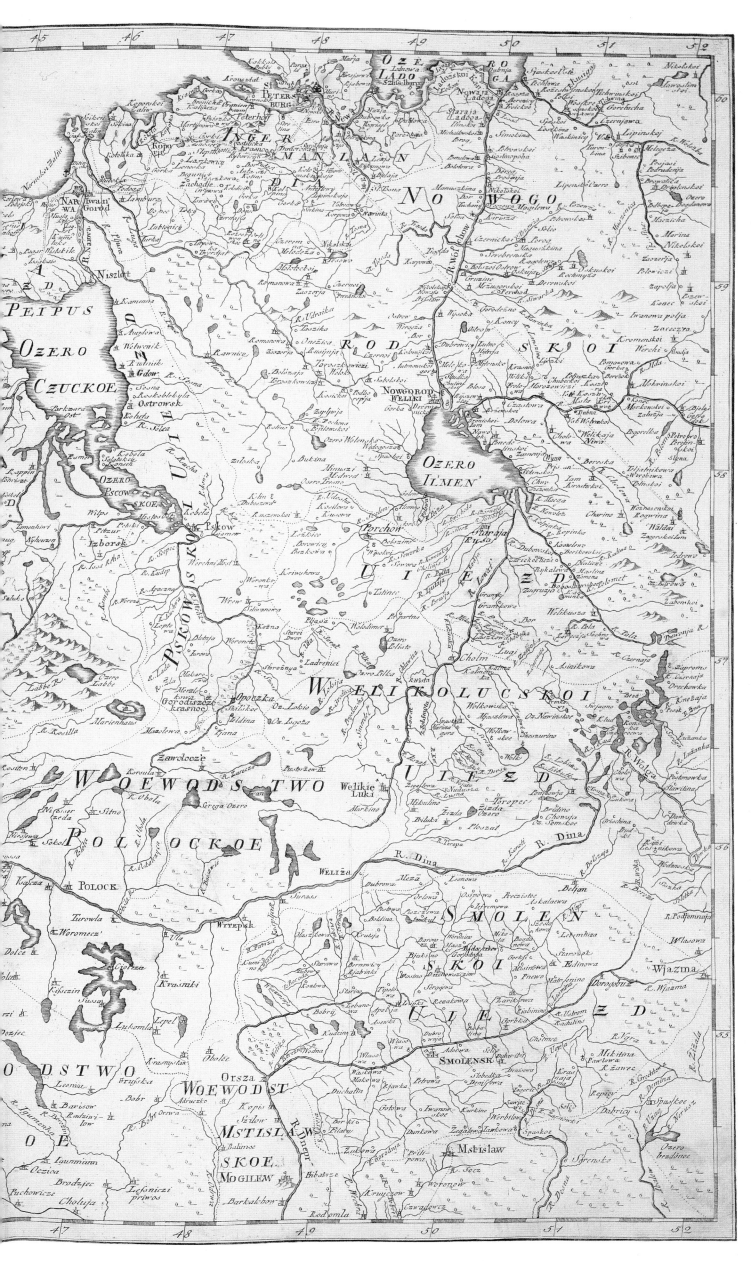

PLATE 6.35 Ducatuum
Estoniae et Livoniae
[Izobrazheniye
gertsogstev Estlyandskogo
i Liflyandskogo] *by
Jacques-Nicolas de l'Isle, St
Petersburg, 1745. This is
the general sheet showing
Estonia and Livonia from
the* Atlas Rossiyaskoy
(otherwise known as the
Atlas russicus) *published by
the Academy of Sciences in
1745 using surveys carried
out during the 1730s under
the direction of the
Frenchman de l'Isle. This is
one of the thirteen sheets
which covered European
Russia at a scale of
1:1,527,000.*

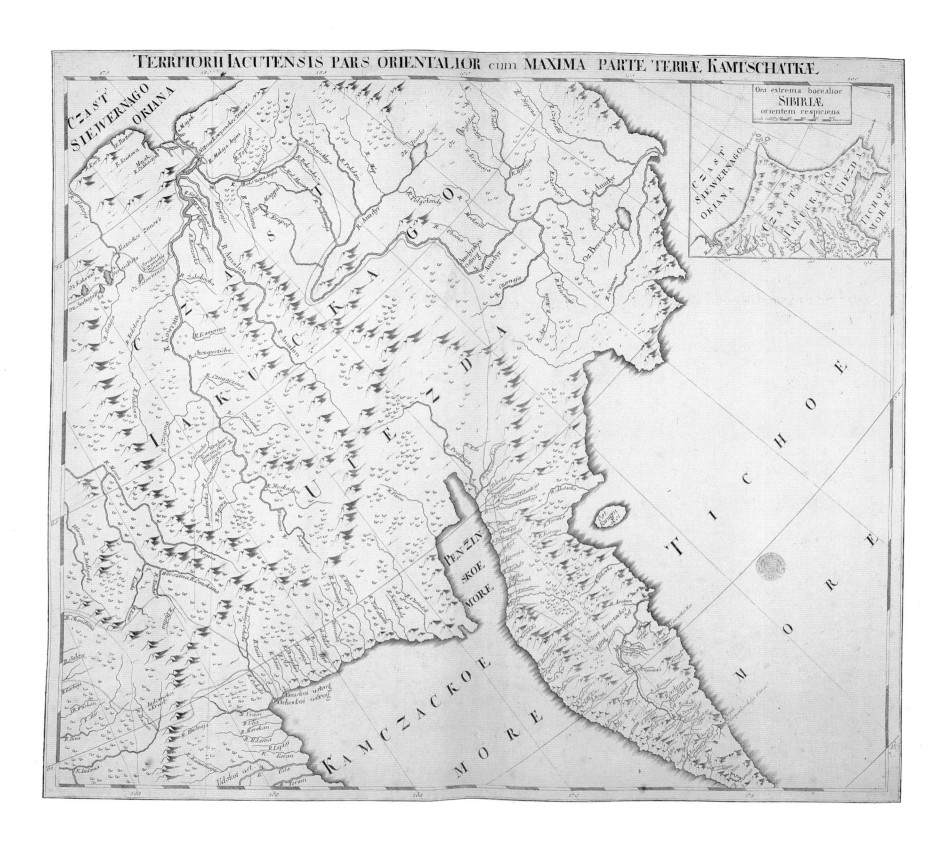

TERRITORII IACUTENSIS PARS ORIENTALIOR cum MAXIMA PARTE TERRÆ KAMTSCHATKÆ

colleagues in St Petersburg, de l'Isle adopted a decidedly hostile attitude towards Russia – whereupon his pension was withdrawn by his former employers, and members of the Academy were henceforth actively discouraged from having any contact with him.

Nearly two decades later, in 1763, Tsarina Catherine II established the General Staff under the command of a Quartermaster-General, a post created some years earlier by Peter the Great. This became the early foundation of the Military Topographical Depot in 1812. In 1816, in the region around Vilna (Vilnius, in Lithuania) which

Russia had acquired in 1795, and somewhat later in Poland (acquired in 1815), Russia began its first scientific triangulation surveys. A base-line was measured in Livonia almost ten-and-a-half kilometres in length. This base proved to be so accurate that it was used as part of the complete survey of the western frontier of Russia, extending in the north from the Arctic shores of northern Finland to Bessarabia on the north banks of the Danube delta in the south.

This new series of surveys stimulated similar works in other European countries, particularly in Sweden where a series of triangles connecting with the Russian system was made in the Aland archipelago between Sweden and Finland (then a Grand Duchy within the Russian Empire). An even more ambitious project, one of international scope, was also mooted: in 1826 the French government proposed that the Russian government participate in a measurement of the forty-eighth latitude, along a line which would have encompassed and connected the surveys of France, Bavaria and Austria thence from Chernovits in Bukovina to the Volga and perhaps even beyond. Had the ambitious project ever been realized, it would have given Europe a continuous arc extending over some 48° of longitude. However, it did not come to fruition.

Surveys in Scandinavia

Denmark surveyed

In Scandinavia, and in particular in Denmark and Sweden, uniform surveys were also in progress. In Denmark this work was carried out under the auspices of the Royal Danish Scientific Society, founded in 1742. The first triangulation commenced in 1761, following a procedure laid down by the Society, beginning with a general survey based on parallel lines which provided reference points for the location of places and features. Field surveys began in 1762, initially with only two surveyors working in the field, led by Professor Thomas Bugge (1740–1815) of the University of Copenhagen. They ran a base-line of 14,515 *alen* (or ells, an ell being equivalent to 24.7 inches or about 627 mm) from Tinghøj out to Brøndby Høj, west of Copenhagen in 1764–1765. The first maps were published as early as 1766, and detailed measurements were completed by 1820 on the scale of 1:20,000. The last maps produced by the survey had appeared by 1834.

The Danish Army General Staff was established by royal decree in 1808 and shortly after, an independent survey, again at 1:20,000, was begun with the intention of publishing a military map series.[25] The 1:20,000 scale is still in use in Denmark for a topographical map series, the Geodætisk Institut series which covers the country in 840 sheets. Additional surveys were published until, in 1830, it was decided to produce a uniform survey reduced to the 1:80,000 scale, the *Militær Topografiske Kort* (Military Topographic-

al Map) of the entire country. The specifications were enshrined in the General Staff technical manual, called *The Art of Topographical Drawing*, after which all topographical mapping activities in Denmark were placed in the capable hands of the Danish War Department.

Sweden surveyed

Across the Öresund, in Sweden, a considerable number of individual provincial maps had been published in the early part of the eighteenth century. General maps of the whole country had also been prepared and issued by the Bureau of Land Surveying between 1739 and 1747.[26] Triangulation survey work began in 1758, with a coastal survey in the southwest of the country facing Denmark from Cimrishamn to the Norwegian frontier near Frederikshall. This work was completed by 1761. Topographical surveys began with Major Gustaf Wilhelm af Tibell (1772–1832), who had served under Napoléon in the Cisalpine Republic as a military engineer and surveyor. Tibell had set up the Swedish Field Survey Corps in 1805, with the object of compiling comprehensive military maps of the country based on topographical surveys and astronomical observations, together with topographical and statistical descriptions. Field surveys were executed at 1:20,000 and special maps at the 1:100,000 scale. The *Fortifikationens-Corps* (the equivalent of the Royal Military Engineers), a body of trained and highly skilled men, was merged with the Field Survey Corps in 1809, to become the Corps of Engineers in 1811. A topographical division, the Topographical Corps, was set up in 1831, and in 1874 all official mapping activities in Sweden were reorganized under the aegis of the General Staff Topographical Division with its headquarters in the capital, Stockholm.

The General Staff 1:100,000 topographical map series for Sweden had its origins in 1815. Initially the sheets were kept in manuscript, all detail being classified secret. In 1826, when the first sheets were directed to be printed from engraved copper plates, all the officers involved were sworn to secrecy and were held individually responsible for all information contained in a given map, including the processes of engraving and printing. The completed survey consisted of 232 sheets printed in four colours, the sheets remaining in print for many years from litho-graphed transfers, regularly revised. General distribution of the 1:100,000 series commenced in 1857, several of the older sheets being produced from fresh surveys. There later followed a much more detailed 1:50,000 topographical map series which forms the basis of modern Swedish topographical mapping.

Norway surveyed

In Norway, the intention was also to provide a national survey. Earlier, parish clergy had been required to produce written descriptions of their parishes and communities for use in topographical descriptions and local mapping of the parish. By 1746, however, only a few parts of southern Norway, in the more settled areas around Christiania (Oslo) and Bergen, had been so mapped, at a scale of 1:100,000. Much of this source material, laboriously gathered over a great number of years, remained little used until the Danish cartographer Christian Jochum Pontoppidan (1739–1807) issued a detailed general map of Norway. The map, entitled *Det Nordlige [-Sydlige] Norge efter Kongelige Allernaadigst Befalning ved Hielp af gode geographiske Korter*, was published at Copenhagen in 1785–1795 in two sheets (Plate 6.37). Pontoppidan had trained in the Danish *Kongelige Landkadetkompagniet* and was a surveyor for almost thirty years (from 1773 to 1801), producing general maps of Scandinavia in 1778 and his famous *Mappa Daniae, Norvegiae et Sueciae* in 1781. Pontoppidan's new map of Norway was accompanied by a printed description (in the manner of d'Anville in Paris) called *Geographisk Oplysning*. This, together with his map and his various treatises on the accurate determination of latitude and longitude, earned Pontoppidan a reputation as a cartographer of meticulous skill and accuracy. Indeed, his maps of Norway, showing five distinct categories of political and ecclesiastical boundaries, were used in the settlement of the frontiers between Norway and Sweden in the absence of more detailed official mapping.

The frequent wars and frontier skirmishes with Denmark and Sweden emphasized the need for accurate surveys of Norway. The official mapping organization, the Norwegian Geographical Survey (first set up in 1833) was begun by the Mathematical Military School, which included

cartography as an important component of the curriculum. The first proposals were for a series on the 1:100,000 scale in fifty-four sheets, which became the so-called *rektangel* (on straightforward rectangular sheets) and *gradteig* (drawn on a graticule on latitudinal and longitudinal lines in the north of the country) series, with a proposed general map at the 1:400,000 scale. In 1805, Norway and Sweden were united under Charles XIII of Sweden. It was intended to carry out topographical surveys of the new united kingdom on a common scale and projection, but agreement on sheet formats and a common prime meridian was never reached, with the result that the two constituent parts of the kingdom maintained separate surveys and map series.

Surveys in Switzerland

In Switzerland, too, topographical map surveys were being undertaken. It requires little imagination to realize that the topography of this country posed its own particular problems. Ever since the map published in the Martin Waldseemüller edition of Ptolemy in 1513, mapmakers had been forced to contend with the difficulties of indicating distances between towns and the proper representation of topography. Most had resorted to the solution of the pictorial map, useful in its way but with little attempt at a representation of linear scale, using the time-honoured device of 'mole-hills' to depict relief, or at least to create an impression of such.

A notable effort in this regard was the *Atlas Suisse* (published in Aarau in 1796–1802) compiled by Johann Heinrich Weiss (1758–1826), Johann Rudolf Meyer (1739–1813) and Joachim Eugen Müller (1752–1833) (Plates 6.38, 6.39, 6.40). The cartographers worked on the project for ten years, up to 1797, at Meyer's own expense. They used a system of hachures and hill-shading engraved onto copper plates, which imparted a remarkable three-dimensional effect to the printed map sheets. The glaciers and other ice-covered areas in the Alps were printed in blue. The series occupied sixteen sheets and covered all of the country on a scale of 1:60,000, the final sheet appearing in 1802. For fifty years the *Atlas Suisse* constituted the best map of the country and of the Alps, and formed the basis of many other maps

PLATE 6.37 (opposite) Det Nordlige Norge . . . 1795 *by Christian Jochum Pontoppidan, copper engraving, Copenhagen, J.G. Blanchensteiner, 1795. This work was the forerunner of the mapping series issued by Norges Geografiske Opmaaling.*

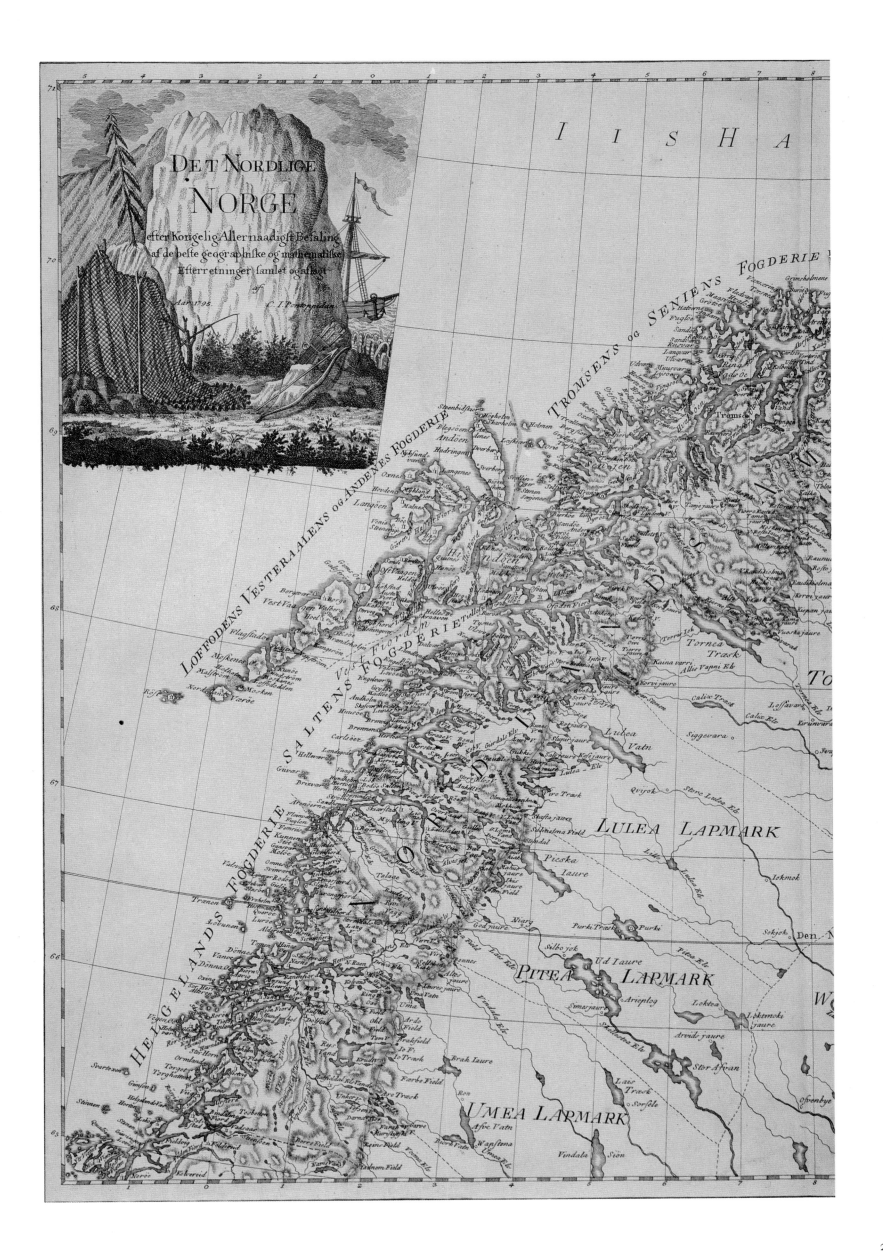

DET NORDLIGE

NORGE

efter Kongelig Allernaadigst Befaling
af de beste geographiske og mathematiske
Efterretninger samlet og afsat

af

Aar 1795.   C. I. Pontoppidan

PARTIE du CANTON de LUCERNE d' UNTERWALDEN d' URI

Echelle en Toises à 6 pieds de FRANCE

PLATE 6.38 *Detail of Lucerne from the* Atlas Suisse *by Johann Heinrich Weiss and Joachim Eugen Müller, published in sixteen sheets with colour printing to show glaciers, Aarau, 1796–1802.*

PARTIE DU C.°° DU VALLAIS DU DÉPARTEMENT DU MONT BLANC

AVERTISSEMENT

PARTIE DU C.°° DU VALLAIS ET LE VERSANT DES EAUX DU PIEMONT

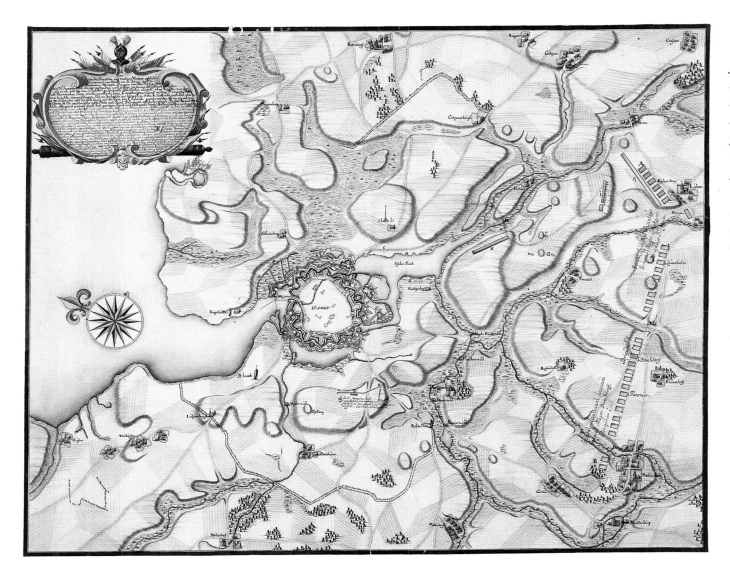

PLATES 6.39, 6.40
*(opposite) Sheets and detail
from the* Atlas Suisse *by
Johann Rudolf Meyer,
Johann Heinrich Weiss and
Joachim Eugen Müller,
published in sixteen sheets
with colour printing to show
glaciers, Aarau, 1796–
1802. The* Atlas Suisse *was
the forerunner of many fine
topographical maps from
Switzerland.*

PLATE 6.41 *(left)* Plan
von die Situation und
Vestung Wismar *by
Heinrich von Scheele,
manuscript in inks and
colours, c. 1712.*

produced in Switzerland. It was only superseded by the appearance of the Dufour maps.

The first uniform national survey of Switzerland was begun in earnest in 1830, by General Guillaume Henri Dufour (1787–1875), of Geneva. The first sheets were published some twelve years later, in 1842. The entire task was completed by 1876 and the whole survey comprised twenty-five sheets at a scale of 1:100,000. 'Far from being a pioneering effort that would require immediate revision, the Dufour atlas proved to be a model of accuracy and artistic delineation, not only for future mapmakers of Switzerland, but for cartographers at large.'[27] The sheets of the atlas were used as the basis for many later surveys at various scales, all of them making reference to the original Dufour maps. Lettering and benchmarks, buildings, roads, boundaries and so on were printed in black; slopes and passes and other physical features which could not be shown by the use of contour lines were depicted using brown hachures, while black hachures were used to indicate rocky outcrops and precipices, thus giving a pictorial representation by imagined oblique lighting. A bronze tint was used to show horizontal views, and all water bodies were printed in blue. All this resulted in the aesthetically very beautiful Swiss topographical map series, still in use today. It is considered by many to be some of the most attractive general-purpose topographical mapping ever published.

The German territories

Similar topographical surveys were being established, or were in the course of preparation, in Germany and the Netherlands. Most of the individual territories of Germany possessed surveys of one kind or another, and indeed most of the twenty-six constituent territories, led by Bavaria, Saxony, Württemberg and Baden, possessed maps dating back at least to the sixteenth century. In Bavaria, for example, a French military engineer in the occupying French forces, Rigobert Bonne (1727–1794) made a survey of the kingdom. The value of such a survey was soon appreciated by Joseph I, who instituted his own topographical survey of Bavaria with the aid of enlisted French

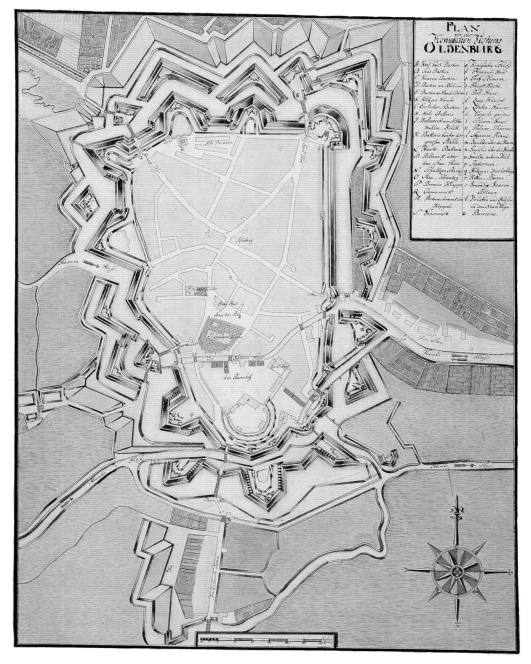

engineers seconded from the French Republic, with the establishment of a Topographical Bureau at Munich. In the 1820s, similar work was begun in Franconia in central southern Germany.

The Netherlands surveyed

Just as other European countries appreciated the necessity of having uniform national mapping surveys, so too did the Netherlands. The lack of unity in the former Republic of the United Netherlands was reflected in its mapping. To be sure, in some districts there existed fine and detailed mapping at a variety of scales and of varying degrees of accuracy, particularly in the western provinces of the country. But in many other less wealthy and less populated parts, the available mapping left much to be desired.

The first triangulation survey of the Netherlands was established by Baron Cornelius Rudolphus Theodorus Krayenhoff (1758–1840), who learned the techniques of surveying from his father, a military engineer and surveyor.[28] Krayenhoff was asked by the Batavian Republic (as the Netherlands was then called) to compile a map of the country, at the scale of 1:115,200, in eight sheets, plus a title-sheet. (This rather odd-looking scale equates to a scale of about one inch to rather less than two miles.) The new map was to be called the *Groote Kaart van de Bataafsche Republiek*. Ever intent on economy, the government plan was to use existing mapping as the basis of the new map, a proper survey being projected only for those areas where good quality mapping was wanting. Krayenhoff soon realized that the best, and indeed the only, solution was to institute a precise triangulation of the entire country. To this end, in 1800 he began by measuring a base-line of 1,000 *Rijnlandsche roeden* (3,767 metres) on the frozen Gouwzee in the north of the country. Progress was rapid and two sheets of the new map were soon at drafting stage. Professor J.H. van Swinden, who carried out the drafting work, had been involved in the mathematical calculations for the French triangulation by Méchain and Delambre and he brought with him his considerable expertise. As a result, Krayenhoff was sufficiently impressed to request government approval to tie the triangulation into the existing French network, so that the whole of western

Europe from Spain to Denmark might be linked by a uniform network of primary triangles.

The request fell upon deaf ears, but Krayenhoff was able to complete his initial primary triangulation work by 1811. Krayenhoff tied his triangulation to the French network at Dunkirk-Mont Cassel in Flanders, giving a network of 162 primary triangles.[29] This was the basis for the resultant *Topographische en Militaire Kaart van het Koninkrijk der Nederlanden* and other topographical maps until 1900 and later (Plate 6.44).

In the meantime, the Batavian Republic was abolished and became the Kingdom of Holland under Louis Napoléon. Mapping activities henceforth were placed in the hands of the War Department. The original eight sheets of the projected map were augmented after 1807 following the incorporation of the German provinces of Ost-Friesland and Jever into the kingdom, giving a sixteen-sheet map. Printing of the map was transferred to Paris during this so-called 'French Period' (which lasted from 1811 to 1813). Some of the sheets were published or even republished, but seven of the sheets were not completed by the time of the collapse of the French Empire in 1815. The following year, the Paris plates were returned to the Netherlands, where they were revised and completed so that in 1823 the original eight sheets were published for the first time in complete form. During their rule, the French had introduced a cadastral survey (see p. 199) in the Netherlands in 1811 for administrative and internal revenue purposes. In the years 1811–1831 cadastral maps for the whole country were issued at a scale of 1:2,500. These did not, however, show topography in any great detail.

Following the final defeat of Napoléon at Waterloo in 1815, the northern Netherlands and the former Austrian Netherlands (Belgium) were united under King Willem I. One of the king's first decrees had been to establish an Army and, in 1814, a Topographical Office, under the Corps of Engineers. This was subdivided in 1816 into the First and Second Bureaus. The Second Bureau came under the command of the General Staff and became known as the Military Reconnaissance Survey. This evolved into a complete mapping service, the *Topographische Dienst*, which still produces the official topographical mapping of the Netherlands at various scales.

Under the capable leadership of the Arnhem-born military engineer Jan Egbert van Gorkum (1780–1832), during the period from 1816 to 1830 the survey produced the 1:25,000 maps of Belgium prior to the separation of Belgium and the Netherlands in 1830. This used the cadastral series as well as the Ferraris 1:11,520 survey. A fresh triangulation survey tied these older surveys into the kingdom's existing network. During these troubled years the survey was quartered at Mons, not far from the French frontier, from 1816 to 1817, then at Kortrijk for three years and finally at Gent for a further ten years. Van Gorkum laid the foundations and the general specification of the modern topographical map in his comprehensive manual, the *Leerboek der Topographie*. But despite van Gorkum's comprehensive and time-consuming work, the manual was, sadly, never published.

In 1820, a royal commission was set up to examine the general state of topographical mapping in the Netherlands. Its most important brief was to determine the types and scales of mapping best suited to government and public requirements. The commission recommended production of a series at 1:10,000, to be reduced to 1:50,000 for printing and general circulation. Most of the recommendations of the commission were never acted upon, largely due to van Gorkum's opposition. The general scheme and the calculations for the 1:50,000 series were eventually adopted in 1842 as the basis for the *Topographische en Militaire Kaart van het Koningrijk der Nederlanden*.[30] The activities of the Military Reconnaissance Survey in Belgium ceased with the outbreak of the revolution and the subsequent partition of the Netherlands into the modern Belgium and the Netherlands in 1830. Van Gorkum transferred his staff from Gent to Leiden north of the border, the town where the lithographic department was later established.

Following the independence of Belgium in 1830, the Dutch Army remained in concentration along the frontier, which ran through sparsely inhabited country in Brabant. A detailed survey was begun in the vicinity of Tilburg, not far from the frontier itself, as the town was then the headquarters of the Army. This General Staff survey was extended in 1839 to cover all of Noordbrabant. Three years later, it was decided to

PLATE 6.42 *(opposite, top)* Plan der Festung Strahlsundt *by Heinrich von Scheele, manuscript in inks and colours, north Germany, c. 1716. A detailed plan of the extensive fortification works to the west of this Baltic port (founded in 1234).*

PLATE 6.43 *(opposite, bottom)* Plan von der Königlichen Vestung Oldenburg, *manuscript in inks and colours, c. 1740. A fine example of eighteenth-century military mapping in Germany. Oldenburg (now in north Germany) was under Danish control at the time this plan was surveyed. Note how the skilful use of watercolours can give a sharp relief effect to the mapping of fortifications.*

230

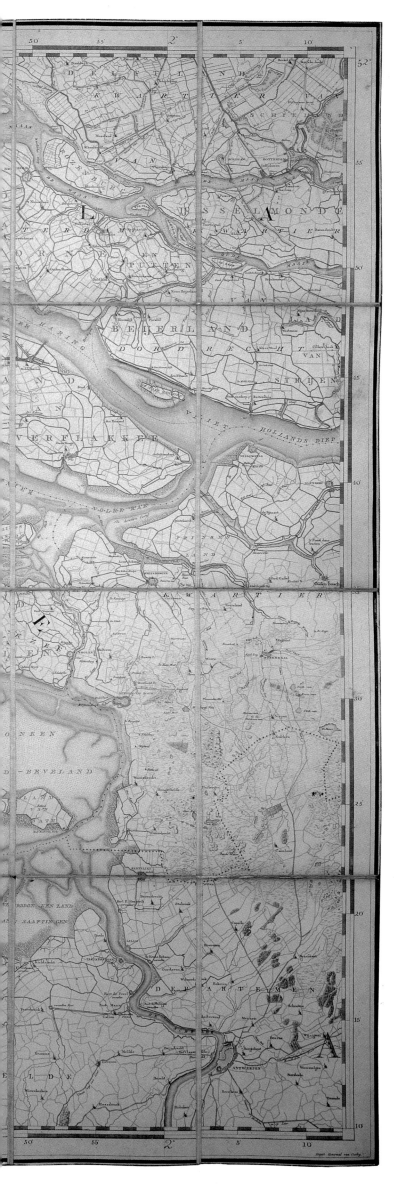

extend the survey to all of the country, along the lines proposed in 1820 by the Royal Commission. Maps surveyed at the 1:25,000 scale were to be reduced to 1:50,000 and printed for distribution from the Topographical Office, which had transferred to The Hague in 1841. Definitive printing and publication did not, however, begin until some nine years later. Official delays and deliberations, and concerns over national security, were the chief reasons for this hold-up. Altogether, all the triangulation surveys were completed by 1855–1859 and sixty-five of the 1:50,000-map series were surveyed and printed by 1864.

PLATE 6.44 *The southwestern sheet showing Zeeland, from the new map of the Netherlands by Baron Cornelius Rudolphus Theodorus Krayenhoff. The map was based on his triangulation surveys begun in 1800 and completed in 1811, which were tied into the existing French network.*

References

1. L.A. Brown, *The Story of Maps*, pages 228–229, 1949.
2. L.A. Brown, *op. cit.*, page 229.
3. R.T. Gould, *The Marine Chronometer: Its History and Development*, page 144, 1923.
4. R.T. Gould, *op. cit.*, page 63.
5. C. Koeman, *The Sea On Paper*, page 48, 1972.
6. J.W. Konvitz, *Cartography in France 1660–1848*, page 7, 1987.
7. J.W. Konvitz, *op. cit.*, pages 7–8.
8. J.W. Konvitz, *op. cit.*, page 21.
9. C. Koeman, *op. cit.*, page 163.
10. R.T. Gould, *op. cit.*, page 144.
11. J.W. Konvitz, *op. cit.*, pages 3–4.
12. C.M. Clode, *The Military Forces of the Crown*, Vol. 1, pages 464–465, 1869; also J.B. Harley and A.Y. O'Donoghue, *The Old Series Ordnance Survey Maps of England and Wales*, pages vii, ix, 1975.
13. William Roy, *Philosophical Transactions of the Royal Society*, Volume 75, part II, 1785.
14. William Roy, *op. cit.*, page 387.
15. J.B. Harley and A.Y. O'Donoghue, *op. cit.*, page xiii.
16. J.B. Harley and A.Y. O'Donoghue, *op. cit.*, page xiii.
17. J.B. Harley and A.Y. O'Donoghue, *op. cit.*, page xiii.
18. C. Close, *The Early Years of the Ordnance Survey*, reprint 1969.
19. E. Close, *op. cit.*
20. William Roy, quoted in Harley and O'Donoghue, *op. cit.*, page xxiii.
21. William Roy, 'An Account Of The Trigonometrical Operation, whereby the Distance between the Meridians of the Royal Observatories of Greenwich and Paris has been determined', in *Philosophical Transactions of the Royal Society*, LXXX, page 111, part 1, 1790.
22. J.B. Harley and A.Y. O'Donoghue, *op. cit.*, page xxiv.
23. L. Bagrow, ed. H.W. Castner, *A History of Russian Cartography up to 1800*, II, page 180, 1975.
24. L. Bagrow and H.W. Castner, *op. cit.*, page 190.
25. B. Bramsen, *Gamle Danmarkskort*, page 142ff, 1975.
26. E. Bratt, *En kronika om kartor över Sverige*, pages 71–80, 1958.
27. L.A. Brown, *op. cit.*, page 273.
28. C. Koeman, *Geschiedenis van de kartografie van Nederland*, page 182ff, Alphen aan den Rijn, 1985.
29. C. Koeman, *op. cit.*, pages 186–187.
30. J.A. van der Linden, *Topographische en Militaire Kaart van het Koningrijk der Nederlanden*, page 20, 1973.

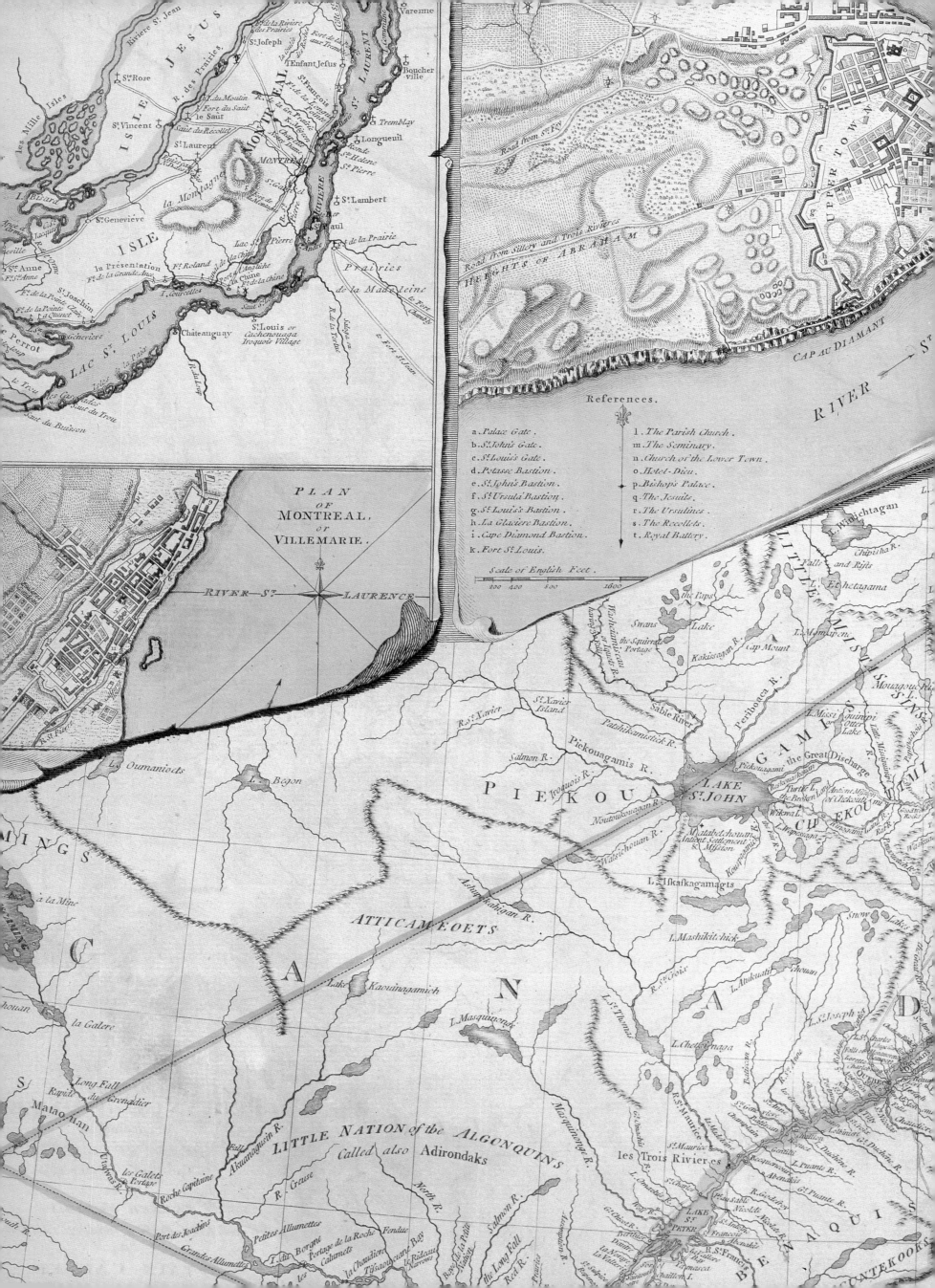

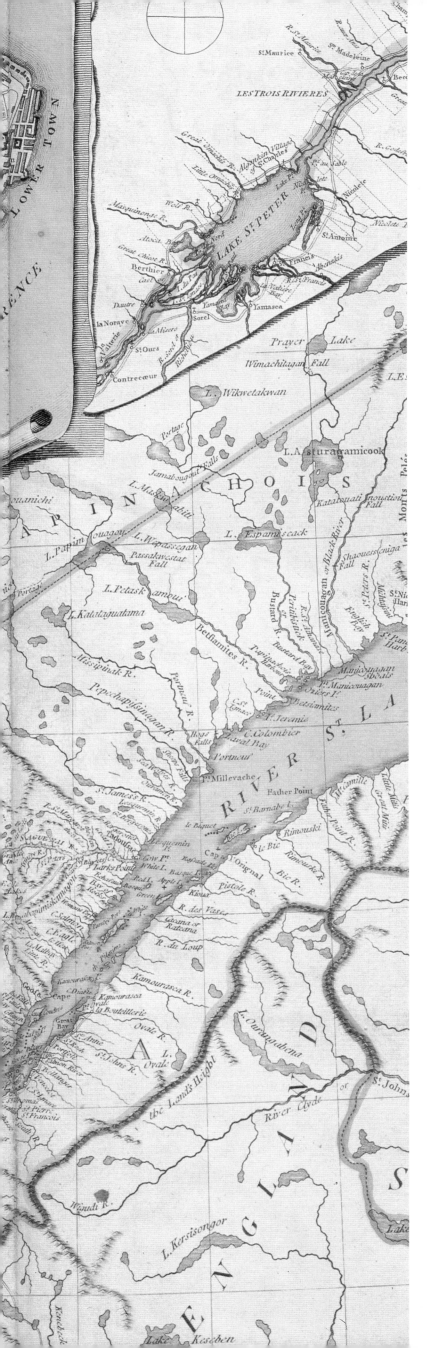

CHAPTER VII

SURVEYS ACROSS THE WORLD

1700 – 1850 AD

BEYOND THE IMMEDIATE confines of Europe, two overseas areas presented themselves to trained surveyors from Britain: the North American colonies and the Indian subcontinent. In North America, away from the more settled parts of the coastal regions and their hinterlands, very little was known of the vast interior. Only a few sporadic sketches existed, made by explorers motivated by the desire to discover what lay beyond the mountains or up the farther reaches of river valleys (Plate 7.3). Some were also driven by the desire to seek profit from trading with Indian tribes or to exploit the local resources (especially the highly lucrative fur trade) (Plate 7.2). At the beginning of the seventeenth century, French missionaries, mostly Jesuit, ventured far into Canada, converting Indians as they went. They established firm settlements, such as Quebec in 1608, Montreal in 1642 and Detroit in 1701. During the late seventeenth century, the French reached far into the interior into the headwaters regions of the Mississippi–Missouri system. By the early 1700s, the basin of the St Lawrence, the Great Lakes region and Mississippi – comprising the territory known as Louisiana – had been largely explored. Louisiana had been settled and partially protected by French forts and outposts, established there from 1639 to 1703.

PLATE 7.1 *Detail from* A New Map of the Province of Quebec, according to the Royal Proclamation of the 2nd of October 1763 *by Captain Jonathan Carver, London, 1775 and later. Anglo-French rivalry in North America was long established. Quebec had been attacked by the English as early as 1629, and was finally granted to England by 1763 in the Treaty of Paris, signed on 2 February.*

PLATE 7.2 *Englishmen trading with North American Indians, copper engraving, c. 1634 from* Historia Americae *by Theodor de Bry.*

PLATE 7.3 *(below)* Louisiana Pars *by Colonel Cadwallader Jones, manuscript in ink, c. 1698.*

Such explorations by the French led them to lay claim to all the area drained by the Mississippi system, almost half a continent in extent. By the eighteenth century, France was actively extending its North American territories from Acadia (later known as Nova Scotia), in a great crescent-like sweep down into Louisiana and the eastern banks of the Mississippi to the Gulf shore, effectively encircling the English colonies (now the Thirteen Colonies). To set the seal on their expansion, the

French established the town of New Orleans in 1718. French interests were in the main taken up in the trade for furs and skins. There was a seemingly inexhaustible supply of these, bought up by traders from the Indians and from European fur trappers all over the Great Lakes region and the upper Mississippi valley.

English colonists were particularly active throughout the seventeenth and eighteenth centuries in North America, notwithstanding several early failures on their part along the Atlantic seaboard. In 1607 Jamestown had been established in Virginia, and the Mayflower colonists had settled in Massachusetts Bay in 1620. By 1733, when Georgia became the Thirteenth Colony, the British Empire in North America was well established, with a prosperous agricultural, fishing and commercial economy.

Naturally, such a situation in North America could not have come about without either war or competition between the major colonial contenders. Anglo-French rivalry was long established. Quebec, for example, had been attacked by the English as early as 1629. The English fur trading empire to the northwest of New France was a growing bait to French interests, based as it was on the almost limitless hunting grounds of the Hudson Bay region (Plate 7.4). Just as in Europe there had been numerous territorial and economic wars between England, France, the Netherlands and Spain, so these conflicts were echoed in North America. The most serious of these, and the one with the farthest reaching consequences, was the French–Indian War of 1754–1760, which effectively halted French territorial ambitions in North America. This war confirmed English power – albeit short-lived – over a great area of North America. The Treaty of Paris in 1763 granted Canada and the lands east of the Mississippi to Britain, while the rest of Louisiana went to Spain as compensation for the earlier French transfer of Florida to Britain.

Short-sighted and not always efficient British colonial administration devised policies and acted in ways which led inevitably to the American Revolution, and loss of the Thirteen Colonies and the birth of the United States of America in the 1770s. British (or Anglo-American) policy towards the native Indians had always been one of elimination or expulsion to make way for Euro-

pean settlers, quite in contrast to the Hispanic policy of assimilation, especially in Mexico. In 1763, the British government declared all lands to the west of the Allegheny and Appalachian ranges, well away from the prosperous seaboard colonies, to be an Indian reserve, beyond the so-called Proclamation Line. Like all such vaguely defined lines and boundaries not marked precisely on paper, the Proclamation Line had no real geographical existence. Far from stemming the westward expansion of the colonists from the seaboard, it actually encouraged colonists to seek land and fortune within and beyond its boundaries, adding to the growing list of grievances against the British government. The Quebec Act of 1774 redrew the boundaries of the new colony far beyond those of the Proclamation, a move seen by the Thirteen Colonies – Virginia and Pennsylvania in particular – as a direct threat, especially as Virginia and Pennsylvania were claiming linear extension of their own territories in this region. Such moves on the part of the British helped spark off the American War of Independence in 1775. The war dragged on until 1783, until the signing of the Treaty of Paris, by which Britain at last formally recognized the establishment and existence of the United States of America.

Mapping the Americas

Such events as these obviously created work for surveyors and mapmakers, and publishers were often required to meet an increasing demand for printed maps with remarkable speed. In the early years, British surveying and mapping was chiefly confined to the coastal regions, largely at the instigation of the Board of Trade and Plantations. The earliest extant product of such work was the map of the eastern part of North America compiled by Captain Cyprian Southack in 1717. (It is

PLATE 7.4 Indians Hunting Beavers *by James Isham, from the Hudson's Bay Company archives.*

PLATE 7.5 *(below)* Carte très curieuse de la Mer du Sud . . . *from the* Atlas Historique *by Henri-Abraham Châtelain, Amsterdam, 1719 and later. One of the most impressive maps of the Americas ever made.*

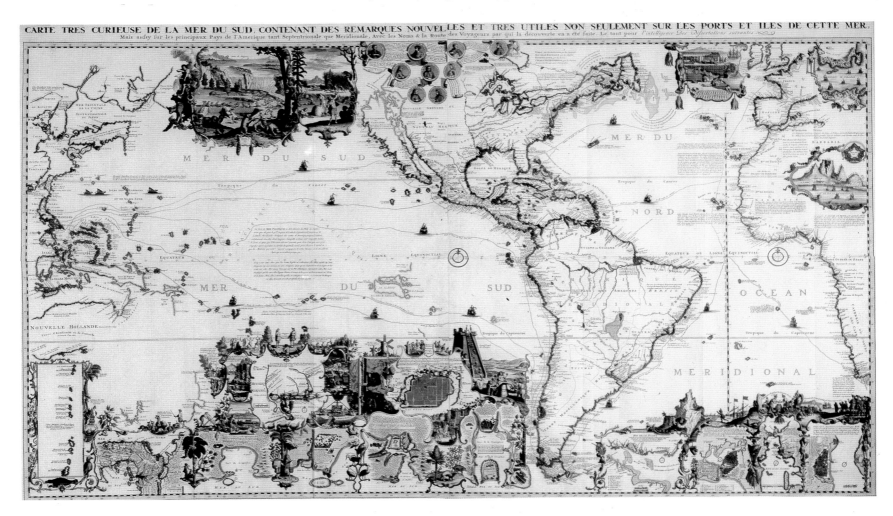

usually known by the title of a later edition, as *A New Chart of the British Empire in North America with the Distinct Colonies granted by Letters Patent from Cape Canso to St Matthias River 1746*). The first issue was drawn to heighten awareness of French political designs on those lands to the west of the Appalachians. It was one of the earliest copper-engraved maps published in North America, and its compiler was also responsible for charts published in *The New-England coasting pilot* atlas in 1730.

Elsewhere, surveyors were active in plotting land grants in response to the stimulus unintentionally provided by the Proclamation Line, as well as speculative colonization ventures in newly constituted provinces floated in London and in parts of continental Europe. With the progress of

settlement and exploration westwards, as well as the threat of war with France, the need for good accurate mapping became a matter of urgency. Pressure exerted in London obliged the Lords Commissioners for Trade and Plantations to encourage surveyors to turn from mapping proprietorial estates and allotments to topographical surveying and mapping. In this respect, an officer of the Board, Thomas Pownall (1722–1855), later to be Governor of Massachusetts, played an important role. Such surveys were often used in the compilation of large general maps.

Henry Popple

One of the most celebrated of these maps is the first large-scale printed map of North America, Henry Popple's *America Septentrionalis. A Map of*

PLATE 7.6 America Septentrionalis. A Map of the British Empire in America with the French and Spanish Settlements adjacent thereto *by Henry Popple, London, 1733. This single-sheet map forms the index to Popple's twenty-sheet survey of North America, the earliest large-scale map published during the colonial period, and the first English map to name all Thirteen Colonies. A series of inset vignette views and small detail maps and plans adds to the comprehensiveness of the survey.*

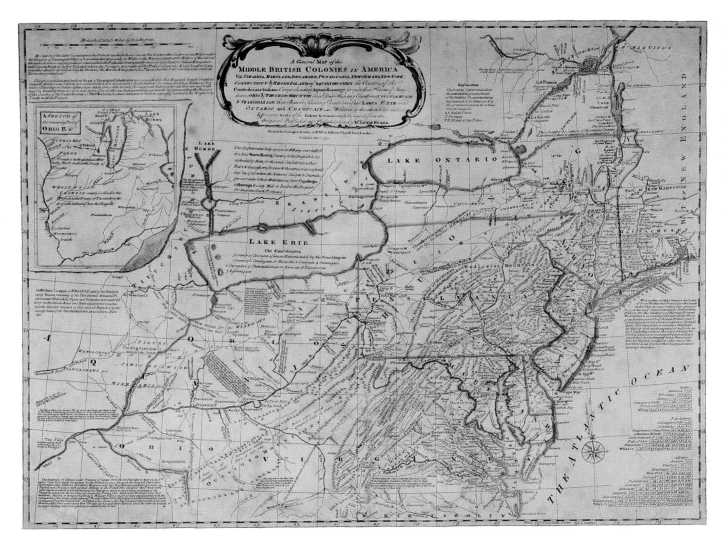

PLATE 7.7 A general Map of the Middle British Colonies in America *by Lewis Evans, Philadelphia, 1755, London, 1771 and later. Evans was commissioned by the Philadelphia Assembly to survey and map the region in 1750. The survey took four years. The resultant map was quoted as an authority in boundary disputes, and contributed in no small measure to informed knowledge of the Ohio region.*

the British Empire in America with the French and Spanish Settlements adjacent thereto, issued in London in 1733 as a large map in twenty sheets (Plate 7.6). It was also the first English map to name all Thirteen Colonies, including the newly settled colony of Georgia, proclaimed in that year. Popple's map gives a cartographic view of the fears of the English, for it was published during a time of conflict between the English and French in Canada and Louisiana, and between the English and Spanish in Florida. In effect, therefore, the Thirteen Colonies saw themselves entirely surrounded. Added to these problems was the constant threat of attacks on the colonists' settlements by Indians allied to the French, leading to the establishment of frontier forts in areas such as the Ohio valley region. Published under the aegis of the Lords Commissioners of Trade and Plantations, Popple's map proved a considerable success. It was also taken up by several foreign publishers, even though it contained many distortions, errors and omissions, and despite complaints from the Lords Commissioners themselves that they considered the map too favourable to French territorial claims. Be that as it may, Popple's map

succeeded in drawing attention to the vulnerability of the English colonies. The map bore the approbation of Dr Edmond Halley who, throughout his long career retained an interest in mapping. He stated: 'I have seen the above mentioned Map, which as far as I am Judge, seems to have been laid down with much Accuracy, and to show the Position of the different Provinces and Islands in that Part of the Globe more truly than any yet extant.'

Lewis Evans

In 1749, the Pennsylvania surveyor Lewis Evans (c. 1700–1756) compiled and published *A Map of Pensilvania, New-Jersey, New-York, and the Three Delaware Counties . . . MDCCXLIX*. It was based on the established longitudes of Philadelphia and Boston and numerous observations of latitude, and was published at the scale of twenty miles to one inch (1:1,267,200). On this basic framework, Evans put the 'Draughts or Discoveries' which had been communicated to him by several landowners and proprietors. He also added information gathered from various route surveys by distance and bearing through and around the mountains and forests: 'No distance could be taken

PLATE 7.8 A Map of the British Colonies in North America . . . by John Mitchell, London, 1775 and later. This is the single most important map in American colonial history. It formed the basis for territorial boundaries drawn up in the treaties to end the French and Indian War and the American Revolution. The map was cited as evidence in boundary disputes as recently as 1932.

PLATE 7.9 A New Map
of the Province of
Quebec, according to the
Royal Proclamation of the
2ⁿᵈ of October 1763 *by
Captain Jonathan Carver,
London, 1775 and later.
The Treaty of Paris of 1763
gave the British possession of
French Canada. This map
shows the first boundaries of
the new British province of
Quebec.*

PLATE 7.9 A New Map
of the Province of
Quebec, according to the
Royal Proclamation of the
2ⁿᵈ of October 1763 *by
Captain Jonathan Carver,
London, 1775 and later.
The Treaty of Paris of 1763
gave the British possession of
French Canada. This map
shows the first boundaries of
the new British province of
Quebec.*

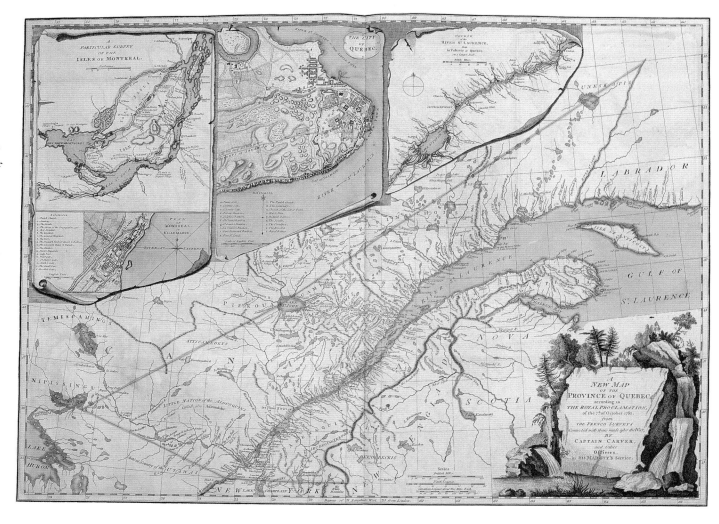

but by actual Mensuration (the Woods being yet so thick)', indicating that surveyors were unable to secure intersecting bearings using compasses.

Six years later, in 1755, there appeared in print perhaps Evans's most famous map, entitled *A general Map of the Middle British Colonies, in America*, at the scale of one inch to fifty miles (1:3,168,000) (Plate 7.7). The map illustrated an essay, *An Analysis of the Middle British Colonies*, printed at Philadelphia. Evans had been commissioned by the Philadelphia Assembly in 1750 to survey and map the region. Because of French claims in this part of North America, in particular in the Ohio valley, much of Lewis's survey work had to be carried out covertly, and it took him some four years to complete the task. Both the map and the essay emphasized the necessity of establishing permanent settlements in the border areas, rather than mere trading posts.

The *Analysis* includes an account of the sort of problems encountered by surveyors in such territory. Evans wrote that: '. . . here there are no Churches, Towers, Houses or peaked Mountains to be seen from afar, no means of obtaining the Bearings or Distances of Places, but by the Compass, and actual Mensuration with the Chain'. Evans made a distinction between what he called 'surveys' and 'computations'. 'We call nothing Surveys but actual Mensurations with a Chain and the course taken with a good Surveying instrument. Courses with a Pocket Compass and computed distances we call Computations.' His map was in great demand and underwent several amendments and many editions through to the early years of the nineteenth century. It was much used during military campaigns in the Seven Years' War of 1756–1763 in the Middle Colonies, and when Pownall, himself a military surveyor of no small ability, issued an edition in 1776, he noted that: '. . . Where local Precision has been necessary this Map has been referred to not simply in private but public Transactions, such as the Great Indian Purchase and Cession'.[1] A few years later, Captain Jonathan Carver used this method for mapping his pioneering route into the upper Mississippi basin in 1766–1768. Both his map and the account of his journey were published in 1778, ten years after he had completed the journey, in the authoritative *Travels through the Interior Parts of North America*, which was the first cartographic description of the trans-Mississippi regions by a colonial surveyor.

Dr John Mitchell

Pownall was also associated with what has become recognized as perhaps the most important single map in colonial American history, *A Map of the British Colonies in North America, with the Roads, Distances, Limits, and Extent of the Settlements, Humbly Inscribed to the Right Honorable The Lords Commissioners for Trade & Plantations* (Plate 7.8). It was first issued in 1755 by Dr John Mitchell (who died in 1768), Virginia-born but living in England, and closely connected with the 'Father of the Colonies', George Montague Dunk, second Earl of Halifax (President of the Board of the Lords Commissioners at the time) during his years in England. Such connections allowed him access to many unpublished or otherwise inaccessible source materials in the compilation of this great map. Colonial governors had also been requested by the Board to furnish Mitchell with individual maps of their provinces. Mitchell's map was referred to in the negotiations for peace for the Treaty of Paris during 1762–1763. Benjamin Franklin himself declared, in a letter to Thomas Jefferson: 'I now can assure you that I am perfectly clear in the Remembrance that the map we used in tracing the Boundary [on 6 December 1782] was brought to the Treaty by the Commissioners from England, and that it was the same that was published by Mitchell twenty years before'.[2] Mitchell's map, on a scale of approximately one inch to forty-three miles (1:2,724,480), was a large one, measuring some 1,370 mm by 1,960 mm. It covered virtually all of the eastern half of North America, from the southern reaches of James Bay and Newfoundland to west of the Mississippi delta. Subsequent editions of Mitchell's map (there were twenty-one in all, published in English, French and Italian) contained extensive engraved historical notes which have been a valuable source for study.

Thomas Jefferys

It was largely due to the efforts of men such as Thomas Jefferys (*c*.1710–1771) that the standards of mapping in Britain advanced so markedly, especially with the advent of trained men from the Academy at Woolwich. Jefferys' career and involvement with mapping seems to have spanned some forty years, from 1732 up to the time of his death in 1771. His reputation as an engraver and publisher was given a considerable fillip in 1746 when he received the title of Geographer to the Prince of Wales, becoming Geographer to the King on the accession of George III in 1761.

In the years after 1750, Jefferys became increasingly involved with the mapping of the North American colonies and the various military campaigns there. The more offensive policy adopted by the British government at the urging of William Pitt, the then Prime Minister, called for large increases in the numbers of troops of all kinds. Attached to these augmented divisions were military surveyors who were trained to conduct topographical surveys. This became all the more necessary when, as a result of the treaty of 1763, Britain acquired control of Canada from France, and Florida from Spain. It soon became obvious that accurate mapping would be needed in order to consolidate British control of their new territories, all the more so since accurate surveys of the former French and Spanish domains were, to all intents and purposes, non-existent.

In 1764, the Board of Trade informed George III that:

. . . we find ourselves under the greatest difficulties arising from the want of exact surveys of these counties in America, many parts of which have never been surveyed at all and others so imperfectly that the charts and maps thereof are not to be depended upon . . . [and that it is recommended] . . . in the strongest manner, that no time should be lost in obtaining accurate surveys of all Your Majesty's North American Dominions but more especially of such parts as from their natural advantages require our immediate attention.[3]

Accordingly, it was proposed that the colonies be divided into Northern and Southern Districts, the dividing line being the Potomac river. A Surveyor-General of Lands was appointed for each, the proposals themselves being drafted by the surveyor Captain (later Major) Samuel Holland (1728–1801). He had carried out careful and highly regarded surveys in Canada, New England, New York and New Jersey, and with every justification was appointed the first Surveyor-General for the Northern District in 1764.

His counterpart for the Southern District was William Gerard DeBrahm (1717–1799), surveyor and military engineer, formerly in the

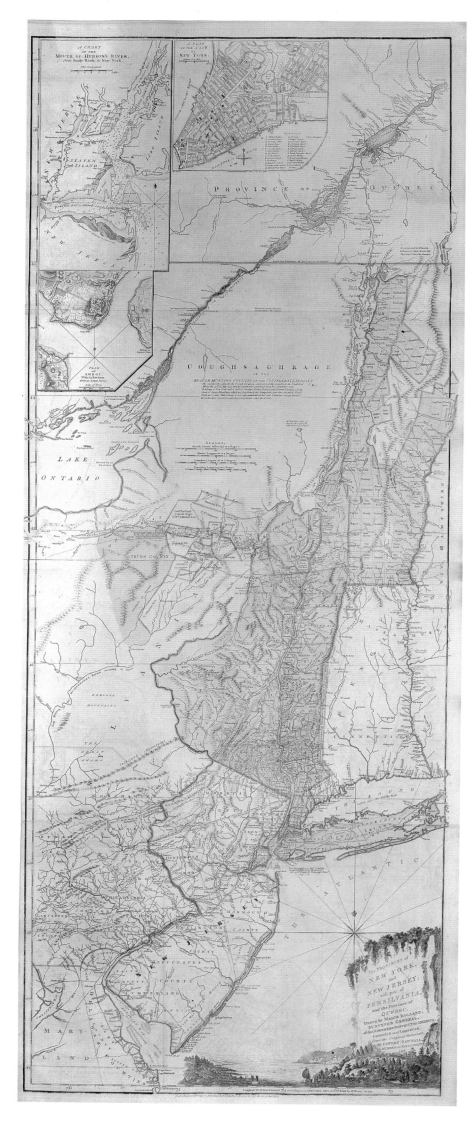

service of Charles VI. DeBrahm arrived in North America from Germany in 1751, founded Bethany in Georgia and became Surveyor-General for the colony in 1754. Only a year later he received the equivalent appointment for the colony of South Carolina. In this capacity, DeBrahm produced his magnificent map, *A Map of South Carolina and a Part of Georgia*, in four sheets, published by Thomas Jefferys in 1757. For the first time, a large district in the southern colonies was mapped accurately by the use of scientific surveys, correctly locating settlements, lagoons and a difficult coast. The map served as the basis for many subsequent maps during the remainder of the century and beyond, and set a new standard of presentation. By 1765, DeBrahm was Surveyor-General for Florida and the whole of the southern District. However, he concentrated his efforts on East Florida, in an attempt to establish a proper survey there. The military surveys now being undertaken in the British North American colonies were based on astronomical observations of latitudes, with control tied to a primary triangulation network started by British military surveyors in New England during the late 1750s. Distances were measured by chain.

One of Thomas Jefferys' most important early maps of part of North America had been issued in 1755 as *A New Map of Nova Scotia and Cape Britain with the adjacent parts of New England and Canada*, accompanied by a memoir written by John Green. It helped ensure Jefferys' good reputation, as the map was instrumental in distinguishing the rival French and British claims in the region. In this manner, Jefferys became a kind of official map publisher to certain government departments.

At this time, Britain still did not have its own official map- or chart-publishing establishment, despite the fact that such a lack had been lamented by several observers. It was, therefore, in the interests of the government that a competent publisher, such as Jefferys, should be entrusted with such matters, and that he be allowed access to official sources and records in the compilation of his maps and charts. Jefferys never received any official salary or contract for such work; at all times he remained an independent publisher with influential official contacts. In effect, his Royal Warrant was an honorary office alongside that of the many other tradesmen who supplied the monarch with their wares. Another fine map engraved and published by Jefferys was the *Map of the most Inhabited part of Virginia containing the whole Province of Maryland with Part of Pensilvania, New Jersey and North Carolina . . . in 1751* by Joshua Fry and Peter Jefferson (Plate 7.12). It was issued for the first time in 1754, in four sheets. Surveyed by order of the Lords Commissioners, it was a highly influential map showing the hinterland and valleys of the Allegheny and Appalachian ranges beyond the Tidewater. Fry, a professor of mathematics, and Jefferson, a surveyor (and father of the future President), had made surveys of the boundary between Virginia and North Carolina in 1749, and incorporated details of it into their new map. The work of John Dalrymple contributed to the detail of the western reaches of the territory shown. The map was acclaimed for its accuracy, in the coastal regions especially, and is the basic cartographical document for eighteenth-century Virginia.[4] The map achieved its widest circulation through the medium of Jefferys' influential *North American Atlas* in 1774 and later (Plate 7.13). It was the first large-scale detailed map of New England.

The well-defined, superior quality of Jefferys'

cartographical output is a just reflection of his own professional skills and of the competence of the people working for him. Jefferys had undoubtedly acquired an extensive geographical knowledge of his own, but he also required the services of an editor, particularly during the years when much of his output was concentrated on the Americas. To this end, he employed as editor Braddock Mead, *alias* John Green (see pp. 171–173). He remained in the employ of Jefferys until his death in 1757, publishing a large number of maps and charts relating to the American colonies.

When peace of a sort was declared between Britain and France a few years later, there was less call for large numbers of maps and charts of the Americas. But Jefferys saw possibilities nearer to home, for in 1759 the Royal Society of Arts had offered a prize of £100 for an original county map on the scale of one inch to one mile (1:63,360). The offer was repeated in 1762 and then on occasion until 1801. The advertisement in 1762 proposed:

. . . to give a sum, not exceeding £100, as a gratuity to any person . . . who shall make an accurate survey of any county upon the scale of one inch to one mile: the sea coasts of all maritime counties, to be correctly

PLATE 7.10 *(opposite)* The Provinces of New York, and New Jersey; with part of Pensilvania, and the Province of Quebec *by Major Samuel Holland and Thomas Pownall, London, 1776 and later. This is the last in a series of surveys carried out by Holland and Pownall and published in the* North American Atlas *of Thomas Jefferys.*

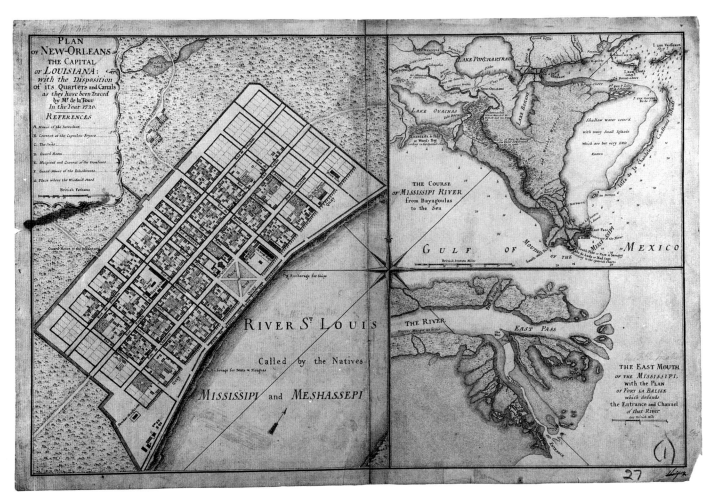

PLATE 7.11 Plan of New-Orleans . . . *by Thomas Jefferys, 1720. This map shows New Orleans only two years after it was founded on the east bank of the lower Mississippi by Captain Celaron de Bienville. The city was built in a systematic way and encircled by a canal. The banks of the Mississippi were raised to prevent the city from flooding.*

laid down, together with their latitudes, and longitudes . . . As further encouragement, the surveyor that will give an exact, and accurate level, and section, of the rivers in any county surveyed, that are capable of being made navigable, shall be entitled to an additional gratuity . . .[5]

From about 1763, therefore, until his death in 1771, Jefferys was involved in the production of some ten original county maps. He acted either as sponsor or engraver, and at no small cost. Unfortunately Jefferys did not receive any reward or recognition for these fine maps – for example, *The County of Bedford*, published in 1767 and *The County of Buckingham*, published in 1770. Moreover, the added burden of these detailed maps, together with the commitments of the rest of his large body of published works, broke Jefferys financially. He was declared bankrupt in 1766, but was somehow able to continue with his publishing activities. He sought and obtained partnerships with other publishers, chief among whom was Robert Sayer (1725–1794), who had been running a successful business in London for a number of years.

An early fruit of this partnership was published in 1768 – *A General Topography of North America and the West Indies*, with one hundred maps, charts and plans. A French-language version was also

available, and it is believed that Sayer must have put up the money to publish the work. Jefferys also published the first set of charts which are associated with the name of James Cook, *A Collection of Charts of the Coasts of Newfoundland and Labrador*, in about 1769.

Better known, of course, for his outstanding achievements in the exploration of the Pacific, Cook received his early training in surveying under Samuel Holland and spent some time on a hydrographic survey of the coast of Labrador and Newfoundland with Michael Lane in the years prior to 1760. Some years after this survey, Jefferys acquired the rights to publish several of the resultant charts.

At some time between 1767 and Jefferys' death in 1771, Sayer acquired a large part of the plate stock and manuscripts of Jefferys' as yet unpublished works. Jefferys' financial situation never recovered, probably because he had been forced to mortgage any profits from the partnership venture to his co-publishers, and to his ultimate successor, William Faden (1750–1836).

The work of Jefferys did not die with him, however. A little before Sayer's own death in 1770, he entered into a partnership with John Bennett (died 1787), who ran a shop on London's Fleet Street, and together they acquired Jefferys' stock. Over the next fourteen or fifteen years, they

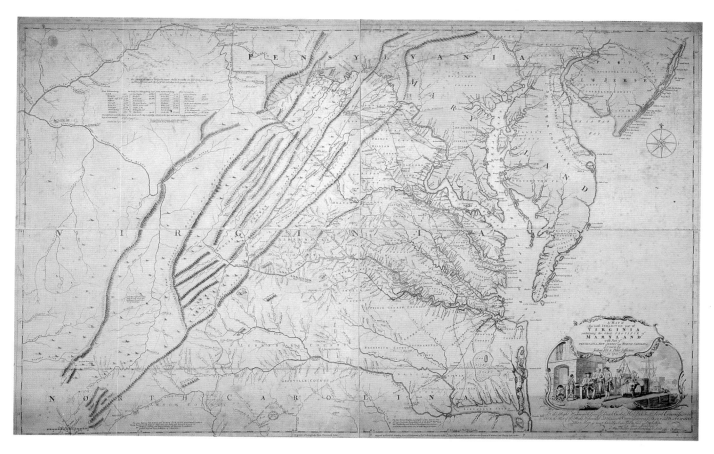

PLATE 7.12 A Map of the most Inhabited part of Virginia containing the whole Province of Maryland with Part of Pensilvania, New Jersey and North Carolina in 1751 *by Joshua Fry and Peter Jefferson, London, 1754 and later. This highly influential map of the colonies of Virginia and Maryland shows the hinterland and valleys of the Allegheny and Appalachian ranges beyond the Tidewater. The map is the basic cartographic document for Virginia in the eighteenth century.*

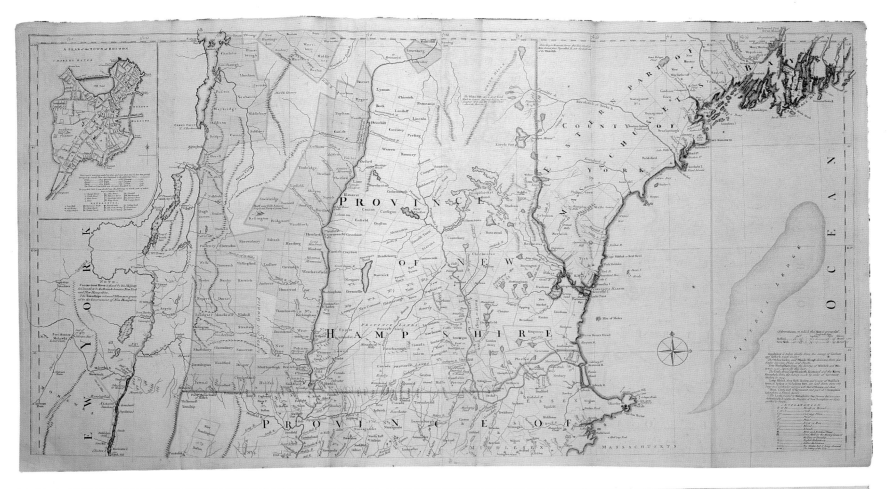

PLATE 7.13 A Map of the most Inhabited part of New
England . . . *from the* North American Atlas *by Thomas
Jefferys, London, 1774 and later. This is the first detailed
large-scale map of New England and one of the earliest printed
maps of Connecticut. It was published in two large folding
sheets at a scale of about seven miles to the inch. The inset
plans show Boston and Boston Harbour.*

issued many of Jefferys' maps and charts in atlases, such as *The North-American Pilot* in 1775; *The West-Indian Atlas* in 1775 and *The American Atlas* in 1776. It seems likely that Jefferys had planned these works before his bankruptcy, and they enjoyed great commercial success under Sayer and Bennett's imprint. Most of them were reissued in revised editions for many years afterwards, into the first decades of the nineteenth century.

India surveyed

The mid-eighteenth century was a time of intense rivalry between several European countries for the profits to be made out of the Indian trade. In order to further their own commercial ambitions, the Honourable East Indian Company early on saw the need for good charts, and from about 1750, the Company began promoting the charting of the coasts of the subcontinent. The first systematic land survey carried out by Europeans in India was that by Major James Rennell (1742–1830) who was in the Bengal Presidency (Plate 7.15). Bengal was the first large area to come under the control of the Company.

Rennel received his early training in surveying in the Royal Navy, volunteering for service in India, but when hostilities between Britain and France ceased in 1763, he quit the Navy and transferred to the East India Company's service. Because of his particular interest in surveying, Rennell soon became aware of the need for accurate mapping of the Company's acquisitions in India. In 1767, a letter to the Court of Directors of the Company stated:

. . . So much depends on accurate surveys both in military operations and in coming at a true knowledge of the value of your possessions, that we have employed everybody on this service who could be spared and were capable of it. But as the work must ever be imperfect, while it is separate and unconnected plans, we have appointed Captain Rennell, a young man of distinguished merit in this branch, Surveyor General, and directed him to one general chart from those already made, and such as are now on hand as they can be collected in . . .[6]

Rennell was thus appointed in 1767, and remained in post for ten years, as the first Surveyor-General of Bengal.

James Rennell

During the years that Rennell spent working in India he instigated and directed a comprehensive survey of the territories of Bengal and Bihar with a three-fold purpose in view: to suit military, administrative (including fiscal) and commercial requirements. Prior to this there existed virtually nothing in the way of systematic planning or mapping, a situation which paralleled almost exactly that which obtained in the North American colonies and the newly acquired former French and Spanish territories. Any mapping which had been carried out was at best sporadic in its coverage, and mostly the work of missionaries or military engineers who had happened to take an interest in a particular area.

Rennell based his survey of Bengal and Bihar on a network of distance and bearing traverses controlled by cross bearings and closed circuits, with additional control provided by astronomical observations of latitudes. On large-scale work, distances were taken by chaining, in other instances by the use of a perambulator, or waywiser (a wheeled instrument with a gauge used for measuring distances), as used by John Ogilby in Britain a century earlier. Rennell and his surveyors (he trained sufficient numbers to form a complete department) also used quadrants for horizontal angular readings as well as for deriving latitudes. Gradually, theodolites were also introduced in order to tighten accuracy. Much work was based on traverses taken along roads and rivers, with lesser detail filled in by eye or estimation (recalling the practice of the surveyors in France a few years earlier, and the experiences of the surveyors in the backwoods of Virginia). The results obtained were remarkable in their accuracy, proving of better quality than the mapping of many European countries. The rigours of the task and the physical conditions under which the men worked took their inevitable toll in terms of illness and injury.

The work by which Rennell's reputation stands even today is the *Bengal Atlas*, the first edition of which was published in London in 1779, two years after his return home on pension. Most of the thirteen maps therein are on a uniform scale of 1:316,800 and were engraved between late 1778

(continued on page 251)

BURMAH

Upper

ARACAN
or
RECCAN

BENGAL

SIAM

COAST OF AVA

PEGU

M A R T A B A N

MOUTHS of the

L O W E R

S I A M

Cheduba I.

Prepares I.

Cocos Islands

Great ANDAMAN Island

Narcondam I.

Barren I.

Great Central

DUNCAN'S Passage
Little Central

Little Andaman Island

ARCHIPELAGO

of

MERGUI

MERGUI

Tenasserim

Carnicobar I.

NICOBAR ISLANDS

SOMBRERE Channel

St GEORGES Channel

Great Nicobar I.

Junkseilon I.

Entrance of the

STRAIT
of
MALACCA

Part of SUMATRA ISLAND

HINDOOSTAN
By J. Rennell F.R.S. 1782.

86 w 87 x 88 y 89 z 90 a 91 b 92 c 93 d 94 e 95 f 96 g 97 h 98 i

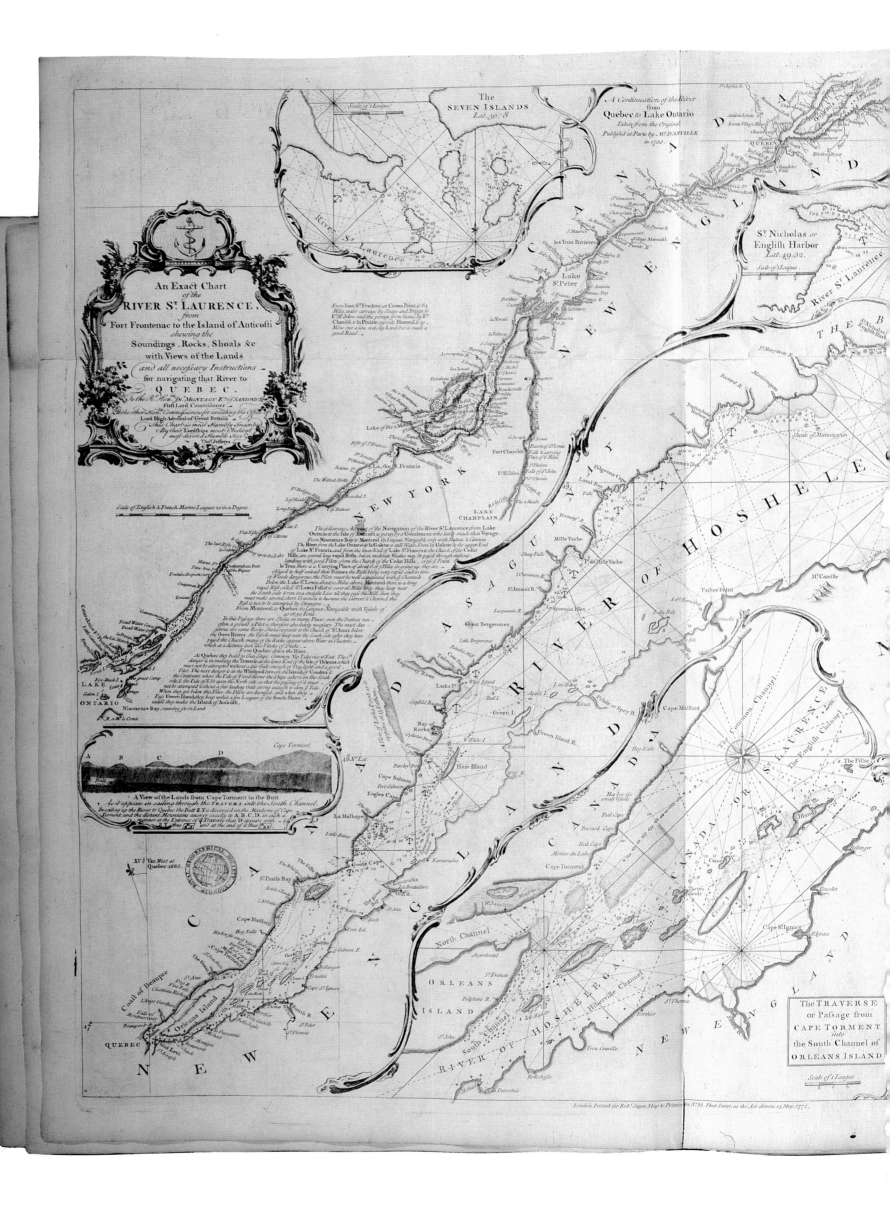

An Exact Chart
of the
RIVER St. LAURENCE,
from
Fort Frontenac to the Island of Anticosti
shewing the
Soundings, Rocks, Shoals &c
with Views of the Lands
and all necessary Instructions
for navigating that River to
QUEBEC.

The SEVEN ISLANDS
Lat: 50°. 8'

A Continuation of the River
from
Quebec to Lake Ontario
Taken from the Original
Published at Paris by Mr D'ANVILLE
in 1755.

St. Nicholas or
English Harbor
Lat. 49.32.

A View of the Lands from Cape Torment to the Butt.
As it appears in sailing through the TRAVERS into the South Channel.

The TRAVERSE
or Passage from
CAPE TORMENT
into
the South Channel of
ORLEANS ISLAND

London, Printed for Robt. Sayer, Map & Printseller, Nº 53. Fleet Street, as the Act directs, 25 May 1775.

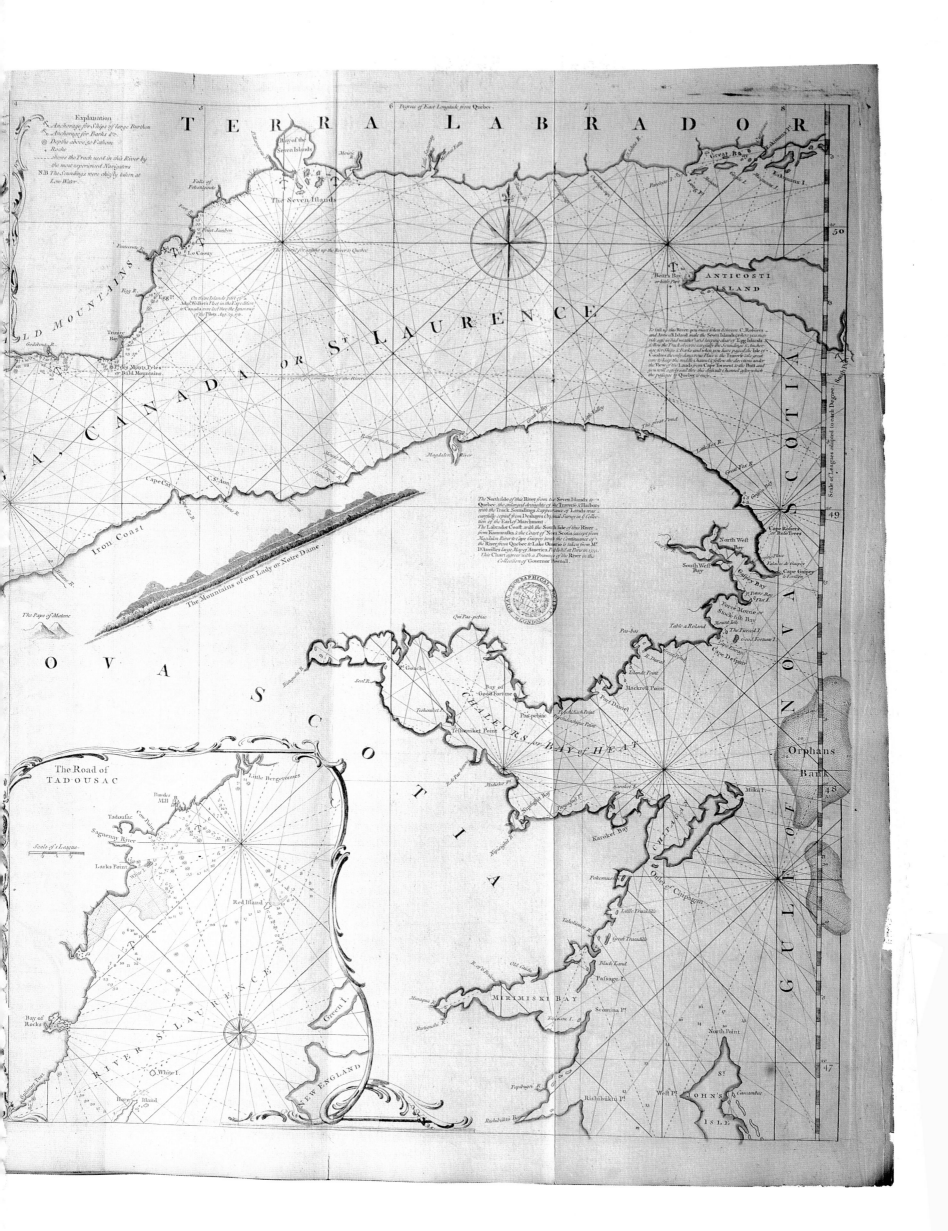

and early 1780. Few copies of the first edition appear to have survived: it seems that the Company vessel carrying copies of the atlas out to India was captured at sea by the Portuguese and they were thus lost. A new edition was quickly prepared, using the original thirteen maps and adding a further seven showing river surveys of the Ganges and general inland navigation. This was achieved by 1781, and reprints were still being made almost fifty years afterwards. The later editions were issued without the general inland navigation map, this having been transferred to Rennell's *Memoir of a Map of Hindoostan*. This book was written to accompany his large general map (entitled simply *Hindoostan*), issued in four sheets at a scale of one equatorial degree to one inch and published in 1782 (Plate 7.16).

The *Memoir*, a remarkable and important work which went through several editions in its own right, contained a critique of the sources used in the compilation of the main map. Among these were East India Company charts communicated by Alexander Dalrymple, the hydrographer to the Company appointed in 1779, as well as route surveys taken by engineers accompanying military campaigns and expeditions. The latter were adjusted to an astronomical framework of latitudes and longitudes obtained for the more important coastal harbours and ports. For the Punjab region in the northwest of India, Rennell had relied on maps and sketches supplied by natives, which gave the names of several rivers and other features. Other sources, such as that for the divisions of northern India into *soubahs* (administrative districts), included a new English translation of the *Ayin Acbaree* and the coastal surveys of Jean Baptiste Nicolas d'Après de Mannevillette. The latter were published in *Le neptune oriental* in Paris in 1745 and revised in 1775. In addition, Rennell also acknowledged the contribution made by Dalrymple about whom he said:

. . . with a liberality, which justly entitles him to the thanks of the public . . . [he] has furnished me from his valuable collection, with every material in it that could contribute towards perfecting my plan. And accordingly, the most valuable of all the new matter that respects the sea coasts (the surveys made by the direction of the Bengal Presidency excepted) is taken from his collection; and also a very considerable

portion of what respects the inland parts of the peninsula, and the northern circars.[7]

With the advance of the British occupying forces in India, Rennell was constantly receiving fresh material from the surveyors and engineers. He issued a second edition of his *Memoir* in 1785, adding a description of the Ganges and the Brahmaputra rivers as well as topographical descriptions communicated by army officers who had fought in recent campaigns against Tipu Sultan. In 1788, Rennell reissued the map, enlarged to one and a half inches to a degree, with further editions following in 1792 and 1793. In the latter cases, the *Memoir* was further augmented by the addition of a brief history of India from Persian, French and other sources.

By the time Rennell's health obliged him to retire and return to England in 1782, he had become the recognized authority on the geography and mapping of India. Indeed, by the time of his death in 1830, he had lived to see the mapping of this vast country established on a scientific and systematic basis.

William Lambton

Initially, more officers were employed to carry out route surveys in Rennell's style, until in 1800 Lieutenant-Colonel William Lambton (*fl.* 1802–1827) obtained the consent of the government of the Madras Presidency to carry out a proper

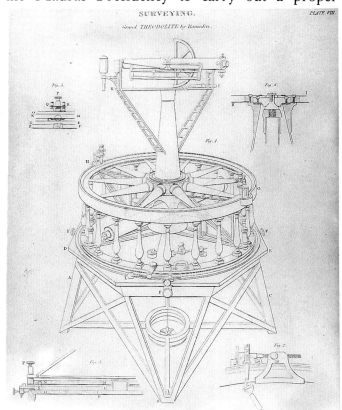

PLATE 7.16 *(opposite)* Hindoostan *by James Rennell, 1782. This map accompanied Rennell's book* Memoir of a Map of Hindoostan, *and was issued in four sheets at a scale of one equatorial degree to one inch. Rennell's mapping in India was a remarkable achievement and stood the test of time well into the next century.*

PLATE 7.17 *(left) The Great Theodolite designed and built by Jesse Ramsden. William Lambton had the instrument shipped out from England to enable him to carry out the first triangulation survey of India. Carrying and setting up an instrument weighing some 90.72 kilograms was no easy task in India's mountainous terrain.*

PLATE 7.18 Plan of
the Trigonometrical
Operations carried on in
the Peninsula of India
from the years 1802 to
1814 inclusive . . . by
Lieutenant Colonel William
Lambton. Lambton was the
first surveyor to use
triangulation to map the
country. The triangulation
surveys fixed points
throughout the subcontinent,
and topographical surveyors
filled in the outline with
details of rivers, roads,
mountains, and other
geographical information.

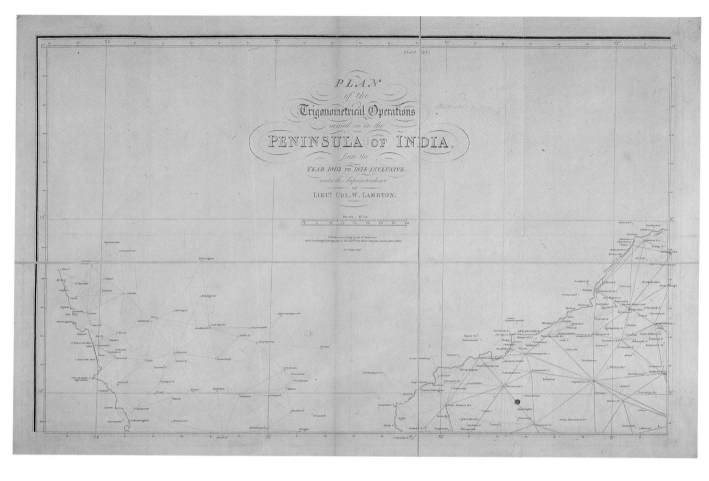

PLATE 7.19 George
(later Sir George) Everest
(1790–1866) joined
William Lambton to
assist with the Great
Trigonometrical Survey of
India, and took over the
leadership on Lambton's
death in 1827.

triangulation survey. Lambton was of the opinion that satisfactory and reliable maps could not be compiled merely by assembling a collection of route surveys. For his project, Lambton had Jesse Ramsden's Great Theodolite shipped out from England (Plates 6.7, 7.17).

Lambton carried his first series of triangles westwards from two measured base-lines, each some 11.27 kilometres long, near Madras and at Bangalore, southwards to Cape Comorin, then northeastwards as far as the seventy-ninth meridian. These were the first of a series of triangles which would take seventy years to complete, having covered more than 3,220 kilometres, reaching into the Himalayas and eventually into Tibet and Xinjiang in China. The Ramsden theodolite was, of course, the same as that which had been used in the less rigorous climate of southern England. Carrying and setting up an instrument weighing some 90.72 kilograms was no easy task in India. Sometimes the flagmen would be terrorized by tigers, at other times they would not be seen for days or weeks before their signal was sighted on some distant hill. On another occasion, when the surveyors were using the great temple at Tanjore as a trigonometrical station and were winching the instrument to the top of the building, a rope broke and dropped the

carefully adjusted theodolite, causing damage to both the instrument and the ancient temple and many of its sculptures. By 1805, Lambton and his team had reached the west coast. On checking his observations he found that the peninsula of India was some sixty-five kilometres narrower than shown on the available maps, Rennell's included. In 1810, he reached Cape Comorin. The Indian government took over the administration of the survey in 1818, establishing the project as the Great Trigonometrical Survey of India.

Later, for the advance up through the jungles of central India, Lambton was joined by George (later Sir George) Everest (1790–1866), a trained military engineer and artillery officer who was blessed with a foul temper and possessed an inextinguishable determination to complete the task (Plates 7.19, 7.20). When Lambton died at the age of seventy, still working and only sixty-five kilometres short of his target at Nagpur, Everest took over. In 1841 he completed the longest meridional (or north-south) arc ever measured, at Dehra Dun in the Himalayas. From the headquarters at Dehra Dun (still the headquarters of the modern Survey of India mapping agency) a longitudinal series of triangles was begun along the border with Nepal skirting the central Himalayas. Malaria is said to have taken an even greater

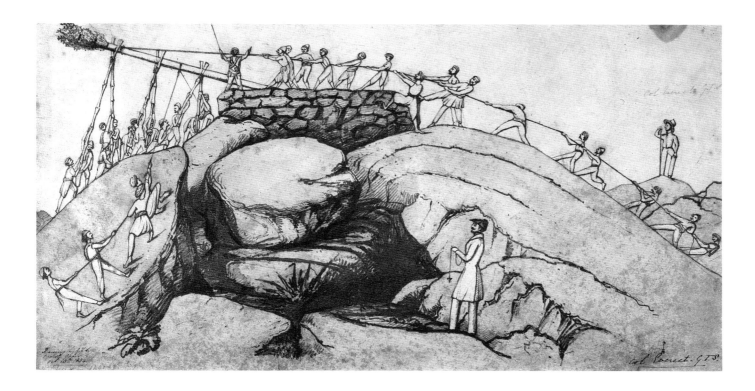

toll of officers and men than the recent military campaigns in the sub-continent.

The work established a set of controlled trigonometrical stations from which the surveyors were able to measure as many as seventy-nine of the area's highest peaks. Each was designated by a Roman numeral and after computation, Everest's successor announced peak XV, at 8,840 metres (29,002 feet), as the highest then known; it was subsequently named Mount Everest, in honour of Sir George in 1856.

To the west, in Kashmir, surveyors were establishing and working from stations at an altitude of more than 5,181 metres. Even the mundane task of erecting a shelter was a matter of endurance, to say nothing of carrying the heavy instruments.

The men would have to wait for a break in the clouds, which could mean waiting for several days, or even weeks, in order to take observations. The Great Trigonometrical Survey of India stands as a lasting achievement in the history of our formidable struggle to map our environment.

No one country can claim distinction for having originated the idea of a national survey. All nations foresaw the importance of detailed maps on a large, workable scale for the defence of the realm and the development of trade and national resources. All that can be said is that some were more successful than others in circumventing the political intrigue, professional jealousy and public lethargy that forever dogged the nations of Europe. The task was endless, and even when work in the field was not stopped by lack of funds, it suffered the ever-present blighting influence of war, either within a country's borders or at its back door. And too, there was always the age-old question – to map, or not to map? The better the map the more useful it would be to an enemy and the more likely to be stolen. In the end, however, the advantages outweighed the risks.[8]

PLATE 7.20 *(above) George Everest supervising the erection of a survey marker while in charge of the Great Trigonometrical Survey of India, a sketch signed and dated, Colonel Everest, 1834.*

PLATE 7.21 *(left) A theodolite designed by Sir George Everest of the Great Trigonometrical Survey of India. (From* The Practical Dictionary of Mechanics *by Edward H. Knight, London, c. 1880.)*

References
1. G.R. Crone, *op. cit.*, page 106.
2. J.J.S. Goss, *The Mapping Of North America*, map 59 (note), 1990.
3. W.W. Ristow's *Bibliographical Note To Thomas Jefferys. The American Atlas*, 1776, page v of facsimile edition of 1974.
4. J.J.S. Goss, *op. cit.*, map 57.
5. Quoted in E.M. Rodger, *The Large-Scale County Maps of the British Isles 1596–1850*, revised edition, pages vi–vii, 1972.
6. S. Cole, *India Within the Ganges*, page 85.
7. S. Cole, *op. cit.*, pages 88–89.
8. L.A. Brown, *op. cit.*, page 275.

Schloß und Vestung Marienberg

Fluß

CHAPTER VIII
TOWN PLANS AND VIEWS
6200 BC – 1900 AD

DETAILED TOWN PLANS and views have been published almost from the earliest days of printing in western Europe in the late fifteenth century, but the idea of the town plan had already been developed in ancient times. Indeed, the earliest known 'town plan' appears to be a wall-painting found at Çatal Hüyük in Turkey, dated about 6200 BC (Plate 8.2). 'Maps' etched on clay tablets were used in Mesopotamia, around 1000 BC, to show results of town surveys. The plan of Nippur is one of the best of these early maps, showing as it does the entire city, with its temples, rivers, parks and city gates. The Greeks also made detailed surveys of colonial settlements, and the Romans had their large plan of Rome, the *Forma urbis Romae*, made some time between AD 203 and 208. From the pre-Christian era, mosaic plans of the port of Ostia have been found, dating from about AD 200.

PLATE 8.1 *Detail of a plan of Würzburg from the* Städte-Atlas *by Johann Baptist Homann issued from Nuremberg during the 1730s and later. The German map publisher Johann Baptist Homann (1663–1724) and his heirs at Nuremberg issued collections of town plans and views covering the main towns of the German Empire and Europe. Note the characteristic heavily coloured plan details.*

Another famous early map is the so-called *Madaba map* of Palestine dating from about AD 560–565 (Plate 8.3). Made in mosaic, with all toponymy in Greek, the map incorporates a pictorial plan of Jerusalem in which many of the most important features may be recognized.

Despite damage wrought during the Iconoclastic controversy in the eighth and ninth centuries, and later during the last years of the nineteenth-century rebuilding of the church in which the mosaic was discovered in 1896, the map survives today as a remarkable monument to Roman and Byzantine skills in mapmaking as well as in the construction of mosaics.

Early European developments

The perspective, or panoramic map developed first in Italy. Perspective plans were made of the cities of Verona in the tenth century, and of Rome in the twelfth century, which consisted of stylized views of the city walls enclosing representations of the cities' most distinctive monuments. Even more stylized are the maps drawn by Matthew Paris, an English monk. He illustrated a pilgrimage itinerary from London to Rome in about 1252, showing representations of the most important places *en route* (Plate 8.4). Down to the late fifteenth century, plans of other Italian cities were drawn in this form. By then the growing trend towards realism in Italian art had led to the making of fully realistic panoramic maps of towns and cities. These were probably commissioned by wealthy burghers for reasons of civic or local pride.

The idea of perspective as if viewed from an elevation – or as if seen suspended from an imaginary balloon – seems to have originated in the late fourteenth century in a view of the Italian city of Padua, made in 1382 by Guido de' Menabui. Another early example is the late-fifteenth-century view of Constantinople from the island book of Christoforo Buondelmonte. Later examples depicting Rome and Florence are known to have been made by Francesco Rosselli, the first

PLATE 8.2 *(right and below) A neolithic wall-painting (right) at Çatal Hüyük, Turkey, dating from around 6200 BC. A modern reconstruction of the plan is shown below. The painting has been interpreted as a plan of a settlement, behind which at centre is a representation of the volcano, Hasan Dağ, erupting.*

PLATE 8.3 *A depiction of houses and churches in Jerusalem on a fragment of the so-called* Madaba *map in mosaic, made in the sixth century. The map is now preserved in fragments at Madaba, Jordan.*

known commercial mapseller, in the fifteenth century. Even seals and medals sometimes bore pictorial representations of cities and towns, such as the seal struck for Ludwig the Bavarian in 1282 which depicts Rome, the seat of his coronation.

The first illustrated travel book to contain properly recognizable and representational town views was the account of a pilgrimage to Jerusalem, written by the German Bernhard von Breydenbach. The *Sanctarum peregrinationem*, first printed in 1486, contained remarkable folding panoramic views of Venice and a detailed panorama of Jerusalem itself as the centrepiece of a perspective 'map' of Palestine (Plate 8.5).

A few years later, in 1493, the most elaborately illustrated book then printed in Europe, the *Liber chronicarum* (or *Weltchronik*) appeared in print. It was the work of the Nuremberg doctor Hartmann Schedel, and was made available in both Latin and in the local vernacular German. This major work, generally known as the *Nuremberg Chronicle*, was printed by the foremost printer of the day in

Nuremberg, Anton Koberger. The thick folio volume contained upwards of 1,900 woodcut pictures, including maps and views, all by or after the celebrated artists Michael Wohlgemuth or Wilhelm Pleydenwurff. Of these illustrations, some 116 were of places identified by name. Bird's-eye views as well as ground-level panoramas were included, but only about a quarter of these towns and cities resembled their real appearance; the rest were almost entirely imaginary. Thus, the same picture was used to illustrate Mainz in Germany and Lyon in France; another picture served for the regions of Hesse in Germany and the whole of Turkey; another for Macedonia in the Balkans and Portugal on the fringes of western Europe.

In 1500, Jacopo de' Barbari published his extraordinary perspective of Venice, entitled and dated simply *Venetie MD* (Plate 8.6). This was printed from six woodcut blocks and measured in all some 1,300 by 2,800 mm, made to give an impression of the size, wealth and commercial

PLATE 8.4 *(right) Part of an itinerary from London to Rome drawn by Matthew Paris, c. 1252. The towns are represented by stylized buildings. Modern itineraries still follow the same general concept of the strip road map.*

PLATE 8.5 *(below) Detail of a map of Palestine with a perspective view of Jerusalem from* Sanctarum peregrinationem *by Bernhard von Breydenbach, large folding woodcut, Mainz, 1486. Designed by the Utrecht-born painter Erhard Reuwich, this map is one of the most famous of all picture maps. Reuwich displays a finely tuned eye for detail.*

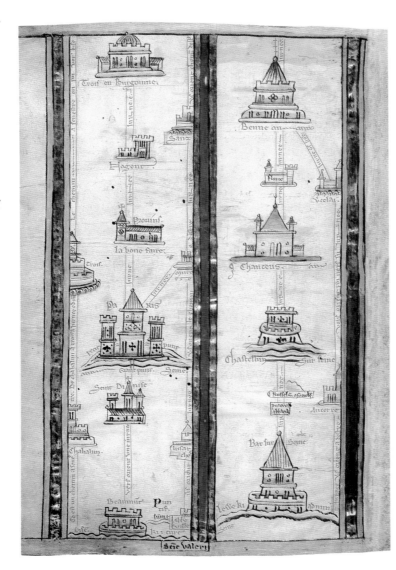

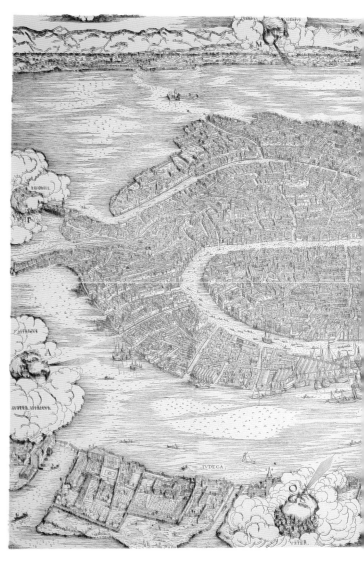

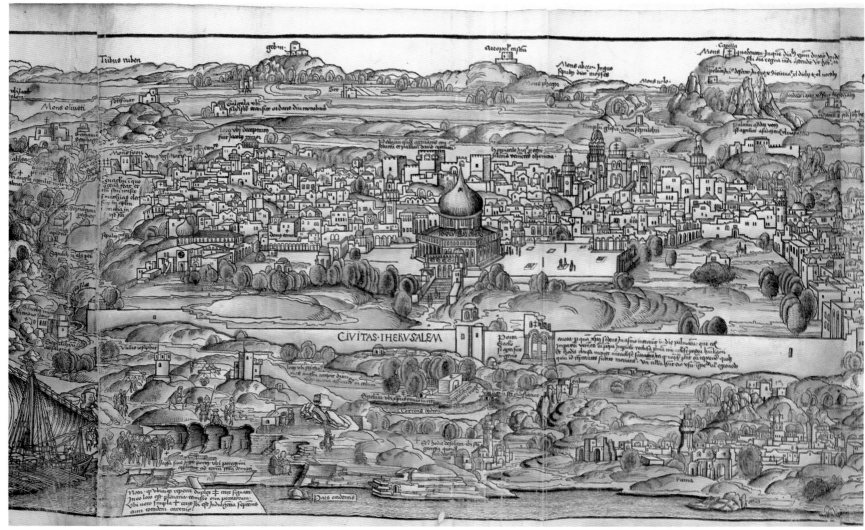

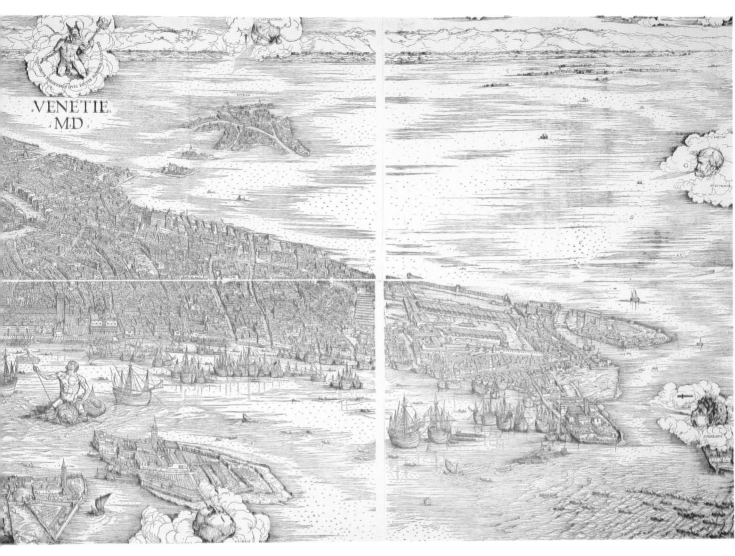

PLATE 8.6 *(left)* Venetie
M D *by Jacopo de'
Barbari, woodcut, six
sheets, Venice, 1500. One
of the most spectacular
town views ever published,
commissioned by one Anton
Kolls, a German merchant
residing in Venice.
Compilation was probably
done in a studio from
separate sketches taken from
high buildings, the whole
being cut on six woodblocks,
which still survive. De'
Barbari's remarkable work
illustrates the realism to
which Renaissance artists
aspired.*

PLATE 8.7 *(left) The
south-central section of the
so-called 'copperplate plan
of London', c. 1553–1559.
This is an engraving from
one of two known surviving
plates of a large plan
assumed to have comprised
twenty sheets.*

259

PLATE 8.8 *(right, centre and far right) Title-pages of Volumes I, V and VI of the* Civitates orbis terrarum *by Georg Braun and Frans Hogenberg, 1572–1617.*

activity of a maritime city at the head of the Adriatic, meeting place of East and West. De' Barbari's realistic perspective shows buildings which are still easily recognizable today, and his masterpiece, together with Francesco Rosselli's more traditional view of Florence, may be seen as the true begetters of the printed perspective city plan which had its greatest flowering in the *Civitates orbis terrarum* by Georg Braun and Frans Hogenberg (see below). Before the appearance of this great work towards the end of the sixteenth century, very few printed books contained more than a mere handful of urban subjects, a great many of which were in any case entirely imaginary in content. The notable exceptions to this rule were such works as Sebastian Münster's *Cosmographia universalis*, a popular work of the 1550s which contained many woodcut town views, panoramas and plans based on actual observation; the *Liber chronicarum* of Hartmann Schedel published a century or so earlier at Nuremberg; and Johann Stumpff's famous history and description of Switzerland, the *Schwyzer chronick* of 1548.

For the most part, however, town plans and views had been issued separately, as *Geschichtsblätter*, or as elaborate, multi-sheet publications intended for display on the walls of great houses or palaces. Examples of these are Jorg Sald's view of Augsburg in 1521 (which measures 800 by 1,910 mm); Cornelis Anthoniszoon's perspective of Amsterdam in 1544 (1,933 by 1,380 mm); Conrad Merian's view of Strasbourg in 1548; the panorama of Lübeck in 1552; and Jacopo de' Barbari's panoramic perspective of Venice, dating from 1500. We can only wonder what the lost twenty-sheet map of London (1553–1559), from which Braun and Hogenberg derived their map of the city, looked like. Two engraved copper plates, at least, are known to have survived, engraved in such extraordinary detail that architectural features on many buildings in the City of London may be seen (Plate 8.7).

The Civitates

The *Civitates orbis terrarum* (or *Civitates* as it is generally known) is one of the great map books of the world, a celebration of the European city in all its many and varied forms. Published in six volumes, over forty-five years from 1572 to 1617,

it is also one of the first 'modern' atlases (Plates 8.8, 8.9); the complete work contains 363 plates which depict in great detail 530 cities and towns as they appeared four centuries ago. It is a work which gives collectors as much pleasure today as it did in its early years.

The *Civitates* incorporates the work of prominent artists, engravers and cartographers of the time in a series of historical perspectives, oblique plans (or bird's-eye views) and town plans, the form perhaps most familiar to the modern reader. Georg Braun (1541–1622), co-compiler with Frans Hogenberg (1535–1590), favoured the oblique view, being of the opinion 'that towns should be drawn in such a manner that the viewer may look into all the roads, and streets and see also all the buildings and open spaces . . . '

Into this remarkable series of engravings, Braun and Hogenberg incorporated an astonishing wealth of detail. By means of these pictures, the compilers presented to the reader an impression of the economy, status, wealth and even the social structure of the towns and cities in Europe – and of the immediately neighbouring regions of Asia and Africa. In addition, wherever space permitted, each subject was enlivened with details of the surrounding countryside. Thus, woods,

PLATE 8.9 *A typical fine early seventeenth-century atlas binding in full morocco, with gilt tooling, on a set of Braun and Hogenberg's* Civitates orbis terrarum.

PLATE 8.10 *(below) A town plan of Lisbon from Volume V (number 2) of the* Civitates orbis terrarum *by Georg Braun and Frans Hogenberg, 1598. The engravings in the* Civitates *included a rich and varied assortment of illustrations showing the trade, customs and habits of the town depicted. In the sixteenth century Lisbon was the centre of a vast overseas empire, hence the inclusion of the sea-going vessels sailing along the coast.*

PLATE 8.11 *Detail of a view of Nuremberg from volume II of the* Civitates orbis terrarum *by Georg Braun and Frans Hogenberg, copper engraving, Cologne, 1575 and later. This engraving, after a view drawn by Cornelius Chaymox, shows how Braun and Hogenberg's views are justly valued as much for their depiction of local costume and customs as for their topographical content.*

pastures, vineyards, orchards, gardens, and even flood- or sea-waters were shown.

At the time of the first publication of the *Civitates*, during the late sixteenth and early seventeenth centuries, water was the most important means of transporting large quantities of trade goods – grains, timber, salt, etc – from one place to another. Therefore, careful attention was given to the correct representation of river-going and sea-going vessels (for example, the engravings show Dutch merchant ships plying in and out of the harbour at Lisbon (Plate 8.10), at Danzig (now Gdańsk) or barges floating down the Rhine, the Thames or the Wisla rivers). Sometimes different types of traffic are shown in the engravings: laden wagons, carriages for the use of nobles, and simply the peddler on foot. Different occupations are portrayed and local costume often shown to gloriously colourful effect (Plates 8.11, 8.14). Indeed, some collectors consider the series to be one of the finest costume books in existence, so detailed are the local and regional costumes worn by the people in the foregrounds. It does not matter in the least that most of the figures are drawn out of proportion to the townscapes; rather, they impart a sense of long perspective, so that the viewer is effortlessly drawn into the centre of the markets of Hamburg, the quays of Bordeaux covered with casks of robust clarets, or the peaceful lanes outside Oxford peopled with strolling academics (Plate 8.12).

But why, and how, were such perspective, or bird's-eye, plans made? The perspective subjects which make up the *Civitates* enabled the mapmak-

er to convey vertical dimensions – the elevations of important buildings, and their architectural features in some instances. At the same time they retained a horizontal dimension, but one which relied on perspective rather than true scale in most cases. The plan and view were thus combined to form a map-view or plan-view, presenting the true ground plan but featuring some, if not all, of the buildings in elevation. By portraying a city in this way, the mapmaker could impress the reader with the grandeur, power and wealth he depicted and, of course, could demonstrate his particular skills in the art of perspective plan-making at the same time as doing so.

A curious feature of the *Civitates* series is that, in nearly every instance, a relatively tranquil scene is depicted. Whatever activity is seen to be taking place, it is a peaceful, everyday kind of activity be it agriculture, viticulture, shipping, trading, or merely displaying local costume to the reader. This is true even in the case of many of the towns of Austria, Hungary and the Spanish Netherlands, even though all of them were at one time or another during the compilation of the six volumes wracked by civil and military conflict. Indeed, many of them witnessed the most appalling atrocities even by our standards of the late twentieth century. Compare the tranquil scenes shown in the *Civitates* with the violent depictions of contemporary events which Hogenberg himself, and others, published, from about 1561 onwards, as *Geschichtsblätter*, illustrating the horrors perpetrated during the religious wars in northern Europe in the struggle for the independence of the Netherlands from Spain. The contrast between the two is stark indeed! It seems almost as if a form of censorship was exercised in the production of many of the engravings in the *Civitates* series. In other words, what we have in Braun and Hogenberg's work is an almost too-perfect ideal of the European town and city way of life in the late sixteenth and early seventeenth centuries.

There is hardly a sign of distress or conflict in the manner in which the inhabitants disport themselves. Not only are there wealthy aristocrats and merchants, as it were taking their bows on presenting their cities to the reader, but in the middle ground of many of the views artisans, labourers, peasants, farmers, small traders and skippers can be seen busy about their various occupations: vines are cultivated in the Rhine valley and in the Loire regions; corn is harvested in southern Spain; flax and cotton are prepared for sale abroad by way of Cadiz, Barcelona and Marseille; wealthy Danzig merchants profit from the lucrative rye trade with Amsterdam; and the proud burghers of Nuremberg rejoice at having secured their profit from trade with other countries. In many instances, the artist Joris Hoefnagel (1542–1600), together with his travelling companions, is included in a French or Spanish scene, or is to be spotted lazing by the wayside on a balmy day.

First and foremost, then, the *Civitates orbis terrarum* is a magnificent collection of pictures, a true pictorial atlas. The descriptive matter printed on the versos is merely supplementary – what nowadays would be considered as caption material. Nevertheless, the text, despite its brevity, should not be ignored, for it contains many facts, some fictions and many speculations from all manner of sources. Braun's purpose was to describe the shape and the settings of the towns and their inhabitants, and what trades and industries flourished there. He sometimes included fulsome praise – perhaps to stimulate sales of the books in those towns – and at other times criticized the physical state of other places. Many descriptions, especially those of towns in France and southern Spain, demonstrate a detailed local knowledge which was probably supplied by Hoefnagel from his own observations. As R. Oehme writes:

The appearance of medieval cities, which today can be reconstructed only with great difficulty from ancient records and documents or architectural remains, has been preserved for posterity by Braun, Hogenberg and their collaborators in a clear and artistic form. Thanks to the abundance of architecturally accurate views and the natural treatment of landscape which characterizes most of the prints, and great variety of the texts, the *Book of Cities* possesses permanent value.[1]

There is a close generic resemblance between the title of the great world atlas of Abraham Ortelius, the *Theatrum orbis terrarum* (first published in Antwerp in 1570), and the *Civitates orbis terrarum* of Braun and Hogenberg. Ortelius was a contemporary of Braun and Hogenberg and his work is quite often considered by collectors to be the rightful companion to that of Braun and Hogenberg. Very often, especially in the case of the German editions, the Ortelius atlas and the Braun and Hogenberg *Civitates* were bound together in a uniform binding of brown morocco with gilt and silver tooling. There is, however, one main difference in the titles. While the Ortelius atlas expanded over the years to cover all the then known world by the time of its final full edition in 1612, the *Civitates* barely stretched beyond Europe. With the hindsight of centuries, this makes the title of the series seem rather grandiose. But that criticism is unfair, especially as the authors are unable to defend their work. Furthermore, it ignores the great pleasure that the work as a whole – and the individual plates – still gives to collectors today.

Indeed, Braun and Ortelius held each other in mutual regard. A few months before Volume I of

PLATE 8.12 *View of Oxford from Volume II (number 2) of the* Civitates orbis terrarum *by Georg Braun and Frans Hogenberg, 1575. Oxford is viewed from the north, without many of the 'dreaming spires' that were yet to grace the townscape.*

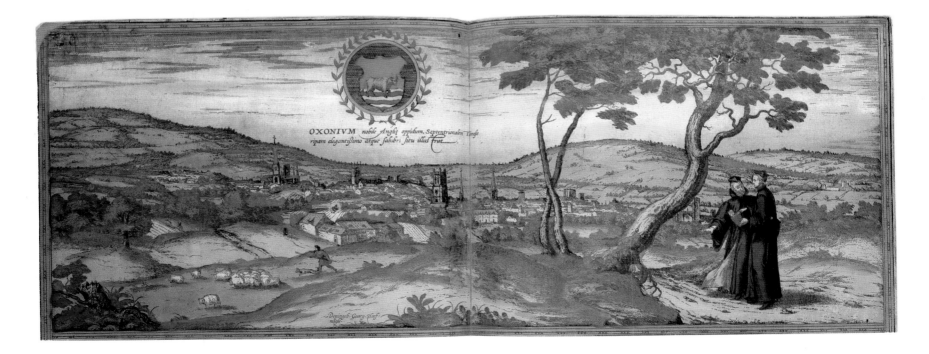

the *Civitates* was first published Braun wrote to Ortelius asking for advice, in a letter dated 31 October 1571:

For various reasons some learned men here in Cologne think that Master Frans's [*i.e.* Hogenberg's] Book of Cities would commend itself more to purchasers if the proper names of places, churches and gates were given in the native language; so as to satisfy both the learned and the unlettered: the learned because they will have the Latin descriptions on the back, the unlettered because each will see his own native town depicted with places named in a form familiar to him. I think the usefulness of this arrangement evident when pictures of cities are sold separately, but the citizens would like them less if they could understand nothing of what they read. For while this is nevertheless the practice in the descriptions [in other words, the engraved maps] of countries in your very beautiful *Theatrum*, and admitting its usefulness to the learned, yet you see how many people are distracted by it; and since Master Frans's subject is a popular one, delighting the eyes even of the unlettered, it would appear sensible to me to accommodate ourselves somewhat to them . . . these are matters, Master Abraham, which I thought of most importance to you and on which no decisions will be taken until we know your considered opinion . . .[2]

The contributors

The chief editor of the *Civitates* series was Georg Braun (1541–1622). He was a cleric in Cologne and spent most of his life in that city. Little else is known about him except that he wrote several, now largely forgotten, theological texts. During the compilation of the *Civitates*, Braun corresponded with town officials as well as with the most important mapmakers and engravers of his time. He even appealed to his readers, in the preface to Volume II, to send in paintings or drawings of their towns and cities if they were not already represented in the work, or to provide more recent depictions of cities already included in earlier volumes. Braun is also thought to have written, or at least edited, most of the descriptive texts printed on the versos of the engraved views and plans of the six volumes.

Prominent among Braun's engravers was Frans Hogenberg (1535–1590) of Mechelen in Belgium. Hogenberg learned the art and techniques

of engraving from his brother, Rémy (or Remigius), who was himself to become famous as the engraver of several of the English regional and county maps compiled by Christopher Saxton in London during the 1570s. Frans Hogenberg engraved many of the plates for Ortelius's *Theatrum* atlas, and he was also the friend of Gerard Mercator, a contemporary of Ortelius. After Frans Hogenberg's death (in 1590) many of the *Civitates* plates were made by Abraham Hogenberg, who is assumed to have been the son of Frans. Among other important engravers who worked for Braun on the project was Simon van den Neuvel, who contributed many plates to the second and third volumes of the series.

It was through his friendship with Ortelius that Georg Braun became acquainted with the Antwerp artist Joris Hoefnagel (1542–1600) (Plate 8.13), who played a vital, and until recently relatively underestimated, part as an artist in the overall design of the series. Hoefnagel was the son of a wealthy family and travelled widely throughout Europe, in particular to England, France and Spain. Hoefnagel lived in Antwerp until 1576 when, like Hogenberg before him, he was driven into exile by the hated tyrant, the Duke of Alba. He then settled in the relatively safe haven of Cologne, and also worked in Austria, Bohemia, Moravia and the Tyrol. In the company of Ortelius, Hoefnagel made extensive travels throughout Italy, collecting material for publication by Braun. Hoefnagel's talent was based on an enthusiasm for knowledge. Through his keen eye for detail, he managed to convey both the structure of the towns and cities and the way of life of their inhabitants. He was also a master of the pure landscape and of local custom, as may be seen, for example, in his well-observed painting of *A Fête at Bermondsey* (*c.* 1570). After Hoefnagel's death in 1600, his son Jakob continued work on the plates for the *Civitates*.

Another very important contributor to the series was Heinrich von Rantzau (1526–1599), commonly known as Rantzovius from his Latinized name. Von Rantzau was the Danish governor of Schleswig-Holstein and lived at Breinburg. He was a close friend and correspondent of Mercator's and he supplied maps, descriptions, plans and views of towns and cities in northern Europe, particularly of Denmark. It is also reasonable to

PLATE 8.13 *Portrait of Joris Hoefnagel (1542–1600), painter, traveller, topographer and engraver, who contributed about one hundred of the town views to the Braun and Hogenberg* Civitates *series.*

GEORGIVS HOEFNAGLIVS PICT. ¡ANTVERPIANVS

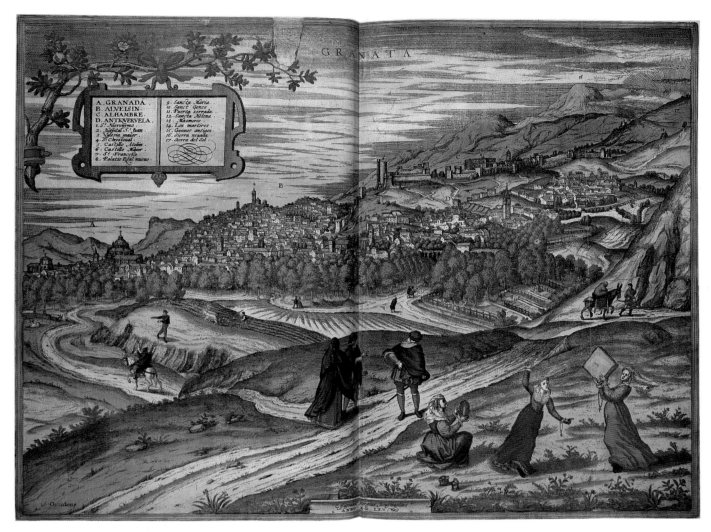

assume that von Rantzau was the author of the texts for the Danish towns and cities that were included in the *Civitates*.

Other sources of information were the older woodcut views used in the Sebastian Münster *Cosmographia* of the 1550s, and the unpublished surveys of towns in the Netherlands by Jacob van Deventer (*c*.1505–1576). Many of the subjects in the six volumes were provided by anonymous artists or were based upon existing engravings or woodcuts by artists and engravers such as Lucas van Valckeborch (who was responsible for the views of Gmunden and Linz in Volume V published in 1598) and Hieronymus Schol (who contributed the beautiful views of Bergen and Stockholm which were published in Volume IV in 1588). Paintings and drawings were contributed by artists such as Anthonij van den Wijngaerde, Pieter Breughel and Egidius van de Rye.

In his preface, Braun praised his collaborators Hogenberg and van den Neuvel with particular admiration: ' . . . whose artistic hands applied all ingenuity and accuracy in the reproduction of the cities and of the buildings and have pictured them with all the architectural details with such correctness, that it is as if one does not see the pictures of the cities, but the cities themselves . . . ' Also singled out by Braun for praise was Hoefnagel, who supplied the lively pictures of Spanish cities, accurately drawn from life (Plate 8.14). The costumed figures and vignettes of local people which enlivened the plans were either by the original artist – as in Hoefnagel's views – or taken from contemporary illustrated costume books such as the famous *Trachtenbuch* of Hanns Weigel and Jost Amman (Nuremberg, 1577). These figures, often theatrical in character, are a great tribute to the compositional skills of the engraver. Although they are drawn on a much larger scale than the rest of the design, they rarely introduce a discordant note. This particular feature of the work is said to have had the additional purpose of preventing the Turks (who at the time were expanding their empire despite defeat at Lepanto in 1571) from using the engravings during their campaigns in southeastern Europe, since their religion prohibited the portrayal of the human figure.

Later developments

The great popular success of the *Civitates* as a whole, and of the individual volumes, inspired a particular fashion for townbooks which lasted

PLATE 8.15 *(right) A town plan of Hamburg from the* Topographia *series by Matthäus Merian, 1640s and later.*

PLATE 8.16 *(below)* Civitas Londini *by John Norden, c. 1600. Published in four sheets together with a processional view below, this map is known in only one complete example, with inset plans of Westminster (left) and London (right). The panel at centre begins:* This description of the moste Famous Citty London, was performed in the yeare of Christe 1600 . . .

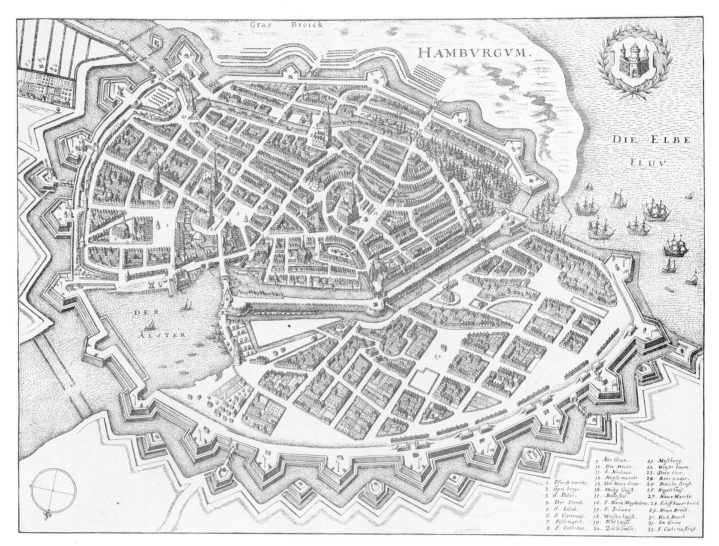

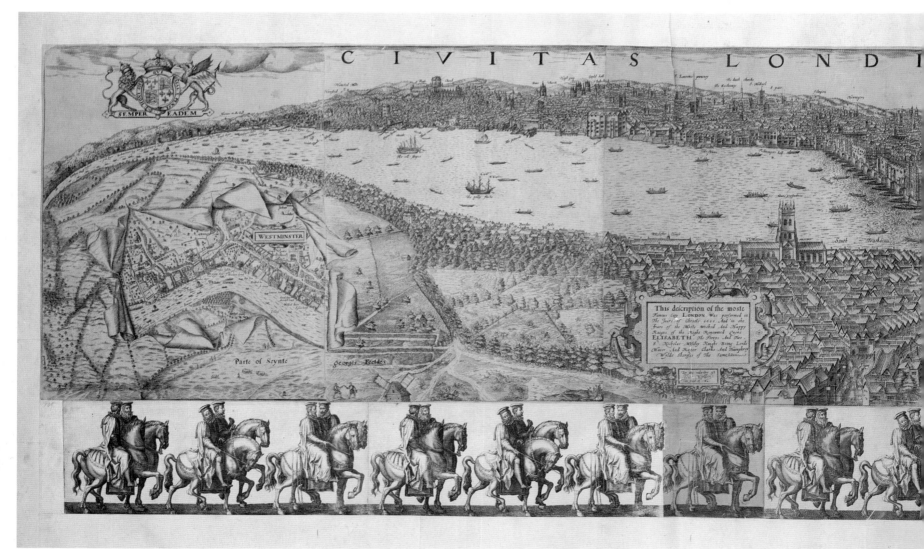

until well into the eighteenth century. Braun even invited others to copy his work, the best examples, notable objects of great beauty and detail in themselves, being the views and plans in a long series issued by the Merian family (Plate 8.15). Their *Theatrum Europaeum*, in twenty-one volumes, began publication in 1640 and ultimately may have been the inspiration for the celebrated Buck town views in England a hundred or so years later. (Samuel and Nathaniel Buck were English topographical artists and engravers working in the eighteenth century, who produced a long series of varied prospects of towns and cities up and down the country. The Buck town views are valued as topographical references because they often presented the same place from different angles.)

Of all the collaborators on the *Civitates* series, Georg Braun was the only one who lived to see the series completed, with the publication of the sixth volume in 1617. After Braun's death in 1622, the plates of the great work lay unused until they were purchased *en bloc* by the leading Amsterdam mapmaker and publisher Joannes Janssonius in 1653. Janssonius reprinted some 232 of the plates,

with only very minor changes such as more fashionable title cartouches, minor re-touches or his imprint. On a few occasions, he commissioned new engravings of older subjects, sometimes including them alongside the earlier subjects in his books. From 1657 onwards, Janssonius issued a large series, in six volumes, with Latin text for all 500 plans and views. Most of them covered Europe, but several new plates showed cities in other parts of the world, especially in Asia. Janssonius's series, with the title *Illustriorum . . . urbium tabulae* (with the name of the appropriate region inserted), covered I *Germania Superior* (two volumes); II *Belgium seu Germania Inferior* (two volumes); III *Europea Septentrionalis*; IV *Gallia et Helvetia*; V *Italia*; and VI *Hispania*.

Years later, in the 1670s and 1680s, many of the original Braun and Hogenberg plates passed to another Amsterdam publisher, Frederick de Wit, who also issued a series of town views. Later still, they came into the hands of the Leiden publisher and print-seller, Pieter van der Aa, who issued a sixty-six-part series of illustrated folio volumes entitled *La galerie agréable du monde* during the 1720s. Many of the impressions from the Braun and Hogenberg plates – by now rather worn – were used for the plates of van der Aa's edition. Only one hundred sets were produced.

PLATE 8.17 *Cambridge, an inset plan of the town on a map of Cambridgeshire by John Speed, 1611. Speed's town plan insets are thought for the most part to have been surveyed by Speed himself, and represent the earliest series of town plans of the British Isles.*

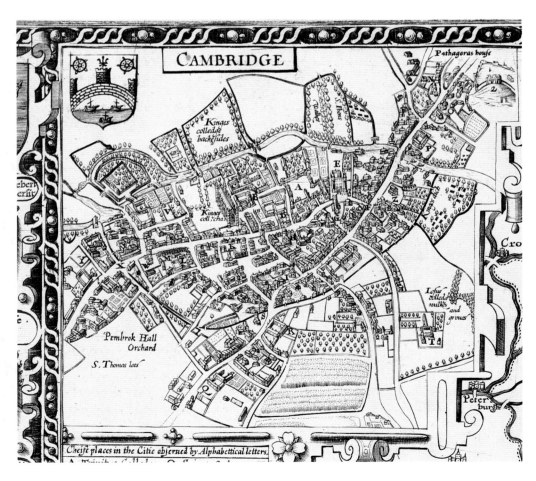

PLATE 8.19 *(opposite)*
Torino *from the Italian
Townbooks series by Joan
Blaeu, Amsterdam, 1663
and later. An example of
how colouring can enhance a
detailed plan. Note the rigid
gridiron plan and also the
citadella dating from 1564.*

PLATE 8.18 *(below)* De
vermaerde koopstadt van
Amsterdam *by Cornelis
Anthoniszoon, woodcut,
from twelve blocks,
Amsterdam, 1544 and
later. A fine, early example
of the separately published
perspective plan, here
embellished with the figure
of Neptune supporting the
arms of Amsterdam to
symbolize the sea-going
merchants of the city.*

Several of the plates subsequently found their way into the hands of yet another Amsterdam publisher, Pieter Mortier. In partnership with Johannes Covens, he issued them in composite collections of maps, plans and views during the 1750s. The later history of the plates still remains a matter of conjecture, although they were known to have been in the possession of the firm of Covens and Mortier in the middle of the nineteenth century. Their ultimate fate is unknown, but it is doubtful whether they survived. Surely the most lasting tribute to the work of Braun and Hogenberg, however, is that the *Civitates* had an influential working life of more than a century and a half.

The Netherlands

As we have seen in Chapter IV, the Netherlands was the centre of mapmaking for the greater part of the sixteenth and seventeenth centuries. During this time, some of the Dutch mapmakers also produced some very fine town plans.

The best-known example from the middle decades of the sixteenth century is the 1544 plan of Amsterdam by Cornelis Anthoniszoon (b.1507) –

a large plan in twelve sheets printed from woodblocks, called *De vermaerde koopstadt van Amsterdam* (Plate 8.18). This cartographic masterpiece may well have drawn its inspiration from Jacopo de' Barbari's great plan-view of Venice of 1500 (see p.259). In various editions, Anthoniszoon's plan continued to be issued until about 1640.

Jacob van Deventer was one of the best-known Dutch mapmakers of the sixteenth century. Van Deventer's greatest project, in effect his life's achievement, was undoubtedly the 214 plans of the towns and cities of the Northern and Southern Netherlands. He received the commission as a result of the general approval of the provincial surveys which he had carried out between 1536 and 1545. The commission was at the command of Philip II 'to visit, measure and describe all the towns throughout our land'.[3] For the work, van Deventer received a retainer of 200 florins a year and a daily subsistence of two florins, plus extra expenses payable for a guide, interpreter (necessary in areas where dialects of Flemish or Friesian, for example, were spoken) and horse transport, according to a document dating from 1559.

Van Deventer's project took some fourteen years. During this time he produced as many as 320 plans, of which about two-thirds have survived, constituting the most comprehensive and trustworthy record of the urban development of any country during the Renaissance period. This was despite the fact that the van Deventer surveys were never made available in printed form with the exception of some of the town plans published in Braun and Hogenberg's *Civitates*. Van Deventer's surveys were carried out for military reasons at the behest of central government during a time of revolt in the Protestant disturbances in the Netherlands. However, none of the published subjects in this series is actually attributed to van Deventer, and there is no mention of his name anywhere in the series. But it has been established[4] that van Deventer's work *was* used by Braun and Hogenberg, either directly, or by way of the plans included in Ludovico Guicciardini's popular history of the Netherlands, published in many editions from 1567 onwards.

Van Deventer's surveys were on a more or less uniform scale of 1:8,000 and were carried out

(continued on page 275)

Names of Places Contain'd in this Mapp.

Old street

Bunhill fields

Artillery ground

More fields

Spitle fields

Mile end

Mile end Green

Goodmans fields

Stepney

Raynes Well

Great Tower Hill
Litle Tower Hill

LONDON

DVRIA FL.

AVGVSTA TAVRINORVM

ERIDANVS FL.

PLATE 8.20 *A plan of London by Joannes de Ram, c. 1700. This beautiful plan is here seen to impressive effect in the fine contemporary hand-colouring which was often employed in Amsterdam in the early eighteenth century.*

PLATE 8.21 *(left)*
Rotterdam *from the famous*
Dutch Townbooks series,
Toonneel der Steden
van de Vereenighde
Nederlanden, *by Joan*
Blaeu, Amsterdam, 1649.
Here the mercantile activity
of a busy port city clearly
can be seen.

PLATE 8.22 *A plan of*
Würzburg from the Städte-
Atlas *by Johann Baptist*
Homann issued from
Nuremberg during the
1730s and later.

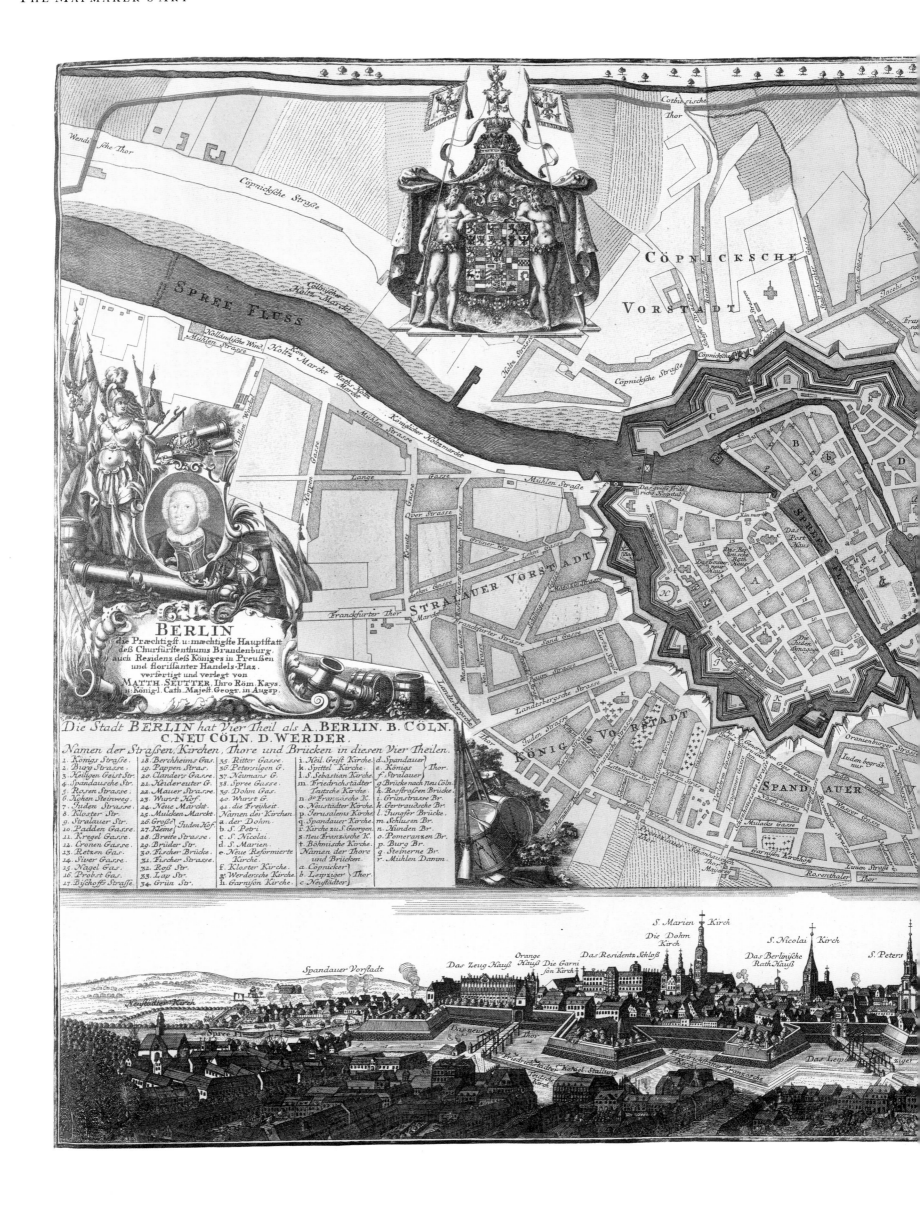

BERLIN
die Prächtigst: u: mæchtigste Hauptstatt
deß Churfürstenthums Brandenburg,
auch Residenz deß Königes in Preußen
und florissanter Handels-Plaz.
verfertigt und verlegt von
MATTH. SEUTTER, Ihro Röm. Kays.
u. Königl. Cath. Majest. Geogr. in Augsp.

Die Stadt BERLIN hat Vier Theil als A. BERLIN. B. CÖLN.
C. NEU CÖLN. D. WERDER.
Namen der Strassen, Kirchen, Thore und Brücken in diesen Vier Theilen.

1. Königs Strasse.	18. Berckheims Gas.	35. Ritter Gasse.	i. Heil: Geist Kirche. d. Spandauer
2. Burg Strasse.	19. Pappen Stras.	36. Petersilgen G.	k. Spittel Kirche. e. Königs Thor.
3. Heiligen Geist Str.	20. Clanders Gasse.	37. Neumans G.	l. S. Sebastian Kirche. f. Stralauer
4. Spandausche Str.	21. Heidereuter G.	38. Spree Gasse.	m. Friedrichstädter h. Brücke nach Neu Cöln.
5. Rosen Strasse.	22. Mauer Strasse.	39. Dohm Gas.	Teutsche Kirche. h. Rosstrassen Brücke.
6. Hohen Steinweg.	23. Wurst Hof.	40. Wurst G.	n. d° Französche K. i. Grünstrasse Br.
7. Juden Strasse.	24. Neue Marckt.	41. die Freyheit.	o. Neustädter Kirche. k. Gertraudische Br.
8. Kloster Str.	25. Mulcken Marckt.	Namen der Kirchen.	p. Jerusalems Kirche. l. Jungfer Brücke.
9. Stralauer Str.	26. Große Juden Hof.	a. der Dohm.	q. Spandauer Kirche. m. Schlusen Br.
10. Padden Gasse.	27. Keine	b. S. Petri.	r. Kirche zu S. Georgen. n. Münden Br.
11. Kregel Gasse.	28. Breite Strasse.	c. S. Nicolai.	s. Neu Französche K. o. Pomeranzen Br.
12. Cronen Gasse.	29. Brüder Str.	d. S. Marien.	t. Böhmische Kirche. p. Burg Br.
13. Retzen Gas.	30. Kircher Brücke.	e. Neue Reformierte	Namen der Thore q. Steinerne Br.
14. Siwer Gasse.	31. Fürcher Strasse.	Kirche.	und Brücken. r. Mühlen Damm.
15. Nagel Gas.	32. Roß Str.	f. Kloster Kirche.	a. Copnicker Thor.
16. Probst Gas.	33. Lap Str.	g. Werdersche Kirche.	b. Leipziger Thor.
17. Bischoffs Strasse.	34. Grün Str.	h. Garnison Kirche.	c. Neustädter

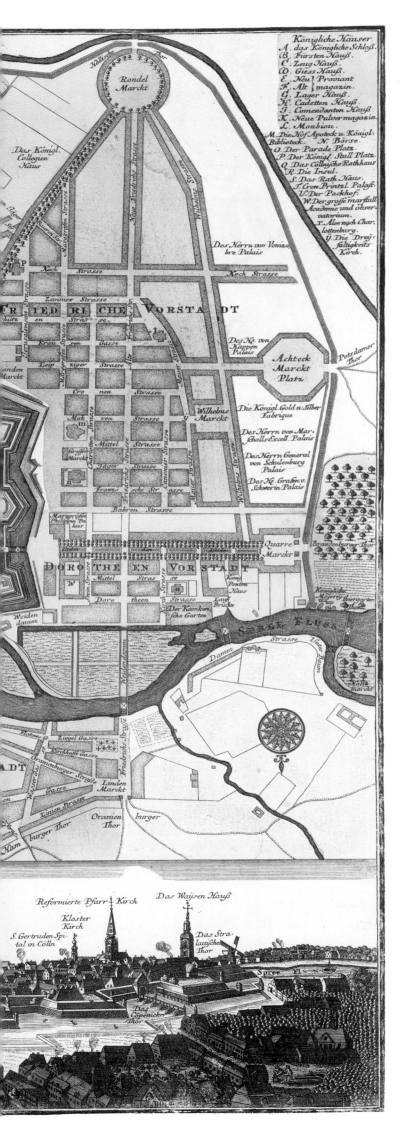

PLATE 8.23 Berlin, die prächtigst. u. mächtigste Hauptstatt des Churfürstenthums Brandenburg *by Georg Matthäus Seutter, copper engraving, Augsburg, c. 1740 or later. The plan shows the core of the city on the Spree river with new suburbs outside the old city walls.*

with little or no assistance as far as we know. As true plans (albeit criticized by some as pictorially inelegant) they provide us today with intricate detailed evidence for the growth of European towns from Roman times. A large body of 152 of van Deventer's plans and fragments of plans which survived the ravages of history were rediscovered in the middle of the nineteenth century and auctioned in 1859, but it was not until 1916 that facsimiles of ninety-seven of the plans were published and made more widely available. (A complete facsimile is now in course of publication as of writing at the beginning of 1993.)

Among the very finest seventeenth-century town plans and atlases are those found in the series of townbooks which Joan Blaeu devoted to the Netherlands (that is, the Southern Netherlands and the United Netherlands in 1648) and to Italy (that is, Piedmont and Savoy and the Church States from 1663 onwards), the latter work continuing in print until the 1720s (Plates 8.19, 8.21). Blaeu's magnificent townbooks of the Netherlands are a continuing object of pride: *Toonneel der Steden, Part I: De Vereenighde Nederlanden* with 128 plans and views, and *Part II: 's Konings Nederlanden* with ninety-five plans and views, which can be seen as a celebration of the pride of the newly independent country having thrown off the Spanish yoke.

Some of Blaeu's maps were adapted from the works of others, such as Antonius Sanderus's *Flandria illustrata* (1641) and Marc Boxhorn's *Theatrum Hollandiae* (1632). Although many were perhaps less than accurate and were often several years out of date by the 1640s, many of the beautifully engraved and highly detailed plans are keenly collected, as are indeed complete sets of the townbooks, on the few occasions that they make an appearance in the auction rooms or in dealers' catalogues. Many of Blaeu's plates were copied by his great competitor Janssonius for his series of townbooks issued during the 1650s.

Germany

The German map publisher Johann Baptist Homann (1663–1724) and his heirs at Nuremberg issued collections of town plans and views in several of their larger composite atlases, often as separate atlases of plans, frequently without title,

PLATE 8.24 Stutgardia
(Stuttgart) by Georg
Matthäus Seutter, issued in
various of his Augsburg
atlases during the 1740s.

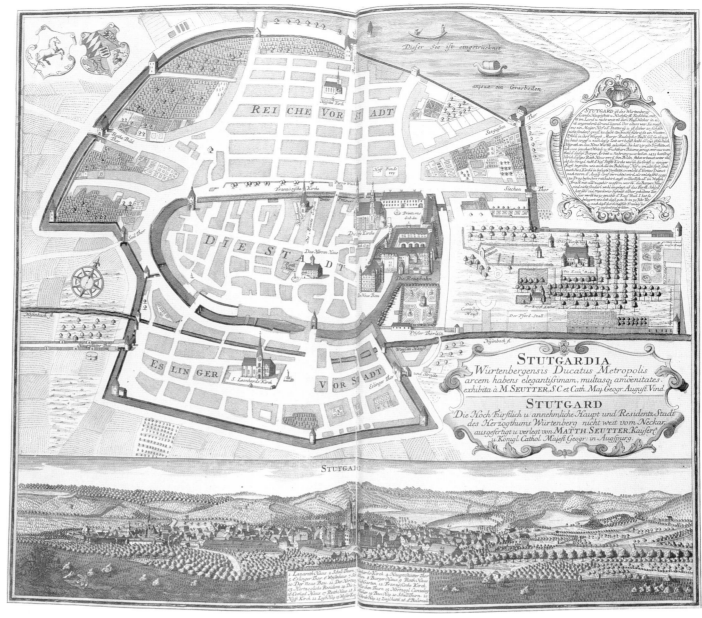

covering the main towns of the German Empire
and Europe (Plates 8.1, 8.22). Characteristic of
these Homann plates are the heavily coloured plan
details covering part of the area, with a (frequently) uncoloured prospect or panoramic view of the
same city along the lower part. Sometimes
Homann's plans and views leave a considerable
amount to the imagination for many towns, even
those far away from Germany, have a distinctly
'German' appearance. Sources are rarely credited,
many plans and views being copied from those
published in contemporary travel books or topographical descriptions. Emphasis is often laid
upon fortified towns and cities in Homann's
collections: remember that wars were an ever-
present feature of life in central Europe in the
eighteenth century and it is quite possible that
Homann issued the German plans especially to
convey the idea of the martial strength of the
towns in the empire. Altogether Homann issued
upwards of 200 individual plans of towns and
cities in his various atlases.

China

It was not only in Europe, of course, that town
plans were being made. The early surviving
Chinese maps are almost entirely pictorial, such as
the Confucian temple map from Suchow drawn in
1193, known from a copy carved in 1247. There
exists, also at the same temple in Suchow, a plan of
the city, drawn in 1193 and carved in stone in
1229 (Plate 8.25). This plan is one of four drawn
by the geographer Huang Chiang for the instruction of the future emperor, to whom Huang was
official tutor. The plans depicted such features as
important buildings, the city walls and the surrounding hills, all superimposed on an outline
ground-plan. The carved version was cut by
Wang Chih-Yuan of Suchow. There exists also an
early plan of the port city of Hangzhou, printed
originally in about 1274 but now known only
from a re-issue made in 1867. This copy is based
upon a manuscript copy made in the eighteenth
century. Both are pictorial plans showing walls,

gates, towers, mountains, trees, and – in the case of the Hangzhou plan – the imperial palace buildings and ships in the port. On many other maps, even from the earliest times, individual fortified places are shown in the form of a basic outline sketch plan.

The early development of local mapping in China (see Chapter II) is illustrated by the fact that, in the time of the emperor Hsi-Ning's reign (1068–1077), ambassadors from Korea received maps on request from county and provincial capitals visited on their travels.[5]

Japan

Large-scale plans of the principal cities and towns in Japan became an important feature of mapmaking in that country in the early years of the Shogunate period (1603–1868). They were produced, often in quite large quantities, over periods of several years and used both for practical purposes as guides and for their decorative and artistic qualities. Probably the earliest town plan is one of Hunai, a district of Edo (the old name for Tokyo), published in 1632. The information on this plan was rendered obsolete by the fire which razed much of the city in 1657. A replacement was prepared by one Otikōti-Dōin at the behest of the government, and was published between 1670 and 1673 in five sections on a scale of 1:3,250. Conventional signs, rather than pictorial devices, were used to depict the topography and buildings of the city. This plan remained the basis for all subsequent maps of the city through to the nineteenth century, even though it was disliked by the map-using public because it was not pictorial

PLATE 8.25 *Part of a rubbing of a plan of Suchow, drawn by Huang Chiang in 1193 and carved on stone by Wang Chih-Yuan in 1229. The principal features of the town, such as important buildings, the city walls and the surrounding hills, are superimposed on an outline ground-plan.*

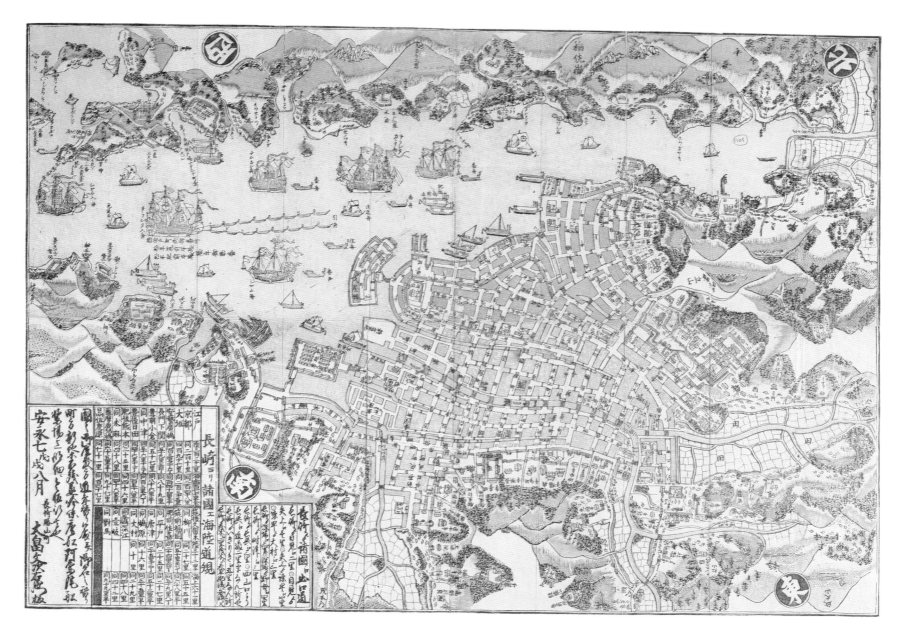

PLATE 8.26 *Map of Nagasaki* [Hishū Nagasaki nozu], *woodblock printing on native paper. Prominent in this plan of Nagasaki is the Dutch trading settlement on the artificial island of Deshima. During the period of isolation (which lasted until the mid-nineteenth century), Nagasaki was the only Japanese port where foreign vessels were allowed to trade.*

in content. Certainly, no similar plan was produced for any other Japanese town or city.

Nevertheless, plans were indeed produced for other towns and cities, showing the central areas in outline plan form and restricting any pictorial content to suburban and surrounding districts — such as, for example, the handsome large woodblock-printed plans of Kyoto in the mid-nineteenth century, made by Takehara Yoshibei showing the grid pattern of the city's streets, dominated by the great Kiyomizu-dera temple on the eastern side of the city. Some of Yoshibei's plans were printed in colour: other temples were represented by yellow squares, important shrines were indicated by pink squares, and imperial residences and palaces were depicted by pink outlines within dark blue.

There was a large market in Japan during the Shogunate period for printed town and city plans, and many have survived in quite large numbers, often in remarkably good condition. A major problem for the collector of these items, however,

is that the same blocks were used many times over for many years, often without alteration. As a result, it can sometimes be difficult to decide whether a given object is an early eighteenth- or nineteenth-century printing, particularly in the case of those plans which bear no maker's name.

A woodcut plan of Nagasaki harbour, dated 1680 (Plate 8.26), was among the earliest of its kind to reach northern Europe, through the collecting activities of the famous orientalist Engelbert Kaempfer (1651–1716). Edo (Tokyo), as the centre of the Tokugawa dynasty, was comprehensively depicted in plans. That by Ishikawa Ryusen, *Edo no ezu*, was made in woodblock in 1689, and gives special emphasis to the residences of the feudal lords (*daimyō*) with their family crests, or *mon*. Japanese mapmakers were accomplished in combining aerial views and plan techniques, often drawing castles, shrines and temples in rather exaggerated proportions. It is worth noting that Japanese maps and plans were intended to be looked at sitting on the floor or standing over them, so that all directions and legends were meant to be read from different angles, rather than in the conventional Western manner. Thus, there is often no obvious top or bottom, north or south, east or west, although gradually north began to be placed at the top of the subject, in the European manner, perhaps as a result of European influence, or maybe as an evolving Japanese practice.

North America

Finally, let us look briefly at the later western town plans, and more specifically at what was being produced in North America. As early as 1556, a plan of Hochelaga (the site of Montreal), the first printed plan of a European settlement in North America, appeared in Giovanni Battista Ramusio's *Delle navigationi* (Plate 8.27). This was followed a century later by Thomas Holme's *A Portraiture of the City of Philadelphia* in 1683, the first printed plan of a United States city; James Lyne's *A Plan of the City of New York* made in 1731; and the rare and beautiful *Plan of the City of New York* by Bernard Ratzer in 1770 (Plate

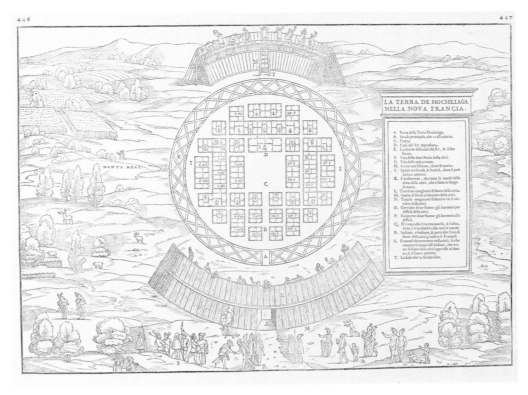

8.29). The latter work shows and locates churches, estates, markets, streets and roads by name in such detail that it is still possible to follow part of the plan in the modern city of New York today.

During the nineteenth century, mapmaking in North America flourished in response to explora-

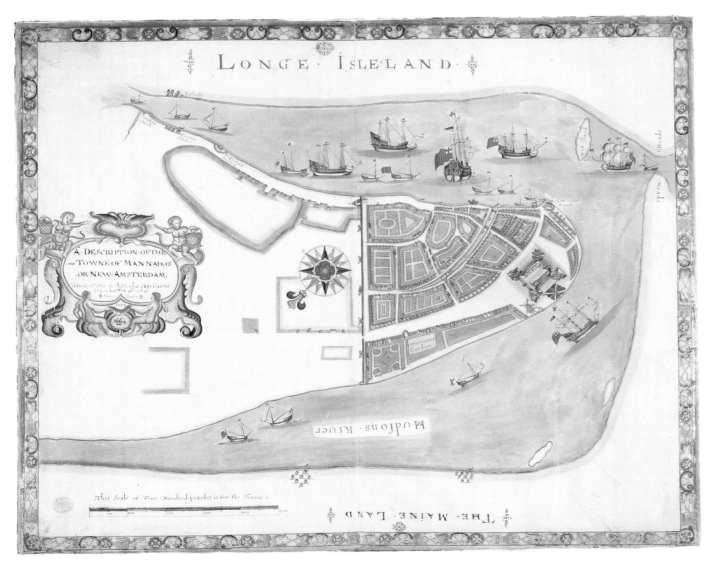

PLATE 8.27 *(above)* La Terra de Hochelaga Nella Nova Francia *from* Delle navigationi et viaggi *by Giovanni Battista Ramusio, woodcut, Venice, 1556 and later. This woodcut is the first printed plan of a European settlement in North America. Hochelaga was a fortified Iroquois Indian village near Monte Real, and is the site of the present-day Montreal.*

PLATE 8.28 *(left)* A description of the Towne of Mannados or New Amsterdam as it was in September 1661, *an anonymous, manuscript plan of lower Manhattan Island. New Amsterdam was the name originally given by the Dutch settlers in 1626. Note that there are English vessels in the harbour, so this plan was probably drawn up in 1664, when the town was taken by the English and renamed New York. Note the fort which gave its name to Battery Park and the pallisaded ditch along the line of present-day Wall Street.*

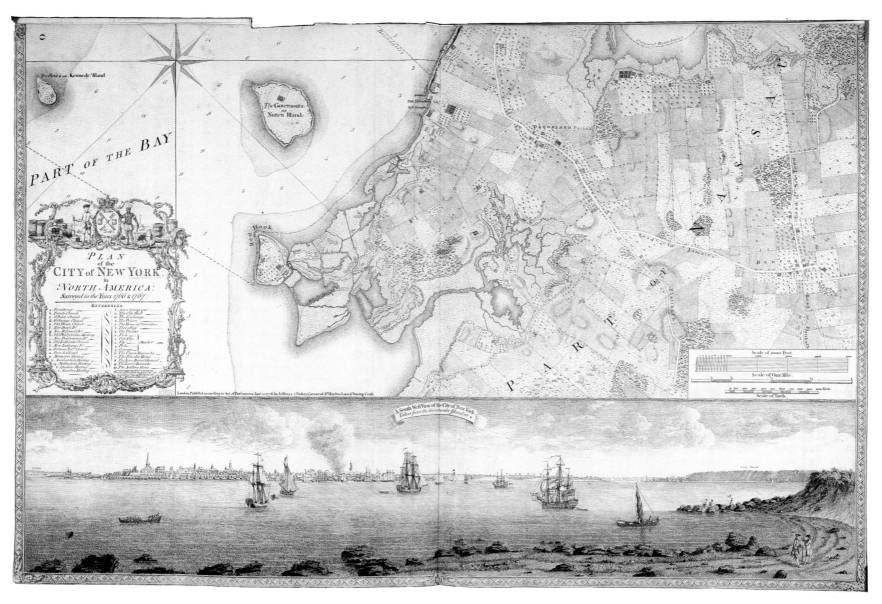

PLATE 8.29 *Detail of the* Plan of the City of New York *by Bernard Ratzer, copper engraving, London, 1776.*

tion, settlement, wars, the rising mobility and literacy of the American population and the drive to exploit natural resources. Up to about 1840, both government agencies and enterprising commercial and speculative companies issued maps and plans. There was a particular need for accurate administrative plans of new or recently founded towns and cities. In Massachusetts in 1794, Osgood Carleton moved the Massachusetts State Legislature to pass a resolution requiring each town to prepare an accurate town plan. In all, some 265 plans for Massachusetts, and one hundred for Maine (which was administered by Massachusetts until 1820) were made, their information being incorporated into state maps. Farther west, the disposal of public lands throughout the nineteenth century was controlled by the General Land Office, established by the Treasury Department in 1812. Under the aegis of the Office, all public land west of the Ohio and Mississippi rivers was to be divided into townships measuring six miles square. The survey began in Ohio in 1785 as a result of the Land

Ordinance Act of that year. Gradually, a specification for township plans was drawn up, with modifications issued in 1831. These required that the plans were to be drawn at a uniform scale of two inches to one mile (1:31,680) on durable paper, and were to represent courses and distances, sections and subdivisions, and to show swampy areas, prairies, roads, Indian trails and similar features.

The opening up of the country, by means of canals and later by railways, brought a westward tide of settlement and the establishment of many towns and cities throughout the nineteenth century. As administration became ever more complex, especially in the industrial East, so the demand for more detail in maps and plans increased, finding expression, for example, in the large-scale fire insurance maps of urban areas, which were produced in very large quantities, to an extremely high standard. The many surviving examples (from between *c.*1852 and 1960) are still highly collectable subjects. One famous producer of these plans was the Sanborn Map and

Publishing Company, established in 1867 in New York, which produced plans for some 13,000 towns and cities in the United States, over a period of nearly a century.

The lithographic process must have been a boon to the producers of maps and plans in an expanding country like the United States in the nineteenth century. The Civil War created a need for rapid dissemination of information on maps and plans for strategic use (see Chapter VII). In the search for mineral resources in the newly settled regions in the West, maps of the gold and silver mining areas, and of the many towns which sprang up almost overnight during the 1860s, were prepared and reproduced in considerable numbers by the lithographic process. Many such plans are visually very pleasing, the basic plan information frequently being accompanied by vignettes of the most important buildings of the town, perhaps an illustration of the railway, or a vignette or two of a park. (The latter may have been an attempt to demonstrate the civilizing virtues of the new settlements, quite in contrast to the popular idea of western towns as primitive and unplanned!) A frequently – and justifiably – cited example is that of the plan of Virginia City, entitled *City of Virginia, Montana. Established July 1863*, surveyed by J.L. Corbett and published in 1868. The town was established during the Montana Gold Rush and is taken as a prime example of the kind of settlement established on the mining frontier. Plans of such towns were made to assist officials in the sale and disposal of town lots and parcels of land, showing blocks, lots, streets and alleys, generally on the traditional American gridiron pattern. The plan of New York published by John Tallis in 1851 is an example perhaps; the monotony of the grid in this instance relieved only by the small vignettes and the elaborately engraved border to frame the plan.

Perhaps the most characteristic expression of American town mapping is the panoramic, or bird's-eye, plan, recalling in spirit if not content the sixteenth-century bird's-eye panoramas of Braun and Hogenberg. In their American form, such plans reached a high level of sophistication. The perspectives showed towns and cities with street patterns, railways, individual buildings and landscape features. They were made from about the late 1860s until as late as the 1920s, providing

a unique view of the urban landscape of America. Produced in large numbers by lithographic methods, they were sold through advertisements or newspaper supplements as promotional aids for land agents, for railway companies wishing to promote settlement and to ensure a captive market for their services, or for mail-order companies and chambers of commerce. Many artists specialized in the production of such subjects, including Albert Ruger, Henry Wellge and O.H. Bailey; the august name of Rand McNally appeared on later examples (Plate 8.30).

PLATE 8.30 Railway Terminal Map of Chicago *from* Atlas of the World *published by Rand McNally & Co*, c. 1887. *Note the clear lines of the traditional American gridiron pattern.*

References
1. R. Oehme, *Old European Cities*, page 45, 1955.
2. Letter printed in the introduction to the facsimile edition of the *Civitates*, 1965.
3. C. Koeman, *Geschiedenis*, page 53, 1985.
4. R.A. Skelton, in introduction to facsimile edition of the *Civitates*, 1965.
5. Joseph Needham, *op. cit.*, pages 549–550.

ASIÆ

PERSIA

MOGOL

EGYPTEN.

AFRI

C.BARDAMASSER.

YEMEN:

ARABIA FELIX

Fartaque

Ormus.

Guadel

Gouzeratte.

CAMBAIA

CÆ

MAGADOXA.

Linea Æquinoctialis.

BIS

MELINDE

MOMBAZA.

PARS

MOZAMBIQUE

INA

COLMA.

SOFFALA.

MADA

GAS

CAR.

CABO DE BONA
ESPERANÇA.

t'AMSTERDAM.
Bij
PIETER GOOS
op het Water inde
Vergulde Zee-
Spiegel.

WASSENDE-GRAADE PASKAART.

OO
IN

CHAPTER IX

THE SEA CHART TRADITION

1500 – 1800 AD

THE SEA CHART, the successor of the portolan chart, has changed little in essence since its inception in the fifteenth century. The first printed collection of nautical, or sea, charts, is believed to be an *Isolario*, or 'Island book', by Bartolommeo dalli Sonetti (so styled after his rhyming descriptions), which appeared in Italy, from the press of Guilelmus Anima Mea Tridinensis in 1485 or 1486. The volume contained forty-nine woodcut charts and maps of the Greek islands and Cyprus, compiled with descriptive verses, or sonnets, written in the Venetian dialect (Plate 9.2). (Many of the islands, including Crete, formed part of the Venetian maritime empire.) The charts are rudimentary and executed in even outline, without printed place-names of any sort. In some instances they show only a scale bar, although each chart is superimposed on a large eight-point compass circle. In many copies of the work, names were added by hand, and some copies are known to have been richly coloured and illuminated in the manner of the manuscript portolan charts and island books of the period. In one sense, Bartolommeo's charts could be considered entirely practical, since they allowed the mariner to insert any relevant place-name or geographical detail suited to his purposes without clutter or superfluous ornamentation.

PLATE 9.1 *Detail of* Oost Indien *by Pieter Goos, printed on vellum, Amsterdam, 1700 or later. Though intended as a nautical navigation chart, the decorative qualities of this impressive work cannot fail to attract the eye. Goos's chart was first issued as early as 1658, and was possibly the earliest newly engraved map to show the Dutch discoveries in Australia down to the voyages of Tasman in 1642–1644.*

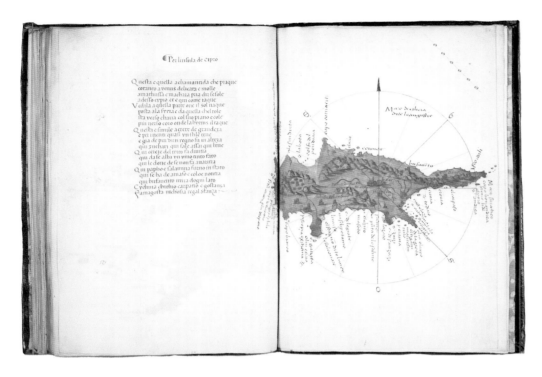

PLATE 9.2 *(above) A map of Cyprus from the* Isolario *by Bartolommeo dalli Sonetti, woodcut, Venice, c. 1485. This work was the first printed 'atlas' of the Greek islands.*

One tribute to the utility of Bartolommeo's charts lies in the fact that the cross (+) symbol (indicating dangerous offshore shoals) is still used today on Admiralty and other nautical charts for the same purpose. Very little is known of Bartolommeo himself, although he claimed that as a ship's crewman, and later as a captain, he made fifteen voyages to the Greek islands, which experience must surely have qualified him extremely well to produce his *Isolario*.

Around one hundred years later, sea charts were obviously proving to be invaluable, as Thomas Blundeville (*c.*1560–1603) wrote in 1589:

Navigation is an Art which teacheth by true and infallible rules, how to governe and direct a Ship from one Port to another, safely, rightly and in shortest time: I say heere safely so farre as it lyeth in mans power to performe. And in saying rightly, I meane not by a right line, but by the shortest and most commodious way that may be found.

PLATE 9.3 *(opposite) A general map of western Europe,* Universe Europe maritime, *published in editions of* Spieghel der Zeevaerdt *by Lucas Janszoon Wagenhaer, copper engraving, engraved by the brothers van Deutecum, Amsterdam, 1584 and later.*

For such a 'most commodious way', Blundeville recommended essential standard equipment: 'an universall Horologe, or Diall, to know thereby the houre of the day in every Latitude, and a Nocturnall able to know thereby the houre of the night'. For the long voyage, he recommended a 'Topographicall instrument to describe thereby those strange Coasts and Countries', also a 'Mariners compasse' and finally, a mariner's chart, called a 'Carde', by means of which the mariner could tell what progress his vessel had made, with the aid of 'certaine Tables made of purpose'.[1]

PLATE 9.4 *(right)* The Mariner's Mirrour *by Lucas Janszoon Waghenaer in the English translation by Anthony Ashley with a frontispiece by Theodor de Bry, London, 1588.*

The Netherlands

Around the time when Blundeville flourished in England, the first uniform collection of sea charts, together with complete sailing directions giving the mariner practically everything he needed to carry out his art, was published at Leiden in the Netherlands in 1584. Taking the form of an atlas, it was compiled by a practising hydrographer and pilot, Lucas Janszoon Waghenaer (1533–1606), and was entitled *Spieghel der Zeevaerdt*. Coverage of the complete atlas was restricted to the shores of northern and western Europe, from Norway to Spain, by way of the shores of the British Isles facing the European mainland and those of the Baltic Sea (Plate 9.4). In other words, the atlas covered those coasts which Dutch vessels were busily plying, in the shipment of goods between the Portuguese and Spanish trading settlements and empires in the East and West Indies.

The charts in the *Spieghel der Zeevaerdt*, engraved by Johannes van Deutecum, were extremely decorative, yet still practical, for they contained many novel features, essential for pilotage in often difficult waters. They had, for instance, the indications of soundings in fathoms, the placing of coastal profiles within the body of the charts (instead of elsewhere in the text of the atlas) and the deliberate distortion of stretches of coastline so that the more difficult passages and entrances to

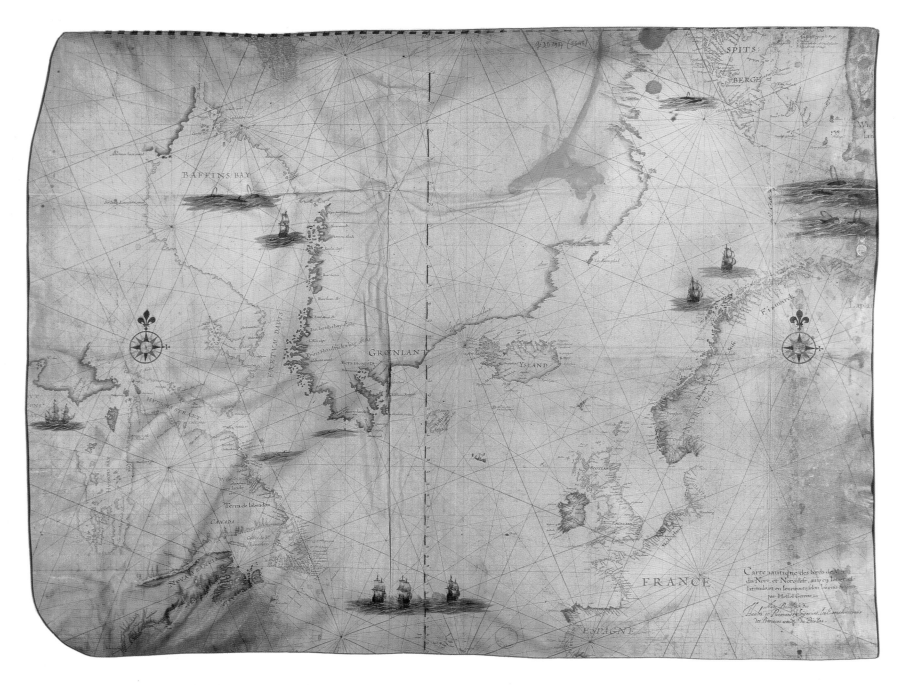

PLATE 9.5 *(above) A chart of the North Atlantic by Hessel Gerritsz, drawn on vellum, Amsterdam, 1608.*

PLATE 9.6 *(opposite, top)* Europa *by Harmen Jansz[oon] en Marten Jansz[oon] Caartschrÿrers tot Edam inde Pascaarte, c. 1610, on vellum manuscript in inks and colours, influenced by Wagenhaer's chart of western Europe.*

PLATE 9.7 *(opposite, bottom) Title-page of* The Light of Navigation . . . *by Willem Janszoon Blaeu (William Johnson), printed by Joannes Janssonius (John Iohnson), 1625.*

harbours could be depicted at a uniform scale. This last practice, in a more extreme manner, is also found in Chinese coastal charts, where the extremely lengthy Pacific coastline of China is rendered as an extended coastline on long charts of up to ten metres in length.

Waghenaer's work proved successful and highly influential, appearing in many editions, translated into Latin, French and English. His name was long commemorated in the English mariners' term 'waggoner', used until the eighteenth century to refer to any sea chart atlas. The English translation of the *Spieghel der Zeevaerdt*, called *The Mariner's Mirrour* (Plate 9.3), was the first English sea chart atlas, and indeed these charts were the earliest ones to be printed in English.

Shortly after the publication of Waghenaer's atlas, there appeared in Amsterdam a sea chart atlas of the Mediterranean, effectively a continuation of Waghenaer's charts for the Mediterranean

region. This was the *Nieuwe Beschrijvinghe ende Caertboek vande Midlandtsche Zee*, compiled by the Dutch Arctic explorer and navigator, Willem Barendszoon (1550–1597), and published in 1595. It served as the standard Dutch collection of charts for Mediterranean navigation during the first part of the seventeenth century. Like Waghenaer's atlas, it contained beautifully engraved charts, resembling in many respects the designs of the best Mediterranean portolan charts, and showing true directions as well as compass variations for different parts of the region.

The name of Blaeu is almost synonymous with mapmaking in the Netherlands in the seventeenth century (see Chapter IV). The firm of Blaeu, founded by Willem Blaeu in 1599, are best known for their fine atlases of regional maps, but they also issued, in earlier years, atlases of sea charts, beginning with a pilot-guide in 1608. This guide, *Het Licht der Zeevaerdt* (Plate 9.7), in-

cluded charts taken from the works of Waghenaer and Barendszoon, and improved upon, covering western, northern and eastern navigations of the coastlines of Europe. It was prefaced by a long introduction and instructions in the art of navigation. Willem Blaeu's atlas was issued in many editions in Dutch, English and French, indicating the virtual monopoly enjoyed by the Amsterdam chart trade in the first half of the century.

The development of the map trade in Amsterdam during the seventeenth century was in essence based on three factors. The greatest incentive was provided by the Dutch voyages to the Arctic, the East Indies, Africa and the West Indies, all of which provided map and chartmakers with new information for incorporation into their products. These maps and charts were distributed in numerous editions throughout the seafaring nations of

PLATE 9.8 *(above)* The Departure of an East Indiaman *by Adam Willaerts, oil on canvas, c. 1640. Dutch voyages to the Arctic, the East Indies, Africa and the West Indies provided map and chartmakers with vital new information.*

PLATE 9.9 *(right) Title-page of* De Zee-Atlas ofte Water-Wereld . . . *by Pieter Goos, 1669.*

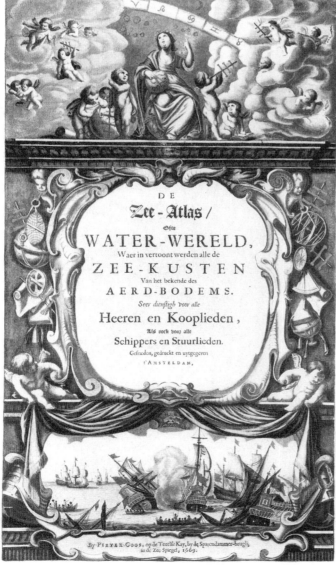

Europe, with the exception of information particular to the interests of the Dutch West India Company and the Dutch East India Company. These rich, powerful and highly organized trading companies were set up and run by wealthy merchants in Amsterdam and the trading ports of the Netherlands. They encouraged and funded far-flung Dutch voyages, sending out fleets of ships on trading missions and also in search of a northeast passage to the spice-rich East (Plate 9.8). The continuing war with Spain provided another incentive, for cartography became a vital tool of modern armies and navies, answering as it did the demand for accurate information. A third factor was the increasing number of land-reclamation projects under way in the Netherlands, which required highly accurate surveying and mapping techniques. All of these factors provided the Dutch chart and map trade with the skills by which it was able to dominate production of land and sea atlases for several decades. The leading publishers, such as the Blaeus, Janssonius, Doncker and others, issued many comprehensive atlases of charts covering the waters and sea lanes of the known world (Plates 9.6, 9.13, 9.14).

Many of these atlases contained charts which

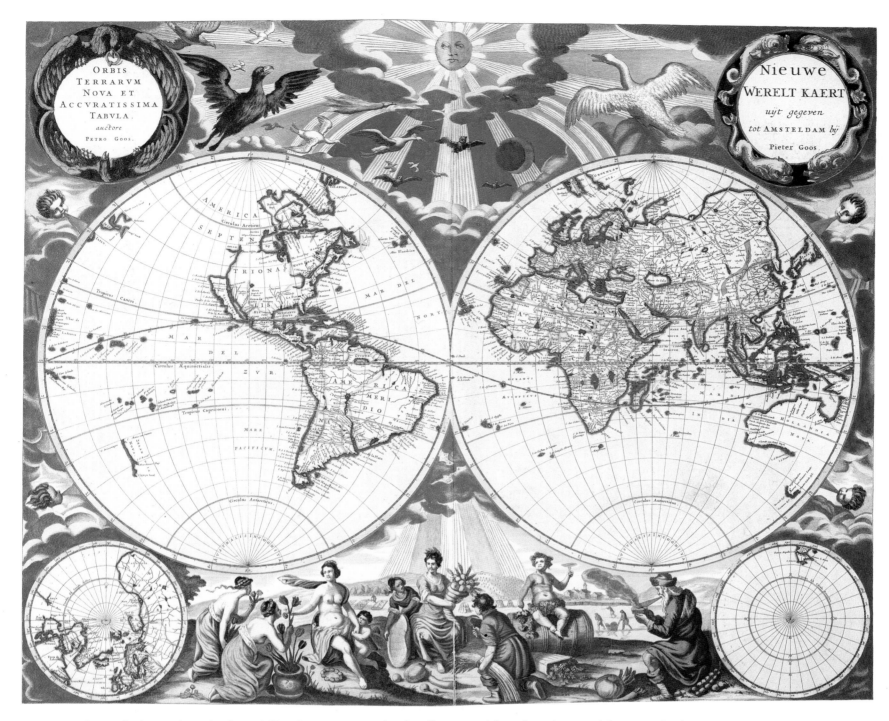

ORBIS
TERRARVM
NOVA ET
ACCVRATISSIMA
TABVLA.
auctore
PETRO GOOS.

Nieuwe
WERELT KAERT
uyt gegeven
tot AMSTELDAM bij
Pieter Goos.

were copies of those in rival publications, or which had been included in earlier atlases issued by particular firms. Hendrick Doncker (*c*.1625–1699) ran a prosperous chart and book business in Amsterdam and in 1655 issued a pilot-guide called the *Lichtende Columne ofte Zeespiegel*. This contained many accurate and up-to-date charts, not only of European waters but, more importantly, of East Indian and Australian waters, and it reflected the progress and achievements of Dutch navigators in the East. One of the most successful of all publishers was Pieter Goos (1616–1675), who gained an excellent reputation with his sea atlas *De Zee-Atlas ofte Water-Wereld* published in several editions and translations between 1666 and 1683 (Plates 9.9, 9.10). Frequently found with rich hand-colouring (sometimes even with gold highlighting on the elaborate cartouches), Goos's

atlas is often considered as the maritime equivalent of the Blaeu *Atlas major* with which it is contemporary. Indeed, some owners of the Blaeu atlas had a copy of Goos's atlas bound uniformly with the Blaeu.

Following the death of Joan Blaeu (Willem Blaeu's son) in 1672, the map and chart trade in the Netherlands fell into decline, but the production of sea charts continued to flourish, largely through the publishing house of the van Keulens. Johannes van Keulen I (*c*.1654–1715) was born in Deventer and founded the publishing house which produced the largest sea atlases issued in the Netherlands, establishing a firm which flourished for two centuries, until 1885: 'the largest unofficial hydrographic office in the world'.[2] The van Keulen atlas, or *Zee-Fakkel* as it is generally known (Plate 9.12), began with coverage of the

PLATE 9.10 *(above) A twin-hemispherical world map from the* Zee-Atlas ofte Water-Wereld *by Pieter Goos, copper engraving, Amsterdam, 1666 or later. Many sea atlases issued in Amsterdam in the seventeenth century included a highly decorative world map, such as this, incorporating figures representing the seasons.*

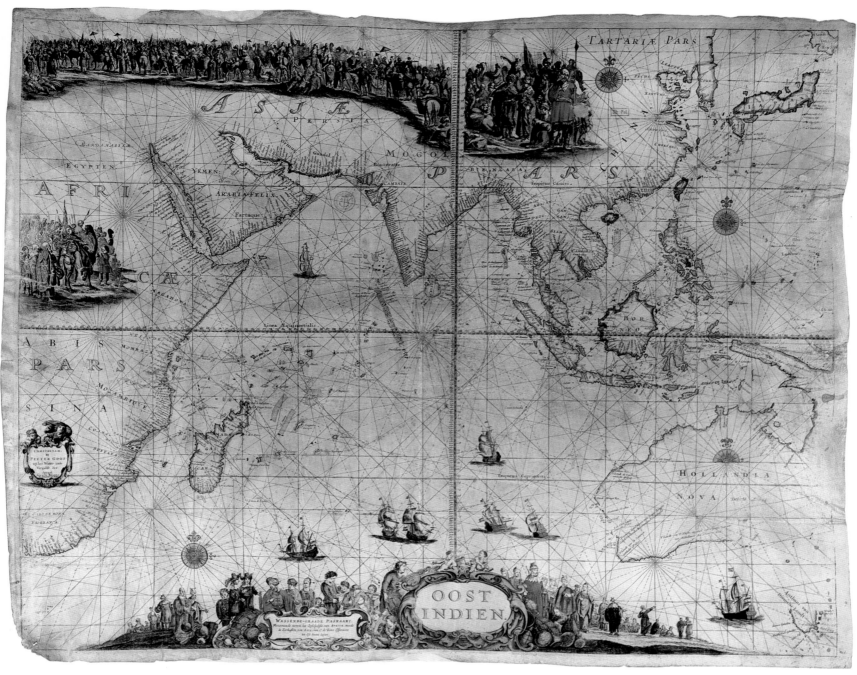

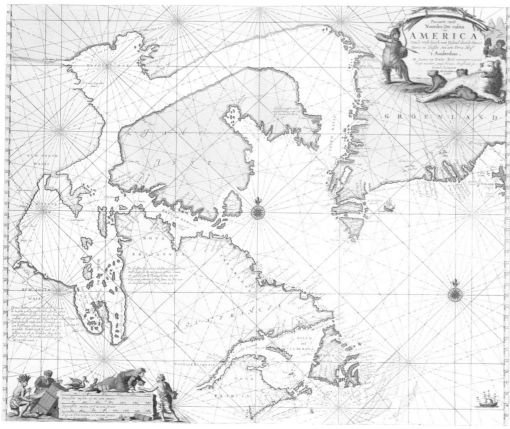

coasts of Europe, and was gradually extended to cover the entire world in five large folio volumes (Plate 9.12). During the eighteenth century, the firm also issued individual charts, particularly of the East Indies, and produced a large number of manuscript charts, often brightly coloured. These charts were presumably intended for presentation or archive purposes, and indeed, a considerable number of them have survived. Each volume of the van Keulen atlas also contained a detailed text or pilot-guide to the waters covered, supplemented with numerous detailed coastal profiles. By the middle of the eighteenth century, however, Amsterdam was long past its primacy as the international centre of hydrographic activity, that honour having passed to the French admiralty and to the English chart trade.

(continued on page 295)

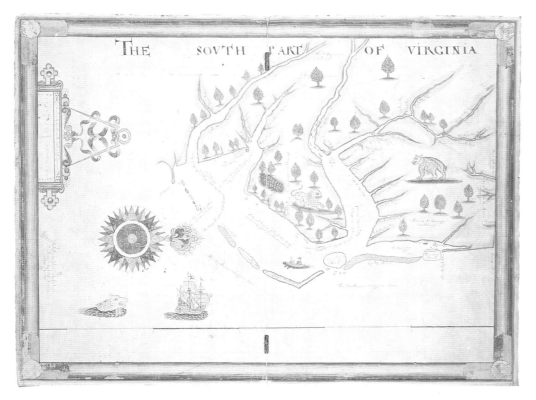

PLATE 9.17 *(above)* The
South Part of Virginia *by
Nicholas Comberford,
drawn at Ratcliffe in east
London c. 1657. A rare
example of a large-scale
chart, here adorned with
trees, a lion and a bear and
the large, very fine compass-
rose. Comberford was
apprenticed to the Drapers'
Company between 1612 and
1620, and seems to have
been quite prolific. Little is
known of him although
Samuel Pepys wrote of him
in 1663, praising 'his
manner of working which is
very fine and labourious'.*

PLATE 9.18 *(right)* Chart
of the South Pacifick
Ocean, Pointing out the
Discoveries made therein
previous to 1764 *by
Alexander Dalrymple,
copper engraving, 1767 or
later. This shows Australia
and New Zealand resulting
from Abel Tasman's
discoveries in the 1640s,
with the tracks of Luis Vaez
de Torres in 1606, Willem
Schonten in 1616 and Jacob
Roggeveen 1722.*

In the middle of the seventeenth century, many
of the English atlases of sea charts were based on
Dutch models, sometimes even using discarded
Dutch plates re-engraved or recut with English
titles and legends. Such were the early beginnings
of the series of atlases put out by John Seller
(*fl.*1664–1697) at the Hermitage in Wapping, to
the east of London. *The English Pilot* began
publication in 1671 and continued under various
guises, editions and re-compilations until as late as
1803. Seller's was the first successful English sea
atlas, even though it did at first use older Dutch
materials. As the work progressed and expanded,

however, so new charts were added to the atlas to
give detailed coverage of the coasts of India, the
Americas and the slaving coasts of West Africa,
for example.

In its early years, Seller's atlas series was
criticized by, among others, Samuel Pepys
(1633–1703), the celebrated diarist and naval
administrator, who commented: 'My lord is, upon
this trial of ours at coming into the Channel,
mightily convinced and angry at Seller's platt
(made on purpose for him for this voyage) proving worse than the Master's old Dutch ones.'[3] It
was largely because of these inaccuracies in Seller's
charts, particularly in his coverage of home waters, that Captain Greenvile Collins (*fl.*1669–
1698) was commanded by the Admiralty to begin
a survey of the coasts of Great Britain. Pepys
noted: 'Seller's maps are at best but copies of the
Dutch, with such improvements as he could make
therein . . . Captain Collins says, and upon view
by comparing the maps, shew me by several
instances that our sea-coasts were better laid down
by Speed [John Speed, who compiled his series of
British county and regional maps, *The Theatre of
the Empire of Great Britaine*, first published in
1611] than they are in our Waggoner.'[4]

After several difficulties, not the least of which
was the ever-familiar lack of financial support and
a general reluctance on the part of the authorities,
Collins' labours finally bore fruit in 1693, with
the publication of *Great Britain's Coasting Pilot*.

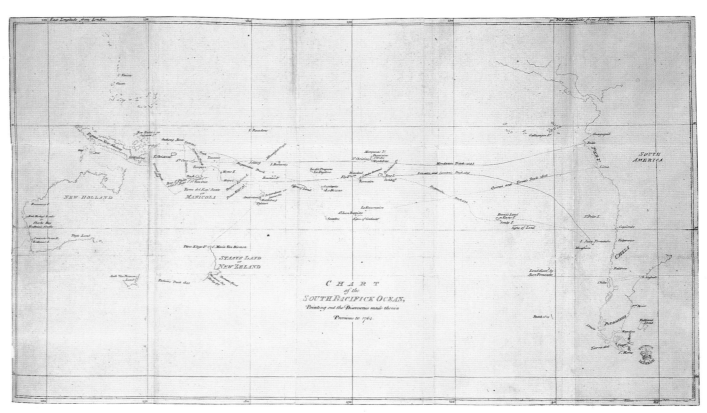

England

One of the most remarkable collections of sea and coastal charts ever compiled was the *Dell'arcano del mare* (Plate 9.15, 9.16) by Sir Robert Dudley (1574–1649), styled Duke of Northumberland and Earl of Warwick. The illegitimate son of the Earl of Leicester, he was a man of science, inventor, engineer, naval commander, and an expatriate Englishman who settled in Florence. Dudley was also the brother-in-law of the English explorer and navigator Henry Cavendish, who gave Dudley access to his logbooks and notes. It was through Cavendish that Dudley became a close friend of the navigators and explorers John Davis and Abraham Kendall, both of whom had been active in American waters.

In 1594–1595, Dudley sailed to the West Indies and explored the coasts of Guyana. On his return to England, he took part in Essex's raid on Cadiz in 1596, for which he was knighted. Dudley later fell into matrimonial difficulties and fell out of favour at the English court, eventually being forced into permanent exile in Florence. His abilities as a naval architect and shipbuilder earned him a powerful reputation and the patronage of Ferdinand II, Grand Duke of Tuscany, to whom Dudley dedicated his work on its publication in Florence in 1646–1647.

Dell'arcano del mare is one of the largest, most remarkable and most important nautical works ever published, and the first to contain charts laid down on the Mercator projection. The atlas was published in six parts, the charts comprising two parts and the other sections containing, among other things, instructions on the manufacture of navigational and surveying instruments and detailed descriptions of all kinds of naval vessels. Wooden models of Dudley's instruments were made, but which unfortunately perished in Florence at the end of the Second World War. A second, enlarged, edition of the atlas was issued in 1661, some years after Dudley's death.

Owing to the size of the large, heavy chart volumes, it is difficult to see how they could have had any practical use at sea. However, a small number of Dudley's charts in reduced format recently came to light, indicating that a smaller edition of the *Arcano* had been planned, presumably for easier use on board ship. These smaller

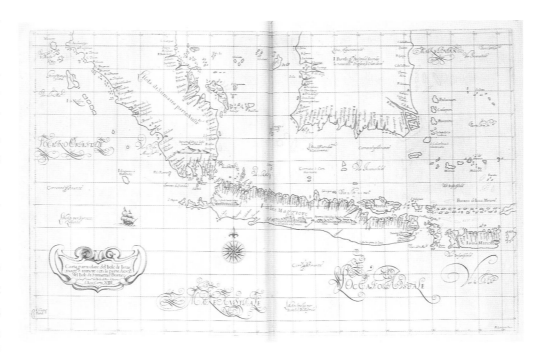

charts are slightly less detailed than their larger counterparts: there was not the space for the repetition of some place-names or for the inclusion of certain fictitious detail such as is found on some of the American folio charts. The same Mercator projection was used on the smaller charts and the clarity of detail would have allowed for relatively easy use by navigators.

Dudley's charts are justly noted for the beauty of the elaborate calligraphy and engraving work, done by Antonio Francesco Lucini, an Italian engraver pupil of Jacques Callot. The actual compilation of Dudley's atlas is surrounded by somewhat romantic legend, for in the preface to the 1661 edition of the *Arcano*, Lucini asserts that he had spent some twelve years working on the plates in seclusion in an obscure Tuscan village, using 5,000 pounds of copper in the process.

PLATE 9.14 *(opposite)* Pascaerte van Oost Indien *by Hendrick Doncker, separately published in c. 1670.*

PLATES 9.15, 9.16 *(above and below) Charts from* Dell'arcano del mare *by Robert Dudley, engraved by A.F. Lucini, Florence, 1646–1661. The first atlas of charts published by an Englishman – and the first to be published using the Mercator projection. At top is a chart of part of the East Indies; below, a chart of the islands of New Guinea.*

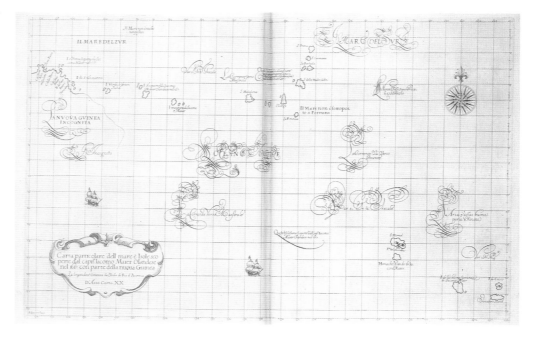

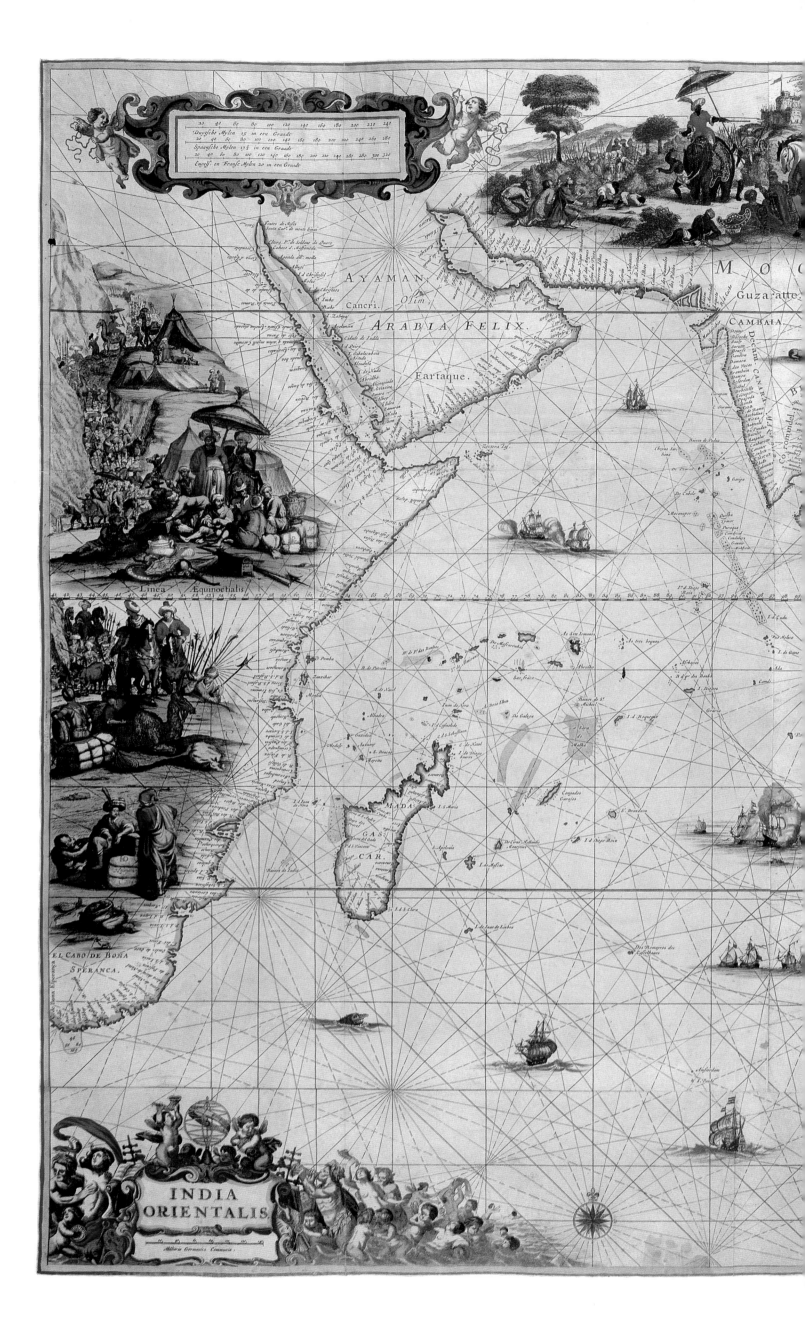

AYAMAN Olim

Cancri.

ARABIA FELIX.

Fartaque.

Linea Æquinoctialis

MADA'

GAS

CAR.

EL CABO DE BONA
SPERANCA.

INDIA
ORIENTALIS.

M O
Guza: atte.

CAMBAIA.

Collins' book, although it did contain some errors, was a landmark in the history of English hydrography, containing as it did the first virtually complete survey in English of the British coasts and offshore islands. It was very successful, appearing in more than fourteen editions up to 1792, with relatively little change of content apart from revisions to the text.

During the American campaigns in the eighteenth century, Joseph Frederick Wallet Des Barres (1721–1824), a military engineer who was born in Switzerland but had trained at Woolwich and settled in England, was posted to North America as a surveyor and accompanied General Wolfe on the Quebec campaign in 1759. Des Barres surveyed Nova Scotia, Newfoundland and, later, the Atlantic seaboard, over a period of ten years. Publication of his surveys was recommended in 1774, but it was to be another ten years before his *Atlantic neptune* saw publication. In four main divisions, it covered Nova Scotia, New England, the St Lawrence, and finally the coasts from New York to the Gulf of Mexico. Des Barres' charts, large in format and highly detailed, are remarkable not only for their accuracy, but also for their engraved and hand-coloured views (Plate 9.19). They served as the primary source for American charts until well into the nineteenth century, with true and magnetic meridians, and longitudes based on that of Greenwich to the east of London.

Numerous chart publishers set up business in London in the eighteenth century, issuing separate charts and collections. One of these was Alexander Dalrymple (1737–1808), hydrographer to the Honourable East India Company from 1779 onwards and hydrographer to the Navy from 1795 to 1808. Dalrymple spent many years collecting charts of the East Indies and the Far East and compiling detailed charts of a large number of the most important stretches of coast and harbours (Plate 9.18). The early beginnings of the Admiralty charts (Plate 9.20) now known to us today can be seen in many of Dalrymple's charts. Also in London, the firm of Mount and Page re-issued some of Seller's charts, adding their own charts in a series of atlases which they published under the general heading of *The English Pilot*. The later editions of the work used materials up to a century old, and were often issued with little revision of the text matter.

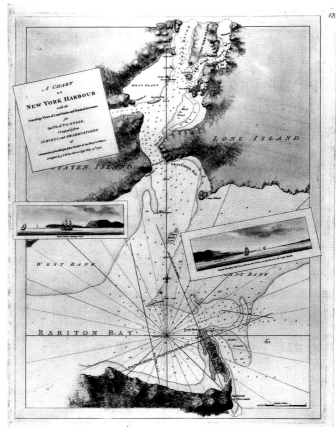

PLATE 9.19 *(left)* A chart of New York harbour *from* Atlantic neptune *by Joseph Frederick Wallet Des Barres*, 1784.

PLATE 9.20 *(below) A chart of Taormina produced by the Admiralty hydrographic survey. Such charts often incorporated beautifully engraved vignette views. Skill in draughtsmanship was a requirement for naval officers.*

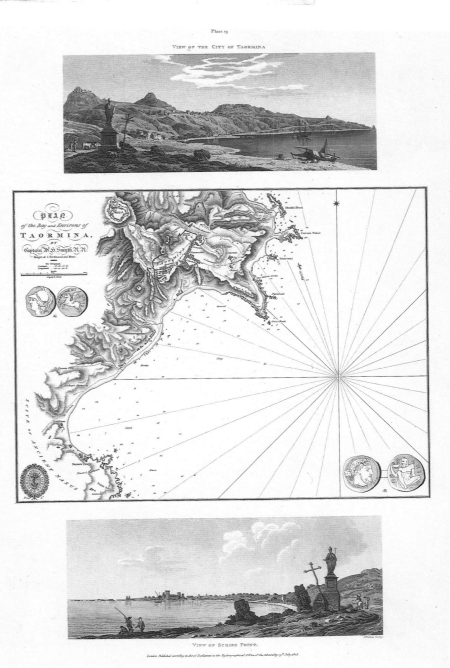

France

At about the time when the chart trade in Amsterdam was falling into decline, the minister of finance to Louis XIV took the initiative to give to France and her navy an important advantage over her rivals in Britain. In 1691, a royal privilege was granted to publish a sea chart atlas, entitled *Le neptune français*. This event marked the beginning of a tradition of chart publishing that was to give France a hydrographical survey a century before its equivalent was established across the English Channel in 1795. The charts of *Le neptune français* were first published in atlas form in Paris in 1693; they were engraved and printed on the Mercator projection according to surveys carried out by several royal-appointed engineers and surveyors. The work was first projected as two large volumes: Volume I covering the Atlantic shores of Europe;

Volume II (which did not appear for some years) intended to cover the Mediterranean. The Dutch issued close copies of the charts, under the imprint of the Amsterdam map- and chart-seller Pieter Mortier, in partnership with Alexis-Hubert Jaillot of Paris. This 'counterfeit' edition, grand and elaborate in conception, was published in 1693, with text editions produced in French, Dutch and English in order to promote sales of the charts in other European countries.

The official French agency, known as the Dépôt des Cartes et Plans de la Marine, was established in 1720. The Dépôt was one of several institutions concerned with maritime affairs and science in eighteenth-century France; there were schools of hydrography set up at Brest, Toulon and Rochefort, while at Lorient on the west coast the Compagnie des Indes maintained its own school and charting establishment which produced many fine and accurate surveys of overseas settlements, such as India. Later in the century, the French made important scientific voyages which were seen as symbolic of the achievements of France in naval science – in particular the voyages made to observe the predicted transits of Venus first in 1761 and again in 1769.

By the 1740s, many of the plates of the original *Le neptune français* had become either very worn, damaged or simply lost, and in 1751 the last of the

PLATE 9.21 *(below left)* Carte de l'Isle de Malte *from* Petit atlas maritime *by Jacques-Nicolas Bellin, Paris, 1764.*

PLATE 9.22 *(below right) Title-page from* Petit atlas maritime *by Jacques-Nicolas Bellin, Paris, 1764.*

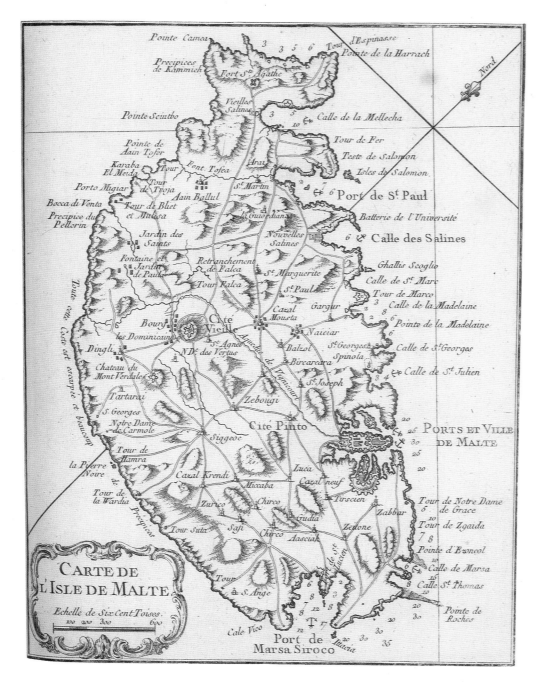

plates were taken over by the navy, who commissioned a new, official edition of the work, to be edited by Jacques-Nicolas Bellin (1703–1772). Bellin, whose name became synonymous with the making of sea charts in eighteenth-century France, spent the greater part of a long career in the French hydrographic service. His most important works were *Le neptune français*, covering the coasts of France (first published in 1753); *Hydrographie française* covering the rest of the world and first published between 1756 and 1765; and the smaller-format *Petit atlas maritime*, in five volumes, containing up to 580 charts and harbour plans of the entire world, published in 1764 (Plates 9.21, 9.22). The new work contained up-to-date charts, early issues of which are sometimes found printed in two colours, black and red: black for the geographical detail, red for the superimposed network of rhumb-lines (lines drawn on sea charts as aids to navigation or course plotting). Later editions had the rhumb-lines engraved directly on to the main plate and printed off in black. The atlas was arranged geographically and editions were issued up to 1800, when they were replaced by editions of the new *Le neptune français*, covering the world in eleven volumes.

Also in France, Jean-Baptiste d'Après de Mannevillette (1707–1780) was an accomplished navigator in the service of the Compagnie des Indes. In 1745 he issued his collection of twenty-two charts, under the title *Le neptune oriental*. The charts were based on accurate and meticulous surveys and covered the coasts of southern Asia and the East Indies. Exactly thirty years later, in 1775, he issued a revised and corrected edition augmented to sixty-three charts. A supplement was issued in 1781. Noteworthy in his atlases was the method adopted for corrections, using paste-on overslips for smaller areas or newly discovered islands. This technique saved considerable effort and expense, for it meant that entire plates did not have to be withdrawn for re-engraving.

A particular feature of French charts of the period is the inclusion of multiple scales of longitude and distance. At least five different prime meridians were shown on French charts: Tenerife, Ferro, the Lizard, London and Paris. Multiple scales would be shown in leagues of different lengths such as French/English leagues (at twenty to a degree), Italian leagues (at seventy-

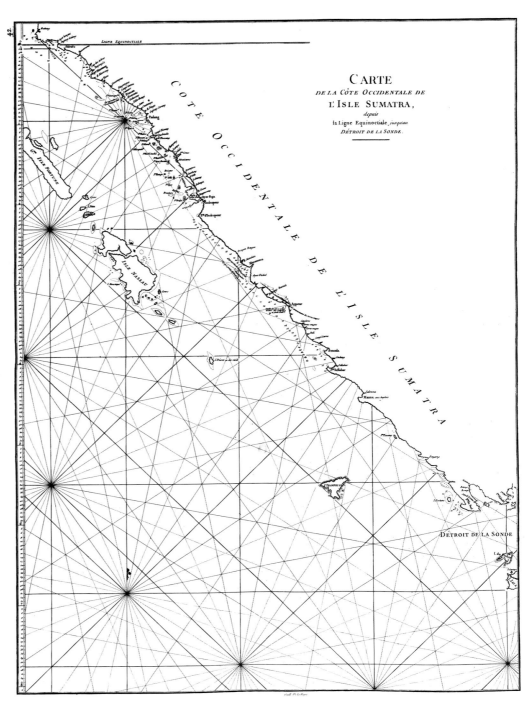

five to a degree), Dutch leagues (at fifteen to a degree), or Spanish (at seventeen-and-a-half to a degree). This illustrates the confusion prior to the adoption, in 1884, of the meridian of Greenwich as the world's prime meridian.

Russia

The foundation of Peter the Great's capital at St Petersburg, and the subsequent erection of the fortress and naval base of Kronshtadt nearby in 1710, encouraged the establishment of hydrographic surveys of the coasts of the Russian Empire in the Baltic, the Black Sea and farther afield. At first, most charts were based on existing Dutch or Swedish surveys in the Baltic, but later naval expeditions were sent out on the initiative of the

PLATE 9.23 *(above)* Carte de la côte occidentale de l'isle Sumatra *by Jean-Baptiste-Nicolas d'Après de Mannevillette, copper engraving, Paris, 1775. This example exhibits a novel and economical method of revising geographical information – namely the use of paste-on correction slips – as at 'I. Troupense' (lower centre) and on the Sumatran coast at Indrapura opposite 'Isle Nassau'.*

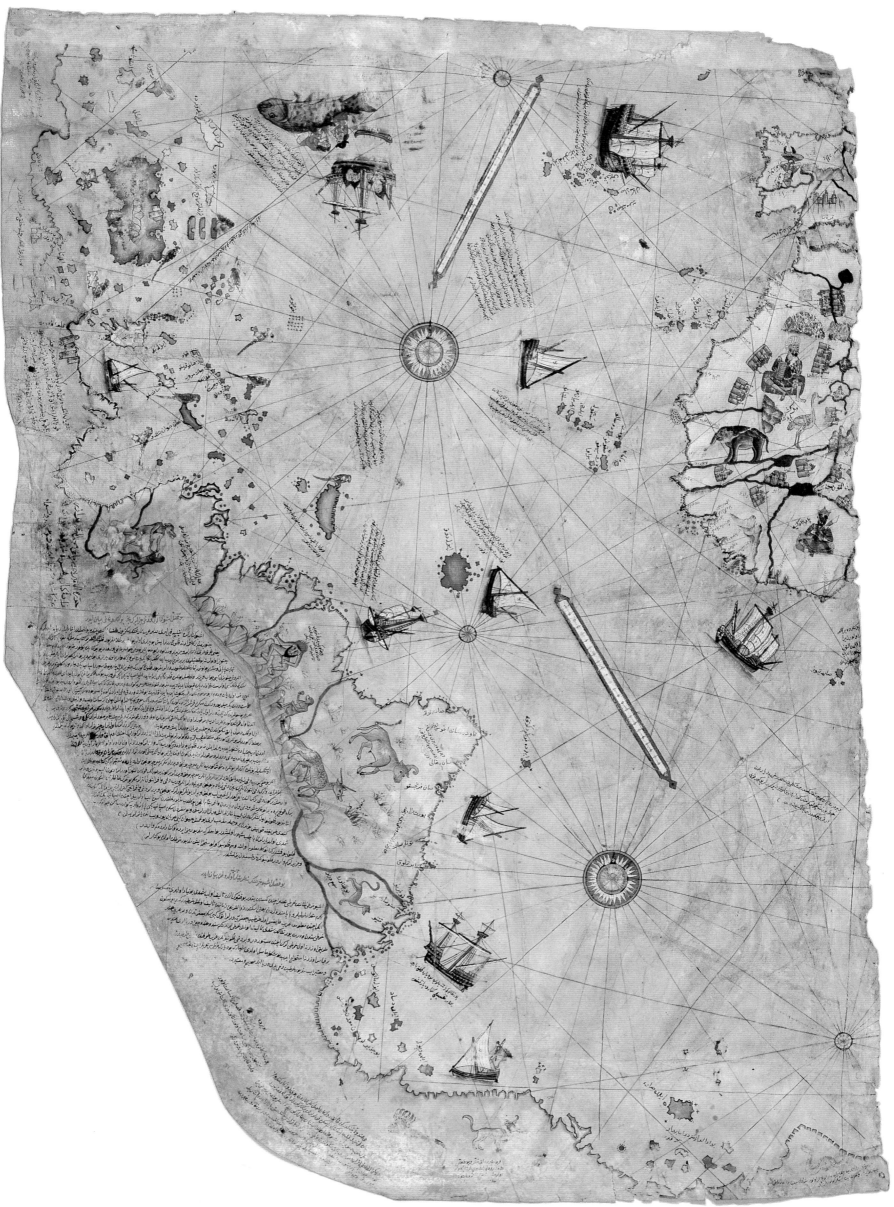

300

Akademiya nauk (The Russian Academy of Sciences) in search of northern sea passages to the Far East and across to Alaska and the Aleutian Islands. Baltic surveys were under the charge of Alexei Nagayev (1704–1781) from 1746, but it was not until 1777 that a special drawing office for charts was established at the St Petersburg Admiralty.

On the southern flanks of the Russian Empire, on the Black Sea, little accurate information was as yet available other than that contained in a few Dutch charts by Nicolaes Witsen, Louis Renard and the van Keulens. Official Russian surveys began in 1755, in the Crimea, under Ivan Bersenev and Lyubim Pustoshkin, which resulted in an eleven-sheet atlas of the Black Sea in 1785. Further surveys in the Sea of Azov, adjoining the Black Sea, followed. The shores of the Caspian also received the attention of surveyors, with accurate surveys appearing in 1764 and 1771–1773. Surveys of the colonies on the Persian shore were published in 1781–1782, followed by an official survey under the auspices of the Admiralty College at the turn of the century. Surveys of the Far Eastern shores were carried out, first by merchants and traders, in the latter half of the

century, especially after the results of Cook's last voyage in the Pacific were published. The Aleutian Islands, in the Bering Sea, were surveyed in 1790–1792 by Gavril Andreyevich Sarychev, who later returned to St Petersburg to continue with surveys of the great rivers of western Russia.

The Far East

The Islamic sea chart tradition is well represented by the lesser known but important work of Admiral Piri Re'is in the *Kitabi-i-Bahriye* written in 1521 (Plate 9.24). This volume includes a collection of Arabic portolans or sailing directions with sailing names, technical terms and names for the features of the Middle East in Arabic or Turkish. The charts disappeared for many centuries and only came to light in Istanbul in 1929. One of them gives a detailed account of Christopher Columbus's first voyage, and Piri Re'is used a chart drawn by Columbus himself, along with information from Arabic and Portuguese sources for his redirection of Africa and Asia.

The Chinese have had a sea-faring tradition for centuries. By Confucian times (551–479 BC),

PLATE 9.24 *(opposite) Fragment of a chart by Piri Re'is showing the Ocean Sea or Atlantic, drawn at Gallipoli in 1513. The chart documents in great detail the result of the first Columbus voyage – and the Turkish admiral himself alludes to his use of a chart drawn by Columbus himself, together with information added from Arabic and Portuguese sources for his redirection of Africa and Asia, with information from Alonso de Ojeda for northern South America.*

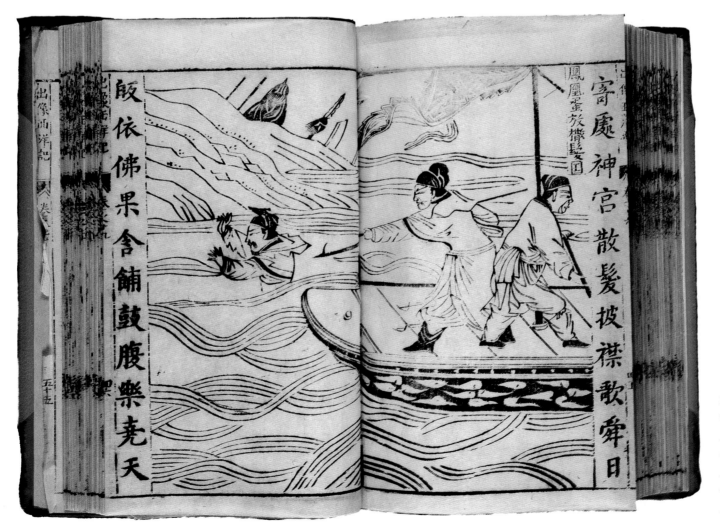

PLATE 9.25 Record of the Western Ocean *by Luo Maodeng, woodblock,* c. 1597. *Admiral Chëng Ho, pictured here in the water, first ventured west, to Hormuz, in 1415.*

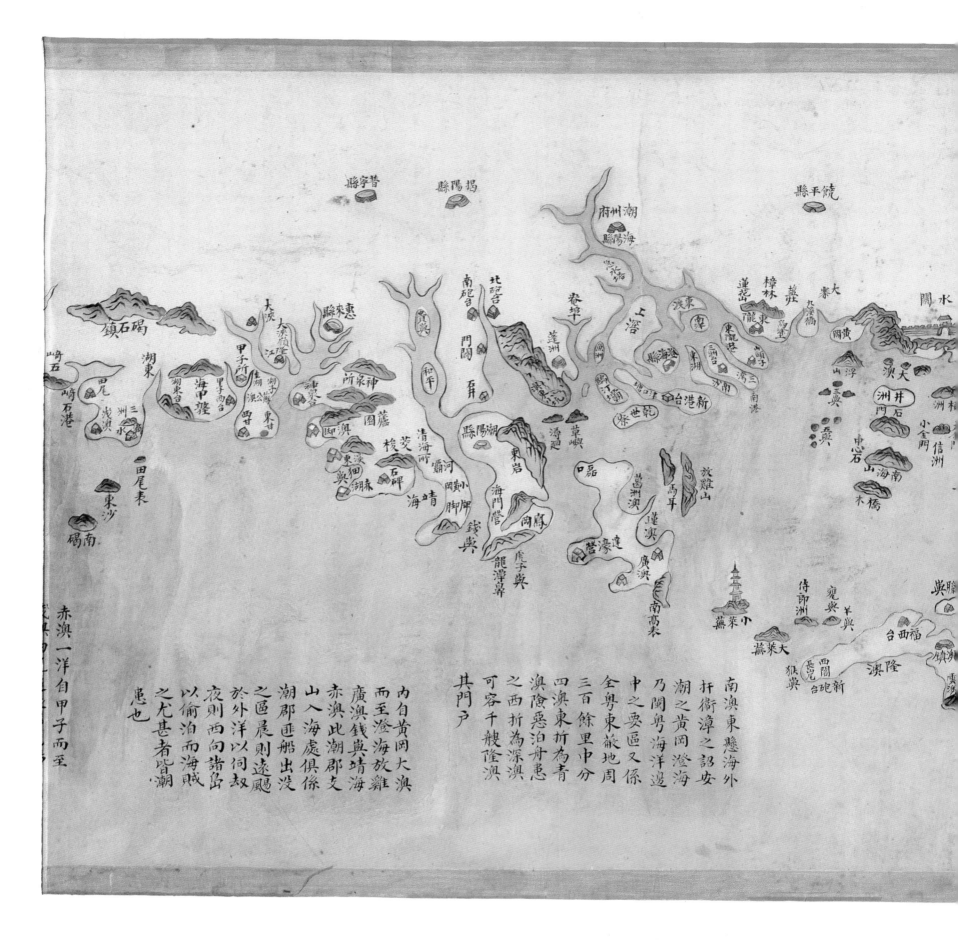

縣字普　　縣陽揭　　　　　　　　　　縣平院

府州潮
驛陽海

南砲臺　北砲臺　　　　　上澄　　　　　　　　　　閣水

鎮石碣

赤澳一洋自甲子而至　　內自黃岡大澳　　其門戶　　　　南澳東懸海外
　　　惠也　　　　　　而至澄海放雞　　　　　　　　　扞衛漳之詔安
　　　　　　　　　廣澳錢澳靖海　　　　　　　　　　潮之黃岡澄海
　　　　　　　　　赤澳此潮郡支　　　　　　　　　　乃閩粵海洋邊
　　　　　　　　　山入海此處俱係　　　　　　　　　　中之要區又係
　　　　　　　　　潮郡匪船出沒　　　　　　　　　　全粵東蔽地周
　　　　　　　　　之區晨則遠颺　　　　　　　　　　三百餘里中分
　　　　　　　　　於外洋以伺叛　　　　　　　　　　四澳東折為青
　　　　　　　　　夜則西向諸島　　　　　　　　　　澳險惡泊舟惠
　　　　　　　　　以偷泊而海賊　　　　　　　　　　之西折為深澳
　　　　　　　　　之尤甚者皆潮　　　　　　　　　　可容千艘隆澳

PLATE 9.26 *Part of the southern coast of China from a coastal navigation chart drawn in the late eighteenth or early nineteenth century, presented in strip form to allow the coastline to be viewed as directly as possible from on board ship.*

navigation was highly organized in the Yangtze region, and in the fourth century BC the Chinese were sailing the high seas. A navy existed in the early western Christian era, and by the seventh century AD the Chinese were the boldest navigators in the Orient. By the twelfth century they controlled the sea lanes of the East Indian archipelago to India, and in the thirteenth century Chinese trading vessels were becoming a considerable threat to Arab traders in the Indian Ocean. During the fifteenth century, the Yung-Le emper-

or sent out a series of expeditions, reaching the Persian Gulf, Arabia and the East African littoral. After this, Chinese naval power waned, but traders from China continued to ply their merchandise throughout the Orient.

A good example of Chinese charts made at the time is one which records the voyages of admiral Chëng Ho, who first ventured west, to Hormuz, in 1415 (Plate 9.25). His map was printed in about 1621 in the form of a strip map some eighteen feet long and folded into forty pages. The

map depicted the route from Nanjing to Hormuz via Java, a distance of about 11,940 kilometres, and was included in a work entitled *Wu Pei Chih* ('Treatise on Military Preparation'). Parts of the route shown are greatly distorted in order to 'squeeze the Indian Ocean sufficiently to allow of representation within the limits of the size of the book'.[5]

Examples of beautifully drawn charts on long silk scrolls, dating from the sixteenth to the nineteenth centuries, also occasionally come to light (Plate 9.26). These were designed to give a comprehensive overview of the entire coast of China, again distorted into a linear format, for military and administrative purposes.

References
1. Thomas Blundeville, *Briefe description of Universal Mappes and Cardes*, 1589.
2. C. Koeman, *The Sea On Paper*, page 2, 1972.
3. H.M. Wallis, *The Compleat Plattmaker*, page 137.
4. J.R. Tanner, 'Samuel Pepys's Naval Minutes', in: *Navy Records Society* LX, pages 135–136, 1926.
5. Joseph Needham, *op. cit.*, page 560.

CHAPTER X

CELESTIAL CHARTS AND GLOBES

600 BC – 1800 AD

THE ASTRONOMY of ancient Babylon seems to have provided the basis for the early Chinese and Greek systems of celestial study. The Babylonians were accomplished mathematicians and astronomers, having developed a system for measuring time which has survived to the present day, for our divisions into 60 and 360 for minutes, seconds and degrees are a direct inheritance. The Babylonians also had a sexagesimal notation system as the basis of a highly accurate system of mathematics. The astronomical researches of the Babylonians are recorded in the form of written texts and tables rather than in any recognizable cartographic form, but circular tablets plotting the positions of groups of stars are known. Needham reports that a number of clay tablets have been found that were once in the library of Assurbanipal (668–626 BC) at Nineveh, which appear to represent planispheres and show circumpolar stars and equatorial lunar stations.[1]

PLATE 10.1 *The northern celestial hemisphere attributed to James Barlow, London, c. 1790. One of a pair of two colourful celestial maps, of more aesthetic value than of any scientific use. The only non-Ptolemaic constellations depicted on this northern map are Antinous, Coma Berenices and Cor Coroli.*

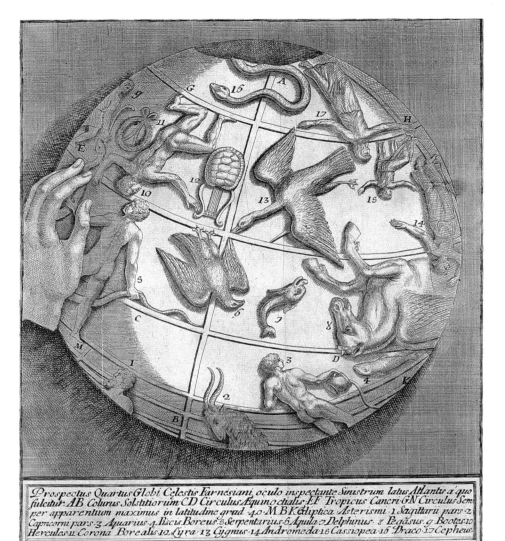

Prospectus Quartus Globi Celestis Farnesiani, oculo inspectante Sinistrum latus Atlantis a quo fulcitur. AB Colurus Solstitiorum CD Circulus Æquinoctialis EF Tropicus Cancri GN Circulus Sem per apparentium maximus in latitudine grad 40. M B K Elliptica Asterismi. 1 Sagittarii pars 2 Capricorni pars 3 Aquarius 4 Piscis Boreus 5 Serpentarius 6 Aquila 7 Delphinus 8 Pegasus 9 Bootes 10 Hercules 11 Corona Borealis 12 Lyra 13 Cignus 14 Andromeda 15 Cassiopea 16 Draco 17 Cepheus

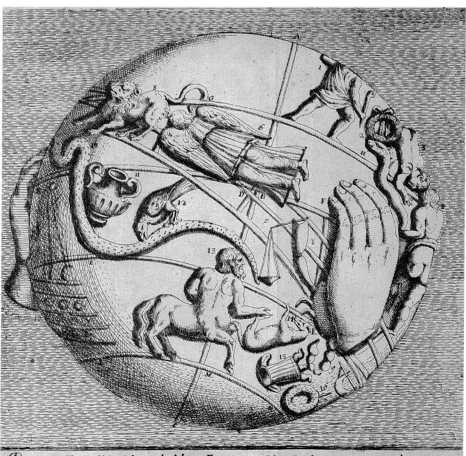

Prospectus Tertius Globi Celestis ab Atlante Farnesiano suffulti, respondens pectori statuæ, oculo constituto in plano Coluri Æquinoctiorum, et inspectante sectionem Autumnalem. A BC. Circulus Ascensionis rectæ ductus per luci dam in Cornu Arietis et per genua Asterismi Virginis D sectio Autumnalis DB Præcessio Æquinoctiorum ætate Ptolemæi EF Circulus Æquinoctialis GH Tropicus Æstivus IK Tropicus Hyemalis LMN Circulus nemquæ apparentium Maximus in lati tudine graduum 40. Asterismi. 1 Bootes 2 Corona Borea 3 Hercules 4 Serpentarius 5 Leo 6 Virgo 7 Libra 8 Chelæ Scorpionis 9 Scorpii cauda 10 Hydri pars 11 Vas 12 Corvus 13 Centaurus 14 Lupus 15 Ara 16 Corona Australis 17 Nauis

In Ancient Greece, observers from early times took an interest in the heavens, naming the stars and constellations after the heroes and heroines of Greek mythology, such as Perseus, Andromeda and the winged horse Pegasus.

Although no celestial globes and charts are known to have survived from these times, details of their existence have been recorded. The Roman writer Cicero mentions that the Greek scientist Thales of Miletus (in about 580 BC) made a celestial globe in the form of a solid sphere.[2] During the early part of the sixth century BC, a pupil of Thales, Anaximander of Miletus, is reputed to have constructed a globe or sphere which is thought to have been a map of the heavens. The astronomer Eudoxus of Cnidos constructed a globe in about 365 BC and also devised a catalogue of stars, which was used by later writers. The geometrician Archimedes of Syracuse (c.287–212 BC) is also believed to have constructed a celestial globe. The Stoic philosopher Crates of Mallos, royal librarian at Pergamon in about 150 BC, is the earliest recorded geographer to have made a globe of the earth. The Greek astronomer Hipparchus (fl. 146–127 BC) recorded the elevation of the Pole Star from different locations on the earth's surface, and he also plotted and compiled celestial charts for various latitudes.

The oldest extant celestial globe is the *Atlante Farnesiano*. It is a Roman copy of an earlier Greek globe and statue and is shown supported on the shoulders of the figure of Atlas. It is thought to have been made some time around AD 150, since the constellations shown on the globe are based on the work of Ptolemy's *Syntaxis*, or *Almagest*. This work, also dating from *circa* AD 150, included a catalogue of the stars and gave instructions on how to construct a celestial globe.

The Far East

The longest continuous tradition of celestial chart-making using cartographic projections from which positions and angular distances could be read off is that of China. Stellar positions were determined by Chinese astronomers as early as the

PLATE 10.2 *(top and bottom) A Roman copy of a Greek globe according to the* Farnese atlas, c. *150 BC. Various constellations and the hands of Atlas are depicted on the celestial globe.*

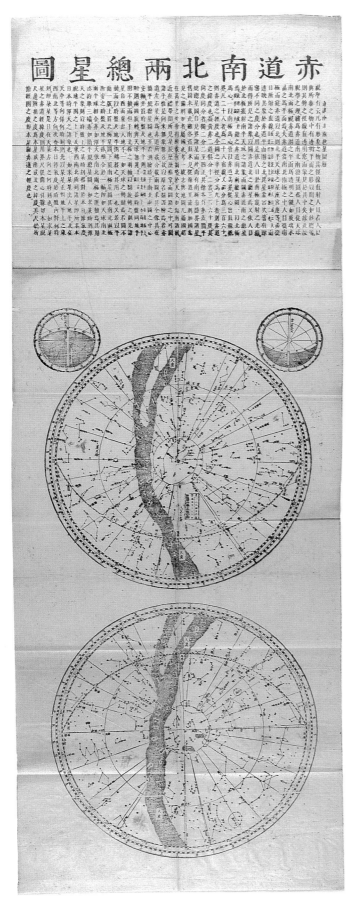

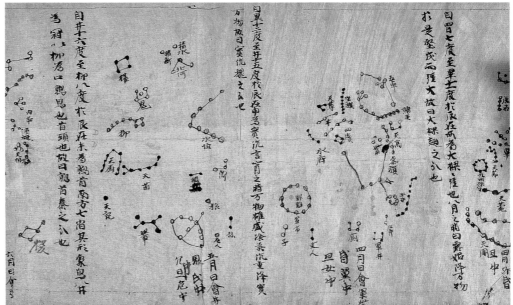

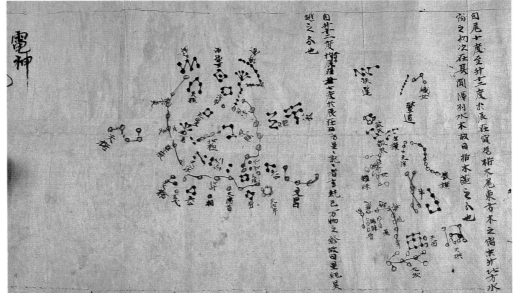

fourth century BC. The Chinese astronomers divided the heavens into twenty-eight sections called *hsiu*, or 'lunar mansions', representing the stages of the moon's progress through the skies, with the pole at their centre. The *hsiu* are represented as long rectangles centred on the Equator and distorted out towards the poles, in just the same way that a modern world map drawn on the Mercator

projection (see Chapter IV) shows Greenland distorted in shape so that it appears to be about as large in area as the continent of Africa, although it is, of course, considerably smaller.

Celestial maps had been made in China as early as the fourth century AD by the astronomer Chhen Cho and a little later (between AD 424 and 453) by Chhien Lo-Chih. The latter used different colours to distinguish the stars whose positions had been determined by the three ancient observers: red for the stars of Shih Shen, black for those of Kan Të and white for the stars of Wu Hsien. None of these maps is known to have survived. Celestial globes were also probably made during the time of Chhien Lo-Chih (AD 435), after a series of star maps by the astronomer Chhen Ho, but none is known to have survived.

The oldest extant Chinese astronomical map dates from AD 940 and was discovered by Aurel Stein at Tunhuang early this century. It is a

PLATE 10.3 *(left)* Map of the two celestial hemispheres of south and north on equatorial co-ordinates [Chido nanbei liang zong xing tu], *attributed to the Jesuit Father Ferdinand Verbiest (1623–1688), woodblock printing, Beijing, c. 1670, thought to be unique.*

PLATE 10.4 *(top and bottom) Chinese star maps on the 'Mercator' projection, manuscript, c. 940. Among the constellations depicted are Orion, Canis Major, Canis Minor, Cancer and Hydra. The colours appear to be keys to commentaries by different astronomers.*

coloured manuscript after Chhien Lo-Chih and depicts the stars in three colours, white, black and yellow, to correspond with the three ancient schools. The map is drawn on a 'projection' resembling that which would become known as the Mercator projection with constellations shown in the traditional method by means of circles linked by lines. It is now to be found in the British Library in London.

A century and a half later, the astronomer Su Sung (1020–1101) published further 'Mercator' projections in his book *Hsin I Hsiang Fa Yao*, or 'New Description of an Armillary Clock'. Published in 1094, it also contained star maps, the oldest of their kind in existence. One of these maps had a straight line across the middle as the

Equator and an arc above to represent the ecliptic. The rectangular boxes of the *hsiu* are clearly seen, with the stars nearest the Equator closer together than those out towards the poles.

The oldest Chinese astronomical map still in existence is the Suchow planisphere, prepared in 1193 for Ning Tsung by the geographer and imperial tutor Huang Shang. The map was engraved on stone in 1247 and is now preserved in the Confucian temple at Suchow.

Other celestial charts were made in Korea, such as that compiled by ten astronomers led by Kwon Keun and engraved, in 1395, for Yi Tai Jo with the title *Thien Hsiang Lieh Tzhu Fën Yeh Chih Thu* ('Positions of the Heavenly Bodies and the Regions they govern').

The Arab world

Greek astronomical traditions were continued by the Arabs in the first century AD. One of the best examples is the manuscript of the early Arab astronomer Abd al-Rahman ibn Umar al-Sufi (AD 903–986) which is called *Kitāb Suwar al-Kawakīb* ('Book of the Fixed Stars') after the Arabic translations of Ptolemy's *Syntaxis* as the *Almagest*. The manuscript illustrates the constellations according to the system of Ptolemy, with each constellation appearing twice: in the first instance as it looks to the observer on the ground; in the second as it might look to an observer from outside the celestial sphere. Stars are distinguished in red, with the figure of the individual constellation, which is distinctly oriental in appearance, drawn in black (Plate 10.5).

Among the finest expressions of Arab knowledge of the techniques and instruments of astronomy is the astrolabe. An astrolabe is a model of the heavens projected on a plane surface and is intended to show the positions of celestial objects at a given time or date, as seen from a given latitude on the earth's surface (Plate 10.6). The astrolabe was probably invented in Greece in the second century BC. Later, it was adopted and refined by the Arabs, who introduced the instrument into western Europe through their conquest of Iberia in the ninth century.

Unfortunately, little remains from these early centuries, although a few fine specimens are still extant. However, some later examples have sur-

PLATE 10.5 *Andromeda from the manuscript* Book of the Fixed Stars [Kitāb Suwar al-Kawakīb] *by Abd al-Rahman ibn Umar al-Sufi, tenth century AD. Andromeda is chained to a rock as a sacrifice to the sea monster Cetus.*

vived. A globe made by the Arabs at Valencia, in Moorish Spain, dating from the eleventh century, is now in Florence, and a twelfth-century brass globe, made in Persia, is preserved in Tehran.

The Copernican revolution

Just as Ptolemy's *Geography* (see Chapter V) held such sway for more than one-and-a-half millennia, so his *Almagest* provided the conventional western conception of the nature of the universe for about 1,400 years. Ptolemy's system placed the earth at the fixed centre of the universe, with the moon, then Mercury, Venus, the sun, Mars, Jupiter and Saturn revolving around the earth. The whole was enclosed by the sphere of the stars which revolved once every twenty-four hours. Johannes de Sacrobosco (*fl.* 1220–1256), whose *Opusculum sphericum* was first printed at Leipzig in about 1560, and Regiomontanus (the Latin name of Johann Müller, 1436–1476), an astronomer of Nuremberg

who wrote his *Tabula directionum* in 1475, were both medieval writers and theorists who speculated on the structure of the universe.

It was, however, the publication, in 1543, of *De revolutionibus orbium caelestium* by Nicolas Copernicus (1478–1543) (Plate 10.7) which marked the end of the acceptance of the geocentric theory of Ptolemy. At the centre of Copernicus's heliocentric system of the universe was the sun, whose position was again fixed. Around the sun revolved the earth (which itself revolved on its axis once every twenty-four hours) on a steady and regular orbit once every year, which was placed between the planets Venus and Mars. Copernicus himself commented:

In the midst of all dwells the sun. For who could set this luminary in another or better place in this most glorious temple than from the place he could at one and the same time lighten the whole? . . . The sun rules the family of the planets as they circle around him.

PLATE 10.6 *A gilt brass planispheric astrolabe by the Persian astronomer Muhammad Mahdī al-Khādim al-Yazī, dated to 1659–1660 AD. Note the constellation figures from the northern hemisphere in the unique secondary star map on the right.*

PLATE 10.7 *A portrait of Nicolas Copernicus (1478–1543). Copernicus was the first astronomer to break with the Ptolemaic tradition which placed the earth at the centre of the universe. In his* De revolutionibus orbium caelestium, *Copernicus put forward the novel theory that the earth and other planets revolved around the sun.*

PLATE 10.8 *(opposite) One of a series of eleven plates depicting the astronomical observatory on the island of Ven in Öresund, established by Tycho Brahe in 1576, which appeared in Volume I of Joan Blaeu's* Atlas major *in 1662.*

PLATE 10.9 *(below) A portrait of the Danish astronomer Tycho Brahe (1546–1601). Brahe challenged both the classical Greek and the Copernican theories of the universe. He proposed a compromise system with the moon and the sun revolving around a central earth. The other planets orbited the sun, while the stars remained on a fixed firmament.*

In Copernicus's system two ideas were expressed: in the first the earth's rotation made the stars appear to revolve daily around the earth, and in the second the sun was fixed and the earth revolved around it once a year. The Church, however, as Campbell notes, 'was strangely slow to decide that by demoting the earth from the centre of things Copernicus had committed the heresy of belittling God's chief creation, Man',[3] for it was only in 1616, during the controversy which surrounded Copernicus's main follower, Galileo, that the work of Copernicus himself was subject to the condemnation of the Church.

By this time, a third concept of the nature of the universe had been devised by the Danish astronomer Tycho Brahe (1546–1601) (Plate 10.9). Brahe's system challenged both the classical Greek and the Copernican systems, but was effectively a compromise. This system had a central earth with the moon and sun revolving around it while the other planets orbited about the sun. The stars, however, remained on a fixed firmament. Brahe produced the first modern catalogue of the stars since that of Ptolemy in the second century. It was to Brahe's observatory on the small island of Ven in Öresund, between Denmark and Sweden, that Willem Janszoon Blaeu, father of Joan Blaeu, travelled in 1594 to study mathematics and astronomy. He became Brahe's assistant and under him, Blaeu learned the science and art of making instruments and globes. Volume I of the Blaeu *Atlas major*, published in 1662, contains a set of eleven plates which describe and illustrate Brahe's observatory, which was founded in 1576 (Plate 10.8). The plates are based on the corresponding woodcut illustrations in Brahe's own astronomical work, the *Astronomiae instauratae mechanicae*, published in 1598.

It is evident that Joan Blaeu included these plates in his atlas as a tribute to his late father and to his father's teacher.[4]

Celestial globes in Europe

In Europe, interest in globes revived during the fifteenth century. The oldest European celestial globe is one made by the philosopher and theologian, Nicolas of Cusa (1401–1464); it is made of wood and glued cloth, with the constellations depicted on the manuscript in ink. Following the manufacture of a pair of celestial and terrestrial engraved globes by the mathematician Gemma Frisius at Leuven in Belgium in 1536–1537, it became common practice to issue globes in such pairs. A strikingly beautiful pair of engraved gilt metal globes dating from 1579 was recently discovered and sold in London in 1990. They are attributed to the workshop of Gerard Mercator.

More famous and vastly more impressive on account of their variety are the globes of the Venetian mapmaker Vincenzo Coronelli (1650–1718). His globes ranged in size from small pocket ones to some four-and-a-half metres in diameter produced for Louis XIV. Coronelli also published his celestial and terrestrial globes in atlas form, comprising the printed gores (shaped sections which could be cut out and pasted on to a sphere to make a globe) (Plate 10.11); the book appeared as the *Libro dei globi* in 1697.

Celestial charts in Europe

Germany

In Europe, the earliest printed charts and maps of the universe and its constellations were published in Germany. A highly diagrammatic depiction of the universe was included in the many woodcut illustrations in the *Liber chronicarum* (commonly

(continued on page 317)

EFFIGIES TYCHONIS BRAHE O.F.
ÆDIFICII ET INSTRUMENTORUM
ASTRONOMICORUM STRUCTORIS.
Aº. DOMINI 1587, ÆTATIS SUÆ 40.

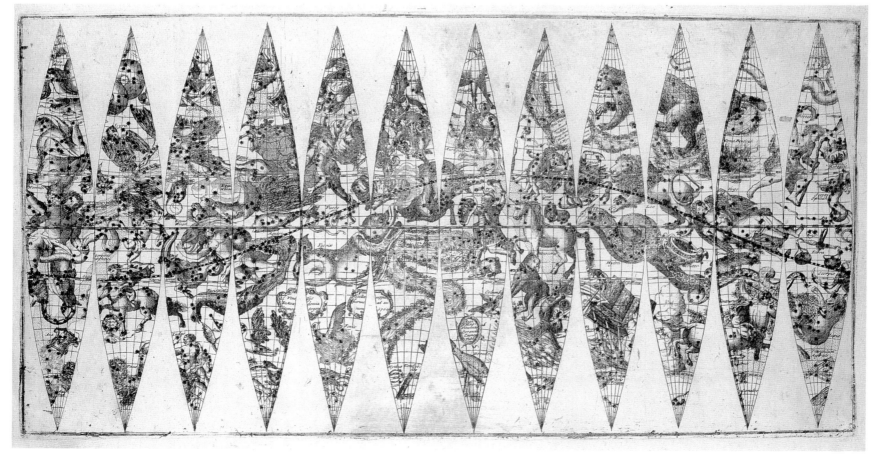

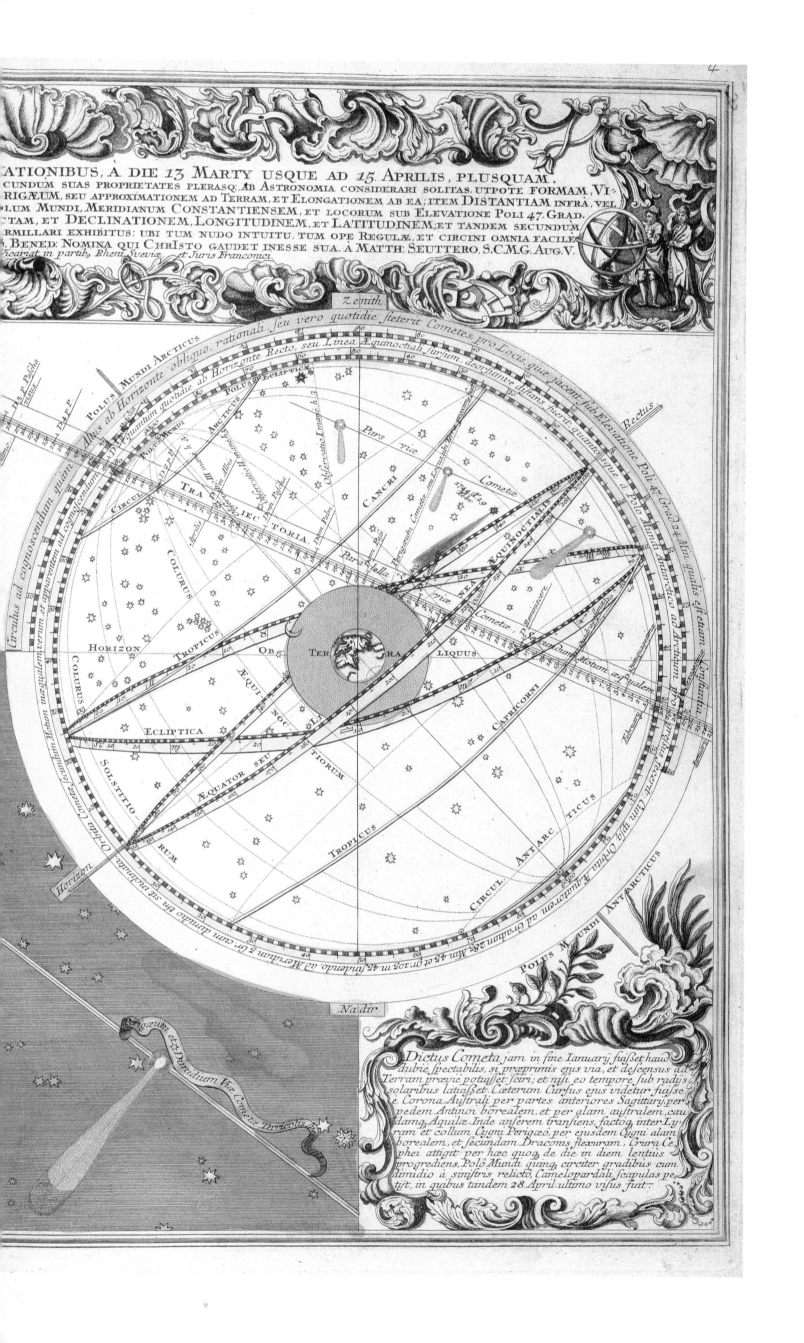

...ATIONIBUS, A DIE *13.* MARTY USQUE AD *15.* APRILIS, PLUSQUAM.
...CUNDUM SUAS PROPRIETATES PLERASQ. AB ASTRONOMIA CONSIDERARI SOLITAS, UTPOTE FORMAM, VI-
...RIGÆUM, SEU APPROXIMATIONEM AD TERRAM, ET ELONGATIONEM AB EA; ITEM DISTANTIAM INFRA, VEL
...LUM MUNDI, MERIDIANUM CONSTANTIENSEM, ET LOCORUM SUB ELEVATIONE POLI *47.* GRAD.
...CTAM, ET DECLINATIONEM, LONGITUDINEM, ET LATITUDINEM, ET TANDEM SECUNDUM
...RMILLARI EXHIBITUS: UBI TUM NUDO INTUITU, TUM OPE REGULÆ, ET CIRCINI OMNIA FACILE
...S. BENED: NOMINA QUI CHRISTO GAUDET INESSE SUA. A MATTH: SEUTTERO, S.C.M.G. AUG. V.
...ricariat in partib. Rheni Sueviæ, et Juris Franconici.

Dictus Cometa jam in fine Ianuarij fuiſſet haud
dubie ſpectabilis, ſi præprimis ejus via, et deſcenſus ad
Terram prævie potuiſſet ſciri; et niſi eo tempore ſub radijs
ſolaribus latuiſſet. Cæterum Curſus ejus videtur fuiſſe
e Corona Auſtrali per partes anteriores Sagittarij, per
pedem Antinoi borealem, et per alam auſtralem, cau
dam q. Aquilæ. Inde anſerem tranſiens, factoq. inter Ly
ram et collum Cygni Perigæo, per ejusdem Cygni alam
borealem, et ſecundam Dracoms flexuram, Crura Ce
phei attigit: per hæc quoq. de die in diem lentius
progrediens, Polo Mundi quinq. circiter gradibus cum
dimidio à ſiniſtris relicto, Camelopardali ſcapulas pe
tijt, in quibus tandem *28.* April. ultimo viſus fuit.

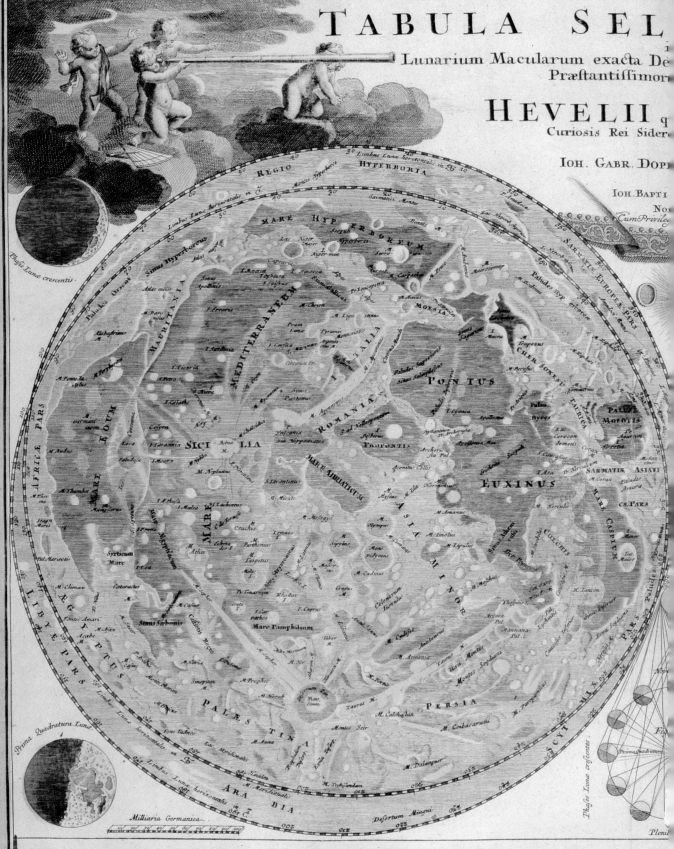

TABULA SEL...

Lunarium Macularum exacta De...
Præstantissimor...

HEVELII q...
Curiosis Rei Sider...

IOH. GABR. DOP...

IOH. BAPTI
Non...
Cum Privile...

Nullum inter corpora cælestia, ex quo tempore Veteres sacræ Uraniæ addicti omnē moverunt lapidem, ut Siderum naturæ & affectiones quam maxime forent in aprico positæ, cunctorum vicit magis admirationem & multiformi ambage (si cum Plinio loqui liceat) torsit contemplantium ingenia, proximum quippe ignorari sidus indignantium quam ipsa Luna, varietate macularum imprimis miranda; sed nec mirari nos subeat, cum medijs tunc destituti, quibus nunc Lunam accuratius inspicere & contemplari nobis hodie datum, oculis scilicet armatis; Hinc etiam deficiente hoc Tuborum opticorum apparatu diversas de Lunæ substantia è maculis nudo oculo visis fovere opiniones non potuere non Antiqui illi rei sidereæ Cultores; alij enim cum Cleartho & Argesinace maculas Lunares nostri Oceani imaginem in Luna, tanquam in speculo conspicuam esse, alij hasce è certis corporibus, quæ Solem inter & Lunam jaceant originem ducere existimarunt; alij Lunam vitream, non quidem exacte pellucidã, sed ex parte opacam; alij partim igneam, partim opacam, putarunt; & quæ sunt multæ aliæ de corporis Lunaris substantia sententiæ.

At multo feliciori successu omnium primus celeberrimus ille Florentinorum Mathematicus Galilæus de Galilæis anno superioris seculi decimo, quo utilissimū Tuborum opticorum inventum luci publicæ tradidit, id negotium tentavit, quod dein Scheinerus & alij satis superq; dedere probatum, imò plures hodie Tubis prædictis ad majorem perfectionem nunc perductis, rem acu quod ajunt multo felicius tangere videntur, si proindubio asserunt, quod Luna innumeris scateat montibus, qui nostros altitudine, habito respectu globi Lunaris ad nostrum, sexagies fere mino-

ris superent; porro quod eædem profunditates, quæ prægrandibus semper ... ambitu suo exteriori, plerumque circulari, mænium ... instar, cinguntur eminentijs, innumeras fere & multo plures, sed non tantas et tam profundas, quem nostra ... hibeat Terra, si huius cavitates suis destituerentur maribus; denique quod partes mul... in Luna obscuræ, quæ sub primo conspectu non apparent profundæ, ideoq; pro mater... liquida, maribus scilicet multorum forsan judicio censendæ, adhibita accuratiori inspectione, teste Viro celeberrimo D.no de la Hire, nihilominus profundæ nec tamen, liqu... deprehendantur; ut hinc haud pauci cum acutissimo Galilæo Lunam pro corpore, ... teriam a Terra diversam habente existimare possent, in qua etiam fortasse substan... tivæ & res creatæ existant, quæ operationes edant ab imaginatione nostra, sicut ... motas, ita, & prorsus alienas; quippe quæ nullam cum nostris similitudinem habe... & proin omnino sint a nostra cogitatione discrepantes.

Quamvis autem Luna profunditatibus et eminentijs quamplurimis sit referta, ... pissime tamen contingit, superficiem Lunæ in certis a Sole distantijs adeo imm... tatum videri, ut magnus ille montium & profunditatum numerus, qui nuper ad... dum distinctissime observari poterat, non amplius tunc sub conspectum cadat; ... huius mutationis ex ipsa figura superiori A intermedia facile patescit, quod scili... profunditates inter noctilunia et quadraturas. Luna crescente a dextris maxim... crescente autem hac a sinistris potissimum altissimorum circumjacentium montium ... obtegantur umbris; et quidem quod insuper tales pro vario Solis ad Lunam po... perpetuo immutentur (quæ proinde etiam noviæ maculæ denominari solent.)

ENOGRAPHICA
n qua
scriptio secundum Nomenclaturam
um Astronomorum
tam
uam RICCIOLI
æ Cultoribus exhibetur
à
ELMAJERO MATH. P.P.
pera
TAE HOMANNI
inbergæ.
io Sac. Cæs. Majest.

PLATE 10.10 *(opposite, top left and centre) The gores for a celestial globe,* Sphaera stellifera *by Willem Janszoon Blaeu, Amsterdam c. 1600. One of the most beautiful of all celestial globes.*

PLATE 10.11 *(opposite, bottom) The gores for a small celestial globe by Vincenzo Maria Coronelli, Venice, c. 1697.*

PLATE 10.12 *(left)* Tabula selenographica *by Johann Baptist Homann, Nuremberg, c. 1720, after Johann Gabriel Doppelmayer.*

nentiæ autem, cum Sol illas à latere illuminat, quam maxime conspicue redduntur, cum è contrario à quadraturis ad oppositionem superficies Lunæ, dum Sol hisce inæqualitatibus magis magisque verticaliter immanere pergit, et omne, quidquid umbrosum ante fuit, pedetentim illuminat, aliam semper exhibeat faciem, ut tandem luminosa et albicans appareat.

Ex hoc fundamento bina nostra Schemata in delineatione macularum notabilem etiam differentiam involvunt, eo quod primum, HEVELIANUM puta, Luna in oppositione cum Sole existente, hoc est, in plenilunio designatum, alterum vero, RICCIOLINUM scilicet, è pluribus Lunæ phasibus in unum corpus fuerit collectum. In denominationibus macularum, utpote signis et significationibus arbitrarijs, dictos Auctores inter se differre hic in aperto videmus, cum Hevelius nomina marium, regionum, fluminum et montium nostrorum imitetur, Ricciolus autem illustrium et de re siderea optime meritorum Astronomorum, complurium præsertim suæ Societatis Mathematicorum nomina pro usu Astronomico sibi elegerit.

Bini circa Lunam limbi se invicem secantes nihil aliud quam motus alicuius in Luna libratorii terminos, intra quos perpetua deprehenditur librationis variatio, subindicant; qui hodie demum per Tubos è diversa macularum nonnullarum mutatione observatus, nec Veteribus olim notus fuit: eandem quippe nobis faciem constantissime semper Lunam obvertere existinantibus: per agit autem hæc motum suum libratorium per quatuordecim circiter dies trigesima sexta tantum.

diametri suæ parte in plagam superiorem ab Austro eorum versus, dum Luna versetur in descendentibus signis, in ascendentibus autem per idem tempus et spatium secundum Herelii et aliorum observationes retrorsum iterum et sic porro vacillare videtur.

Eodem tempore, menstruo nempe spatio Lunam quoque orbitam suam, dum porro et retro librationem absolvit, peragrare, et pro vario situ diversas phases, hoc est luminis figurationes varias proat figura media inferior B, subindicat, simul exhibere deprehendimus, cum pars Lunæ illuminata mox crescere, mox decrescere, pro maiori vel minori Lunæ a Sole distantia debeat, quæ sane luminis non propriæ sed a Sole mutuati, signa sunt indubia: interim non obstante, quod lumen quoddam debile haud multo ante et post novilunia Lunæ quasi innatum, de quo olim multæ inter Astronomos movebantur lites, maculas Lunares nonnihil reddat conspicuas, cum extra omne dubium sit positum, hoc suam originem a Terræ nostræ superficie duodecies, et quod excedit, maiori quam illa Lunæ, radios Solis tunc temporis omnium copiosissimos in illam reflectente habere, eò quod hac reflexione cessante, ipsum etiam putativum lumen nonnunquam plane cum ipsa Luna in Eclipsibus disparuerit.

Ultimo denique loco duplices pro Lunæ Mensuræ longitudinariæ notandæ quoque remunt, quarum unam pro distantiis et magnitudine macularum ut et diametro Lunari, quæ secundum Hevelium 494 mensuratur milliaribus, per Germanica milliaria definiendis, nec Veteribus olim notus fuit, alteram pro quantitate Eclipsium Lunarium tam secundum digitos Eclipticos quam eorum partes exacte describenda, huic tabulæ apposuimus.

PLATE 10.13 Cometa, qui Anno Christi *1742* apparvit *from* Atlas novus *by Matthäus Seutter, Augsburg, c. 1745. One of a suite of celestial plates in Seutter's atlases, showing the comets of 1618–1619, 1642, 1683 and March–April 1742.*

the planets, eclipses of the sun and moon, and the positions of the constellations in the firmament.

Apian broadened the scope of the *Astronomicon* by including a variety of mechanisms for astrological purposes, such as for finding the hour of conception given the moment of birth. The book has been described as 'the most spectacular contribution of the book-maker's art to sixteenth-century science',[5] but it is now rarely found in a fine and complete state. Apian's book, incidentally, also provides the first illustration of the discovery that comets always move with their tails pointing away from the sun.

On these early charts, the constellations were represented by their imagined figures as well as by name. At about this time, several texts were published using illustrations of the constellations, such as those produced by the Roman Alessandro

PLATE 10.14 *(left)* Imagines coeli septentrionales cum duodecim imaginibus zodiaci *by Albrecht Dürer, Nuremberg, 1515. One of the earliest printed star charts, here of the northern celestial hemisphere.*

PLATE 10.15 *(below) A woodcut illustration of the northern skies from* Astronomicum Caesareum *by Peter Apian, Ingolstadt, 1540. The rich hand-colouring seen on this plate is typical of the period.*

known as the *Nuremberg Chronicle*), compiled by Hartmann Schedel and published in Nuremberg in 1493. Schedel's plan shows the earth sitting at the centre of all things, surrounded by spheres representing the elements of water, air and fire, the moon and the planets then known, and finally the constellations of the zodiac.

In 1515, maps of the universe represented by the northern and southern celestial hemispheres were made by Albrecht Dürer and published as woodcuts bearing the titles *Imagines coeli Septentrionales cum duodecim imaginibus zodiaci* (Plate 10.14) and *Imagines coeli Meridionales*. These maps used stellar co-ordinates that had been determined by Johann Stabius, with the stars located by the mathematician Konrad Heinfogel in their Ptolemaic positions. Dürer himself drew the figures of the constellations.

One of the most impressive and elaborate sixteenth-century books of celestial charts was compiled by the astronomer and mathematician Peter Apian (also known as Apianus and sometimes by his native name, Bienewitz). Apian (1495–1552) is widely known for his *Cosmographia sive descriptio totius orbis* which was first published in 1524, and reissued in many editions and translations throughout the sixteenth century. His major work, however, was the *Astronomicon Caesareum*, published at Ingolstadt in 1540, which contained charts and elaborate diagrams of the universe (Plate 10.15). Many of these featured volvelles (revolving discs), richly hand-coloured and intended to show the movements of

PLATE 10.16 *The constellation of Cygnus (the Swan) from the first printed star atlas,* De le stelle fisse libro uno *by Alessandro Piccolomini, 1540. The comparative brightness of the stars is indicated by letters, with 'A' representing the brightest star.*

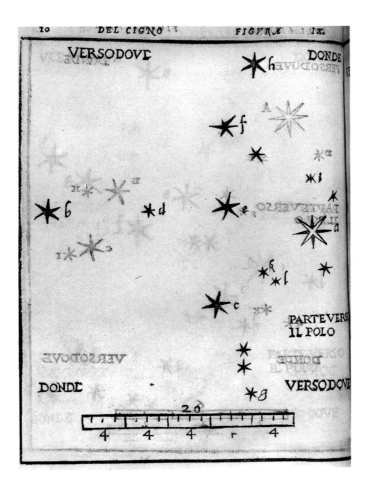

Piccolomini (1508–1678), which contained up to forty-eight woodcut charts, in several editions, including *De le stelle fisse libro uno*, printed in 1540 (Plate 10.16). On his charts, Piccolomini used letters of the Roman alphabet to distinguish individual stars, a system later adopted by other chartmakers in the sixteenth and seventeenth centuries. Other, smaller charts of the heavens, superficially resembling those of Dürer, were devised by the German geographer Johannes Honter (1498–1549) and published in 1541.

The first real atlas of the universe appeared in 1603, at Ulm in Germany. This was the *Uranometria* by the Bavarian astronomer Johann Bayer (Plate 10.18), which contained a series of beautiful and elaborate charts engraved by Alexander Mair. The *Uranometria* proved to be an extremely popular work, being reprinted in many editions up to 1703, and providing the basis for a number of celestial atlases published in Europe until well

PLATE 10.17 *Charts from* Coelum stellatum christianum *by Julius Schiller, 1627. Schiller's atlas was an attempt to reinterpret the constellations in the guise of Christian symbolism.*

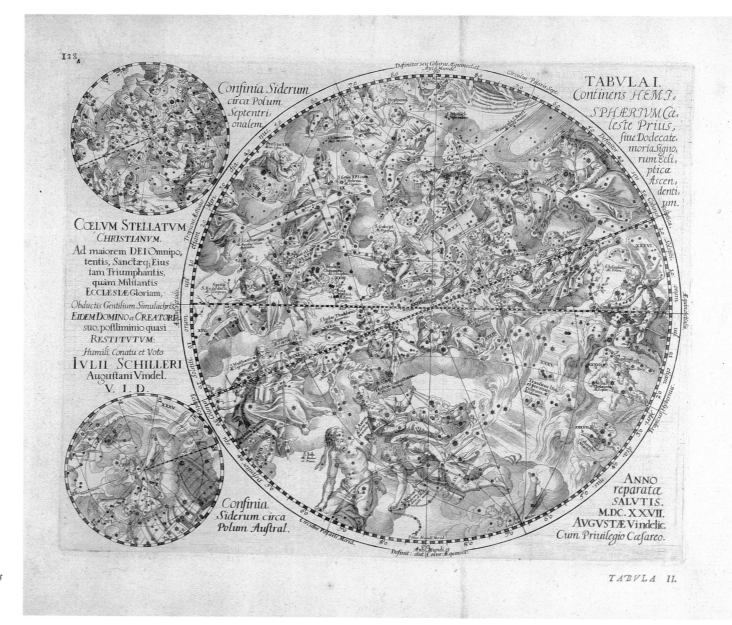

into the eighteenth century. For his charts, Bayer devised the method of using Greek, as well as Roman, letters to identify individual stars, a system still used today. Bayer was able to identify more than 1,700 stars from the first to the sixth magnitudes of brightness.

Another atlas published in Germany in this period was the *Coelum stellatum christianum*, issued at Augsburg in 1627 by Julius Schiller (who died in the same year). Schiller was devoutly Roman Catholic and his atlas was an attempt to redraw and rename the familiar, pagan constellations from a Catholic standpoint, as a system of Christian symbolism and iconography (Plate 10.17). Schiller's atlas was the result of meticulous and careful observation and preparation, incorporating the most up-to-date astronomical information, with contributions from many of the leading astronomers of the time, among them Tycho Brahe, Johannes Bayer and Johannes Kepler, in a series of finely engraved charts. These show the original twelve signs of the zodiac transformed into the twelve apostles. The constellations of the northern and southern celestial hemispheres appear, respectively, as figures from the New and Old Testaments: for example, Pegasus becomes the archangel Gabriel in Schiller's system, and Hercules is transformed into the Three Magi. In each

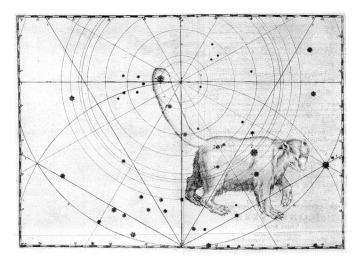

PLATE 10.18 *Chart from* Uranometria *by Johann Bayer, 1603, copper engraving, Augsburg, 1603. The constellation of the 'Little Bear' (otherwise known as the 'Plough') can be clearly seen.*

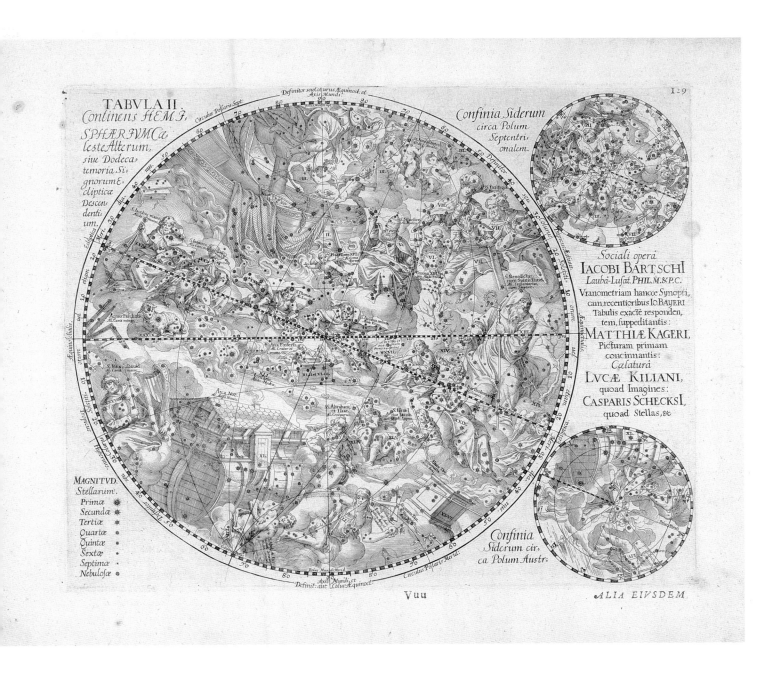

century (see Chapter V). However, they also produced some fine celestial and selenographical (lunar) charts based on the observations of such astronomers as Johann Gabriel Doppelmayer (1677–1750), whose charts were published by Homann as *Atlas coelestis* at Nuremberg in 1742. The charts of Homann and Seutter are found in some eighteenth-century atlases, particularly those published in Germany. They are also frequently found incorporated into the larger Homann composite atlases as a body of star charts, sometimes accompanied by a *Tabula selenographica* (or twin-hemispherical map of the moon) (Plate 10.12) based on the map of the same name compiled by the Polish-born astronomer Johannes Hevelius (1611–1687) in 1647. Hevelius also published a lavishly illustrated book, *Cometographia*, in 1688, describing the origin and nature of comets (Plate 10.19). This book is very occasionally encountered today, and when seen in full colour is a magnificent work.

Work in England

In England, the sixteenth century ended on a high note for astronomy when John Blagrave (1550–1611), instrument maker, mathematician and surveyor, devised an elaborate celestial chart in 1596 to accompany the book on his little-known invention, the uranical astrolabe, entitled *Astrolabium uranicum generale*. The celestial chart was engraved by Benjamin Wright, who was famous for several maps and charts. Blagrave's chart incorporated information and tables for use with his astrolabe – which he was prompted to make from a desire to improve upon existing instruments – as well as information on the signs of the zodiac and tables of celestial motion. His chart shows such discoveries and observations as the comet of 1596, *Cometa 1596*, which he placed at the hindfoot of the constellation *Ursa major*.

During the seventeenth century in England, astronomy developed as an important branch of the natural sciences, due in no small degree to the labours of the first Astronomer Royal, John Flamsteed (1646–1719), appointed in 1675. Flamsteed was so committed to perfection and accuracy in his work that he published very few of his observations in his lifetime. Indeed, his contemporaries sometimes accused him of suppressing and hoarding information, and his relationships with his

PLATE 10.19 *(above)*
Hemisphaerum australe *from* Cometographia *by Johannes Hevelius, 1688.*

PLATE 10.20 *(below)*
Cassiopea Cepheus Ursa Minor draco *from the posthumous* Atlas coelestis *by John Flamsteed, London, 1729.*

chart, Latin letters are used to distinguish the most important stars. While Schiller's atlas never received universal acceptance among astronomers, it nevertheless remains an interesting contribution to the history of celestial chartmaking.

Johann Baptist Homann (1663–1724) of Nuremberg and Georg Matthäus Seutter (1678–1757) of Augsburg and Vienna were both prominent cartographers in Germany in the eighteenth

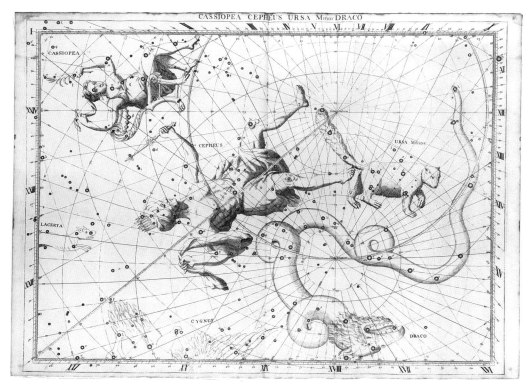

ZODIACUS STELLATUS CUJUS LIMITIBUS PLANETARUM OMNIUM VISIBILES VIÆ COMPREHENDUNTUR. Autore Jo: Seller Serenifimi Reg: Hydrographo.

fellows, such as Edmond Halley (his successor) and Isaac Newton were frequently strained.

The foundation of the observatory at Greenwich in 1675 was born out of a need for accurate observations of the heavens in an attempt to solve the most pressing problem facing navigators at the time, the precise determination of longitude. Flamsteed's appointment as Astronomer Royal spurred hopes that England would be the first nation to give the world of navigation the solution to the problem of finding longitude at sea; but it soon became apparent that Flamsteed was not content to publish the results of his observations in a hurried attempt to claim such glory. Indeed, his catalogue, the *Stellarum inerrantium catalogue brittanicus*, was not published until 1725, some years

after his death, and his charts did not appear until 1729, when they were issued as the *Atlas coelestis* (Plate 10.20). (The same title had been given by Cellarius to his atlas of 1660, but with charts very different in appearance.) In Flamsteed's charts the stars are shown according to the co-ordinates for 1690 and are identified by Bayer's system, with the use of Greek and Roman letters to distinguish the brighter objects, and with the additional help of a system of numbers, still known as 'Flamsteed's Numbers'. The figures of the constellations are drawn and engraved in classical style after drawings by the artist Sir James Thornhill (1675–1734), who had been commissioned to paint the ceiling of the dome of St Paul's Cathedral in London. Flamsteed's clarity and his painstaking

PLATE 10.21 Zodiacus stellatus . . . *from the* Atlas maritimus *by John Seller, London, 1679.*

PLATE 10.22 *(right and opposite) The paired northern (right) and southern (opposite) celestial hemispheres attributed to James Barlow, London, c. 1790. Of more aesthetic appeal than of any scientific value.*

attention to accuracy and detail ensured that his atlas, published posthumously in 1725, became the most important one of its kind published during the eighteenth century.

Other celestial atlases issued in England at about this time include the various editions of the small-format *Atlas coelestis*, a pocket atlas published by the chartmaker John Seller in London between about 1675 and 1690 in conjunction with his similar-sized atlases of sea charts and regional maps (Plate 10.21). They are all now quite scarce. More or less contemporary with Seller's charts were those issued by another London mapmaker, Philip Lea (*fl.*1660s–1700). His charts of the northern and southern celestial hemispheres, made around 1686, were printed and sold (appropriately enough) from his establishment at the 'Atlas and Hercules' in Cheapside, London. Robust and

handsome in appearance, Lea's circular charts are framed in a squared-off neoclassical egg-and-dart border. In a patriotic touch, the name of the minor constellation *Canes venatici* was changed to *Cor Caroli Regis Martyris* ('The Heart of King Charles the Martyr'), said to have been so created by Halley in memory of Charles I, who had been executed in 1649.

Somewhat later, in 1750, came an English atlas based largely upon Johann Bayer's *Uranometria* – the work by John Bevis (1695–1771) entitled *Uranographia britannica*. It had as its allegorical frontispiece the figure of Frederick, Prince of Wales, dressed as Caesar and being presented with a copy of the atlas by Urania. Bevis's atlas is now rare; few copies appear to have been printed and only a small number of copies are now recorded. In his charts Bevis used Bayer's system of indicat-

ing the stars, but any which are not shown in Bayer's original work are distinguished by the use of decorative Gothic letters.

The decorative tradition of English celestial charts continued until late in the eighteenth century. A chart by James Barlow, from about 1790, extends the Ptolemaic tradition into the southern skies, during the great age of exploration in the southern hemisphere below the tropic of Capricorn (Plate 10.22). Charles II is commemorated in *Robur Carolinum*, a constellation set near the southern celestial pole, symbolizing the royal oak in which the king is said to have hidden at Boscobel. The southern skies had their complement of beasts in steady progression, such as *Hydrus* (the watersnake), *Pavo* (the peacock), *Piscis volans* (the flying fish), *Columba Noachi* (Noah's dove) and many more. Numerous new

constellations were added to fill the southern skies, no doubt to commemorate scientific and technical achievements made during the eighteenth century, many of which had become, or were to become, essential aids to navigation. Among them were *Horologium* (the clock), *Pyxis nautica* (the mariner's compass), *Telescopium* and *Fornax chemica* (the chemical furnace), perhaps in commemoration of Antoine Lavoisier, the French chemist who established that combustion is a form of chemical action, and who coined the word 'oxygen'.

The French tradition

In France, too, celestial charts were being produced, prominent among which were those made by Augustin Royer (*fl.* 1670s–1700), architect to Louis XIV. Royer's atlas, *Cartes du ciel*, issued in Paris in 1679, was based on the works of Edmond

323

PLATE 10.23 *(previous page)* Planisphaeri coeleste *by Frederick de Wit, c. 1680. This spectacular map of the heavens shows the northern and southern hemispheres with traditional representations of the constellations and signs of the zodiac.*

Halley, Jacob Bartsch (who first named the southern constellation of *Crux australia* or the Southern Cross) and the *Harmonia macrocosmica* of Andreas Cellarius (see below). The atlas continued in print until 1708, and during its lifetime several new constellations were given particular depictions. Some of these appear to have been devised by Royer himself to appease the French temperament, such as the figure *Sceptum* in the northern celestial hemisphere, drawn as the hand of justice, and a *fleur-de-lys* sceptre placed at the feet of Pegasus and so situated as to appear above Paris when on the meridian of the city. Another of Royer's creations appeared on his charts of the southern celestial hemisphere in the figure of the constellation *Lilium* to represent the royal French *fleur-de-lys*, as if to symbolize French pretensions to colonial power in the terrestrial southern hemisphere. Royer was an extremely skilled artist as well as being a very able draughtsman, befitting his architectural practice, and his charts are handsome, elegant and refined in appearance.

Work in the Netherlands

One of the finest illustrated books published in Amsterdam in the seventeenth century, rivalling in sheer beauty the great series of atlases issued by the Blaeus, was the *Atlas coelestis seu harmonia macrocosmica*. It was compiled by Andreas Cellarius (who was probably German or Polish by birth, but resident at Hoorn in Noordholland as rector of the Latin school there), and is generally considered the most beautiful celestial atlas ever published (Plate 10.24). Cellarius's work, the title of which translates poetically as 'Celestial atlas, or the harmony of the universe', contains twenty-nine extremely elaborate and decorative maps and charts depicting the Ptolemaic and Copernican systems and Brahe's compromise system, with a further group representing variations on all three. The allegorical title-page (a feature common to many atlases of the time) represents astronomers paying homage to their muse, Urania.

A significant feature of Cellarius's charts is that some of them portray the heavens as projected on

PLATE 10.24 Coeli stellate christiani haemisphaerium prius *(as depicted by Julius Schiller) from the finest of all star atlases, the* Atlas coelestis seu harmonia macrocosmica, *by Andreas Cellarius, Amsterdam, c. 1660. Note that the constellations of Gemini, Cancer, Leo, Virgo, Libra and Scorpius have been replaced by Schiller's new constellations of Jacob (the major), John, Thomas, Jacob (the minor), Philip and Bartholomew. The constellation of Argo Navis is now represented by Noah's ark.*

to the terrestrial globe – in other words, they show how the earth's surface might appear to an observer from the heavens looking through the constellations themselves. When the charts are seen in full original colour – and there are many examples of this work available for study in institutional collections the world over – an almost three-dimensional effect can be perceived, so that the zodiacal figures seem to be suspended above the surface of the globe. Surrounding each spherical chart or diagram Cellarius provides illustrations of astronomers and allegorical figures, but whether such embellishments are the result of his own inspiration we do not know.

It may fairly be said that any celestial atlas issued after that of Cellarius is but a pale imitation. It could even be argued that the beautiful celestial gores made by Coronelli (see p.312) cannot compare with the charts of Cellarius in terms of sheer beauty. Nevertheless, the gores which Coronelli made for his larger celestial globes during the late seventeenth and early eighteenth centuries have a particular appeal of their own because of the unusual shape of each gore plate in his *Libro dei globi*. Such gores are often collected and mounted together in northern and southern celestial hemispherical segments or, occasionally, as complete sets of twelve-gore segments. Coronelli's constellation figures appear with allegorical costume and many classical accoutrements, but because of the purpose for which they were ultimately intended the segments were not decorated as in Cellarius's atlas.

Celestial charts may never have been as important to the history of mapmaking as charting the earth. Nevertheless, the study of celestial charts has proved itself to be of just as much interest to the map enthusiast as any other branch of cartography. As G.S. Snyder wrote:

In the history of cartography, the study of celestial charts has come to assume a footnote status, relegated to minor chapters in the classic works on maps and mapmaking . . . a function of science and other fields tangential to cartography . . . This unusual treatment stems, in part, from some basic differences between the two genres. Whereas terrestrial maps derived from actual exploration by land and sea, charting the sky depended entirely on the limited capabilities of the naked eye. As the earth was a physical realm that could be described by pictographic symbols representing mountain ranges, forests, and rivers, the heavens were open to interpretation, to the use of images from mythology and religion to create constellations representing the positions of the stars and planets . . .[6]

PLATE 10.25 *Atlas holding the earth to view, from an Ottens composite atlas compiled in Amsterdam. This is a typical allegorical atlas frontispiece of the later seventeenth century.*

References
1. Joseph Needham, *Science and Civilisation in China, III*, pages 254–256, 1959.
2. Cicero, *De Republica*, I, 14.
3. T. Campbell, *Early Maps*, page 20, 1981.
4. J.J.S. Goss, *Blaeu's the Grand Atlas of the Seventeenth-Century World*, page 18, 1990.
5. O. Gingerich, *Journal for the History of Astronomy* II, pages 168–171, 1971.
6. G.S. Snyder, *Map of the Heavens*, page 7, 1984.

CHAPTER XI

CURIOSA

1300 – 1900 AD

THE OFTEN FERTILE imaginations of mapmakers have on occasion come up with remarkable notions of imaginary lands, satire, distortions (accidental or intentional) of geographical truth, anthropomorphism and so on, all of which delight and entertain the latter-day collector of old maps. Some of these cartographical curiosities are well known to collectors, others rather less so.

The realms of the imagination played a considerable role in the design of the medieval *mappaemundi*: 'in the earlier world maps the geographical element was only one of many: the map was a vehicle for conveying every kind of information – zoological, anthropological, moral, theological, historical'.[1] Paradise, Eden and other imaginary lands of innocence featured in such maps up to a millennium ago. The best-known examples of these are the Hereford (*c.*1276) and the Ebstorf *mappaemundi* depicting Africa (*c.*1339), featuring an abundance of all kinds of fauna, including unicorns and other fabulous beasts (see Chapter II).

PLATE 11.1 *Detail of* Aspice Paulinam Pauli sub imagine gente *from an atlas of the archbishopric of Cologne, the* Prodromus geographicus, *by Johannes Michael Gigas, Cologne, c. 1620. The so-called* Pauluskarte *is a remarkable example of the portrayal of a person in cartographic form. The apostle Paul is, in an imaginative manner, superimposed on a map of the region around Münster in northwestern Germany.*

PLATE 11.2 *(right) An
early map of Europe, drawn
to resemble the human form,
by Opicinus de Canistris
(c. 1296 – c. 1300). The
map was drawn to illustrate
a text written between 1334
and 1338, probably for the
papal court at Avignon. The
outline appears to have been
adapted from portolan
charts.*

PLATE 11.3 *(opposite,
top)* Aspice Paulinam
Pauli sub imagine gente
*from an atlas of the
archbishopric of Cologne,
the* Prodromus
geographicus, *by Johannes
Michael Gigas, Cologne,
c. 1620. The so-called*
Pauluskarte *is one of the
most elusive of all curiosa.*

PLATE 11.4 *(opposite,
bottom)* Geography
Bewitched! *or, a droll
caricature map of
Scotland, printed by Bowles
and Carver, London,
c. 1780. Ingenious in
design, Scotland is depicted
in jocular mood as a hunch-
backed clown.*

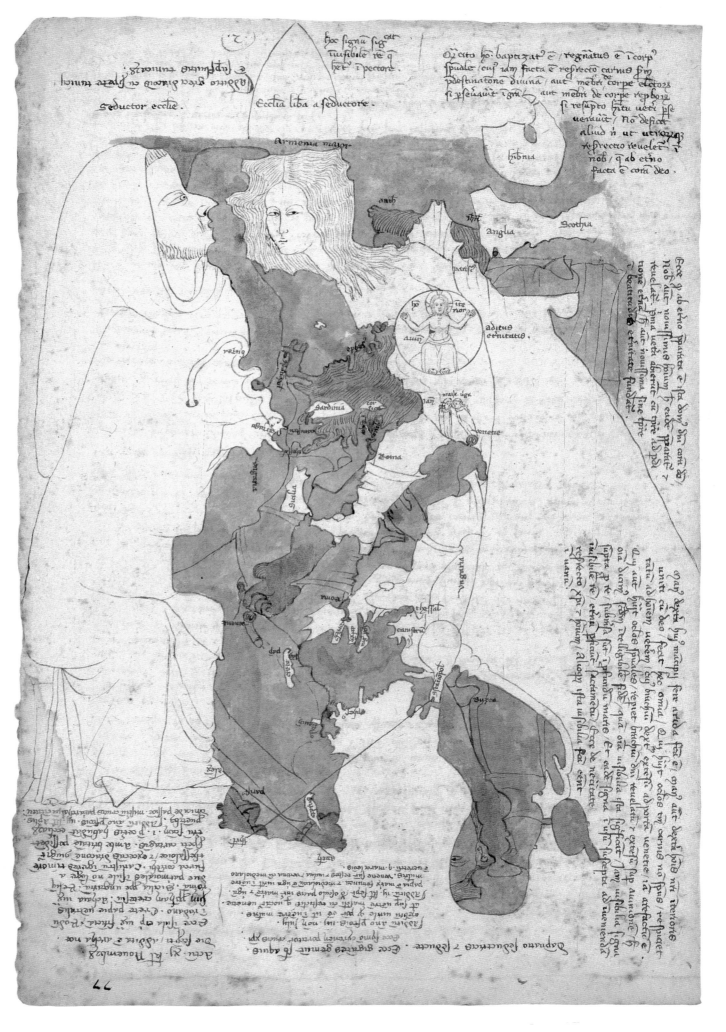

The idea of combining a map with a human or animal figure was known before the application of printing became widespread in the West. For example, during the fourteenth century, Opicinus de Canistris depicted the Mediterranean in a human form. Somewhat later came the famous caricature of Europe as *Europa regina* (Plate 11.2), sometimes also seen as *Europa . . . in forma virginis*, after Johann ('Bucius') Putsch (1516–1542), which was widely published throughout Europe in the sixteenth century. The outlines of the continent form the robes of an imperial monarch, the crowned head of whom is the Iberian peninsula – presumably to symbolize the view that Spain was the crown of Europe. The right hand carries the orb (Sicily), the left the sceptre, which touches the British Isles, thus symbolizing an alliance between Charles V and Henry VIII.

Another remarkable example of the portrayal of a person in cartographic form is found in the very rare atlas of Johannes Michael Riese (known as Gigas). His *Prodromus geographicus hoc est Archiepiscopatus Coloniensis . . . descriptio nova* was published in Cologne by Abraham Hogenberg in 1620. The map in question is the so-called *Pauluskarte* (Plates 11.1 11.3). Here, the apostle Paul is, in a highly imaginative manner, superimposed on a map of the region around Münster in northwestern Germany. The map, properly entitled *Aspice Paulinam Pauli sub imagine gente*, is dedicated to Archbishop Ferdinand I of Cologne.

A later instance of the human form doing cartographical service is found in Olof Rudbeck's work *Laponia illustrata*, published in 1701, which describes the author's journeys through Lapland. In Rudbeck's depiction of the Baltic region, the arms of the Baltic Sea suggested to him the outline of Charon, the ancient ferryman of Styx:

He put me in mind of what has been affirmed by some Modern Authors of the Shape or whole extent of the *Baltick* Sea, to represent the posture of a Gyant, which, if taken with some grains of allowance, may perhaps challenge the same probability, as the Representations made by some Geographers of other countries; as of *Europe*, like a *Virgin*; of *Holland*, like a *Lyon &c*. Take then this vast tract of our *Baltick* Sea . . . you will find it to represent an exact Map, the shape of an Old Gyant bending his Head forward, with a crooked Back.[2]

Geography Bewitched!
or, a droll *Caricature MAP of* SCOTLAND.
London.Printed for Bowles & Carver, No.69 St.Pauls Church Yard, 4 June 1794.

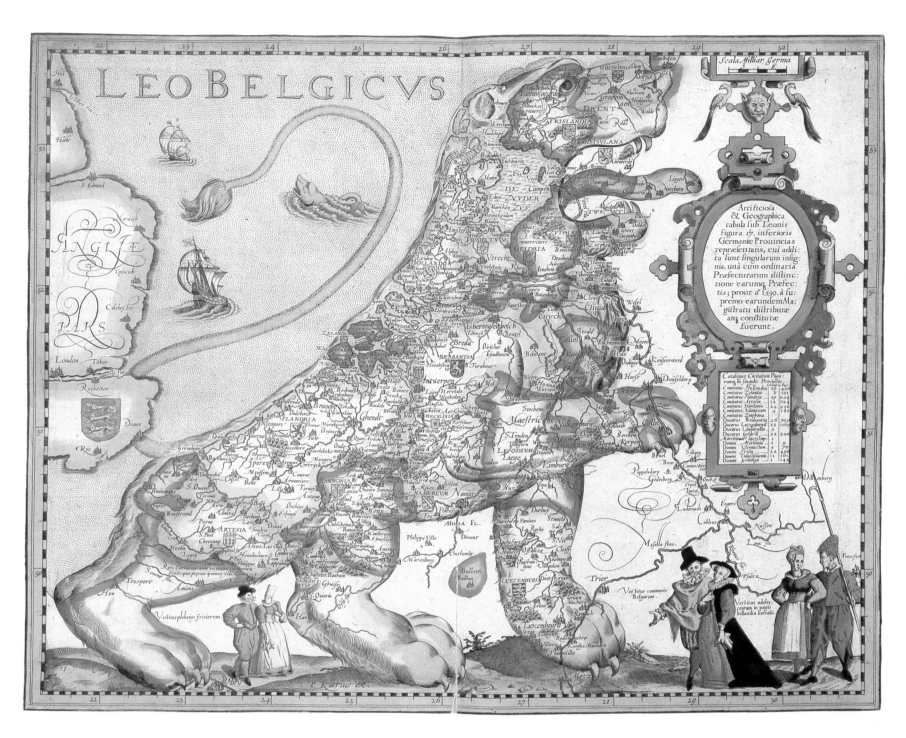

PLATE 11.5 De Leone
Belgico *by Michael
Eitzinger, c. 1590. The
lion is a symbol of the
emerging power of the
Netherlands (the beast
figures on most of the
provincial arms). The* Leo
Belgicus *is one of the most
popular and enduring of
cartographic curiosities.*

In England maps of the British Isles, under the
general title of *Geography Bewitched!*, were published in 1780. Ingenious in design, England
appears as a jolly, pipe-smoking, beer-swilling
character astride a large fish, while Scotland is
depicted as a hunch-backed clown seated on a large
rock (Plate 11.4). During the nineteenth century,
a delightful series of cartoon maps called *Geographical Fun. Humourous Outlines of Various Countries*, devised by William Harvey (who wrote
under the pseudonym 'Aleph'), was published in
1869. The series comprises twelve vividly
chromolithographed 'maps' designed to represent
the character of a nation in the form of a caricature. Thus, England is represented by Britannia
and Prussia by the figure of Friedrich Wilhelm
kneeling before Bismarck, who is himself looking
eastwards. Further south, Garibaldi looms over

Corsica and Sardinia, represented by the papal
crown and the Pope respectively.

Animal and plant maps

The depiction of an animal in cartographical form
is much less common than the use of the human
form. Even so, the most celebrated of all cartographical curiosities must be the so-called *Leo
Belgicus*, which made its first appearance in 1583
in *De Leone Belgico, eiusque topographica atque
historica descriptione*, by the Austrian historian,
Michael Eitzinger.[3] The inspiration for the idea
of the *Leo Belgicus* may not now be immediately
obvious, but it is the pictorial symbolization of the
strength of the United Netherlands. After all, the
lion has long been a symbol of power and strength
throughout history – think of the famous Lion

PLATE 11.6 Leo Belgicus
by Johannes van Deutecum,
first issued in 1598. The
portraits of Phillip II of
Spain, Margaret of Parma,
the Duke of Alva, Don
Juan of Austria and others
are included in the borders to
symbolize the then struggle
for power exacted in this
corner of Europe.

PLATE 11.7 A version of
the Leo Belgicus by C.J.
Visscher, issued c. 1611–
1621. The seated lion
symbolizes the Twelve-Year
Truce (1609–1621)
between Spain and the
United Netherlands. This is
the second state with slightly
trimmed borders.

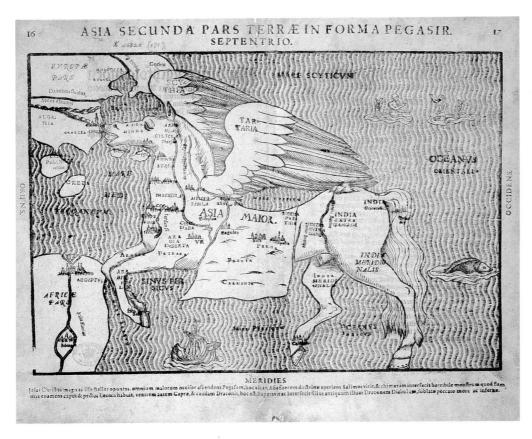

PLATE 11.8 *(above)*
Asia secunda pars terrae
in forma Pegasir *from
the biblical travel book*
Itinerarium sacrae
scripturae *by Heinrich
Bünting, 1581. A highly
imaginative view of Asia
which requires considerable
imagination to see the form
of the continent or vice
versa.*

Gate at Mycenae, the city of Agamemnon, the earliest recorded coat of arms, dating back to about 1800 BC. Also, many of the individual provinces of the United Netherlands bore a lion in one form or another in their own crests, so drawing the whole country in the shape of the animal would appear, logically, to be an outward graphic representation of that unity and strength. With the benefit of four centuries of hindsight, the political outline of the Netherlands and Belgium in the late sixteenth century could well suggest the outline of a crouched lion.

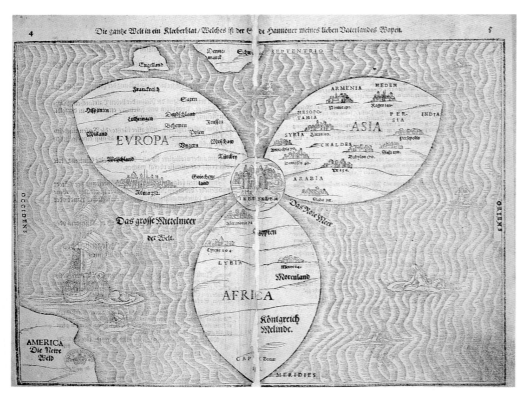

Several variants of the *Leo Belgicus* were made over the decades (Plates 11.5, 11.6, 11.7), but the only version to enjoy a wide circulation was that of Famiano Strada, who used the design for the engraved title-page of his history of the Dutch wars, *De Bello Belgico*, published in Rome in 1632. This is the most frequently encountered version of the 'map', illustrating as it did some ninety editions of Strada's book in Latin, French, Italian, Spanish, Dutch and English published between 1632 and 1794.

The *Itinerarium sacrae scripturae* of Heinrich Bünting, first published in 1581, is well known for its illustrations. This work, a popular account of the geography of the Bible written in the form of a travel book, also contained cartographical oddities. Asia was drawn in the form of Pegasus (Plate 11.8) and the world was depicted in the distorted outline of a clover-leaf (Plate 11.9) – *Die gantze Welt in ein Kleberblatt, Welches in der Stadt Hannover, meines lieben Vaterlandes Wapen.* In this 'map' the centre of the leaf is the holy city of Jerusalem and the three petals surrounding it form the continents of Asia, Africa and Europe, the design of the whole alluding to the crest of Bünting's home town, Hannover.

Political maps

The many wars throughout Europe in the nineteenth century spawned a series of political cartoon maps by Frederick W. Rose. One of the best known examples of these is the *Serio-Comic War Map for the Year 1877* (Plate 11.11), which shows Europe under threat from Russia. The latter is depicted as an octopus with its tentacles reaching out to grasp the most accessible parts of the European continent. One wounded tentacle is labelled as Crimea, recalling the defeat in the Crimean War. Other tentacles reach out to the Balkans, another encircles Poland and yet another has Finland in its grasp. Many years later, in 1899, Rose made another version of the 'octopus map', this time called *Angling in Troubled Waters.* This version shows several countries of Europe represented by portraits of their monarchs or national characters. Tsar Nicholas II draws in the parts of his vast empire on fishing lines, John Bull

(continued on page 339)

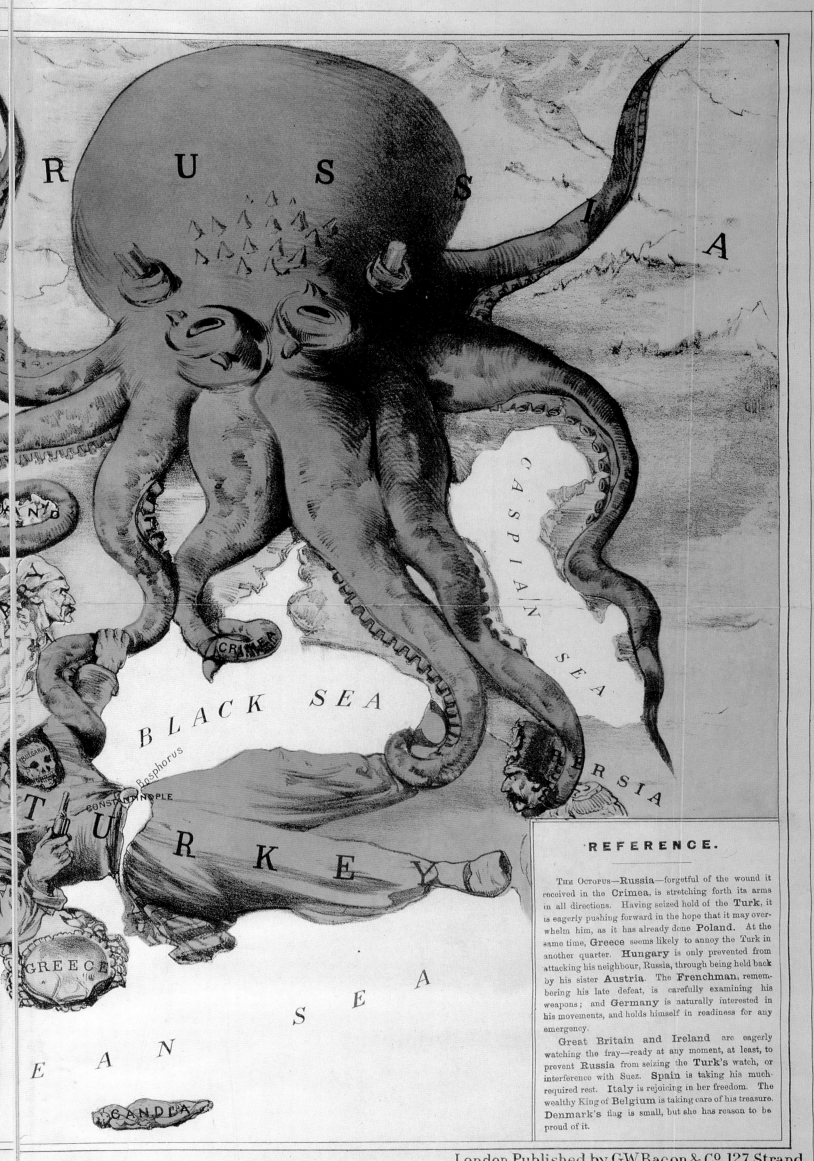

REFERENCE.

THE OCTOPUS—Russia—forgetful of the wound it received in the Crimea, is stretching forth its arms in all directions. Having seized hold of the Turk, it is eagerly pushing forward in the hope that it may overwhelm him, as it has already done Poland. At the same time, Greece seems likely to annoy the Turk in another quarter. Hungary is only prevented from attacking his neighbour, Russia, through being held back by his sister Austria. The Frenchman, remembering his late defeat, is carefully examining his weapons; and Germany is naturally interested in his movements, and holds himself in readiness for any emergency.

Great Britain and Ireland are eagerly watching the fray—ready at any moment, at least, to prevent Russia from seizing the Turk's watch, or interference with Suez. Spain is taking his much-required rest. Italy is rejoicing in her freedom. The wealthy King of Belgium is taking care of his treasure. Denmark's flag is small, but she has reason to be proud of it.

London, Published by G.W. Bacon & Cº, 127, Strand.

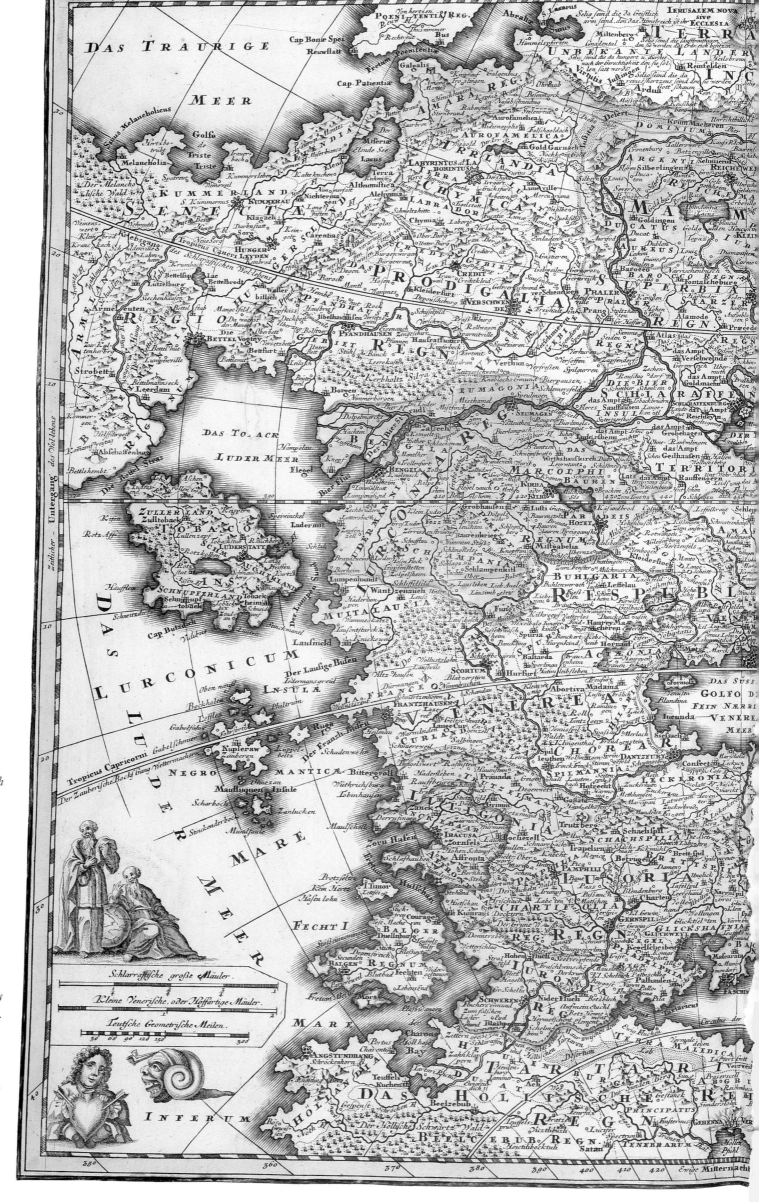

PLATE 11.9 *(opposite below)* Die gantze Welt in ein Kleberblatt *by Heinrich Bünting, 1581. Bünting sought to honour his home town of Hannover by this clover-leaf 'map' of the world. The clover leaf appears on the town's crest.*

PLATE 11.10 *(right)* Accurata Utopiae Tabula . . . Schlaraffenlandes Neu-erfundene lächerliche Land-Tabell *by Matthäus Seutter, c. 1740. Seutter's imaginary Schlaraffenland was a land of vice, made up of nineteen countries, each the fount of a particular vice or sin.*

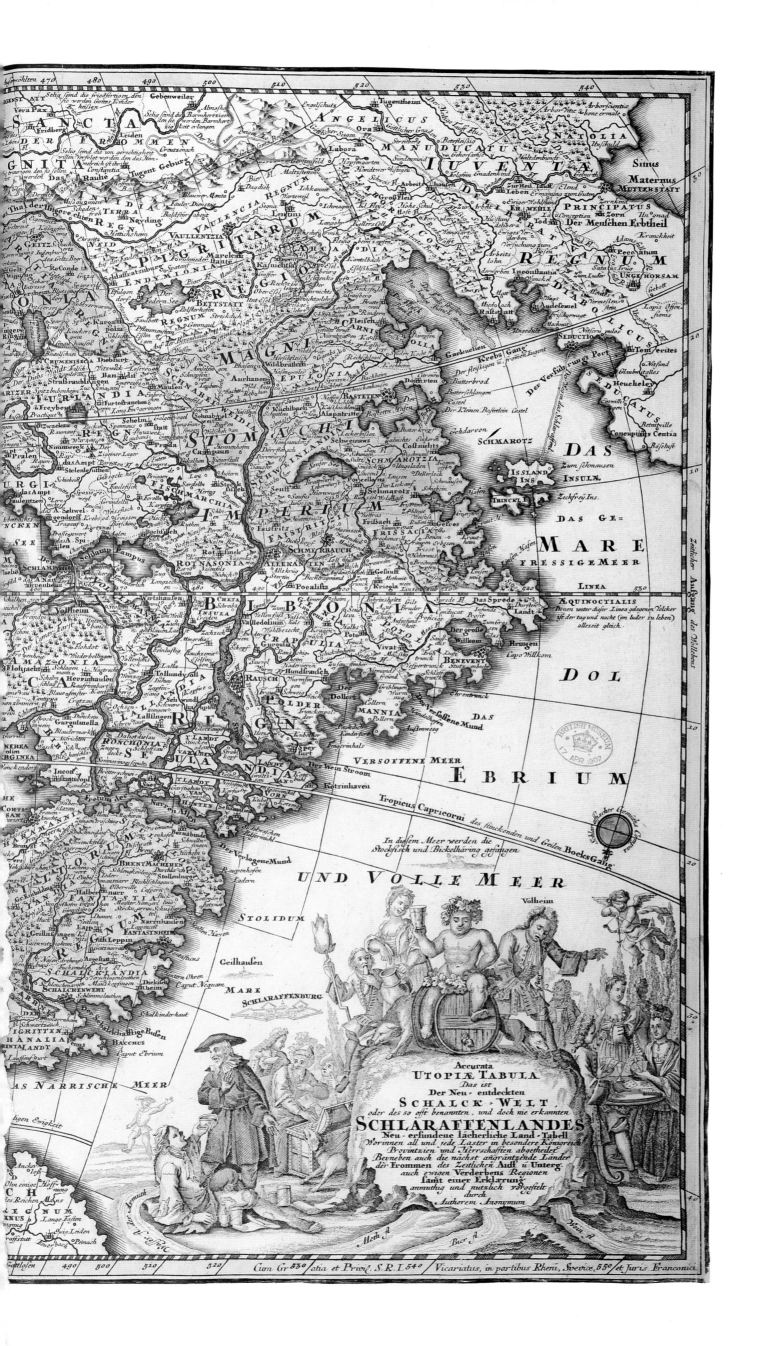

Accurata
UTOPIÆ TABULA
Das ist
Der Neu-entdeckten
SCHALCK-WELT
oder des so offt benannten, und doch nie erkannten
SCHLARAFFENLANDES
Neu-erfundene lächerliche Land-Tabell
Worinnen all und jede Laster in besondere Königreich
Provintzien und Herrschafften abgetheilet
Beyneben auch die nächst angräntzende Länder
der Frommen des Zeitlichen Auff u. Unterg.
auch ewigen Verderbens Regionen
samt einer Erklärung
annuthig und nutzlich vorgestellt
durch
Authorem Anonymum

SERIO-COMIC WAR MAP
FOR THE YEAR 1877.
BY F. W. ROSE.

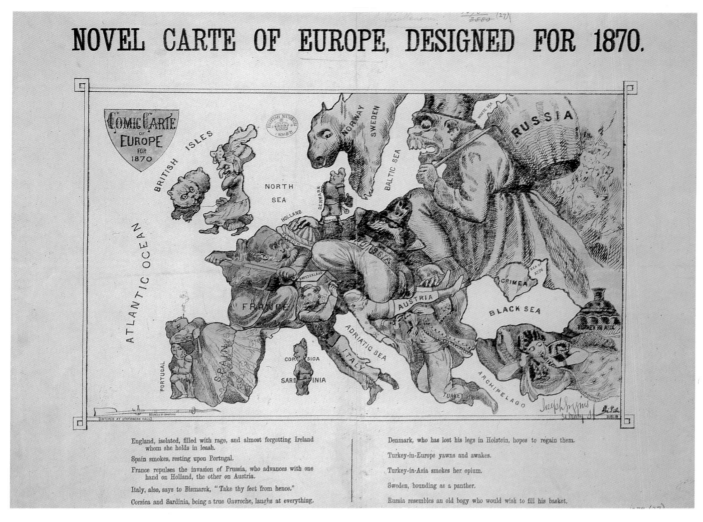

NOVEL CARTE OF EUROPE, DESIGNED FOR 1870.

England, isolated, filled with rage, and almost forgetting Ireland whom she holds in leash.

Spain smokes, resting upon Portugal.

France repulses the invasion of Prussia, who advances with one hand on Holland, the other on Austria.

Italy, also, says to Bismarck, "Take thy feet from hence."

Corsica and Sardinia, being a true Gavroche, laughs at everything.

Denmark, who has lost his legs in Holstein, hopes to regain them.

Turkey-in-Europe yawns and awakes.

Turkey-in-Asia smokes her opium.

Sweden, bounding as a panther.

Russia resembles an old bogy who would wish to fill his basket.

stands angling in the North Sea and the Turkish sultan angles for Crete in the Mediterranean, having lost the island to Greece after the war of 1897. Meanwhile, Spain looks wistfully out into the Atlantic, mourning the loss of the last of her once-substantial American colonies in 1898.

Myth and fantasy

Cartographical myth and fantasy play a part in several maps available to the collector today. In this respect, the west coast of North America occupies centre stage, in the form of the 'island' of California, a notorious example of geographical confusion. During the sixteenth century California appeared, correctly, as a large peninsula of North America. During the seventeenth and eighteenth centuries, however, that peninsula was cast adrift into the Pacific to become a large island.

Practically every mapmaker of note included a map of the 'island' of California in his atlases in one form of outline or another, from the 1620s until the end of the eighteenth century. In 1625 the English collection of voyages and travels by Samuel Purchas, called *Purchas His Pilgrimes*, included an engraved map of North America after

Henry Briggs titled *The North Part of America . . . and upon ye West the large and goodly Iland of California*. The map incorporates the legend:

California sometimes supposed to be a part of ye western continent but since a Spanish Charte taken by ye Hollanders it is found to be a goodly Ilande: the length of the west shoare beeing about 500 leagues from Cape Mendocino to the South Cape there of Called Cape St Lucas: as appeareth both by that Spanish Chart and by the relation of Francis Gaule whereas in the ordinairie Charts it is sett downe to be 1,700 Leagues.[4]

This map is one of the most notorious in the history of North American cartography (Plate 11.14). It was compiled from information collected by Sebastian Vizcaino and Antonio de la Ascensión from the Spanish expedition to the west coast in 1602, for the purpose of locating a safe haven for the fleets out of the Spanish colony of the Philippines. Henry Briggs wrote his *Treatise of the Northwest Passage to the South Sea* in 1622, based on that Spanish account, stating that California was 'found to be a goodly Ilande', after having claimed to have seen a map captured by the Dutch navigators which showed the peninsula separate

PLATE 11.13 The Evil
Genius of Europe by W.
Coney, tinted lithograph,
London, 1859. Napoleon
III is here portrayed as 'the
evil genius' threatening to
expel Austria from northern
Italy, and about to try on the
Italian boot.

from the American mainland. Since the northern extent of the Gulf of California was as yet unexplored, it was only natural to believe that it might possibly join the Pacific Ocean, thereby rendering California indeed as an island.

A lesser-known cartographical oddity which occurs from time to time in collections, and in some eighteenth-century German composite atlases, is a map of an imaginary land, Schlaraffenland, which at a glance might be taken for a distorted outline of part of Sweden and Denmark.

A good example of a map of Schlaraffenland is included in an atlas issued by Matthäus Seutter during the 1740s (Plate 11.10). According to Seutter, Schlaraffenland was a utopia – a land of idleness and luxury. G. Hill comments:

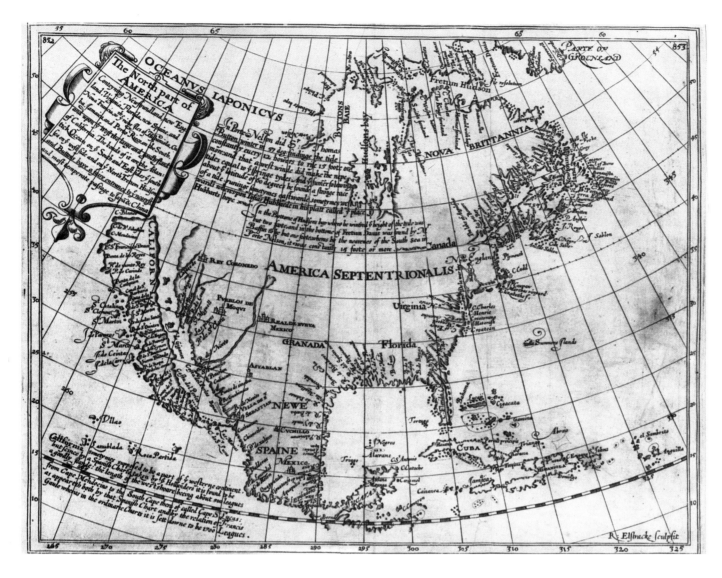

The best known description of it [Schlaraffenland] is in a poem by the sixteenth-century Meistersinger Hans Sachs, who stresses the elements of food, money and lethargy. Chickens, geese and pigeons fly around ready cooked, waiting to be eaten with a minimum of effort, and every house is surrounded by a hedge of sausage. Seutter's map expands this considerably, his Schlaraffenland becomes the land of all vice. It is made up of nineteen different countries, each the home of a particular vice, and is surrounded by four others: the kingdoms of Youth and Old Age, Terra Sancta Incognita, and Tartari Regnum – the nether regions. Altogether these lands fill a complete hemisphere from 360° to 540° longitude [and therefore physically impossible!]. The geography of the various countries is worked out in great detail, and is described at length in a 396-page book that was published at the same time in about 1730. The numerous place-names on the map are nearly all puns, such as Alamode, Bacchanalia and Cortisan; many of them are extremely crude. To the north is New Jerusalem, in the unknown country of the pious; to the south is the kingdom of Hell, where all the inhabitants of Schlaraffenland will eventually arrive . . .[5]

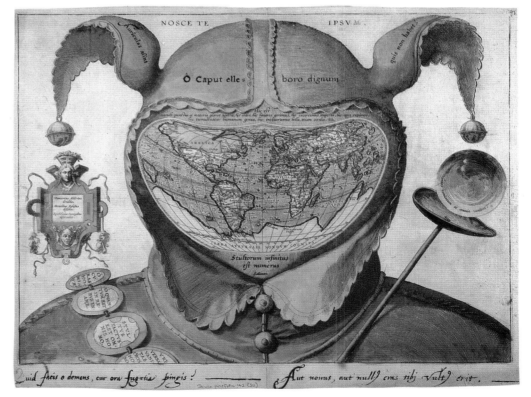

References
1. P.D.A. Harvey, *Medieval Maps*, page 19, 1991.
2. G. Hill, *Cartographical Curiosities*, page 41, 1978.
3. H.A.M. van der Heijden, *Leo Belgicus*, page 9ff, 1990; also R.V. Tooley, *Leo Belgicus. An Illustrated List*, Map Collectors' series 7, 1963.
4. Samuel Purchas, *Purchas His Pilgrimes*, 1625.
5. G. Hill, *op. cit.*, page 58.

CHAPTER XII

AESTHETICS

1400 – 1750 AD

CARTOGRAPHY IS OFTEN considered to be an art form in its own right and the story of maps is in many ways a reflection of the changes in art history over the years. Maps are collected today as much for their aesthetic appeal as for their historical interest. Since the Second World War, and with the publication of many books and articles on old maps, there has been a considerable increase of interest in the collecting of old maps both for decorative purposes and for financial investment. Many fine collections, general and specialized, have been formed by private individuals as well as institutions over the years for various purposes: to study the historical geography of a particular region, be it an English colony, a French province or a German dukedom; to research into the spread of settlement across the New World; or to investigate changing ideas about the shape of the world.

PLATE 12.1 *Detail of* Carta marina et descriptio septentrionalium terrarum . . . Anno D[omi]ni *1539 by Olaus Magnus, woodcut on nine sheets, Venice, 1539. This was the most important map of the northern regions, and the source map for generations of cartographers throughout the sixteenth and early seventeenth centuries. The map is remarkable for its wealth of picturesque detail, the knowledge embodied therein and the very art of its execution. It is reproduced here from a modern hand-coloured facsimile, and is shown in its entirety overleaf, top.*

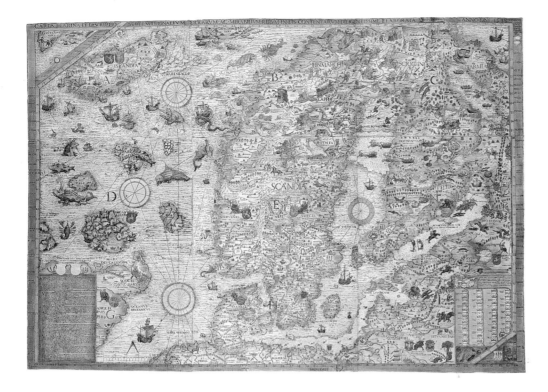

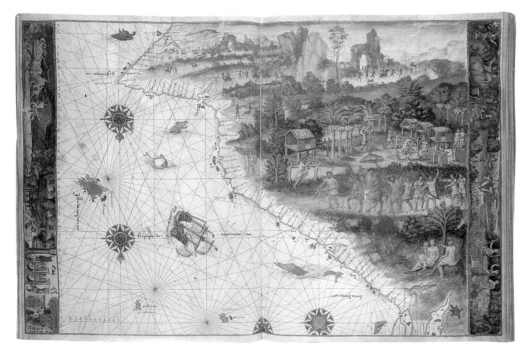

However, the idea of using maps as a means of embellishing one's own domestic surroundings is by no means a new one. Dr John Dee, the Elizabethan mathematician and mystic, described in 1570 the reasons why people acquired maps:

Some, to beautify their Halls, Parlors, Chambers, Galeries, Studies, or Libraries with, some other for their own journeys directing into far lands, or to understand other men's travels, liketh, loveth, getteth, and useth, Maps, Charts, and Geographical Globes . . .[1]

If a dozen map collectors are asked why they collect or study maps, they will very likely give a dozen different answers, all of them justifiable. Indeed, such a simple survey could be taken of over a hundred people, and the same result might be obtained. Ptolemy himself, considered the differing concerns of geography (relating to the entire world) and chorography (relating to particular places): using the analogy of a portrait, he stated that geography deals with the description of the entire head, chorography with individual features such as the eyes or the ears. If the maxim that Nature abhors a vacuum is accepted, then blank uncharted spaces on maps were not acceptable to the eye of the beholder. Mercator and many of his contemporaries gave the public value for money in this sense. What better way, for instance, of balancing the lands surrounding the North Pole than by placing a vast continent in the Antipodes, centred upon the South Pole? Such cartographic imagination had to wait another two centuries to be verified as cartographic fact, but in the meantime the mysterious *Terra incognita* in the south was to provide a rich source of ideas with which to fill and decorate maps. Of course, the mapmakers' creativity need not — and did not — stop with 'imaginary' continents. Like all good

PLATE 12.2 *(left, top)* Carta marina et descriptio septentrionalium terrarum . . . Anno D[omi]ni *1539 by Olaus Magnus, woodcut on nine sheets, Venice, 1539.*

PLATE 12.3 *(left, centre) Part of Java la Grande on an anonymous chart probably made in Dieppe in about 1547, from the so-called 'Vallard atlas'. The work is crowded with ethnographic details, including a busy village scene.*

PLATE 12.4 *(left, bottom)* Islandia *by Abraham Ortelius from the* Theatrum Orbis Terrarum, *Antwerp, 1585. This highly decorative and fanciful map of Iceland features a fantastic collection of sea monsters. Note also the polar bears balancing on icebergs at top right.*

craftspeople, these early mapmakers took pride in their work and often decorated their maps to improve their appearance (Plates 12.1, 12.2, 12.3, 12.4). Gradually, some maps became of interest for their appearance alone.

Early printing techniques

To appreciate the aesthetics of old maps one must first understand the methods of production available at the time. Most of the old maps which become available to the collector are printed by one of several methods (Plates 12.5, 12.6). Each of these methods has its own characteristics which impose particular features on the finished product. Broadly speaking, these methods or processes fall into three groups: the relief process, the intaglio process and the design process. In the relief method, the design to be inked is left in relief, the unprinted parts being cut away from the surface of the woodblock or engraved metal plate. In the intaglio process, the design is engraved on a metal plate, such as copper or brass, by the use of a graving tool (as in line-engraving) or eaten out with an acid (as in etching). Afterwards, the plate is inked, the surplus ink wiped off, and the plate is then passed through a press with a sheet of dampened paper which draws up the ink in the incised lines of the design on the metal. In the surface process, the design is drawn, rather than cut or engraved, on a specially prepared surface, such as that of a lithographic stone.

One feature common to all of these processes is that the design (including, of course, all lettering) is drawn in reverse on the plate or block. The technique of drawing or cutting all of the design and lettering for a map demanded considerable skill. It was a time-consuming process and any errors had to be carefully expunged from the plate or block to ensure that as little trace as possible would be left on the finished printed map. Manuscript maps and charts, of course, required no printing process, but the skills needed to make a usable map were no less exacting.

The process used in the printing of a map can sometimes be a clue to the date of its production. Both the woodcut (or relief) process and the copper-plate engraving (or intaglio) process date from the earliest period of the application of printing in mapmaking, around the late fifteenth and early sixteenth centuries. Woodcuts had some

initial advantages which made them more popular with the early mapmakers. The technique had already had a long period of trial and development by the time the first maps came to be printed. In Europe, those towns and cities where wood-engraving flourished as an art (such as Nuremberg, Strasbourg, Basel and Augsburg) were also the places where geographical science was particularly developed. To make an impression from a cut woodblock inked up for printing requires less pressure than printing from an engraved metal plate. Therefore a simpler kind of press could be used, often less expensive and cumbersome to set up than its metal counterpart. Much pressure has to be brought to bear upon an inked metal plate in order to force the paper to take up the design

PLATE 12.5 *A typical letterpress printer's workshop by Abraham von Werdt, woodcut, c. 1660. The two printers on the right are inking the letterpress type-formes with leather ink-pads. At centre can be seen the boxes containing types.*

PLATE 12.6 *(below) Interior of an intaglio printer's workshop, by Abraham Bosse, etching, Paris, c. 1642.*

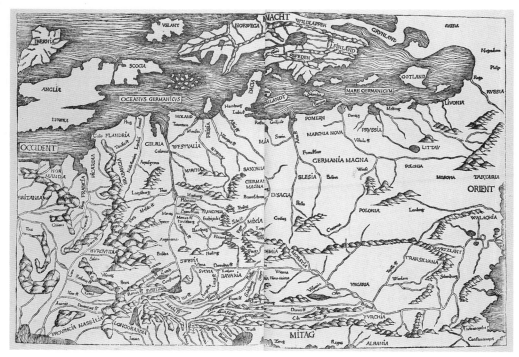

PLATE 12.7 *A map of central and eastern Europe from the* Nuremberg Chronicle, *woodcut, compiled, designed and printed at Nuremberg in 1493 after Hieronymus Münzer. It is one of the earliest obtainable printed maps of the region, but it does repeat errors from an earlier manuscript drawn some time between 1439 and 1454.*

cleanly (Plate 12.6). Both the cut woodblock and any type for letterpress to be printed on a map had their printing surfaces in quite sharp relief. Both could be fitted together in a printer's forme and the map and text printed off in one operation, with obvious benefits in terms of cost and time. Most early printed maps, from the late fifteenth century onwards, appeared in books, so that if any maps were to be printed from engraved metal plates for inclusion in a book, the printer was required to put the sheets through his press at least a second time in order to print maps and illustrations in

those spaces expressly left in the letterpress. It is largely because of this factor that metal engraving as a medium for the production of maps came to perfection later on in the sixteenth century with the rise in demand for sheet maps and, more particularly, atlas maps.

Although printing from both woodblocks and metal plates was already in use by the time the first printed maps appeared, it was some years before these techniques began to be applied to the reproduction of maps in books. Among the earliest printed maps were those copied from the illustrated manuscripts of the latter Middle Ages, such as the diagrammatic world maps of Isidore of Seville (Plate 2.2) and Macrobius, or the maps inspired by the ideas of Ptolemy. An early edition of Ptolemy with maps was printed from copper-engraved plates at Bologna in 1477, and another at Rome in 1478 (reprinted in 1490, 1507 and 1508), but these represented almost the entire output of maps produced from metal plates during the fifteenth and sixteenth centuries. It is true, therefore, that the woodcut method held sway as the medium for the production of printed maps for several decades to come, until well into the middle of the sixteenth century, despite the fine technical achievement of the use of metal plates in the editions of Ptolemy's maps (see Chapter V).

PLATE 12.8 *Detail of* Venetie M.D. *by Jacopo de'Barbari, woodcut, six sheets, Venice, 1500. One of the most striking town views ever published. Contrast de'Barbari's work with the woodcuts issued only a few years previously in the* Nuremberg Chronicle *of 1493 (above).*

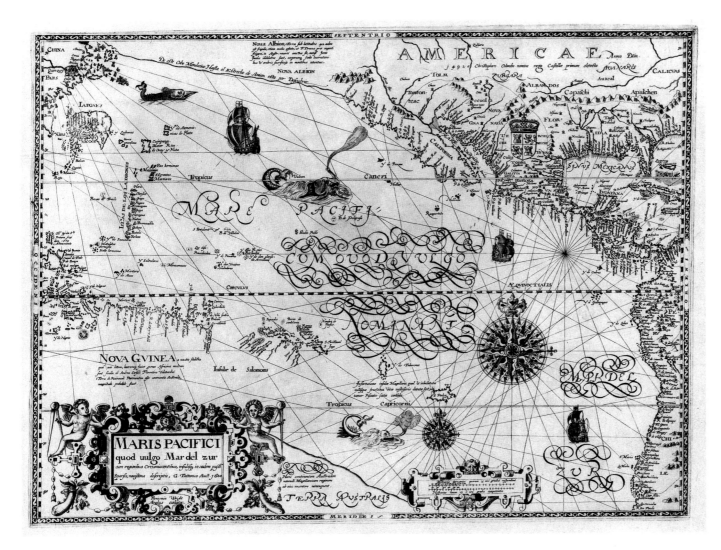

PLATE 12.9 Maris Pacifici quod vulgo Mar del Zur *by Gabriel Tatton, copper engraving, London, 1600. Note the fine features of this copper engraving: the subtle shading and profuse ornamental detail.*

The tonal range which could be achieved by the use of woodblocks was considerably more limited than that which could be achieved with metal plates (Plates 12.7). In general, a woodcut surface has only two tones, black and white, but a skilled block-cutter could often create remarkable effects by the use of shading techniques, such as stippling or line-shading. A glance at the great plan view of Venice made in 1500 by Jacopo de' Barbari reveals the work's almost incredible detail and accuracy, created in the new realistic style of the time in Italy (Plate 12.8). The metal engraver, on the other hand, could achieve far more subtle ranges of shading, lettering and detail by using the fine point of his engraving tool, ideally suited to the profuse and often robust detail of Renaissance ornament (Plate 12.9). He could also work much faster than the woodblock-cutter, thereby placing him at an advantage in terms of his output, in spite of the fact that the woodcut was as yet cheaper and simpler to produce.

Maps in books, either as text illustrations or as maps bound in separately from the letterpress, continued to be printed from woodblocks for many years. Until the end of the sixteenth cen-tury, and even into the seventeenth century in some Italian towns, they were found in important books and geographical texts which had a life parallel to those of the maps and early atlases printed from engraved metal plates. In this re-spect, one of the most important and most widely used books of its day was the *Cosmographia universalis* by Sebastian Münster of Basel. This book was printed in many editions and in many translations between 1550 and 1628, some of the original woodblocks being used throughout the entire period. Indeed, in the editions published after 1588 there was even a group of woodcut maps of the modern world cut in the 'copperplate' style in emulation of the copper-engraved maps in the *Theatrum orbis terrarum* atlas of Abraham Ortelius, first published in 1570.

A feature which prolonged the life of many woodblocks used for map production, Münster's included, was the use of lettering printed from cast metal type, or from stereotype plates cut from lines of cast type inserted into slots cut in the surface of the woodblock. The technique had obvious commercial advantages in that it saved considerable time and money, but the effects were frequently crude in both execution and appearance. Anything up to 3,000 impressions might be taken from a woodblock in the production runs of popular works, such as those of Münster. Nevertheless, woodcut maps have a particular charm and quaintness of their own and sometimes the very technique can impart a sense of age far beyond the reality. Because of this, such maps have a loyal following among many map collectors today.

By the middle of the sixteenth century, there was a wider demand in Europe for separately printed sheet maps. Mapmakers in the Netherlands, already accomplished in the working of different metals in the manufacture of nautical and scientific instruments, were able to meet this demand. The dimensions of the maps were sometimes very large, as in the case of the great world map of Mercator, printed in Duisburg in 1569, the *Nova et aucta orbis terrae descriptio ad usum navigantium emendate accomodata*, which was composed of eighteen sheets, and measured some 1,350 by 1,980 mm. One of the greatest and most influential maps ever compiled, it is a true work of art in its own right, complete with ornamental designs, allegorical figures and legends, ornamental ships and sea monsters, as well as legendary islands in the Atlantic Ocean – none of which, however decorative they were, has any real relevance to the actual geographical knowledge demonstrated by the map itself.

It is easy to disparage such features as mere space-fillers for want of more reliable information, but it would be wrong to dismiss the achievement represented by Mercator's map. To maintain a uniformity of line and lettering over such a large area was no mean feat, even for such an accomplished calligrapher as Mercator.

It was only in 1570, about a century after the appearance of the first printed maps in western Europe, that the production of maps from engraved copper plates, with descriptive text in letterpress to accompany each map, became established with the appearance of the *Theatrum orbis terrarum* atlas compiled by Abraham Ortelius (Plates 4.14, 4.15, 4.17, 12.12, 12.13, 12.14). While this move created a book of maps of more or less uniform appearance reflecting the style of its period, it also effectively fossilized the style of the maps in this atlas. Because the copper from which the plates were made was then, as now, an

expensive metal, the plates had to be treated with great care, and one plate may have had to serve for anything up to thirty or forty years. One curious result of this is that, in the case of Ortelius's atlas, the later editions (up to 1612) often contained maps which were first cut in 1570 and bound along with maps engraved only a half dozen years or so before, often in a quite different style.

The setting of the text on the versos of the maps created problems too. Type was scarce and very expensive in the sixteenth and seventeenth centuries. Immediately after a book was printed, the type had to be used again in the next book at the printer's establishment. Thus, a printer would be in the habit of making up large runs of sheets ready for future editions of an atlas or book. Very occasionally errors would occur, so that a map might be printed on a sheet bearing the description of another region. In such instances, a sheet of the correct text had to be cut up and pasted over the existing text. Such cases are, however, quite rare, which says much for the care these early printers took in assembling atlases and books: little was wasted, in order to recoup as much of the initial financial investment as possible.

Sometimes, in an attempt to modernize an atlas without resorting to the heavy financial outlay of commissioning fresh plates, the old plates would be altered or retouched. For example, in the middle of the seventeenth century, when the plates of the Amsterdam publisher Joannes Janssonius were sold off, they were bought up by various other mapsellers and publishers for their own atlases. The outmoded cartouche designs and other decorative features of the styles of the 1630s and 1640s (when many of Janssonius's map plates were first engraved) were often hammered out of the plate and the map detail left intact. After this, new, more up-to-date designs of cartouche, vignette or other embellishment were then engraved on to the old plate in the space left by the hammering-out process. So it was that many of Janssonius's plates enjoyed a new lease of life in the atlases of Moses Pitt in the 1680s with embellishments in the more ornamental rococo style that was popular at the time.

To cite another example, some years ago an atlas compiled by the German map publishers Homann's Heirs of Nuremberg came to light. Nestling among the heavily engraved, robust designs of the German publisher's maps, each boldly coloured in bright washes and very much in the style common to German atlases of the first half of the eighteenth century, was a copy of Willem Blaeu's map of Frankfurt which was first issued in the 1630s. In itself, this was not unusual. Close examination of the plate, however, showed that it was but a shadow of its former glory; it was very worn, had been retouched in places and had also been coloured in the same manner as its companions in the atlas.

The Blaeu map, incidentally, also showed extensive signs of damage, with cracks and chips in the plate margins, evidence perhaps of the tragic damage suffered during the disastrous fire which broke out one night in February 1672 at Blaeu's printing house in Amsterdam, a fire which effectively put an end to his activities as the greatest map publisher of the day.

Colour

In discussing the aesthetics of old maps, one point arises perhaps more often than any other, the question of colour applied to the maps. Throughout the long history of printed maps, colour has been used to supplement and complement the

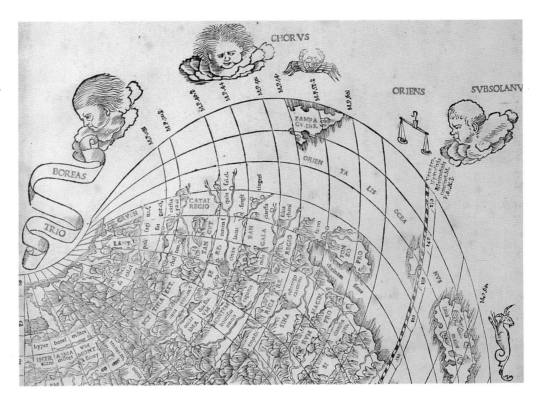

PLATE 12.10 *Detail of the cordiform world map from the Venice edition of Ptolemy, 1511. The map was printed in two colours and is an early example of the application of colour printing to map production.*

cartographic information and the symbols used. Very early engravers were often also accomplished miniaturists and painters who added colour to their products in the manner of illuminated manuscripts and charts. As a rule, however, most early woodcut maps and those maps produced in the fifteenth and sixteenth centuries by the Italians were issued and sold without applied colour. Italian mapmakers very rarely applied colours to their finely engraved maps, preferring the subtle use of the engraving tool to provide gradations of shade in their maps. These are beautifully engraved, but frequently sparse-looking, and often reminiscent of the severity of early Renaissance classical architectural books, books with which the mapmakers were no doubt familiar.

In the late fifteenth century, however, a tradition was set which is still in use today for maps printed in colour: blue was used for seas, lakes, rivers and other areas of water; woods and forests were painted green; roads were indicated in yellow or brown; houses, other buildings or town symbols would be coloured red or blue; mountains were shown in brown or ochre shading highlighted with red, and so on. Colours for boundaries were generally arbitrary in choice; or a combination of colours became peculiar to a particular mapmaker. The intention of applying colour was doubtless to catch the eye of the prospective purchaser. Publishers and mapsellers in those days were no less skilled at the job of selling their wares than are the high-powered advertisers of today.

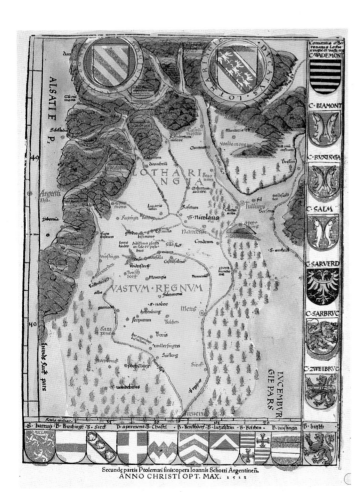

PLATE 12.11 *Lotharingia (Lorraine) from the edition of Ptolemy edited by Martin Waldseemüller, published at Strasbourg in 1513. The map, which is printed in three colours, red, black and ochre, is of great interest in the history of map printing as it illustrates the early desire for colour in map reproduction.*

PLATE 12.12 *(above)*
Flandriae comitatus
descriptio *by Abraham
Ortelius, copper engraving,
c. 1590. This striking map
of Flanders exemplifies
Ortelius's distinctive
colouring style. His maps
were hand-coloured in bold,
bright colours.*

PLATES 12.13, 12.14
*(opposite, top and bottom)
Two editions of* Americae
sive Novi Orbis, nova
descriptio *by Abraham
Ortelius, copper engraving,
c. 1570 (top) and c. 1585
(bottom). Note the gradual
changes in colouring style
and the altered outline of
South America.*

In 1570, Abraham Ortelius brought about a new development when he set up his business in Antwerp, describing himself as an *afzetter van kaerten* (colourist of maps). His atlases were hand-coloured in bold, bright, sometimes thickly applied colour, certainly intended to impress and to last, since some of his colours and colour combinations appear as bright today as they must have been during Ortelius's own time.

Over the forty or so years during which the *Theatrum* atlas was produced, gradual changes in the style of colouring were introduced, so that a print of a map issued in 1570 and coloured at the time can have a completely different appearance from a print of the same map issued in, say, 1603 and coloured in the style of that period. The *Atlas major* issued by the Blaeus in 1662 contains maps which were, at the time, anything up to fifty years

old, and almost unchanged. Early editions of the Blaeu atlas, from the single-volume *Appendix* of 1630 onwards, were coloured with darker — and somewhat richer — colours than those used in the later editions. It is quite true to say that, with care, the age of a coloured Blaeu map — or an Ortelius too for that matter — can be recognized by the manner in which it is coloured.

This is not to suggest, however, that colour was not used on maps before Ortelius. As early as 1511, an edition of Ptolemy was printed at Venice with woodcut maps printed in red and black (Plates 12.10), and two years afterwards another edition of Ptolemy was printed at Strasbourg by Johannes Schott, containing a map of Lorraine in three colours: black, red and ochre (Plates 12.11). This was a truly remarkable feat indeed, considering that problems of register — in other words,

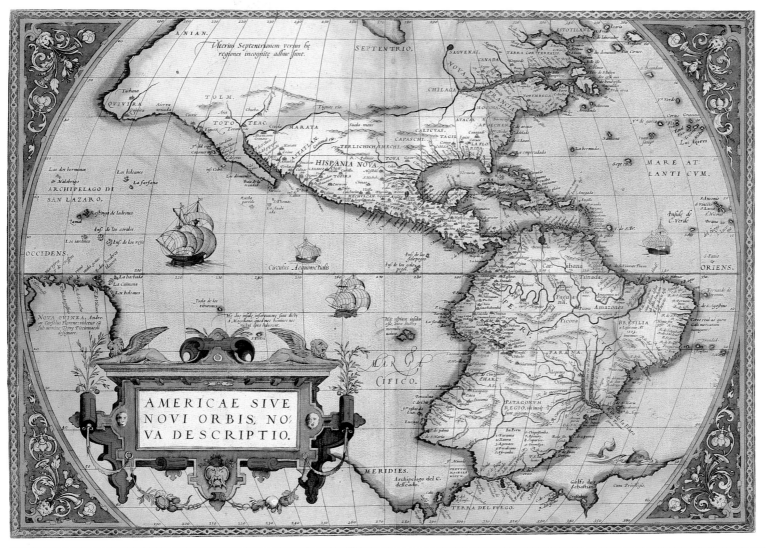

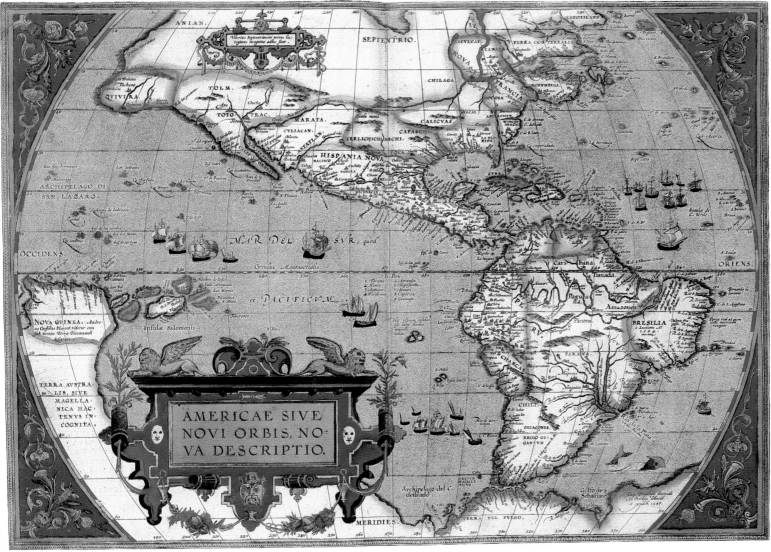

PLATE 12.15 *Effigies ampli regni auriferi Guineae in Africa, attributed to Luis Teixeira, Amsterdam, Huych Allard, 1602 or later. Engraved by Baptista van Deutecum, this remarkable and beautiful map shows considerable detail in the Senegal and Gold Coast regions after Portuguese sources.*

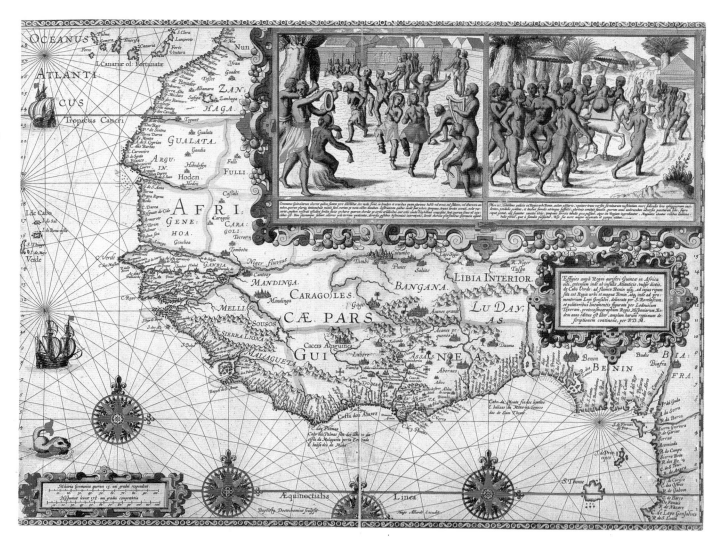

ensuring that colours were printed in the exact place on a map – were to keep map colouring a manual process until the real development of colour printing during the first half of the nineteenth century. When colours *were* used on maps in the early years of cartography, they were applied in flat washes.

Once again, it was in northern Europe, in the Netherlands, that the art of illumination was adapted and applied to the colouring of maps. Illumination developed to such an extent that it became an independent trade, practised by the St Luke's Guild at Antwerp, for example, where Ortelius worked. Specialists set up their own workshops to colour maps to order for private clients or for other publishers, so that maps could be had either plain or coloured. This trade is still active today, for there are many very fine colourists of maps and prints in business, emulating the styles and colours of the old craftsmen. There is, however, a certain cachet to maps in what is termed 'contemporary' colour – that is, colour applied at or about the time of the original printing of a map or print. Of course, as there are only finite quantities of old maps in circulation,

modern colourists will often produce strikingly beautiful examples of hand-colouring, taking much greater care to achieve the desired results than might have been the case with colourists working on larger quantities of the same maps in, say, the sixteenth century.

The Dutch and Flemish mapmakers continued to produce maps, during the seventeenth century in particular, which were ever more decorative, presenting their colourists with further opportunities to express their art (Plates 12.15, 12.21, 12.22). It became fashionable to use outline colours to complement the engraving of a map, with the cartouches and other decorative features richly coloured and frequently highlighted by the addition of gold or silver. Perhaps the best example of this type of work is that of the Amsterdam colourist Dirk van Santen. In the 1660s and 1670s, he coloured maps made by the leading mapmakers of the day, and even complete atlases intended for presentation to the nobility. Van Santen added large amounts of gold to his colouring, recalling the best of the manuscript illuminators of earlier times (Plate 10.8). The fretwork and tracery, the scrollwork of cartouches, and the little figures holding up banners were all depicted in brilliant colours. The polder atlases of the seventeenth and eighteenth centuries present further examples of the colouring skills of the Dutch tradition (Plate 12.16).

In 1701, John Smith wrote *The Art of Painting in Oyl*, in which he set out the manner of colouring certain features: '*Crowns*, or anything representing Gold with Yelloe . . . the Hair of Men or Women with Tincture of *Myrrh* . . . the flesh of Women or Boys, with very little of the Tincture of *Cochinele*, in a large Quantity of Water, and Garments either with thin Green shadowed with thicker . . . or with *Vermillion* shaded with *Carmine*'. For features such as sailing vessels, Smith suggested 'painting the Hull . . . with *Umber*, the Sails with Tincture of *Myrrh*, and the Flags with *Vermillion* or *Blue Bice*; and if they are represented as firing their Guns, let all the *Smoak* be done with very thin *Bice*'. Borders and other frame designs were to be treated thus: 'as for the Margent, or square stick of Degrees . . . which goes round the map, let that be coloured either with Yelloe or Red-lead, or Crimson, none but those three Colours serving well for this purpose'. Coats of arms and shields were to be brightly coloured and emblazoned in their correct colours and gilded if necessary; vignettes and illustrations of people and animals, instruments, produce, tools and anything else chosen to embellish the map were to have characteristic colouring 'according to the nature of it'.[2]

Beautiful as these originally coloured maps are, one of their main disadvantages is that of possible discoloration. Often, over the centuries, the pigments used in early colours slowly reacted with the natural moisture content of the paper and so caused discoloration, offsetting or even deterioration of the paper itself, problems which can require costly restoration processes. It used to be said that early colouring could be recognized by the fact that the verdigris pigments used in the making of green paints would, over the years, cause a brownish discoloration on the reverse of the maps or prints. While this is quite true in many cases, the rule does not always hold, as so much depends on the physical conditions under which a map is kept over the years. The better these conditions, the better the quality of paper used for the original printing and the greater the care with which the colours were applied, the less likely it is that deterioration will take place.

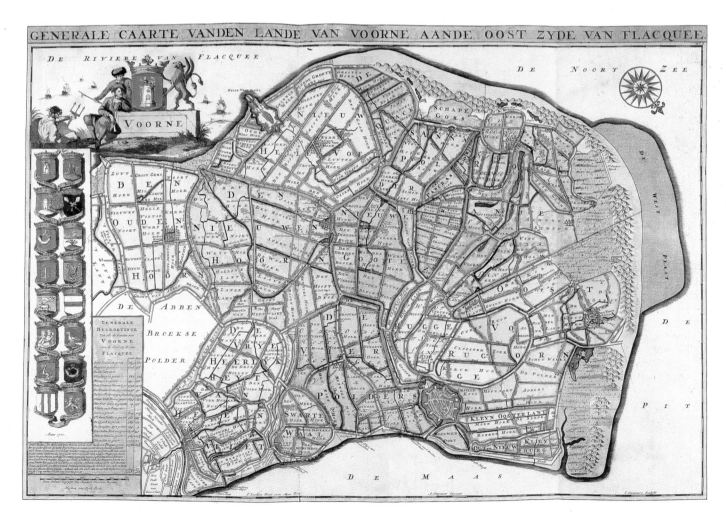

PLATE 12.16 Generale caarte vanden lande van Voorne aande oost zyde van Flacquee *by Heijman van Dijck, copper engraving, c. 1700. This striking polder map exemplifies the Dutch colourist skills of the period.*

353

PLATES 12.17, 12.18
(right and below) Ireland
*by Jan Baptist Vrients from
his later editions of
Ortelius's atlas, 1603 and
later, after Baptista
Boazio, 1599. Only three
examples of the original are
known to have survived.
Engraved by Renold
Elstrache, it has been
described as 'the earliest
English printed map of
Ireland with any pretensions
to detail'. This smaller
version,* Irlandiae accurata
descriptio *(Plate 12.17,
right) was used in the later
editions of Abraham
Ortelius's* Theatrum orbis
terrarum *after 1616. This
map includes fictitious
islands, such as 'Elstraches
ile' and 'Baptistes rock' off
the Ulster coast. Compare
the relative merits of both
coloured and uncoloured
editions.*

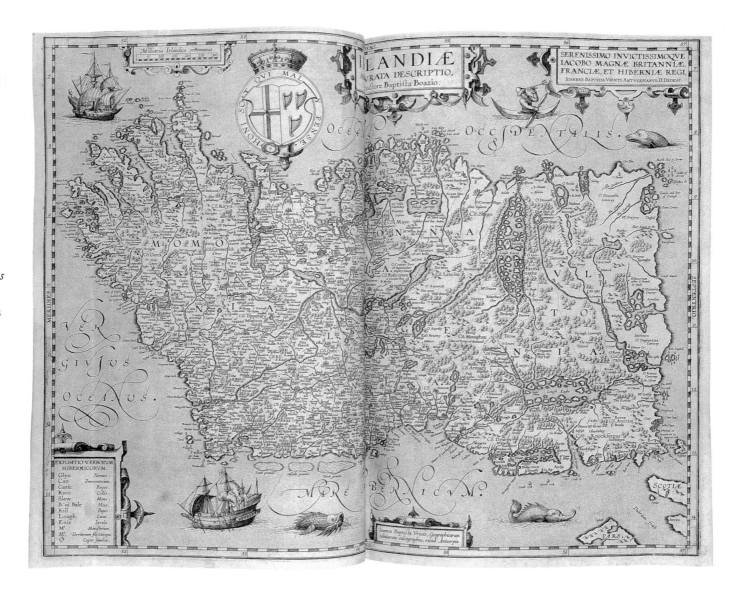

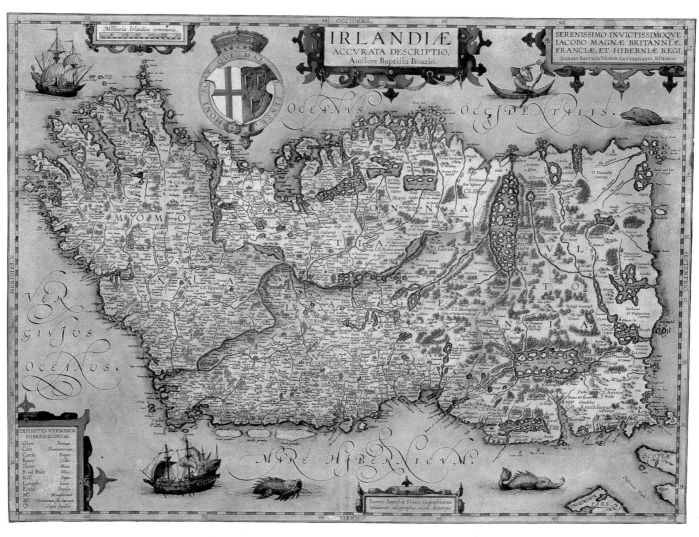

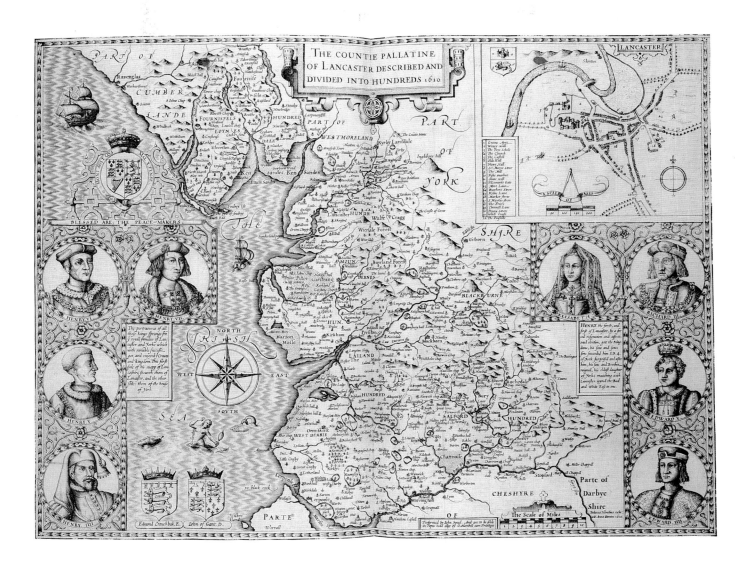

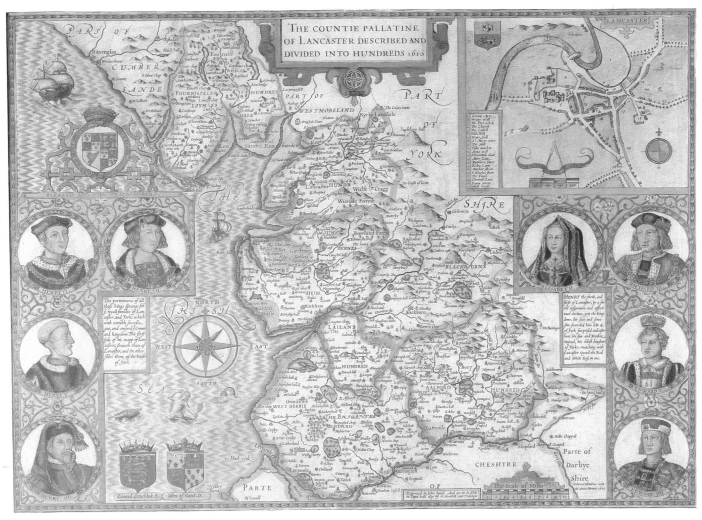

PLATES 12.19, 12.20 *(above and left) Two editions of* The Countie Pallatine of Lancaster *described by John Speed, copper engraving, London, 1611 and later. This beautiful map of Lancashire is taken from Speed's famous atlas,* Theatre of the Empire of Great Britaine. *Decorative features include portraits of the rival houses of the Lancastrians and Tudors. The inset town plan is a typical feature of Speed's county maps. Note the striking aesthetic effect of the early uncoloured edition: the finely engraved intense black linework is set against a creamy white background.*

To colour or not to colour?

Should an uncoloured map be coloured or not? Many modern collectors prefer their maps to be left uncoloured, just as they were originally issued. It is argued that colouring removes bibliographical evidence, that it deceives and that it is irreversible. Further, as there are only a limited number of original uncoloured maps available, the more often these are coloured, the fewer of them there are that remain. This is often reflected in the prices which collectors will pay for the finest examples of uncoloured maps – as much as, and sometimes more than, the sums paid for maps in the best 'contemporary' colouring. My own view is that if a map is pleasing to its new owner in its original state, then it should be left in that state. Let us take as an example an early edition of a John Speed English county map, from the first edition of his *Theatre of the Empire of Great Britaine*, published in 1611. The originals of these fine maps, engraved by Dutch craftsmen, are outstanding examples of the engraver's art, finely printed in an intense black which, seen against the background of the creamy-white thick paper of the early editions, helps to make aesthetically delightful compositions which have no need to be coloured (Plate 12.19). Later printings, up to 1676, often show signs of plate wear and were not always so well printed. In such cases there is no harm in having the maps coloured, provided this is carried out carefully and sympathetically. This is a personal view: no two collectors will always be of the same mind. That, surely, is one of the great pleasures of the study of old maps.

Origins and inspirations

From early on in the history of decorative mapping, designers, engravers and cartographers used a variety of sources as inspiration for the design of their maps. Many mapsellers dealt also in decorative and other prints. Abraham Ortelius, for example, possessed several albums of prints by the German master Albrecht Dürer,[3] although none of the decorative devices incorporated by Ortelius in his maps can be directly attributed to Dürer. If we look at some of the embellishments in the maps of Jodocus Hondius, such as his *Vera totius expeditionis nauticae*, (c.1595),[4] we can see four little *putti* (winged cherubs) which are mirror images of the same figure in Dürer's *The Dream*. Again, the twin-hemispherical world map in the Blaeu *Atlas major* of 1662 shows allegorical representations of the four seasons (Plates 4.28, 12.23).[5] These are taken from the 1592 series by the Italian artist Antonio Tempesta, again in mirror images (Plate 12.24).

Other embellishments were taken from sources in the Netherlands, such as the works of the artist Hendrik Goltzius. Several of his woodcuts and wood-engravings were in the possession of the Blaeus and some of them are known to bear their imprint. The Rijksprentenkabinet in the Netherlands possesses an album containing a collection of 236 cartouche designs[6] nearly all of which come from maps published in editions of Ortelius's *Theatrum orbis terrarum* between 1601 and 1612. The collection must have been assembled when the atlas was commonly available, for no-one thought twice about cutting up such a fine book to make a collection of cartouches!

Until well into the seventeenth century the *Theatrum* proved to be rich inspiration for cartouche designs. The process also applied in reverse – Ortelius adapted the engraved title of Jacob Florisz's *Veelderhande cierlijke Compertimenten* (Antwerp, Hans Liefrinck, 1564) for the title-cartouche of his *Theatrum* map of Gelderland, in Utrecht, *Gelriae, Cliviae . . . verissima descriptio*.[7] A similar design appears in his general map of America. Both of these were included in the first edition of the *Theatrum*. Again, his map of Mexico, *Hispaniae novae . . . 1579* uses a cartouche design, engraved by Frans Huys in 1555, taken from the design book by Hans Vredeman de Vries, the *Multarum variumque protractionum*.

Even the famous caricature map, the *Leo Belgicus* (see p.332–333), 'borrowed' its engravings. The version issued by Johannes van Deutecum the younger in 1598 used other engravings as inspirations for the design elements in the medallion

(continued on page 362)

PLATE 12.21 *(opposite)* Typus orarum maritimarum Guinae, Manicongo & Angolae ultra promontorium Bonne Spei usque, *drawn and engraved by Arnold Florent van Langren for Jan Hugghen van Liuschoten's* Itinerario, *Amsterdam, 1596. Recognisable views of St Helena and Ascension are shown.*

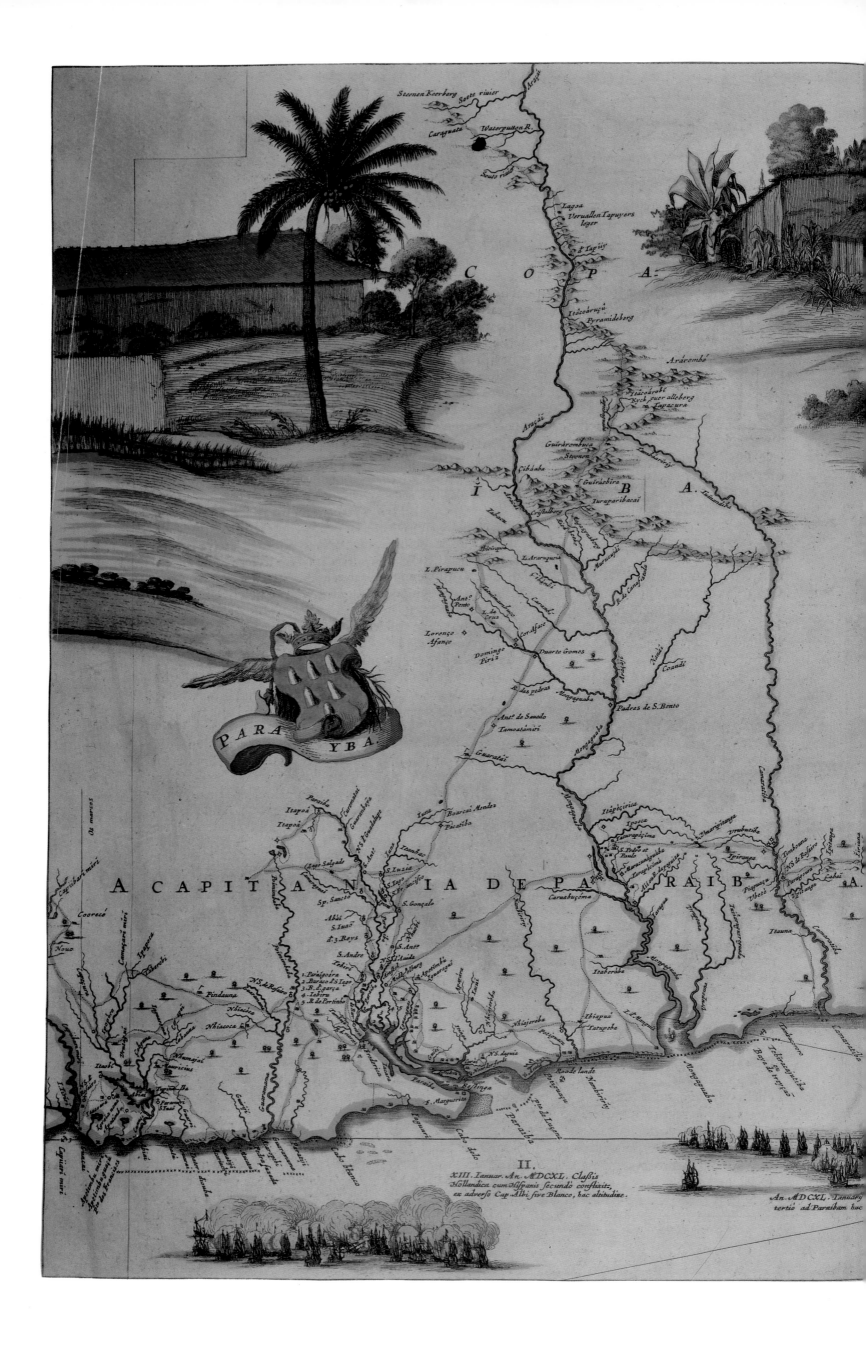

GVINEÆ PARS ME LEGHE TEN

A. Serra Lisona
I. Roßa
Cago Chibo ale

AEQVINOCTIA

S. Paulo

Vegia

OCEANVS

I. de S. Matheus

Abrolho

I. de Fernando de Loronha

Rocas

C. de S. Roque

Paraiba
Os Petiguares
Pernambuco
Olinda
C. de S. Augustino
S. Aleixo
R. Terceiro
Sitiamni

I. ęemçaon

AETHIOPICVS

I. de S. Helena

I. Trimidade

I. ęemçaon

S. Maria Dangos

I. de Martim Vaz

I. dos Pitos

ASCENSION

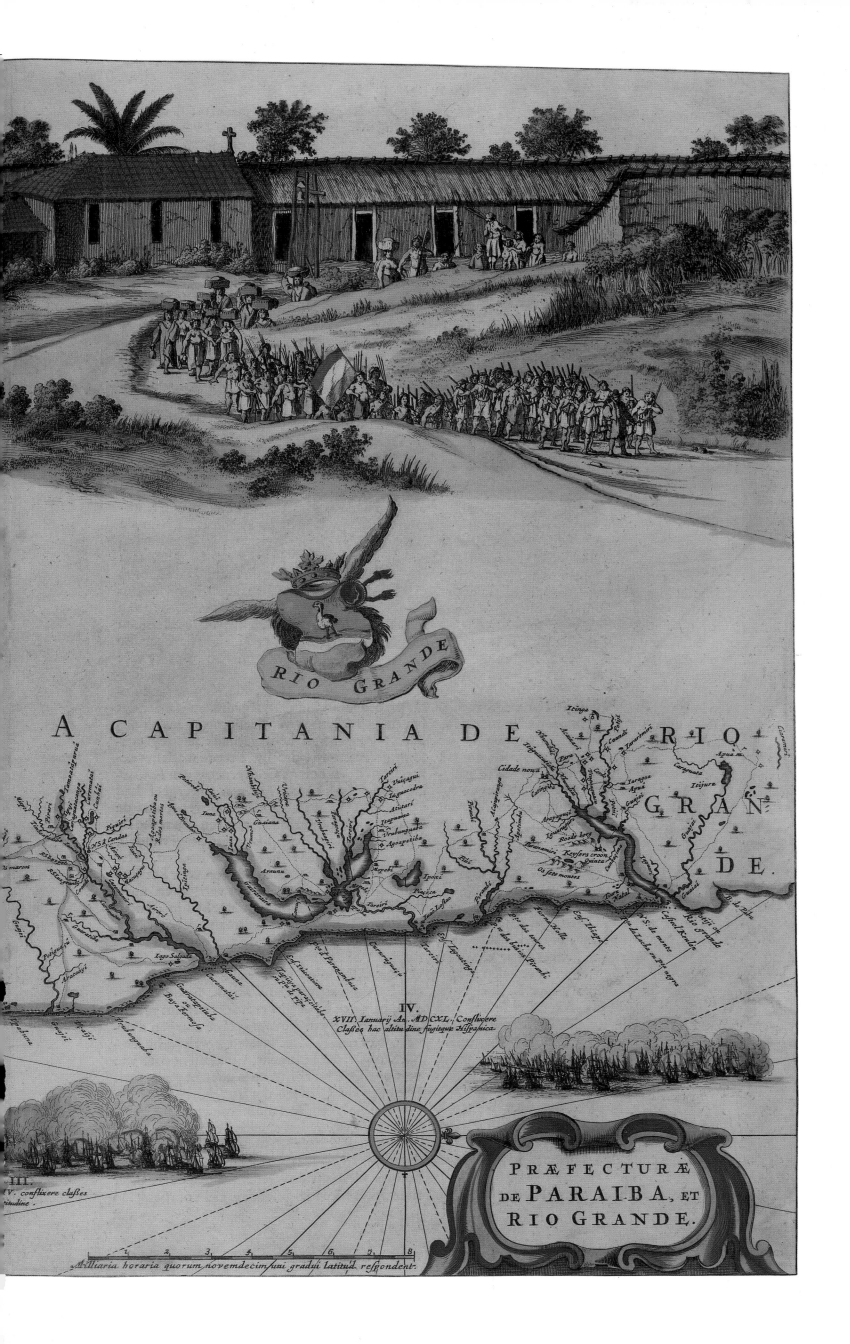

A CAPITANIA DE RIO GRANDE

RIO GRANDE

IV.

XVII Ianuarij An. MDCXL, Conflixere
Classes hac altitudine fugitque Hispanica.

III.

V. conflixere classes
titudine.

PRÆFECTURÆ
DE PARAIBA, ET
RIO GRANDE.

Milliaria horaria quorum novemdecim uni gradui latitud. respondent.

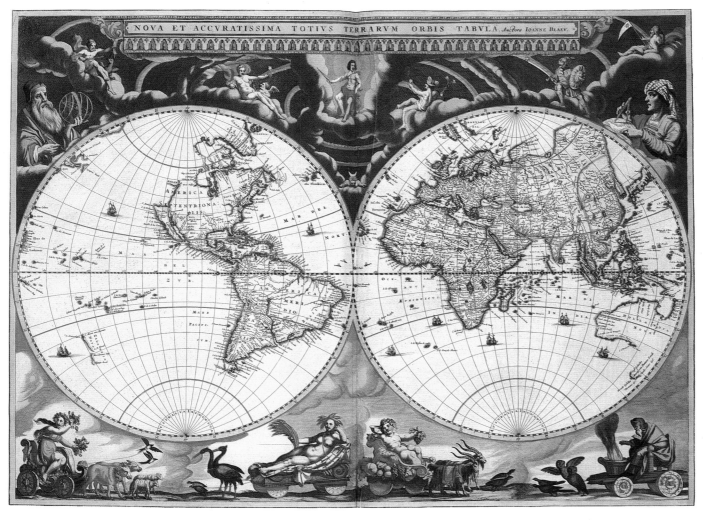

PLATE 12.22 *(opposite)*
Praefecturae de Paraiba, et Rio Grande by Joan Blaeu from the Atlas major, *1662. The large pictorial vignettes illustrate local life and conditions in Brazil. The procession of Indians at top right is illustrated after a painting of Frans Janszoon Post.*

PLATE 12.23 *(left)* Nova et accuratissima totius terrarum orbis tabula *by Joan Blaeu from the* Atlas major, *1662. The allegories of the four seasons are based on drawings by Antonio Tempesta below.*

PLATE 12.24 *(below)*
The Four Seasons *by Antonio Tempesta, 1592. The seasons run clockwise: spring, summer, autumn, winter.*

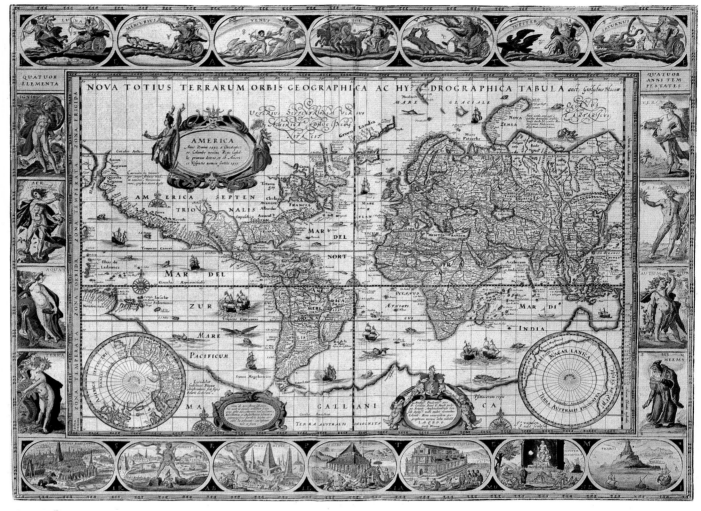

PLATE 12.25 *(right, with detail above)* Nova totius terrarum orbis geographia ac hydrographica tabula *by Willem Blaeu, 1606 and later. Celebrated as one of the supreme examples of the mapmaker's art, Blaeu's map contains a wealth of decorative detail; such vignettes as Autumn (above) and Ignis (beneath) illustrate the aesthetic appeal of Blaeu's genius.*

PLATES 12.26, 12.27 *(opposite, top and bottom)* Cyprus insula *by Willem Blaeu, c. 1635. The arresting figure of Venus drawn in a shellboat (at lower right) was influenced by an engraving by Hendrik Goltzius. The engraving recalls the vignette of Venus appearing in the top frieze of Blaeu's 1606 world map (Plate 12.25).*

portraits of the political figures involved in the Dutch Revolt. For example, the portraits of Philip II, the Duke of Alva, Archduke Albert of Austria, William of Orange, and others were taken from engraved subjects by Hieronymus and Antonie Wiericx.

One of the best examples of such 'design quarrying' is to be found in the beautiful world map on the Mercator projection of 1606,[8] which was used in the Blaeu atlases for many years (Plates 4.27, 12.25). The Blaeu map is decorated with no fewer than twenty-two border vignettes, taken from allegorical designs of the four elements, the four seasons and so on. Some are in mirror image, others are not. Cyprus in the Blaeu atlases, *Cyprus insula* (Plate 12.26) showing Venus (Aphrodite) drawn in a shellboat by two swans, is influenced by an engraving by Hendrik Goltzius. The engraving itself recalls the vignette in the aforementioned world map symbolizing the planet Venus (Plate 12.27).

There are also examples of seventeenth-century maps which incorporate original designs by famous artists of the day, rather than adaptations of existing designs. A particular example of this practice is the work of the Flemish artist David

Vinckeboons.[9] The Blaeu world map of 1605 has, in the lower half of the eastern hemisphere, a very large and ornate cartouche design after Vinckeboons. (The original designs for this map are now in the Staatliche Graphische Sammlung in Munich.) The famous series of Bible maps engraved by the Van Deutecum brothers for Pieter Plancius contain designs which illustrate biblical events after Vinckeboons' drawings.

Most map collectors are familiar with the Blaeu atlas maps from the 1630s onwards. These decorative pieces often contain cartouches after the designs and drawings of contemporary artists. While the identities of the Blaeus' map engravers remain almost entirely unknown, it has been shown that many of the cartouches were designed by Pieter Janszoon, during a long career working for the Blaeus.[10] A collection of these designs was put together by the seventeenth-century Amsterdam art dealer Jan Pieterszoon Zomer (1641– 1724), a pupil of Janszoon. Janszoon's style changed little over the years: the cartouches in the atlas volumes covering the British Isles are thought to have originated from the hand of Janszoon. Many other designs are very similar and it is possible either that Janszoon himself drew

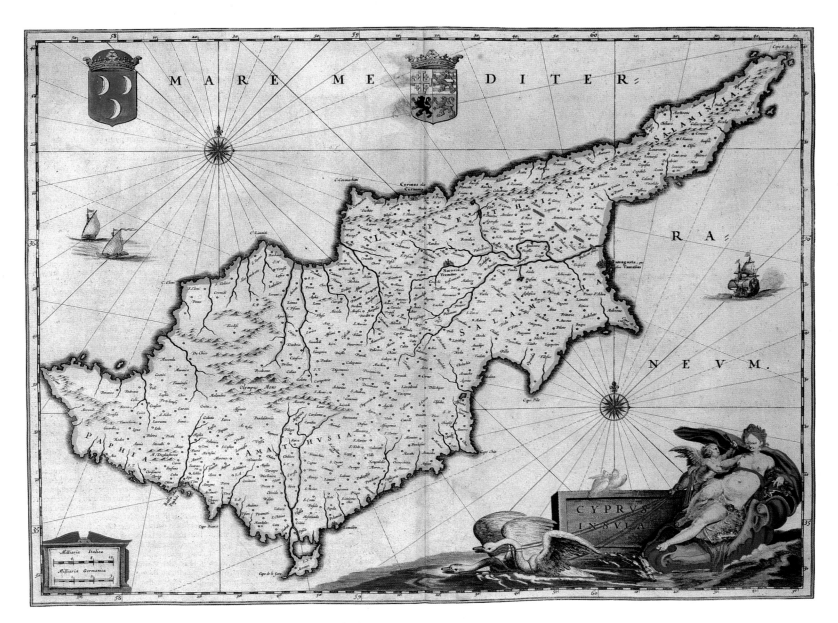

the original designs or that his pupils, in turn, did so in emulation of their master.

Another Dutch artist, Nicolaes Berchem, made elaborate designs for Nicolaes Visscher the elder in the 1650s.[11] His series depicting the four elements appears in the beautiful spandrel designs of Visscher's world map *Orbis terrarum nova et accuratissima tabula* of 1658. The original drawings for these designs found their way to Austria and are now kept at the Albertina Museum in Vienna. Berchem later produced several designs for Frederick de Wit, such as the cartouches and vignettes found on the charts in his *Atlas maritimus ofte Zee Atlas* of 1675.

All of these works have one thing in common – whether their designs were specially prepared for the map, or borrowed from another source, they have, undeniably, added greatly to the overall appeal of the project. The dictionary defines aesthetics as 'The branch of philosophy concerned with concepts such as beauty and taste'. There are, thankfully, as many views on beauty and taste as there are map collectors today.

References
1. Dr. John Dee, 1570.
2. John Smith, *The Art of Painting in Oyl*, page 106, 1701.
3. J.F. Heijbroek and M. Schapelhouman, eds., *Kunst in kaart. Decoratieve aspecten van de cartografie*, page 19, 1989.
4. R.W. Shirley, *The Mapping of the World*, page 188, 1983.
5. R.W. Shirley, *op. cit.*, page 428.
6. The Rijksprentenkabinet, Inv. boeken I, page 775, 1934.
7. Heijbroek and Schapelhouman, *op. cit.*, page 23.
8. J.J.S. Goss, *Blaeu's the Grand Atlas of the Seventeenth-Century World*, pages 24–25, 1990.
9. J.J.S. Goss, *op. cit.*, page 65.
10. J.J.S. Goss, *op. cit.*, page 73ff.
11. J.J.S. Goss, *op. cit.*, page 76ff.

SELECT BIBLIOGRAPHY

The following is by no means intended to be an exhaustive bibliography on the subject; compilation of such a list would fill a series of large volumes. It is, however, intended as a guide for readers who wish to explore the wide-ranging and constantly expanding body of literature on cartography and on old maps in particular. It is not for this author to make qualitative judgments on the books and other sources cited in this list, that is for others to do. The reader who is beginning to take an interest in the subject is advised to read as many titles as possible, for no one source can provide all the answers. But, while reference materials are a valuable aid to study, it must be stressed once again that there is no substitute for studying old maps themselves, whether in a dealer's stock, in one's own collection however large or small, at the auction houses or in libraries. The list which follows is not confined to materials in the English language; most of the works cited in languages other than English contain a resumé in English, or are

sufficiently illustrated so that anyone unfamiliar with the language of publication can derive both pleasure and information from the contents. Specialist dealers' catalogues also frequently contain valuable information on individual maps and atlases, while the specialized catalogues published by the leading auction houses, such as Sotheby's and Christie's, often contain detailed descriptions of travel books, atlases and maps which are of value as references in themselves. A selected list of catalogue-issuing dealers and auction houses will be found at the end of the following list. In addition, certain non-cartographical titles have been included where these have been found useful as sources of information for historical contexts.

The dates given in the bibliography are, where possible, the latest editions and may vary from the dates given in the references at the end of each chapter, as these older editions are the ones I referred to in writing this book.

Books

Adams, P. G. *Travellers and Travel Liars 1660-1800*, New York, Dover Publications, Inc., 1980

Agache, R., *et al*. *Cartes et figures de la terre*, Paris, Centre Georges Pompidou, 1980

Alden, J. *Pioneer America*, London, Hutchinson, 1966

Averdunk, H. and Muller-Reinhard, J. *Gerhard Mercator und die Geographen unter seinen Nachkommen*, reprint edition, Amsterdam, Theatrum Orbis Terrarum Ltd, 1979

Avezac de Castera-Macaya, M.A.P. d' *Martin Hylacomylus Waltzemüller: ses ouvrages et ses collaborateurs*, reprint edition, Amsterdam, Meridian Publishing Co., 1980

Bachmann, F. *Die alten Städtebilder. Ein Verzeichnis der graphischen Ortsansichten von Schedel bis Merian*, Leipzig, Verlag Karl W. Hiersemann, 1939

Bagrow, L., Castner, H.W., *ed. A History of the Cartography of Russia up to 1600[-1800]*, 2 volumes, Wolfe Island, The Walker Press, 1975

Bagrow, L. *ed.* Skelton, R.A. *History of Cartography*, revised and enlarged edition, London, C.A. Watts & Co. Ltd, 1964

Barraclough, G., *ed. The Times Atlas of World History*, revised edition, London, Times Books Limited, 1988

Benevolo, L. *Die Geschichte der Stadt*, Frankfurt am Main and New York, Campus Verlag, 1982

Beresiner, Y. *British County Maps Reference and Price Guide*, Woodbridge, The Antique Collectors' Club, 1983

Billington, R.A. *Westward Expansion. A History of the American Frontier*, revised edition, London and New York, Collier Macmillan, 1974

Bom, G.D. *Bijdragen tot eene geschiedenis van het geslacht 'Van Keulen' als Boekhandelaars, Uitgevers, Kaart- en Instrumentsmakers in Nederland; een biblio-cartographische studie*, reprint edition, Amsterdam, Meridian Publishing Co., 1962

Boomgaard, J.E.A. *Holland in kaart en prent*, Weesp, Fibula-Van Dishoeck; Tielt, Drukkerij-Uitgeverij Lannoo pvba, 1984

Bramsen, B. *Gamle Danmarkskort. En historisk oversigt med bibliografiske noter for perioden 1570-1770*, third edition, Copenhagen, Rosenkilde og Bagger, 1975

Bratt, E. *En kronika om kartor över Sverige*, Stockholm, Generalstabens Litografiska Anstalt, 1958

Brown, L.A., *introd. The World Encompassed. An exhibition of the history of maps held at the Baltimore Museum of Art October 7 to November 23, 1952*, Baltimore, The Trustees of the Walters Art Gallery, 1952

Brown, L.A. *The Story of Maps*, reprint edition, New York, Dover Publications Inc., 1977

Buisseret, D., *ed. From Sea Charts to Satellite Images. Interpreting North American History through Maps*, Chicago and London, The University of Chicago Press, 1990

Burke, G.L. *The Making of Dutch Towns. A Study in Urban Development from the Tenth to the Seventeenth Centuries*, London, Cleaver-Hume Press Ltd, 1956

Campbell, T. *Early Maps*, New York, Abbeville Press, Inc., 1981

Campbell, T. *The Earliest Printed Maps 1472-1500*, London, The British Library, 1987

Cavelti Hammer, M. *Der Weg zur modernen Lankarte 1750-1865. Die Schweiz und ihre Nachbarländer im Landkartenbild. Von Cassini bis Dufour*, Köniz, Edition Plepp, 1989

Chambers, M., Grew, R. *et al. The Western Experience*, fifth edition, New York, McGraw-Hill, Inc., 1991

Chubb, T. *The Printed Maps in the Atlases of Great Britain and Ireland. A bibliography, 1579-1870*, reprint edition, Folkestone and London, Dawsons of Pall Mall, 1974

Close, C. *intro.* Harley, J.B. *The Early Years of the Ordnance Survey*, reprint edition, Newton Abbot, David & Charles Reprints, 1969

Cocq, M.L. le *Premières images de la terre*, Paris, Joël Cuénot, 1977

Cortazzi, H. *Isles of Gold. Antique Maps of Japan*, New York and Tokyo, John Weatherhill, Inc., 1983

Croiset van Uchelen, T., Horst, K. van der, and Schilder, G. *Theatrum Orbis Librorum. Liber Amicorum presented to Nico Israel on the occasion of his seventieth birthday*, Utrecht, HES Publishers and Forum Antiquarian Booksellers, 1989

Crone, G.R. *Maps and their Makers. An introduction to the history of cartography*, fifth edition, Folkestone, Wm Dawson & Son Ltd, 1978

Cumming, W.P. *Mapping the North Caroline Coast. Sixteenth-Century Cartography and the Roanoke Voyages*, Chapel Hill, Division of Archives and History North Carolina Department of Cultural Resources, 1988

Cumming, W.P. *The Southeast in Early Maps. With an annotated check list of printed and manuscript regional and local maps of Southeastern North America during the Colonial Period*, Chapel Hill, The University of North Carolina Press, 1962

Cumming, W.P., Hillier, S.E., Quinn, D.B. and Williams, G. *The Exploration of North America 1630-1776*, London, Elek Books Ltd, 1974

Cumming, W.P., Skelton, R.A. and Quinn, D.B. *The Discovery of North America*, London, Elek Books Ltd, 1971

Dahlgren, E.W. *Les débuts de la cartographie du Japon*, reprint edition, Amsterdam, Meridian Publishing Co., 1977

Delano-Smith, C. and Ingram, E.M. *Maps in Bibles 1500-1600. An Illustrated Catalogue*, Geneva, Librairie Droz S.A., 1991

Delpar, H., *ed. The Discoverers. An Encyclopedia of Explorers and Exploration*, New York, McGraw-Hill Book Company, 1980

Denucé, J. *Oud-Nederlandsche Kaartmakers in betrekking met Plantijn*, 2 volumes, reprint edition, Amsterdam, Meridian Publishing Co., 1964

Deursen, A.T. van *Het kopergeld van de Gouden Eeuw*, 4 volumes, Assen, Van Gorcum, 1978-1981

Donkersloot de Vrij, M. *Topografische kaarten van Nederland vóór 1750. Handgetekende en gedrukte kaarten, aanwezig in de Nederlandse rijksarchieven*, Groningen, Wolters-Noordhof bv, 1981

Dörflinger, J. *Die Österreichische Kartographie im 18, und zu beginn des 19. Jahrhunderts unter besonderer berücksichtigung der Privatkartographie zwischen 1780 und 1820. 1. Band: Österreichische karten des 18. Jahrhunderts*, Vienna, Verlag der Österreichischen Akademie der Wissenschaften, 1984

Duncan, T.B. *Atlantic Islands, Madeira, the Azores and the Cape Verdes in Seventeenth-Century Commerce and Navigation*, Chicago and London, The University of Chicago Press, 1972

Duroselle, J-B. *transl.* Mayne, R. *Europe. A History of its Peoples*, London, Viking, 1990

Eerde, K.S. van *Wenceslaus Hollar. Delineator of His Time*, Charlottesville, The University Press of Virginia, for The Folger Shakespeare Library, 1970

Eerde, K.S. van *John Ogilby and the Taste of His Times*, Folkestone, Wm Dawson & Sons Ltd, 1976

Elliot, J. *The City in Maps: urban mapping to 1900*, London, The British Library, 1987

Ermen, E. van *The United States in Old Maps and Prints*, Tielt, Uitgeverij Lannoo, 1990

Evans, I.M. and Lawrence, H. *Christopher Saxton. Elizabethan Map-maker*, Wakefield, Wakefield Historical Publications, and London, The Holland Press, 1979

Fell, R.T. *Early Maps of South-East Asia*, Singapore, Oxford University Press, 1988

Fernández-Armesto, F., *ed. The Times Atlas of World Exploration*, London, Times Books, 1991

Fite, E.D. and Freeman, A. *A Book of Old Maps delineating American History from the Earliest Days down to the Close of the Revolutionary War*, reprint edition, New York, Dover Publications, Inc., 1969

Fontaine Verwey, H. de la *Uit de Wereld van het Boek*, 3 volumes, Amsterdam, Nico Israel, 1979-1982

Franklin, W. *Discoverers, Explorers, Settlers. The Diligent Writers of Early America*, Chicago and London, Chicago University Press, 1979

Glanville, P. *London in Maps*, London, The Connoisseur, 1972

Glaser, L. *America on Paper. The First Hundred Years*, Philadelphia, Associated Antiquaries, 1989

Gole, S. *India within the Ganges*, New Delhi, Jayaprints, 1983

Goss, J.J.S. *The Mapping of North America. Three*

centuries of map-making 1500-1860, Secaucus, 1990

Goss, J.J.S *Blaeu's the Grand Atlas of the 17th Century World*, London, Studio Editions, 1990

Goss, J.J.S. *Braun & Hogenberg's The City Maps of Europe. A Selection of 16th Century Town Plans & Views*, London, Studio Editions, 1992

Gróf, L.L. *Carta Hungarica. Térképgyüjtemény (1540-1841)*, Budapest, Interpress, 1988

Gross, H. *Zur Entstehungs-Geschichte der Tabula Peutingeriana*, reprint edition, Amsterdam, Meridian Publishing Co., 1980

Hakluyt, R. *Divers voyages touching the discoverie of America, and the Ilands adjacent unto the same, made first of all by our Englishmen, and afterward by the Frenchmen and Britons*, London, Thomas Woodcocke, 1582

Harley, J.B. and Woodward, D. ed. *The History of Cartography. Volume One. Cartography in Prehistoric, Ancient, and Medieval Europe and the Mediterranean*, Chicago and London, The University of Chicago Press, 1987 [Volumes 2-6 are in preparation]

Harms, H. *Themen alter Karten*, Oldenburg, Ernst Völker, 1979

Harvey, P.D.A. *The History of Topographical Maps, Symbols, Pictures and Surveys*. London, Thames and Hudson, 1980

Harvey, P.D.A. *Medieval Maps*, London, The British Library, 1991

Hauber, E.D. *Versuch Einer umständlichen Historie der Land-Charten*, Ulm, Daniel Bartholomäi, 1724 [facsimile reprint, Karlsruhe, Fachhochschule Karlsruhe, 1988]

Heijbroek, J.F. and Schapelhouman, M. ed. *Kunst in kaart. Decoratieve aspecten van de cartografie*, Utrecht, HES Uitgevers, 1989

Heijden, H.A.M. van der *The oldest maps of the Netherlands. An illustrated and annotated carto-bibliography of the 16th century maps of the XVII Provinces*, Utrecht, HES Publishers, 1987

Heijden, H.A.M. van der *Leo Belgicus. An illustrated and annotated carto-bibliography*, Alphen aan den Rijn, Uitgeverij Canaletto, 1990

Hodson, D. *County Atlases of the British Isles published after 1703. Volume I Atlases published 1704 to 1742 and their subsequent editions; Volume II Atlases published 1743 to 1763 and their subsequent editions*, Tewin, The Tewin Press, 1984-1989 [further volumes in preparation]

Holmes, N. *Pictorial Maps*, London, The Herbert Press, 1992

Honour, H. *The New Golden Land. European Images of America from the Discoveries to the Present Time*, New York, Pantheon Books, 1975

Hough, S.J. *The Italians and the Creation of America. An Exhibition at the John Carter Brown Library, Brown University*, Providence, 1980

Howse, D. and Sanderson, M. *The Sea Chart. An Historical Survey based on the Collections in the National Maritime Museum*, Newton Abbot, David & Charles, 1973

Humphreys, A.L. *Old Decorative Maps and Charts*, London, Halton & Truscott Smith, Ltd; New York, Minton, Balch & Company, 1926

Hyde, R. *Gilded Scenes and Shining Prospects, Panoramic Views of British Towns 1575-1900*, New Haven, Yale Center for British Art, 1985

Hyde, R. *Panoramania! The art and entertainment of the 'all-embracing' view*, London, Trefoil Publications Ltd, 1988

Jolig, K. *Niederländische Einflüsse in der deutschen Kartographie besonders des 18. Jahrhunderts*, reprint edition, Amsterdam, Meridian Publishing Co., 1980

Keay, J., ed. *The Royal Geographical Society History of World Exploration*, London, Paul Hamlyn Publishing, 1991

Keuning, J. *Petrus Plancius. Theoloog en Geograaf 1552-1622*, Amsterdam, P.N. van Kampen & Zoon NV, 1946

Keuning, J. and Donkersloot de Vrij, M., eds *Willem Jansz. Blaeu. A biography and history of his work as a cartographer and publisher*, Amsterdam, Theatrum Orbis Terrarum Ltd, 1973

Klein, C.M. *Maps in Eighteenth-Century British Magazines. A Checklist. The Hermon Dunlap Smith Center for the History of Cartography Occasional Publication No. 3*, Chicago, The Newberry Library, 1989

Koeman, C. *The History of Lucas Janszoon Waghenaer and his 'Spieghel der Zeevaerdt'*, Amsterdam, Theatrum Orbis Terrarum Ltd, 1964

Koeman, C., ed. *Wolfenbütteler Forschungen Band 7: Land- und Seekarten im Mittelalter und in der frühen Neuzeit*, Munich, Kraus International Publications, 1980

Koeman, C. *The sea on paper. The story of the Van Keulens and their 'Sea-torch'*, Amsterdam, Theatrum Orbis Terrarum Ltd, 1972

Koeman, C. *Atlantes neerlandici. Bibliography of terrestrial, maritime and celestial atlases and pilotbooks, published in the Netherlands up to 1800*, 5 volumes, Amsterdam, Theatrum Orbis Terrarum Ltd, 1967-1971

Koeman, C. *Joan Blaeu and his Grand Atlas*, Amsterdam, Theatrum Orbis Terrarum Ltd, 1970

Koeman, C. *Geschiedenis van de kartografie van Nederland. Zes eeuwen land- en zeekaarten en stadsplattegronden*, second edition, Alphen aan den Rijn, Uitgeverij Canaletto, 1985

Koeman, C. and Homan, H.J.A. *Atlantes neerlandici. A supplement to the Volumes I-V and a bibliography of geographical, celestial and thematic atlases published in the Netherlands between 1880 and 1940*, Alphen aan den Rijn, Uitgeverij Canaletto, 1985

Koepp, D.P., ed. *Exploration and Mapping of the American West. Selected Essays. Occasional Paper No. 1, Map and Geography Round Table of the American Library Association*, Chicago, Speculum Orbis Press, 1986

Konvitz, J.W. *Cartography in France 1660-1848. Science, engineering, and statecraft*, Chicago and London, The University of Chicago Press, 1987

Lanman, J.T. *Glimpses of History from Old Maps. A Collector's View*, Tring, Map Collector Publications Ltd, 1989

Laor, E. and Klein, S. *Maps of the Holy Land. Cartobibliography of Printed Maps, 1475-1900. Based on the Eran Laor Collection at the Jewish National and University Library, Jerusalem*, New York, Alan R. Liss, Inc.; Amsterdam, Meridian Publishing Co., 1986

Leader, J.T. *Life of Sir Robert Dudley*, reprint edition, Amsterdam, Meridian Publishing Co., 1977

Linden, J.A. van der *Topographische en Militaire Kaart van het Koningrijk der Nederlanden*, Bussum, Fibula-van Dishoeck, 1973

Links, J.G. *Townscape Painting and Drawing*, London, B.T. Batsford Ltd, 1972

Lister, R. *Old Maps and Globes: with a list of cartographers, engravers, publishers and printers concerned with printed maps and globes from c.1500 to c.1800*, second edition, London, Bell & Hyman, 1979

Martin, R.M., ed. Potter, J. introd. *The Illustrated Atlas of the Nineteenth Century World*, London, Studio Editions, 1989

Mercator Society, The *English Mapping of America 1675-1715. An Informal Selection of Printed and Manuscript Maps Produced During the Formative Years of the English Map Trade*, New York, The Mercator Society, The New York Public Library, 1986

Meurer, P.H. *Fontes Cartographici Orteliani. Das "Theatrum Orbis Terrarum" von Abraham Ortelius und seine Kartenquellen*, Weinheim, VCH Act Humaniora, 1991

Meurer, P.H. *Atlantes colonienses. Die Kölner Schule der Atlaskartographie 1570-1610*, Bad Neustadt an der Saale, 1988

Mickwitz, A-M. and Miekkavarra, L. *The A.E. Nordenskiöld Collection in the Helsinki University Library. Annotated Catalogue of Maps made up to 1800*, 3 volumes, Stockholm, Almqvist & Wiksell International for Helsinki University Library, 1979-1984

Mingroot, E. van and Ermen, E. van *Scandinavia in old maps and prints*, Knokke, Mappamundi Ltd, 1987

Moreland, C. and Bannister, D. *Antique Maps: A Collector's Handbook*, London, Longman, 1983

Morison, S.E. *The European Discovery of America. The Northern Voyages AD 500-1600*, New York, Oxford University Press, 1971

Morison, S.E. *The European Discovery of America. The Southern Voyages AD 1492-1616*, New York, Oxford University Press, 1974

Morris, A.E.J. *History of Urban Form. Prehistory to the Renaissance*, London, George Godwin Ltd, 1974

Mumford, L. *The City in History. Its Origins, Its Transformations, and Its Prospects*, London, Secker & Warburg Ltd, 1961

Murray, J.J. *Vlaanderen en Engeland. De invloed van de Lage Landen op Engeland ten tijde van de Tudors en de Stuarts*, Antwerp, Mercatorfonds, 1985

National Maritime Museum. *Catalogue of the Library. Volumes 3: Atlases & Cartography*, 2 volumes, London, Her Majesty's Stationery Office, 1971

Nebenzahl, K. *A Bibliography of Printed Battle Plans of the American Revolution 1775-1795*, Chicago and London, The University of Chicago Press, 1975

Needham, J. *Science and Civilisation in China. Volume 3: Mathematics and the Sciences of the Heavens and the Earth*, Cambridge, Cambridge University Press, 1979

Newby, E. *The Mitchell Beazley World Atlas of Exploration - a 4,000 year journey in the company of heroes*, London, Mitchell Beazley Publishers Ltd, 1975

Nordenskiöld, A.E.F. *Facsimile-Atlas to the Early History of Cartography*, reprint edition, New York, Dover Publications, Inc., 1973

North, J.D. *Stars, Minds and Fate. Essays in ancient and medieval cosmology*, London and Ronceverte, The Hambledon Press, 1989

North, J.D. *The Universal Frame, Historical essays in astronomy, natural philosophy and scientific method*, London and Ronceverte, The Hambledon Press, 1989

Ortroy, F. van *L'oeuvre cartographique de Gérard et de Corneille de Jode*, reprint edition, Amsterdam, Meridian Publishing Co., 1963

Ortroy, F. van *Bibliographie de l'œuvre de Pierre Apian*, reprint edition, Amsterdam, Meridian Publishing Co., 1963

Osley, A.S. *Mercator. A monograph on the lettering of maps, etc. in the 16th century Netherlands with a facsimile and translation of his treatise on the italic hand and a translation of Ghim's Vita Mercatoris*, London, Faber and Faber, 1969

Parry, J.H. *The Age of Reconnaissance, Discovery, Exploration, and Settlement, 1450-1650*, Cleveland and New York, The World Publishing Company, 1963

Parry, J.H. *The Discovery of South America*, London, Paul Elek, 1979

Parry, J.H. *The Discovery of the Sea. An illustrated history of men, ships and the sea in the fifteenth and sixteenth centuries*, New York, The Dial Press, 1974

Pelletier, M. et al. *A la découverte de la terre. Dix siècles de cartographie. Trésors du Département des Cartes et Plans mai-juillet 1979*, Paris, Bibliothèque Nationale, 1979

Penrose, B. *Travel and Discovery in the Renaissance 1420-1620*, Cambridge (Massachusetts), Harvard University Press, 1967

Polk, D.B. *The Island of California. A History of the Myth*, Spokane, The Arthur H. Clark Company, 1991

Pounds, N.J.G. *An historical geography of Europe*, Cambridge, Cambridge University Press, 1990

Reinhartz, D. and Colley, C.C. *The Mapping of the American Southwest*, College Station, Texas A&M University Press, 1987

Reps, J.W. *The Making of Urban America. A history of city planning in the United States*, Princeton, Princeton University Press, 1965

Reps, J.W. *Cities of the American West. A History of Frontier Urban Planning*, Princeton, Princeton University Press, 1979

Richter, H. *Olaus Magnus Carta marina 1539*, Lund, Skånska Centraltryckeriet, 1967

Richter, H. *Naturvetenskarpernas historia i Sverige intill år 1800. Del I. Geografiens historia i Sverige intill år 1800*, Stockholm, Almqvist & Wiksells Boktryckeri AB, 1959

Ristow, W.W. *A la Carte, Selected Papers on Maps and Atlases*, Washington, DC., Library of Congress, 1972

Ritchie, G.S. *The Admiralty Chart. British naval hydrography in the nineteenth century*, London, Hollis & Carter, 1967

Sandler, C. *Johann Baptista Homann, die Homännischen Erben, Matthäus Seutter und ihre Landkarten*, reprint edition, Amsterdam, Meridian Publishing Co., 1979

Schäfer, D. *Portuguese Exploration to the West and the Formation of Brazil 1450-1800*, Providence, The John Carter Brown Library, 1988

Schama, S. *The Embarrassment of Riches. An Interpretation of Dutch Culture in the Golden Age*, London, William Collins Sons and Co., Ltd, 1987

Schilder, G. *Australia unveiled. The share of the Dutch navigators in the discovery of Australia*, Amsterdam, Theatrum Orbis Terrarum Ltd, 1976

Schilder, G. *Monumenta cartographica neerlandica I-III*, Alphen aan den Rijn, Uitgeverij Canaletto, 1986-1990 [further volumes in preparation]

Schilder, G. Krogt, P. van der and Clercq, S. de *ed. Marcel Destombes (1905-1983). Contributions sélectionnées à l'Histoire de la Cartographie et des Instruments scientifiques*, Utrecht, HES Publishers; Paris, A.G. Nizet, 1987

Schilder, G. and Krogt, P. van der, *ed. Miscellanea cartographica. Contributions to the history of cartography*, Utrecht, HES Publishers, 1988

Scholten, F.W.J. *Militaire topografische kaarten en stadsplattegronden van Nederland 1579-1795*, Alphen aan den Rijn, Uitgeverij Canaletto, 1989

Schwartz, S.I. and Ehrenberg, R.E. *The Mapping of America*, New York, H.N. Abrams, Inc., 1980

Seifert, T. *Bayerische Staatsbibliothek. Die Karte als Kunstwerk. Dekoratieve Landkarten aus Mittelalter und Neuzeit*, Unterscheidenheim, Verlag Dr. Alfons Uhl, 1979

Shirley, R.W. *The Mapping of the World. Early Printed World Maps 1472-1700*, London, The Holland Press Ltd, 1983

Shirley, R.W. *Early Printed Maps of the British Isles 1477-1650. The completely revised and updated edition*, East Grinstead, Antique Atlas Publications, 1991

Shirley, R.W. *Printed Maps of the British Isles 1650-1750*, Tring, Map Collector Publications Ltd; London, The British Library, 1988

Skelton, R.A. *Decorative Printed Maps of the 15th to 18th Centuries*, London, Spring Books, 1965

Skelton, R.A. *Explorers' Maps. Chapters in the Cartographic Record of Geographical Discovery*, London, Routledge & Kegan Paul, Ltd, 1958

Skelton, R.A. *County Atlases of the British Isles 1579-1800. A Bibliography, 1579-1703*, London, Carta Press, 1970

Smith, C.T. *An Historical Geography of Western Europe before 1800*, London, Longmans, 1967

Snyder, G.S. *Maps of the Heavens*, London, André Deutsch Ltd, 1984

Stevens, H.N. *Ptolemy's Geography. A brief account of all the printed editions down to 1730*, London, 1905

Stommel, H. *Lost Islands. The Story of Islands That Have Vanished from Nautical Charts*, Vancouver, University of Vancouver Press, 1984

Stone, J.C. *The Pont Manuscript Maps of Scotland. Sixteenth century origins of a Blaeu atlas*, Tring, Map Collector Publications Ltd, 1989

Stott, C. *Celestial Charts*. London, Studio Editions, 1991

Strauss, G. 'A Sixteenth-Century Encyclopedia: Sebastjan Münster's *Cosmography* and Its Editions' in: Carter, C.H. *ed. From the Renaissance to the Counter-Reformation. Essays in honour of Garret Mattingly*, London, Jonathan Cape, 1966

Suárez, T. *Shedding the Veil. Mapping the European discovery of America and the World . . . 1434-1865*, Singapore, River Edge and London, World Scientific Publishing Co., Ltd, 1992

Szathmáry, T. *Descriptio Hungariae, Magyar-országéserdély nyomtatott térképei I 1477-1600*, Fusignano, privately published for the author, 1987 [volume II in preparation]

Thompson, M.M. *Maps for America. Cartographic products of the U.S. Geological Survey and others*, Washington, D.C., U.S. Department of the Interior, U.S. Geological Survey, 1979

Thrower, N.J., *ed. The Compleat Plattmaker. Essays on Chart, Map, and Globe Making in England in the Seventeenth and Eighteenth Centuries*, Berkeley, Los Angeles and London, University of California Press, 1978

Tooley, R.V. *Collectors' Guide to Maps of The African Continent and Southern Africa*, London, Carta Press, 1969

Tooley, R.V., Bricker, C. and Crone, G.R. *Landmarks of Mapmaking. An Illustrated Survey of Maps and Mapmakers*, Oxford, Phaidon Press Ltd, 1976

Tooley, R.V. *Tooley's Dictionary of Mapmakers*, Tring, Map Collector Publications Ltd, 1979. New edition in preparation.

Tooley, R.V. *Maps and Map-Makers*, seventh edition, New York, Dorset Press (by arrangement with B.T. Batsford, Ltd, London), 1987. New edition in preparation.

Tooley, R.V. *The Mapping of Australia*, London, The Holland Press, 1979

Tyacke, S.J., *ed. English Map-Making 1500-1650. Historical Essays*, London, The British Library, 1983

Tyacke, S.J. *London Map-Sellers 1660-1720. A collection of advertisements for maps placed in the London Gazette 1668-1719 with biographical notes on the mapsellers*, Tring, Map Collector Publications Ltd, 1978

Uzielli, G. and Amat Di S. Filippo, P. *Mappamondi, carte nautiche, portolani ed altri monumenti cartografici specialmente italiani dei secoli XIII-XVII*, reprint edition, Amsterdam, Meridian Publishing Co., 1967

Vrij, M. de *The world on paper. A descriptive catalogue of cartographical material published in Amsterdam during the seventeenth century*, Amsterdam, Theatrum Orbis Terrarum Ltd, 1967

Wallis, H.M. and Robinson, A.H. *ed. Cartographical Innovations. An International Handbook of Mapping Terms to 1900*, Tring, Map Collector Publications Ltd, 1987

Wallis, H.M. and Tyacke, S.J. *ed. My Head is a Map. Essays & Memoirs in honour of R.V. Tooley*, London, Francis Edwards and Carta Press, 1973

Weddle, R.S. *The French Thorn. Rival explorers in the Spanish Sea, 1682-1762*, College Station, Texas A&M University Press, 1991

Wheat, J.C. and Brun, C.F. *Maps and Charts published in America before 1800: a bibliography*, second, revised edition, London, The Holland Press Ltd, 1985

Williams, G. and Frost, A. *Terra Australis to Australia*, Melbourne, Oxford University Press, 1988

Wilson, A. and Wilson, J.L. *The Making of the Nuremberg Chronicle*, Amsterdam, Nico Israel, 1976

Wilson, E. *The Story of the Blue Back Chart*, London, Imray, Laurie, Norie & Wilson, Ltd, 1937

Wilson, D. *The Circumnagivators*, London, Constable and Company Ltd, 1987

Woodward, D., *ed. Art and Cartography, Six Historical Essays*, Chicago and London, The University of Chicago Press, 1987

Woodward, D., *ed. Five centuries of map printing*, Chicago and London, The University of Chicago Press, 1975

Woodward, D. *The Maps and Prints of Paolo Forlani. A Descriptive Bibliography. The Hermon Dunlap Smith Center for the History of Cartography Occasional Publication No. 4*, Chicago, The Newberry Library, 1990

Periodicals

Acta cartographica. A series of monographs and studies on the history of cartography, reprinted from periodicals since 1800, Vol 1-, Amsterdam Theatrum Orbis Terrarum Ltd, 1968 [in continuation]

Caert-Thresoo. Tijdschrift voor de geschiedenis van de kartografie in Nederland, Vol. I, no. 1-, commenced 1982, quarterly publication, Alphen aan den Rijn, Uitgeverij Canaletto, 1982- [in continuation]

Cartographica Helvetica. Fachzeitschrift für Kartengeschichte, 1-, commenced 1990, biannual publication, Murten, 1990- [in continuation]

Imago Mundi. The Journal of the International Society for the History of Cartography, I-, commenced 1935, annual publication (various places, currently), London, 1935- [in continuation]

IMCoS Journal. Journal of the International Map Collectors' Society, 1-, commenced 1980, three or four issues a year, London, 1980- [in continuation]

The Map Collector, 1-, commenced 1977, quarterly publication, Tring, Map Collector Publications Ltd, 1977- [in continuation]

Selected Catalogue-Issuing Auctioneers and Dealers

(current addresses may be obtained from the latest issue of *The Map Collector*)

DENMARK – COPENHAGEN: Rosenkilde og Bagger

FRANCE – PARIS: Louis Lœb–Larocque; CHARTRES: Patrick et Elisabeth Sourget

GERMANY – HAMBURG: D.F. Dörling; MUNICH: Monika Schmidt; Zisska & Kistner; OSNABRÜCK: H. Th. Wenner; KÖNIGSTEIN: Reiss & Auvermann

NETHERLANDS – AMSTERDAM: A.L. van Gendt; Nico Israel; C. Broekema; R. Putman; GELDROP: Paulus Swaen; UTRECHT: J.L. Beijers

SWEDEN – STOCKHOLM: Ronnells Antikvariat AB

UNITED KINGDOM – LONDON: Sotheby's; Christie's; Phillips; Tooley & Adams; Jonathan Potter Ltd; Robert Douwma Prints & Maps Ltd; Bernard Quaritch Ltd; Maggs Brothers Ltd; Bernard J. Shapero Ltd; InterCol Ltd; The Map House Ltd; J.A.L. Franks Ltd; CHESTER: Richard Nicholson; SWINDON: Dominic Winter; UCKFIELD: Ivan R. Deverall

UNITED STATES OF AMERICA – CHICAGO: Kenneth Nebenzahl Inc.; KING OF PRUSSIA: W. Graham Arader, III, NEW YORK: Sotheby's; Christie's; Swann Galleries; Richard B. Arkway; Martayan Lan; Thomas Suárez; OLD FIELD: Jo Ann and Richard Casten; PHILADELPHIA: Philadelphia Print Shop, Ltd; WILLIAMSBURG: Paul Roberts Stoney; SANTA FE: R. and D. Fitch; SAN FRANCISCO: John D. Scopazzi

LIST OF ILLUSTRATIONS

10.12 *Tabula selenographica* by Johan Baptist Homann, Nuremberg, *c.*1720, after Johann Gabriel Doppelmayer. The British Library, London (Map Library).

10.13 *Cometa, qui Anno Christi 1742 apparvit* from *Atlas novus* by Matthäus Seutter, Augsburg, *c.*1745. The Library of Congress, Washington, DC., U.S.A.

10.14 *Imagines coeli septentrionales cum duodecim imaginibus zodiaci* by Albrecht Dürer, Nuremberg, 1515. © National Maritime Museum, Greenwich, London.

10.15 A woodcut illustration of the northern skies from *Astronomicum Caesareum* by Peter Apian, Ingolstadt, 1540. © National Maritime Museum, Greenwich, London.

10.16 The constellation of Cygnus (the Swan) from the first printed star atlas, *De le stelle fisse libro uno* by Alessandro Piccolomini, 1540. The Royal Astronomical Society, London.

10.17 Charts from *Coelum stellatum christianum* by Julius Schiller, 1627. The British Library, London (Map Library).

10.18 Chart from *Uranometria* by Johan Bayer, 1603, copper engraving, Augsburg, 1603. The British Library, London.

10.19 *Hemisphaerum australe* from *Cometographia* by Johannes Hevelius, 1688. The Royal Astronomical Society, London.

10.20 *Cassiopea Cepheus Ursa Minor draco* from the posthumous *Atlas coelestis* by John Flamsteed, London, 1729. © National Maritime Museum, Greenwich, London.

10.21 *Zodiacus stellatus . . .* from the *Atlas maritimus* by John Seller, London, 1679. The Library of Congress, Washington, DC.

10.22 The paired northern and southern celestial hemispheres attributed to James Barlow, London, *c.*1790. The British Library, London (Map Library).

10.23 *Planisphaeri coeleste* by Frederick de Wit, *c.*1680. Jonathan Potter Ltd., London.

10.24 *Coeli stellate christiani haemisphaerium prius* (as depicted by Julius Schiller) from *Atlas Coelestis seu harmonia macrocosmica* by Andreas Cellarius, Amsterdam, *c.*1660. Jonathan Potter Ltd., London.

10.25 Atlas holding the earth to view, from an Ottens composite atlas compiled in Amsterdam, *c.*1650. © National Maritime Museum, Greenwich, London.

11.1 Detail from *Aspice Paulinam Pauli sub imagine gente* from an atlas of the archbishopric of Cologne, the *Prodromus geographicus*, by Johannes Michael Gigas, Cologne, *c.*1620. Westfälisches Landesmuseum, Munich.

11.2 A map of Europe by Opicinus de Canistris (*c.*1296–*c.*1300). Biblioteca Apostolica Vaticana, Rome.

11.3 *Aspice Paulinam Pauli sub imagine gente* from an atlas of the archbishopric of Cologne, the *Prodromus geographicus*, by Johannes Michael Gigas, Cologne, *c.*1620. Westfälisches Landesmuseum, Munich.

11.4 *Geography Bewitched!* or, *a droll caricature map of Scotland*, printed by Bowles and Carver, London. Jonathan Potter Ltd., London.

11.5 *De Leone Belgico* by Michael Eitzinger, *c.*1590. Courtesy Sotheby's, London.

11.6 *Leo Belgicus* by Johannes van Deutecum, first issued in 1598. Courtesy Sotheby's, London.

11.7 A version of the *Leo Belgicus* by C. J. Visscher, *c.*1611–1621. Courtesy Sotheby's, London.

11.8 *Asia secund pars terrae in forma Pegasir* from the biblical travel book *Itinerarium sacrae scripturae* by Heinrich Bünting, 1581. The British Library, London.

11.9 *Die gantze Welt in ein Kleberblatt* by Heinrich Bünting, 1581. The British Library, London.

11.10 *Accurata Utopiae tabula . . . Schlaraffenlandes Neu-erfundene lächerliche Land-Tabell* by Matthäus Seutter, *c.*1740. The British Library, London (Map Library).

11.11 *Serio-Comic War Map of Europe for the Year 1877*, commonly known as the 'octopus map', by Frederick Rose. Courtesy Sotheby's, London.

11.12 *Novel Carte de Europe designed for 1870* by Frederick Rose. Courtesy Sotheby's, London.

11.13 *The Evil Genius of Europe* by W. Coney, tinted lithograph, London, 1859. Courtesy Sotheby's, London.

11.14 *The North part of America . . . and upon ye West the large and goodly Iland of California* by Henry Briggs, London, 1625. The British Library, London (Map Library).

11.15 An anonymous world map in the visor of a fool's cap, Antwerp, *c.*1590, Douce.Portfolio. 142(92) 'Fool's Cap World'. The Bodleian Library, Oxford / The Bridgeman Art Library, London.

12.1 Detail of *Carta marina et descriptio septen-*
12.2 *trionalium terrarum . . . Anno D[omo]ni 1539* by Olaus Magnus, woodcut on nine sheets, Venice 1539. Map Collector Publications Ltd.

12.3 Part of Java la Grande on an anonymous chart probably made in Dieppe in about 1547, from the so-called 'Vallard atlas'. The Huntington Library, San Marino, California.

12.4 *Islandia* by Abraham Ortelius from the *Theatrum orbis terrarum*, Antwerp, 1585. Courtesy Sotheby's, London.

12.5 A letterpress printer's workshop by Abraham von Werdt, woodcut, *c.*1660. © The Board of Trustees of the Victoria & Albert Museum, London.

12.6 Interior of an intaglio printer's workshop by Abraham Bosse, etching, Paris, *c.*1642. The Board of Trustees of the Victoria & Albert Museum, London.

12.7 A map of central and Eastern Europe from the *Nuremberg Chronicle*, woodcut, compiled, designed and printed at Nuremberg in 1493 after Hieronymus Münzer. The British Library, London (Map Library).

12.8 Detail of *Venetie M.D.* by Jacopo de'Barbari, woodcut, six sheets, Venice, 1500. The British Library, London.

12.9 *Maris Pacifici quod vulgo Mar del Zur* by Gabriel Tatton, copper engraving, London, 1600. Courtesy Sotheby's, London.

12.10 Detail of the cordiform world map from the Venice edition of Ptolemy, 1511. The British Library, London (Map Library).

12.11 *Lotharingia* (Lorraine) from the edition of Ptolemy edited by Martin Waldseemüller, published at Strasbourg, 1513. The British Library, London (Map Library).

12.12 *Flandriae comitatus descriptio* by Abraham Ortelius, copper engraving, *c.*1590. Courtesy Sotheby's, London.

12.13 Two editions of *Americae sive Novi Orbis*
12.14 *nova descriptio* by Abraham Ortelius, copper engraving, *c.*1570 (12.13) and *c.*1585 (12.14). Courtesy Sotheby's, London.

12.15 *Effigies ampli regni auriferi Guineae in Africa*, attributed to Luis Teixeira, Amsterdam, Huych Allard, 1602 or later. Courtesy Sotheby's, London.

12.16 *Generale caarte vanden lande van Voorne aande oost zyde van Flacquee* by Heijman van Dijck, copper engraving, *c.*1700. Courtesy Sotheby's, London.

12.17 *Irlandiae accurata descriptio* by Jan Baptist Vrients from the later editions of Abraham Ortelius's *Theatrum orbis terrarum* after 1616, after Baptista Boazio, copper engraving, 1599. The British Library, London (Map Library).

12.18 *Ireland* by Jan Baptist Vrients from his later editions of Abraham Ortelius's *Theatrum orbis terrarum*, 1603 and later, after Baptista Boazio, copper engraving, 1599. Courtesy Sotheby's, London.

12.19 Two editions of *The Countie Pallatine of*
12.20 *Lancaster* described by John Speed, copper engraving, London, 1611 and later. Courtesy Sotheby's, London.

12.21 *Typus orarum maritimarum Guinae Manicongo & Angolae ultra promontorium Bonne Spei usque*, drawn and engraved by Arnold Florent van Langren for Jan Hugghen van Linschoten's *Itinerario*, Amsterdam, 1596. The British Library, London (Map Library).

12.22 *Praefecturae de Paraiba, et Rio Grande* by Joan Blaeu from the *Atlas major*, 1662. © Royal Geographical Society, London.

12.23 *Nova et accuratissima totius terrarum orbis tabula* by Joan Blaeu from the *Atlas major* 1662. © Royal Geographical Society, London.

12.24 *The Four Seasons* by Antonio Tempesta, 1592. Reproduced by courtesy of the Trustees of the British Museum, London (Department of Prints and Drawings).

12.25 *Nova totius terrarum orbis geographia ac hydrographica tabula* by Willem Blaeu, 1606 and later. © Royal Geographical Society, London.

12.26 *Cyprus insula* by Willem Blaeu, *c.*1635. © Royal Geographical Society, London.

INDEX